release 5

Stata Reference Manual
Release 5
Volume 2
G-O

Stata Press
College Station, Texas

Stata Press, 702 University Drive East, College Station, Texas 77840

The suggested citation for this software is

StataCorp. 1997. *Stata Statistical Software: Release 5.0* College Station, TX: Stata Corporation.

Title

> **generate** — Create or change contents of variable

Syntax

$\big[$ **by** *varlist*: $\big]$ **generate** $\big[$ *type* $\big]$ *newvar* $\big[$ *:lblname* $\big]$ =*exp* $\big[$ **if** *exp* $\big]$ $\big[$ **in** *range* $\big]$

$\big[$ **by** *varlist*: $\big]$ **replace** *oldvar* =*exp* $\big[$ **if** *exp* $\big]$ $\big[$ **in** *range* $\big]$ $\big[$, **nopromote** $\big]$

set seed #

set type $\big\{$ byte $\mid$ int $\mid$ long $\mid$ float $\mid$ double $\mid$ str# $\big\}$

Description

generate creates a new variable. The values of the variable are specified by =*exp*. Also see [R] **egen** for extensions to **generate**.

replace changes the contents of an existing variable. Since **replace** alters data, the command may not be abbreviated.

set seed # specifies the initial value of the random number seed used by the **uniform()** function. # should be specified as a positive integer.

set type specifies the default type assigned to new variables (such as by **generate**) when the storage type is not explicitly specified. Caution should be exercised when using this command.

Options

nopromote prevents **replace** from promoting the variable type to accommodate the change. For instance, consider a variable stored as an integer type (**byte**, **int**, or **long**) and assume you **replace** some values with nonintegers. By default, **replace** will change the variable type to a floating point (**float** or **double**) and thus correctly store the changed values. Similarly, **replace** will promote **byte** and **int** variables to longer integers (**int** and **long**) if the replacement value is an integer but too large in absolute value for the current storage type. **replace** will promote strings to longer strings. **nopromote** prevents **replace** from doing this; instead, the replacement values are truncated to fit into the current storage type.

(Compatibility with previous releases note: Automatic variable promotion was added in Stata 4.0. If you set **version** to 3.1 or less, Stata will return to its old behavior and thus old programs and ado-files will work; see [R] **version**.)

1

Remarks

generate and replace

generate and replace are used to create new variables and modify the contents of existing variables, respectively. Although the commands do the same thing, they have different names so that you do not accidentally replace values in your data. The details of expressions are covered in [U] **20 Functions and expressions**.

Stata for Windows and Stata for Macintosh users be sure to see [R] **edit**.

▷ Example

You have a dataset containing the variable age2, which you have previously defined as age^2 (i.e., age^2). You have changed some of the age data and now want to correct age2 to reflect the new values:

```
. generate age2=age^2
age2 already defined
r(110);
```

When you attempt to re-generate age2, Stata refuses, telling you that age2 is already defined. You could drop age2 and then re-generate it, or you could use the replace command:

```
. replace age2=age^2
(204 real changes made)
```

When you use replace, you are informed as to the number of actual changes made to the data.

◁

You can explicitly specify the storage type of the new variable being created by putting the *type*, such as byte, int, long, float, double, or str8, in front of the variable name. Not specifying a type is equivalent to specifying float. (More correctly, it is equivalent to specifying the default type set by the set type command; see below.)

You may also specify a value label to be associated with the new variable by including ':*lblname*' after the variable name. This is seldom done since you can always associate the value label later by using the label define command; see [U] **19.6.3 Value labels**.

▷ Example

Among the variables in your data is name containing the first and last name of each person. You wish to create a new variable called lastname, which you will then use to sort the data. name is a string variable, and you type

```
. generate lastname=substr(name,index(name," ")+1,.)
type mismatch
r(109);
```

Since you did not explicitly specify the storage type, Stata attempted to create a float variable called lastname equal to your string expression. Stata realized it could not do that, so it complained and did nothing. You meant to type

```
. generate str12 lastname=substr(name,index(name," ")+1,.)
```

◁

▷ Example

You wish to create a new variable `age2` that is the variable `age` squared. You realize that since `age` is an integer, `age2` will also be an integer and `age2` will certainly be less than 32,766. You therefore decide to store `age2` as an `int` to conserve memory:

```
. generate int age2=age^2
(9 missing values generated)
```

Preceding `age2` with `int` told Stata that the variable was to be stored as an `int`. After creating the new variable, Stata informed us that 9 missing values were generated. Whenever `generate` produces missing values, it informs you.

◁

See [U] **20 Functions and expressions** and [U] **34 Commands for dealing with categorical variables** for more information and examples. Also see [R] **recode** for a convenient way to recode categorical variables.

❑ Technical Note

If you specify the `if` modifier and/or `in` *range*, the *=exp* is evaluated only for those observations meeting the specified condition and/or in the specified range. The other observations of the new variable are set to missing:

```
. generate int age2=age^2 if age>30
(112 missing values generated)
```

❑

▷ Example

`replace` can be used to change just a single value as well as to make sweeping changes to your data. For instance, say you enter data on the first five odd and even positive integers and then discover that you made a mistake:

```
. list
        odd     even
1.       1        2
2.       3        4
3.      -8        6
4.       7        8
5.       9       10
```

Notice that the third observation is wrong; the value of `odd` should be 5, not −8. We can use `replace` to repair the mistake:

```
. replace odd=5 in 3
(1 real change made)
```

We could also have repaired the mistake by typing `replace odd=5 if odd==-8`.

◁

set seed

set seed # reinitializes the seed for the pseudo-random number generator uniform() and should be specified as a positive integer. If a negative number is specified, it will be made positive. The seed determines the sequence of pseudo-random numbers produced by uniform(). When Stata comes up, it initializes the seed to 123456789, an easy-to-remember nonrandom number that in no way affects the pseudo-randomness of the numbers produced by uniform(). Since Stata initializes the seed to a constant, however, Stata produces the same sequence of random numbers (measured from the start of the session) unless you reinitialize the seed. The seed you select affects only the sequence, not the pseudo-randomness. Without loss of pseudo-randomness, the seed may be set to small numbers; e.g., set seed 2. See [U] **20.3.2 Statistical functions** for details and formulas.

set type

When you create a new variable and do not specify the storage type for the variable, say by typing generate y=x+2, the new variable is made a float. That is, it is made a float if you have not issued the set type command. If earlier in your session you typed set type double, then the new variable would be made a double.

We recommend that set type float and set type double be the only possibilities you consider. Many of Stata's features are implemented as ado-files, and some ado-files do not explicitly specify the storage types of their working variables. While this is especially true of ado-files written by others, this is even true of some of our ado-files. It is understood that such sloppiness on our part is inexcusable, but in the meantime you should not set type int since some ado-files may then produce incorrect results. set type double, on the other hand, is quite safe.

Methods and Formulas

You can do anything with replace that you can do with generate. The only difference between the commands is that replace requires that the variable previously exist, whereas generate requires that the variable be new. In fact, inside Stata, generate and replace are the same code! Since Stata is an interactive system, however, we force a distinction between replacing existing values and generating new ones so that you do not accidentally replace valuable data while thinking that you are instead creating another new piece of information.

Also See

[U] **19 Data**, [U] **20 Functions and expressions**

[R] **edit**, [R] **egen**, [R] **recast**, [R] **recode**, [R] **rename**

Title

glm — Generalized linear models

Syntax

glm *depvar* [*varlist*] [*weight*] [if *exp*] [in *range*] [, <u>f</u>amily(*familyname*)

    <u>l</u>ink(*linkname*) <u>noc</u>onstant <u>s</u>cale(x2|dev|#) [<u>ln</u>]<u>o</u>ffset(*varname*) disp(#)

    <u>ef</u>orm <u>l</u>evel(#) <u>i</u>terate(#) <u>l</u>tol(#) <u>i</u>nit(*varname*$_\mu$) <u>nolog</u>]

glmpred [*type*] *newvar* [, <u>a</u>ll [<u>d</u>eviance|<u>m</u>u|<u>p</u>earson|xb|<u>s</u>tdp]]

where *familyname* is one of

    <u>g</u>aussian | <u>ig</u>aussian | <u>b</u>inomial [*varname*$_N$|#$_N$] | <u>p</u>oisson| <u>nb</u>inomial [#$_k$] |

    <u>ga</u>mma

and *linkname* is one of

    <u>i</u>dentity | <u>l</u>og | <u>log</u>it | <u>p</u>robit | <u>c</u>loglog | <u>o</u>power# | <u>p</u>ower# | <u>nb</u>inomial

aweights, fweights, and iweights are allowed; see [U] **18.1.6 weight**.

glm shares the features of all estimation commands; see [U] **26 Estimation and post-estimation commands**.

To reset problem-size limits, see [R] **matsize**.

glm may be used with sw to perform stepwise estimation; see [R] **sw**.

Description

    glm fits generalized linear models.

    glmpred, for use after glm, creates *newvar* containing predicted means, predicted linear predictors, residuals, and the like.

Options

family(*familyname*) specifies the distribution of *depvar*; family(gaussian) is the default.

link(*linkname*) specifies the link function; the default is the canonical link for the family() specified.

noconstant specifies that the linear predictor has no intercept term, thus forcing it through the origin on the scale defined by the link function.

scale(x2|dev|#) overrides the default scale parameter. By default, scale(1) is assumed for the discrete distributions (binomial, Poisson, negative binomial) and scale(x2) is assumed for the continuous distributions (Gaussian, gamma, inverse Gaussian).

scale(x2) specifies the scale parameter be set to the Pearson chi-squared (or generalized chi-squared) statistic divided by the residual degrees of freedom, as recommended by McCullagh and Nelder (1989) as a good general choice for continuous distributions.

scale(dev) sets the scale parameter to the deviance divided by the residual degrees of freedom. This provides an alternative to scale(x2) for continuous distributions and over- or under-dispersed discrete distributions.

scale(#) sets the scale parameter to #. For example, using scale(1) in family(gamma) models results in exponential-errors regression. Additional use of link(log) rather than the default power(-1) for family(gamma) essentially reproduces Stata's ereg command (see [R] **weibull**) if all the observations are uncensored.

[ln]offset(*varname*) specifies an offset to be added to the linear predictor. offset() specifies the values directly: $g(E(y)) = \mathbf{x}\beta + varname$. lnoffset() specifies the exponentiated values: $g(E(y)) = \mathbf{x}\beta + \ln(varname)$. lnoffset() is most useful with Poisson-like data where *varname* records the person-years of exposure to some hazard and y (*depvar* in the syntax diagram) records the observed number of "deaths".

disp(#) multiplies the variance of *depvar* by # and divides the deviance by #. The resulting distributions are members of the quasi-likelihood family; see McCullagh and Nelder (1989) for a detailed description. The option may be appropriate for use with moderately overdispersed binomial or Poisson data to adjust the standard errors of the regression coefficients, which otherwise are too small.

eform displays the exponentiated coefficients and corresponding standard errors and confidence intervals as described in [R] **maximize**. For family(binomial) link(logit) (i.e., logistic regression), exponentiation results in odds ratios; for family(poisson) link(log) (i.e., Poisson regression), exponentiated coefficients are rate ratios.

level(#) specifies the confidence level, in percent, for confidence intervals. The default is level(95) or as set by set level; see [U] **26.4 Specifying the width of confidence intervals**.

iterate(#) specifies the maximum number of iterations allowed in estimating the model; iterate(50) is the default. You should rarely need to specify iterate().

ltol(#) specifies the convergence criterion for the change in deviance between iterations; ltol(1e-6) is the default.

init(*varname*$_\mu$) specifies *varname*$_\mu$ as the initial estimate for the mean of *depvar*. This can be useful with models that produce convergence difficulties, for example, family(binomial) models with power or odds-power links.

nolog suppresses the iteration log.

all, used with glmpred, specifies the prediction is to be made for all observations possible. The default is to restrict the calculation to the estimation sample.

deviance specifies that glmpred is to calculate the deviance residuals. Deviance residuals are recommended by McCullagh and Nelder (1989) and by others as having the best properties for examining goodness of fit of a GLM. They are approximately normally distributed if the model is correct. They may be plotted against the fitted values or against a covariate to inspect the model's fit. Also see the pearson option below.

mu specifies that glmpred is to calculate $g^{-1}(\mathbf{x}\widehat{\beta})$, the predicted value of y. mu is the default if no options are specified.

pearson specifies that **glmpred** is to calculate the Pearson residuals. Be warned that Pearson residuals often have markedly skewed distributions for non-Normal family distributions. Also see the **deviance** option above.

xb specifies that **glmpred** is to calculate the linear predictor $\mathbf{x}\widehat{\beta}$.

stdp calculates the standard error of the linear predictor.

Remarks

glm fits generalized linear models of y with covariates $\mathbf{x}$:

$$g\big(E(y)\big) = \mathbf{x}\beta, \qquad y \sim F$$

In the above, $g(\ )$ is called the link function and F the distributional family. Substituting various definitions for $g(\ )$ and F results in a surprising array of models. For instance, if y is distributed Gaussian (normal) and $g(\ )$ is the identity function, we have

$$E(y) = \mathbf{x}\beta, \qquad y \sim \text{Normal}$$

or linear regression. If $g(\ )$ is the logit function and y is distributed Bernoulli, we have

$$\text{logit}\big(E(y)\big) = \mathbf{x}\beta, \qquad y \sim \text{Bernoulli}$$

or logistic regression. If $g(\ )$ is the natural log function and y is distributed Poisson, we have

$$\ln\big(E(y)\big) = \mathbf{x}\beta, \qquad y \sim \text{Poisson}$$

or Poisson regression, also known as the log-linear model. Other combinations are possible.

Although **glm** can be used to estimate linear regression (and, in fact, does so by default), this should be viewed as an instructional feature; **fit** and **regress** produce such estimates more quickly and, in the case of **fit**, numerous post-estimation commands are available to explore the adequacy of the fit; see [R] **fit** and [R] **regress**.

In any case, you specify the link function using the **link()** option and the distributional family using **family()**. The allowed link functions are

Link function	glm option
identity	link(identity)
log	link(log)
logit	link(logit)
probit	link(probit)
complementary log-log	link(cloglog)
odds power	link(opower #)
power	link(power #)
negative binomial	link(nbinomial)

Link function **identity** is defined as $y = y$.

Link function **log** is defined as $\ln(y)$.

Link function **logit** is defined $\ln\big(y/(1-y)\big)$, the natural log of the odds.

Link function **probit** is defined $\Phi^{-1}(y)$, where $\Phi^{-1}(\ )$ is the inverse Gaussian cumulative.

Link function `cloglog` is defined $\ln\big(-\ln(1-y)\big)$.

Link function `opower` is defined $\big[(y/(1-y))^n - 1\big]/n$, the power of the odds. The function is generalized so that `link(opower 0)` is equivalent to `link(logit)`, the natural log of the odds.

Link function `power` is defined as y^n. Specifying `link(power 1)` is equivalent to specifying `link(identity)`. The power function is generalized so that $y^0 \equiv \ln(y)$, and thus `link(power 0)` is equivalent to `link(log)`. Negative powers are, of course, allowed.

Link function `nbinomial` is defined $\ln\big(y/(y+k)\big)$ where $k = 1$ if `family(nbinomial)` is specified and $k = \#_k$ if `family(nbinomial` $\#_k$`)` is specified.

The allowed distributional families are

Family	glm option
Gaussian (normal)	family(gaussian)
inverse Gaussian	family(igaussian)
Bernoulli/binomial	family(binomial)
Poisson	family(poisson)
negative binomial	family(nbinomial)
gamma	family(gamma)

`family(normal)` is allowed as a synonym for `family(gaussian)`.

The binomial distribution can be specified as (1) `family(binomial)`, (2) `family(binomial` $\#_N$`)`, or (3) `family(binomial` $varname_N$`)`. In case 2, $\#_N$ is the value of the binomial denominator N, the number of trials. Specifying `family(binomial 1)` is the same as specifying `family(binomial)`; both mean that y has the Bernoulli distribution with values 0 and 1 only. In case 3, $varname_N$ is the variable containing the binomial denominator, thus allowing the number of trials to vary across observations.

The negative binomial distribution can be specified as (1) `family(nbinomial)` or (2) `family(nbinomial` $\#_k$`)`. Omitting $\#_k$ is equivalent to specifying `family(nbinomial 1)`. The value $\#_k$ enters the variance and deviance functions; typical values range between .01 and 2; see the technical note below.

You do not have to specify both `family()` and `link()`; the default `link()` is the canonical link for the specified `family()` (except for `nbinomial`):

Family	Default link
family(gaussian)	link(identity)
family(igaussian)	link(power -2)
family(binomial)	link(logit)
family(poisson)	link(log)
family(nbinomial)	link(log)
family(gamma)	link(power -1)

If you do specify both `family()` and `link()`, note that not all combinations make sense. You may choose among the following combinations:

	identity	log	logit	probit	cloglog	power	opower	nbinomial
Gaussian	x	x				x		
inverse Gaussian	x	x				x		
binomial	x	x	x	x	x	x	x	
Poisson	x	x				x		
negative binomial	x	x				x		x
gamma	x	x				x		

❏ Technical Note

Some `family()` and `link()` combinations result in models already estimated by Stata. These are

family()	link()	Other Stata estimation command
gaussian	identity	regress or fit
binomial	logit	logit or logistic
binomial	probit	probit (see note 1)
poisson	log	poisson
nbinomial	log	nbreg (see note 2)
gamma	log	ereg (see note 3)

Note 1: For probit estimation, `glm` and `probit` will produce the same coefficients, but the standard errors will be only asymptotically equivalent because probit is not the canonical link for the binomial family. If the binomial denominator is not 1, the equivalent maximum-likelihood command is `bprobit`; see [R] **probit** and [R] **glogit** *(sic)*.

Note 2: Family negative binomial, log-link models—also known as negative binomial regression—are used for data with an overdispersed Poisson distribution. Although `glm` can be used to estimate such models, use of Stata's maximum-likelihood `nbreg` command is probably preferable. In the GLM approach, one specifies `family(nbinomial #_k)` and then searches for a $\#_k$ that results in the deviance-based dispersion being 1. `nbreg`, on the other hand, finds the maximum-likelihood estimate of $\#_k$ and reports a confidence interval for it; see [R] **nbreg** and Rogers (1993). Of course, `glm` allows links other than log and for those links, including the canonical `nbinomial` link, you will need to use `glm`. As with `probit`, `glm`-reported standard errors will be only asymptotically equivalent to those produced by `nbreg` because log is not the canonical link for the negative binomial family.

Note 3: `glm` can be used to estimate exponential regressions, but this requires specifying `scale(1)`. As with probit, the `glm`-reported standard errors will be only asymptotically equivalent to those produced by `ereg` because log is not the canonical link for the gamma family. `glm` cannot be used to estimate exponential regressions on censored data.

❏

▷ Example

In general, where there is overlap between a capability of `glm` and that of some other Stata command, we recommend using the other Stata command. Our recommendation is not due to some inferiority of the GLM approach. Rather, it is that those other, more specialized commands, by being specialized, provide options and ancillary commands missing in the broader `glm` framework. Nevertheless, `glm` does produce the same answers where it should.

In [R] **logistic**, we estimate a model based on data from a study of risk factors associated with low birth weight (Hosmer and Lemeshow 1989, appendix 1). We can reestimate the model using `glm`:

```
. glm low age lwt race2 race3 smoke ptl ht ui, f(bin) l(logit)

Iteration 1 : deviance =  202.0426
Iteration 2 : deviance =  201.4504
Iteration 3 : deviance =  201.4480
Iteration 4 : deviance =  201.4480

Residual df  =       180              No. of obs =        189
Pearson X2   =  182.0193              Deviance    =   201.448
Dispersion   =  1.011218              Dispersion  =  1.119156
```

```
Bernoulli distribution, logit link
----------------------------------------------------------------------------
     low |    Coef.   Std. Err.      z    P>|z|     [95% Conf. Interval]
---------+------------------------------------------------------------------
     age |  -.0271003   .0364499   -0.743   0.457    -.0985408    .0443402
     lwt |  -.0151508   .0069258   -2.188   0.029    -.0287251   -.0015766
   race2 |   1.262647   .5264052    2.399   0.016     .2309121    2.294382
   race3 |   .8620792   .4391467    1.963   0.050     .0013673    1.722791
   smoke |   .9233448    .400821    2.304   0.021     .1377502     1.70894
     ptl |   .5418365   .3462469    1.565   0.118    -.1367948    1.220468
      ht |   1.832518   .6916239    2.650   0.008     .4769599    3.188076
      ui |   .7585134   .4593739    1.651   0.099    -.1418428     1.65887
   _cons |   .4612239   1.204575    0.383   0.702      -1.8997    2.822147
----------------------------------------------------------------------------
```

glm, by default, presents coefficient estimates whereas logistic presents the exponentiated coefficients—the odds ratios. glm's eform option reports exponentiated coefficients and glm, like Stata's other estimation commands, replays results.

```
. glm, eform
Residual df   =         180                 No. of obs =          189
Pearson X2    =    182.0193                 Deviance   =      201.448
Dispersion    =    1.011218                 Dispersion =     1.119156

Bernoulli distribution, logit link
----------------------------------------------------------------------------
     low | Odds Ratio  Std. Err.      z    P>|z|     [95% Conf. Interval]
---------+------------------------------------------------------------------
     age |   .9732636   .0354754   -0.743   0.457     .9061587    1.045338
     lwt |   .9849634   .0068216   -2.188   0.029     .9716836    .9984247
   race2 |   3.534767   1.860719    2.399   0.016     1.259748    9.918309
   race3 |   2.368079   1.039934    1.963   0.050     1.001368    5.600136
   smoke |   2.517698   1.009146    2.304   0.021     1.147689    5.523101
     ptl |   1.719161   .5952542    1.565   0.118     .8721492    3.388773
      ht |   6.249602   4.322374    2.650   0.008     1.611169    24.24173
      ui |    2.1351    .9808091    1.651   0.099     .8677577     5.25337
----------------------------------------------------------------------------
```

These results are the same as reported in [R] **logistic**.

◁

▷ Example

More interesting is the use of glm to estimate models that cannot be carried out by other Stata commands. We use data from an early insecticide experiment, given in Pregibon (1980). The variables are ldose, the log dose of insecticide; n, the number of flour beetles subjected to each dose; and r, the number killed.

```
. list
        ldose       n       r
1.     1.6907      59       6
2.     1.7242      60      13
3.     1.7552      62      18
4.     1.7842      56      28
5.     1.8113      63      52
6.     1.8369      59      53
7.     1.8610      62      61
8.     1.8839      60      60
```

The aim of the analysis is to estimate a dose-response relationship between p, the proportion killed, and X, the log dose.

As a first attempt, we will formulate the model as a linear logistic regression of p on ldose; that is, take the logit of p and represent the dose-response curve as a straight line in X:

$$\ln\big(p/(1-p)\big) = \beta_0 + \beta_1 X$$

Since the data is grouped, we cannot use Stata's logistic command to estimate the model. Stata does, however, already have a command for estimating a logistic regression on data organized in this way, and we could type

```
. blogit r n ldose
(output omitted)
```

Instead, we will estimate the model using glm:

```
. glm r ldose, family(binomial n) link(logit)
Iteration 1 : deviance =   11.4517
Iteration 2 : deviance =   11.2325
Iteration 3 : deviance =   11.2322
Iteration 4 : deviance =   11.2322
Iteration 5 : deviance =   11.2322

Residual df  =        6                  No. of obs =          8
Pearson X2   =  10.02679                 Deviance   =  11.23221
Dispersion   =  1.671132                 Dispersion =  1.872034

Binomial (N=n) distribution, logit link
-------------------------------------------------------------------------
      r |     Coef.    Std. Err.      z     P>|z|    [95% Conf. Interval]
--------+----------------------------------------------------------------
  ldose |   34.27034   2.912141    11.768   0.000    28.56265    39.97803
  _cons |  -60.71747   5.180713   -11.720   0.000   -70.87149   -50.56346
-------------------------------------------------------------------------
```

The only difference between blogit and glm in this case is how they went about obtaining the answer, although this difference is hidden from us. blogit secretly expands the data to contain 481 observations (the sum of n) so that it could run Stata's standard, individual-level logistic command. glm, on the other hand, uses the information on the binomial denominator directly. We specified family(binomial n), meaning variable n contains the denominator. Parameter estimates and standard errors from the two approaches do not differ.

An alternative model, which gives asymmetric sigmoid curves for p, involves the complementary log-log or cloglog function:

$$\ln\big(-\ln(1-p)\big) = \beta_0 + \beta_1 X$$

There is no equivalent Stata command to estimate the cloglog model; we must use glm.

```
. glm r ldose, family(binomial n) link(cloglog)
Iteration 1 : deviance =   3.5692
Iteration 2 : deviance =   3.4466
Iteration 3 : deviance =   3.4464
Iteration 4 : deviance =   3.4464

Residual df  =        6                  No. of obs =          8
Pearson X2   =  3.294685                 Deviance   =  3.446418
Dispersion   =  .5491142                 Dispersion =  .574403
```

```
Binomial (N=n) distribution, cloglog link
------------------------------------------------------------------------------
       r |      Coef.   Std. Err.       z    P>|z|     [95% Conf. Interval]
---------+--------------------------------------------------------------------
   ldose |   22.04118    1.799365    12.249   0.000      18.51449    25.56787
   _cons |  -39.57232    3.240291   -12.213   0.000     -45.92318   -33.22147
------------------------------------------------------------------------------
```

The complementary log-log model is preferred; note that the deviance for the logistic model, 11.23, is much higher than the cloglog model's 3.45.

This example also shows the advantages of the glm command—one can vary assumptions easily. Note the minor difference in what we typed to obtain the logistic and cloglog models:

```
. glm r ldose, family(binomial n) link(logit)
. glm r ldose, family(binomial n) link(cloglog)
```

Were this not a manual and were we performing this work for ourselves, we would have typed the commands in a more abbreviated form:

```
. glm r ldose, f(b n) l(l)
. glm r ldose, f(b n) l(cl)
```

◁

▷ Example

After glm estimation, glmpred may be used to obtain various predictions based on the model. We mentioned in the previous example that the complementary log-log link seemed to fit the data better than the logit link. Below, we go back and obtain the fitted values and deviance residuals:

```
. quietly glm r ldose, f(binomial n) l(logit)
. glmpred mu_logit
. glmpred dr_logit, deviance
. quietly glm r ldose, f(binomial n) l(cloglog)
. glmpred mu_cl
. glmpred dr_cl, d
. list r mu_logit dr_logit mu_cl dr_cl
           r    mu_logit    dr_logit        mu_cl       dr_cl
  1.       6     3.45746     1.28368      5.58945     0.18057
  2.      13     9.84167     1.05969     11.28067     0.55773
  3.      18    22.45139    -1.19611     20.95422    -0.80330
  4.      28    33.89761    -1.59412     30.36942    -0.63439
  5.      52    50.09584     0.60614     47.77644     1.28883
  6.      53    53.29092    -0.12716     54.14273    -0.52367
  7.      61    59.22216     1.25107     61.11331    -0.11879
  8.      60    58.74297     1.59398     59.94723     0.32495
```

Note that in 6 out of the 8 cases, $|dr\_logit| > |dr\_cl|$.

◁

❑ Technical Note

Stata's xi command prefix may be used with glm. Let us pretend that in the above example, we had ldose, the log dose of insecticide; n, the number of flour beetles subjected to each dose; and r, the number killed—all as before—except now we have results for three different kinds of beetles. Our hypothetical data includes beetle containing the values 1, 2, and 3.

```
. list
         beetle      ldose           n           r
 1.           1      1.6907          59           6
 2.           1      1.7242          60          13
 3.           1      1.7552          62          18
 4.           1      1.7842          56          28
 5.           1      1.8113          63          52
 6.           1      1.8369          59          53
 7.           1      1.8610          62          61
 8.           1      1.8839          60          60
 9.           2      1.6907          56           7
10.           2      1.7242          62           2
   (output omitted )
23.           3      1.8610          64          23
24.           3      1.8839          58          22
```

Let us assume that, at first, we wish to merely add a shift factor for type of beetle. We could type

```
. xi: glm r i.beetle ldose, f(bin n) l(cloglog)
i.beetle               Ibeetl_1-3    (naturally coded; Ibeetl_1 omitted)

Iteration 1 : deviance =    77.8983
Iteration 2 : deviance =    73.7830
  (output omitted )
Iteration 7 : deviance =    73.7651

Residual df  =        20                  No. of obs  =         24
Pearson X2   =  71.89011                  Deviance    =  73.76506
Dispersion   =  3.594506                  Dispersion  =  3.688253

Binomial (N=n) distribution, cloglog link
------------------------------------------------------------------------------
        r |      Coef.   Std. Err.      z    P>|z|     [95% Conf. Interval]
----------+-------------------------------------------------------------------
Ibeetl_2 |  -.0910396   .1059318    -0.859   0.390    -.2986621    .1165828
Ibeetl_3 |  -1.836058   .1303533   -14.085   0.000    -2.091546   -1.580571
   ldose |   19.41558   .9989705    19.436   0.000     17.45764    21.37353
   _cons |  -34.84602   1.801892   -19.339   0.000    -38.37767   -31.31438
------------------------------------------------------------------------------
```

We most certainly find evidence that the insecticide works differently on the third kind of beetle. We might now check whether the curve is merely shifted or also differently sloped:

```
. xi: glm r i.beetle*ldose, f(bin n) l(cloglog)
i.beetle               Ibeetl_1-3    (naturally coded; Ibeetl_1 omitted)
i.beetle*ldose         IbXldo_#      (coded as above)
Iteration 1 : deviance =    54.4141
Iteration 2 : deviance =    50.1942
  (output omitted )
Iteration 6 : deviance =    50.1697

Residual df  =        18                  No. of obs  =         24
Pearson X2   =  49.28442                  Deviance    =  50.16972
Dispersion   =  2.738023                  Dispersion  =  2.787207

Binomial (N=n) distribution, cloglog link
------------------------------------------------------------------------------
        r |      Coef.   Std. Err.      z    P>|z|     [95% Conf. Interval]
----------+-------------------------------------------------------------------
Ibeetl_2 |  -.7993241   4.586652    -0.174   0.862    -9.788996    8.190348
Ibeetl_3 |   17.78741   4.624834     3.846   0.000       8.7229    26.85192
   ldose |   22.04118   1.799356    12.249   0.000      18.5145    25.56785
IbXldo_2 |   .3838675   2.544069     0.151   0.880    -4.602417    5.370152
IbXldo_3 |    -10.726   2.548176    -4.209   0.000    -15.72033   -5.731665
   _cons |  -39.57232   3.240274   -12.213   0.000    -45.92314    -33.2215
------------------------------------------------------------------------------
```

We find that the (complementary log-log) dose-response curve for the third kind of beetle has roughly half the slope of that for the first kind.

The results here are unimportant—the data is fictional—what is important is that xi can be combined with glm just as it can with any other Stata estimation command; see [R] **xi**. Also see [U] **34 Commands for dealing with categorical variables**; what is said there concerning linear regression is equally applicable to any GLM model.

❑

❑ Technical Note

After glm estimation you may perform any of the post-estimation commands you would perform after any other kind of estimation in Stata; see [U] **26 Estimation and post-estimation commands**. If, continuing with the previous example, you wanted to test the joint significance of all the interaction terms, you could type

```
. testparm I*
 ( 1)   Ibeetl_2 = 0.0
 ( 2)   Ibeetl_3 = 0.0
 ( 3)   IbXldo_2 = 0.0
 ( 4)   IbXldo_3 = 0.0
           chi2(  4) =   243.56
        Prob > chi2 =    0.0000
```

If you wanted to print the variance-covariance matrix of the estimators, you type correlate, _coef (to see it as a correlation matrix) or correlate, _coef cov (to see the covariances themselves).

You can even use predict to obtain the linear prediction and the standard error of the predictions, but for other predicted values, you use the glm-specific glmpred estimation command.

If you use the linktest post-estimation command, do not forget to specify the family() and link() option on the linktest command; see [R] **linktest**.

❑

Saved Results

In addition to standard post-estimation results, glm saves in the global S_# macros:

S_1	number of observations	S_3	overall deviance
S_2	residual degrees of freedom	S_4	Pearson χ^2.

Acknowledgments

glm was written by Patrick Royston of the Royal Postgraduate Medical School, London. The original version of this routine was published in Royston (1994). Royston's work, in turn, was based on a prior implementation by Joseph Hilbe, first published in Hilbe (1993).

Methods and Formulas

`glm` and `glmpred` are implemented as ado-files.

The canonical reference on GLM is McCullagh and Nelder (1989). The term generalized linear model is due to Nelder and Wedderburn (1972), and many people use the acronym GLIM for GLM models. This usage is due to the classic GLM software tool GLIM by Baker and Nelder (1985).

`glm` obtains results by iteratively reweighted least squares (IRLS) as described in McCullagh and Nelder (1989). The implementation here, however, allows user-specified weights, which we denote v_j for the jth observation. Let M be the number of "observations" ignoring weights. Define

$$w_j = \begin{cases} 1 & \text{if no weights are specified} \\ v_j & \text{if fweights or iweights are specified} \\ Mv_j/(\sum_k v_k) & \text{if aweights are specified} \end{cases}$$

The number of observations is then $N = \sum_j w_j$ if fweights are specified and $N = M$ otherwise. Each IRLS step is performed by `regress` using w_j to multiply the weights.

Let d_j^2 denote the squared deviance residual for the jth observation:

For the Gaussian family, $d_j^2 = (y_j - \widehat{\mu}_j)^2$.

For the Bernoulli family (binomial with denominator 1),

$$d_j^2 = \begin{cases} -2\ln(1 - \widehat{\mu}_j) & \text{if } y_j = 0 \\ -2\ln(\widehat{\mu}_j) & \text{otherwise} \end{cases}$$

For the Binomial family with denominator m_j,

$$d_j^2 = \begin{cases} 2y_j\ln(y_j/\widehat{\mu}_j) + 2(m_j - y_j)\ln\big((m_j - y_j)/(m_j - \widehat{\mu}_j)\big) & \text{if } 0 < y_j < m_j \\ 2m_j\ln\big(m_j/(m_j - \widehat{\mu}_j)\big) & \text{if } y_j = 0 \\ 2y_j\ln(y_j/\widehat{\mu}_j) & \text{if } y_j = m_j \end{cases}$$

For the Poisson family,

$$d_j^2 = \begin{cases} 2\widehat{\mu}_j & \text{if } y_j = 0 \\ 2\big(y_j\ln(y_j/\widehat{\mu}_j) - (y_j - \widehat{\mu}_j)\big) & \text{otherwise} \end{cases}$$

For the gamma family, $d_j^2 = -2\big(\ln(y_j/\widehat{\mu}_j) - (y_j - \widehat{\mu}_j)/\widehat{\mu}_j\big)$.

For the inverse Gaussian, $d_j^2 = (y_j - \widehat{\mu}_j)^2/(\widehat{\mu}_j^2 y_j)$.

For the negative binomial,

$$d_j^2 = \begin{cases} 2\ln(1 + k\widehat{\mu}_j)/k & \text{if } y_j = 0 \\ 2y_j\ln(y_j/\widehat{\mu}_j) - 2[(1 + ky_j)/k]\ln[(1 + ky_j)/(1 + k\widehat{\mu}_j)] & \text{otherwise} \end{cases}$$

The deviance residual calculated by `glmpred` is $d_j = \text{sign}(y_j - \widehat{\mu}_j)\sqrt{d_j^2}$. The overall deviance reported by `glm` is $D^2 = \sum_j w_j d_j^2$. The dispersion of the deviance is D^2 divided by residual degrees of freedom.

Define the Pearson residual calculated by `glmpred` as

$$r_j = \frac{y_j - \widehat{\mu}_j}{\sqrt{V(\widehat{\mu}_j)}}$$

where $V(\widehat{\mu}_j)$ is the family-specific variance function.

$$V(\widehat{\mu}_j) = \begin{cases} \widehat{\mu}_j(1 - \widehat{\mu}_j/m_j) & \text{if binomial or Bernoulli } (m_j = 1) \\ \widehat{\mu}_j^2 & \text{if gamma} \\ 1 & \text{if Gaussian} \\ \widehat{\mu}_j^3 & \text{if inverse Gaussian} \\ \widehat{\mu}_j + k\widehat{\mu}_j^2 & \text{if negative binomial} \\ \widehat{\mu}_j & \text{if Poisson} \end{cases}$$

The Pearson χ^2 reported by `glm` is $\sum_j w_j r_j^2$. The corresponding dispersion is χ^2 divided by residual degrees of freedom.

References

Baker, R. J. and J. A. Nelder. 1985. *The Generalized Linear Interactive Modelling System, release 3.77.* Oxford: Numerical Algorithms Group.

Hilbe, J. 1993. sg16: Generalized linear models. *Stata Technical Bulletin* 11: 20–28. Reprinted in *Stata Technical Bulletin Reprints*, vol. 2, pp. 149–159.

Hosmer, D. W., Jr. and S. Lemeshow. 1989. *Applied Logistic Regression.* New York: John Wiley & Sons.

McCullagh, P. and J. A. Nelder. 1989. *Generalized Linear Models.* 2d ed. London: Chapman & Hall.

Nelder, J. A. and R. W. M. Wedderburn. 1972. Generalized linear models. *Journal of the Royal Statistical Society*, Series A, 135: 370–384.

Pregibon, D. 1980. Goodness of link tests for generalized linear models. *Applied Statistics* 29: 15–24.

Rogers, W. H. 1993. sg16.4: Comparison of nbreg and glm for negative binomial. *Stata Technical Bulletin* 16: 7. Reprinted in *Stata Technical Bulletin Reprints*, vol. 3, pp. 82–84.

Royston, P. 1994. sg22: Generalized linear models: revision of glm. *Stata Technical Bulletin* 18: 6–11. Reprinted in *Stata Technical Bulletin Reprints*, vol. 3, pp. 112–121.

Also See

[U] **20.5 Accessing coefficients and standard errors**, [U] **26 Estimation and post-estimation commands**

[R] **fit**, [R] **lincom**, [R] **linktest**, [R] **logistic**, [R] **nbreg**, [R] **poisson**, [R] **predict**, [R] **regress**, [R] **st stweib**, [R] **sw**, [R] **test**, [R] **testnl**, [R] **vce**, [R] **weibull**, [R] **xi**, [R] **xtgee**

Title

> **glogit** — Logit and probit on grouped data

Syntax

> **blogit** *pos_var pop_var rhsvars* [*if exp*] [, *logit_options*]
>
> **bprobit** *pos_var pop_var rhsvars* [*if exp*] [, *probit_options*]
>
> **glogit** *pos_var pop_var rhsvars* [*if exp*] [*in range*] [, <u>level</u>(#) or]
>
> **gprobit** *pos_var pop_var rhsvars* [*if exp*] [*in range*] [, <u>level</u>(#)]

These commands share the features of all estimation commands; see [U] **26 Estimation and post-estimation commands**, but also see the warning below.

To reset problem-size limits, see [R] **matsize**.

Description

blogit and **bprobit** produce maximum-likelihood logit and probit estimates on grouped ("blocked") data; **glogit** and **gprobit** produce weighted least squares estimates. In the syntax diagrams above, *pos_var* and *pop_var* refer to variables containing the total number of positive responses and the total population.

All commands, typed without arguments, redisplay previous estimation results.

Warning: Although these commands share the features of all estimation commands, **predict** returns the index, not the probability, after **glogit** and **gprobit**. See *Methods and Formulas* below for instructions on obtaining predicted probabilities.

See [R] **logit**, [R] **logistic**, and [R] **probit** for obtaining maximum-likelihood estimates on ungrouped (individual or micro) data.

Options

logit_options refers to the options allowed by the **logit** command; see [R] **logit**. Most importantly, these include **level()** and **or**; see below.

probit_options refers to the options allowed by the **probit** command; see [R] **probit**. Most importantly, this includes **level()**.

level(#) specifies the confidence level, in percent, for confidence intervals. The default is **level(95)** or as set by **set level**; see [U] **26.4 Specifying the width of confidence intervals**.

or reports the estimated coefficients transformed to odds ratios, i.e., e^b rather than b. Standard errors and confidence intervals are similarly transformed. This option affects how results are displayed, not how they are estimated. **or** may be specified at estimation or when replaying previously estimated results.

Remarks

Maximum-likelihood estimates

blogit produces the same results as logit and logistic, bprobit as probit, but the "blocked" commands accept data in slightly different "shape". Consider the following two datasets:

```
. use xmpl1, clear

. list

     agecat    exposed      died       pop
1.        0          0         0       115
2.        0          0         1         5
3.        0          1         0        98
4.        0          1         1         8
5.        1          0         0        69
6.        1          0         1        16
7.        1          1         0        76
8.        1          1         1        22

. use xmpl2, clear

. list

     agecat    exposed    deaths       pop
1.        0          0         5       120
2.        0          1         8       106
3.        1          0        16        85
4.        1          1        22        98
```

These two datasets contain the same information; observations 1 and 2 of xmpl correspond to observation 1 of xmpl2; observations 3 and 4 of xmpl11 correspond to observation 2 of xmpl2; and so on.

The first observation of xmpl11 says that, for agecat==0 and exposed==0, 115 subjects did not die (died==0). The second observation says that, for the same agecat and exposed groups, 5 subjects did die (died==1). In xmpl2, the first observation says that there were 5 deaths out of a population of 120 in agecat==0 and exposed==0. These are two different ways of saying the same thing. Both of these datasets are transcriptions from the following table reprinted in Rothman (1986, 187) for age-specific deaths from all causes for tolbutamide and placebo treatment groups (University Group Diabetes Program 1970):

	Age through 54		Age 55 and above	
	Tolbutamide	Placebo	Tolbutamide	Placebo
Dead	8	5	22	16
Surviving	98	115	76	79

The data in xmpl11 is said to be "fully relational", which is computer jargon meaning that each observation corresponds to one cell of the table. Stata typically prefers data in this way. The second form of storing this data in xmpl2 is said to be "folded", which is computer jargon for something less than fully relational.

blogit and bprobit deal with "folded" data and produce the same results as logit and probit would if the data had been stored in its "fully relational" representation.

▷ Example

For the tolbutamide data, the fully relational representation would have been preferred: You could then use `logistic`, `logit`, and any of the epidemiological table commands; see [R] **logistic**, [R] **logit**, and [R] **epitab**. Nevertheless, there are occasions when the folded representation seems more natural. With `blogit` and `bprobit`, you avoid the tedium of having to unfold the data:

```
. use xmpl2, clear
. blogit deaths pop agecat exposed, or
Logit Estimates                                 Number of obs =      409
                                                chi2(2)       =    22.47
                                                Prob > chi2   =   0.0000
Log Likelihood =  -142.6212                     Pseudo R2     =   0.0730
------------------------------------------------------------------------
_outcome | Odds Ratio   Std. Err.      z     P>|z|    [95% Conf. Interval]
---------+--------------------------------------------------------------
  agecat |   4.216299   1.431519    4.238   0.000     2.167361   8.202223
 exposed |   1.404674    .4374454   1.091   0.275      .7629451  2.586175
------------------------------------------------------------------------
```

Had we not specified the `or` option, results would have been presented as coefficients rather than odds ratios. The estimated odds ratio of death for tolbutamide exposure is 1.40, although the 95% confidence interval includes 1. (By comparison, this same data, in its fully relational form, was used in [R] **epitab** to demonstrate the `cs` command. The Mantel–Haenszel weighted odds ratio was 1.40 with a 95% confidence interval of 0.76 and 2.58.)

We can see the underlying coefficients by replaying the estimation results and not specifying the `or` option:

```
. blogit
Logit Estimates                                 Number of obs =      409
                                                chi2(2)       =    22.47
                                                Prob > chi2   =   0.0000
Log Likelihood =  -142.6212                     Pseudo R2     =   0.0730
------------------------------------------------------------------------
_outcome |    Coef.    Std. Err.      z     P>|z|    [95% Conf. Interval]
---------+--------------------------------------------------------------
  agecat |   1.438958    .3395203   4.238   0.000      .7735101  2.104405
 exposed |   .3398053    .3114213   1.091   0.275     -.2705692   .9501798
   _cons |  -2.968471    .33234    -8.932   0.000     -3.619846  -2.317097
------------------------------------------------------------------------
```

◁

▷ Example

`bprobit` works like `blogit`, substituting the probit for the logit likelihood function.

```
. bprobit deaths pop agecat exposed
Probit Estimates                                Number of obs =      409
                                                chi2(2)       =    22.58
                                                Prob > chi2   =   0.0000
Log Likelihood = -142.56478                     Pseudo R2     =   0.0734
------------------------------------------------------------------------
_outcome |    Coef.    Std. Err.      z     P>|z|    [95% Conf. Interval]
---------+--------------------------------------------------------------
  agecat |   .7542049    .170969    4.411   0.000      .4191118  1.089298
 exposed |   .1906236    .1666057   1.144   0.253     -.1359176   .5171649
   _cons |  -1.673973    .1619592 -10.336   0.000     -1.991407  -1.356539
------------------------------------------------------------------------
```

◁

Weighted least squares estimates

▷ Example

You have state data on the number of marriages (`marriage`), the total population aged 18 years or more (`pop18p`), and the median age (`medage`). The data excludes Nevada, and so has 49 observations. You create a new variable called `medage2` equal to age squared by typing `generate medage2=medage^2` and now wish to estimate a logit equation for the marriage rate:

```
. glogit marriage pop18p medage medage2
Weighted least squares logit estimates for grouped data:
```

Source	SS	df	MS		Number of obs =	49
					F(2, 46) =	12.05
Model	.743083768	2	.371541884		Prob > F =	0.0001
Residual	1.41852928	46	.030837593		R-squared =	0.3438
					Adj R-squared =	0.3152
Total	2.16161305	48	.045033605		Root MSE =	.17561

Logit	Coef.	Std. Err.	t	P>|t|	[95% Conf. Interval]	
medage	-.7581404	.2964699	-2.557	0.014	-1.354903	-.1613775
medage2	.0113728	.0048501	2.345	0.023	.00161	.0211356
_cons	8.243371	4.525708	1.821	0.075	-.8664067	17.35315

◁

▷ Example

You could just as easily have estimated a grouped-probit model by typing `gprobit` rather than `glogit`:

```
. gprobit marriage pop18p medage medage2
Weighted least squares probit estimates for grouped data:
```

Source	SS	df	MS		Number of obs =	49
					F(2, 46) =	17.88
Model	.085135818	2	.042567909		Prob > F =	0.0000
Residual	.109525156	46	.002380982		R-squared =	0.4374
					Adj R-squared =	0.4129
Total	.194660974	48	.004055437		Root MSE =	.0488

Probit	Coef.	Std. Err.	t	P>|t|	[95% Conf. Interval]	
medage	-.4469112	.1162244	-3.845	0.000	-.6808588	-.2129637
medage2	.006902	.0018857	3.660	0.001	.0031063	.0106977
_cons	4.958584	1.78923	2.771	0.008	1.357051	8.560117

◁

Saved Results

See [R] **maximize** for results stored by `blogit` and `bprobit`.

See [R] **regress** for results stored by `glogit` and `gprobit`.

In addition, each of these commands stores its name in `S_E_cmd` and the name of the dependent variable in `S_E_depv`.

Methods and Formulas

blogit, bprobit, glogit, and gprobit are implemented as ado-files.

Maximum-likelihood estimates

The results reported by blogit and bprobit are obtained by maximizing a weighted logit or probit likelihood function. Let $F(\ )$ denote the normal or logistic likelihood function. The likelihood of observing each observation in the data is then

$$F(\beta x)^s \left(1 - F(\beta x)\right)^{t-s}$$

where s is the number of successes and t is the population. The term above is counted as contributing $s + (t - s) = t$ degrees of freedom. All of this follows directly from the definition of logit and probit.

Weighted least squares estimates

The logit function is defined as the log of the odds ratio. If there is one explanatory variable, the model can be written

$$\log\left(\frac{p_j}{1 - p_j}\right) = \beta_0 + \beta_1 x_j + \epsilon_j$$

where p_j represents successes divided by population for the jth observation. (If there is more than one explanatory variable, simply interpret β_1 as a row vector and x_j as a column vector.) The large sample expectation of ϵ_j is zero and its variance is

$$\sigma_j^2 = \frac{1}{n_j p_j (1 - p_j)}$$

where n_j represents the population for observation j. We can thus apply weighted least squares to the observations with weights proportional to $n_j p_j (1 - p_j)$.

As a practical matter, the left-hand-side logit is calculated as the $\log(s_j / f_j)$, where s_j represents the number of successes and f_j represents the number of failures. The weight is calculated as $(s_j f_j)/(s_j + f_j)$.

You can calculate the predicted probabilities by typing

```
predict bx
generate varname=1/(1+exp(-bx))
```

For gprobit, write $F(\ )$ for the cumulative normal distribution, and define z_j implicitly by $F(z_j) = p_j$, where p_j is the fraction of successes for observation j. The probit model for one explanatory variable can be written

$$F^{-1}(p_j) = \beta_0 + \beta_1 x_j + \epsilon_j$$

(If there is more than one explanatory variable, simply interpret β_1 as a row vector and x_j as a column vector.)

The expectation of ϵ_j is zero and its variance is given by

$$\sigma_j^2 = \frac{p_j(1 - p_j)}{n f^2 \left(F^{-1}(p_j)\right)}$$

where $f(\ )$ represents the normal density (Amemiya 1981, 1498). We can thus apply weighted least squares to the observations with weights proportional to $1/\sigma_j^2$.

You can calculate the predicted probabilities by typing

```
predict bx
generate varname=normprob(bx)
```

References

Amemiya, T. 1981. Qualitative response models: A survey. *Journal of Economic Literature* 19: 1483–1536.

Hosmer, D. W., Jr., and S. Lemeshow. 1989. *Applied Logistic Regression*. New York: John Wiley & Sons.

Judge, G. G., W. E. Griffiths, R. C. Hill, H. Lütkepohl, and Tsoung-Chao Lee. 1985. *The Theory and Practice of Econometrics*. 2d ed. New York: John Wiley & Sons.

Rothman, K. J. 1986. *Modern Epidemiology*. Boston: Little, Brown and Company.

University Group Diabetes Program. 1970. A study of the effects of hypoglycemic agents on vascular complications in patients with adult onset diabetes. *Diabetes* 19, supplement 2: 747–830.

Also See

[U] **20.5 Accessing coefficients and standard errors**, [U] **26 Estimation and post-estimation commands**

[R] **clogit**, [R] **lincom**, [R] **logistic**, [R] **logit**, [R] **maximize**, [R] **mlogit**, [R] **ologit**, [R] **predict**, [R] **probit**, [R] **test**, [R] **testnl**, [R] **vce**, [R] **xi**

Title

> **gph** — Low-level graphics

Syntax

gph open $\left[\text{, saving}(\textit{filename})\right]$

gph close

gph clear $\#_{r_1}\ \#_{c_1}\quad \#_{r_2}\ \#_{c_2}$

gph pen #

gph text $\quad\#_r\ \#_c\quad \#_{rotation}\quad \#_{alignment}\quad \textit{text}$

gph font $\#_{\Delta r}\ \#_{\Delta c}$

gph vtext $\textit{varname}_r\ \textit{varname}_c\ \textit{varname}_{str}\ \left[\text{if } \textit{exp}\right]\ \left[\text{in } \textit{range}\right]$

gph line $\quad\#_{r_1}\ \#_{c_1}\quad \#_{r_2}\ \#_{c_2}$

gph vline $\textit{varname}_r\ \textit{varname}_c\ \left[\text{if } \textit{exp}\right]\ \left[\text{in } \textit{range}\right]$

gph vpoly $\quad\textit{varname}_{r_1}\ \textit{varname}_{c_1}\quad \textit{varname}_{r_2}\ \textit{varname}_{c_2}\ \ldots\ \textit{varname}_{r_p}\ \textit{varname}_{c_p}$
$\quad\left[\text{if } \textit{exp}\right]\ \left[\text{in } \textit{range}\right]$

gph box $\quad\#_{r_1}\ \#_{c_1}\quad \#_{r_2}\ \#_{c_2}\quad \#_{shade}$

gph point $\quad\#_r\ \#_c\quad \#_{\Delta c}\quad \#_{symbol}$

gph vpoint $\textit{varname}_r\ \textit{varname}_c\ \left[\ \textit{varname}_{\Delta c}\ \textit{varname}_{symbol}\ \right]\ \left[\text{if } \textit{exp}\right]\ \left[\text{in } \textit{range}\right]$
$\quad\left[\text{, size}(\#_{\Delta c})\ \text{symbol}(\#_{symbol})\ \right]$

gph arc $\quad\#_r\ \#_c\quad \#_{\Delta c}\quad \#_{\phi_1}\ \#_{\phi_2}\quad \#_{shade}$

graph $\ldots\ \left[\text{, bbox}(\textit{bounding\_box})\ \ldots\right]$

The graphics screen is

$$(r_{\min}, c_{\min}) = (0,0) \qquad\qquad (0, 32000) = (r_{\min}, c_{\max})$$

$$(r_{\max}, c_{\min}) = (23063, 0) \qquad (23063, 32000) = (r_{\max}, c_{\max})$$

A *bounding_box* is defined as 7 comma-separated integers

$\#,\ \#,\ \#,\ \#,\ \#,\ \#,\ \#$

with the interpretation

$r_{\text{top}},\ c_{\text{left}},\quad r_{\text{bottom}},\ c_{\text{right}},\quad \textit{text height } \Delta r,\ \textit{text width } \Delta c,\quad \textit{rotation}$

A mapping is defined as $(y_{\min}, y_{\max}, x_{\min}, x_{\max}, a_y, b_y, a_x, b_x)$ such that the value (y, x) is mapped to screen coordinates (r, c) via

$$r = a_y y + b_y \qquad \text{if } y_{\min} \le y \le y_{\max}$$
$$c = a_x x + b_x \qquad \text{if } x_{\min} \le x \le x_{\max}$$

Description

gph provides programmers with access to Stata's low-level graphic routines. With these, virtually any graph can be programmed.

In addition, the high-level **graph** command has option **bbox**(*bounding_box*) that instructs **graph** to place its graphical output in the portion of the screen specified. Thus, programmers may use any high-level **graph** command as a subroutine.

gph commands may appear only inside a **program define**; gph commands may not be typed interactively.

Remarks

In order to understand Stata's low-level graphics capabilities, you must first learn to think of a graph in the way Stata thinks about it: like a matrix with rows and columns. The top left of the screen is labeled $(r_{min}, c_{min}) = (0, 0)$. The bottom right of the screen is $(r_{max}, c_{max}) = (23063, 32000)$. When you instruct gph to do anything, you instruct it in this metric.

Let us define a rectangle as $(r_1, c_1; r_2, c_2)$. Thus, the graphics screen is the rectangle $(0, 0; 23063, 32000)$.

The gph open and gph close commands

gph open opens the graphics screen; none of the other gph commands may be used until you have executed this command.

Once **gph open** has been executed, all of Stata's normal text output is suppressed. You could list the data, for instance, and **list** will run fine, but nobody will ever see the output because Stata discards it.

When you execute **gph close**, graph mode is closed and Stata returns to its normal behavior.

Thus, the simplest low-level graph program would read:

```
program define mygph
        gph open
        gph close
end
```

When you execute this program, the result will be an empty graphics screen.

The other gph commands

gph clear $\#_{r_1}$ $\#_{c_1}$ $\#_{r_2}$ $\#_{c_2}$ clears the specified rectangle. You need to use this command only when creating dynamic graphics. After **gph open**, the entire area is already cleared. **gph clear** is for clearing a subarea later.

gph pen # sets the current pen, where $0 \leq \# \leq 9$. After **gph open**, the pen is set to 1. All gph commands draw their graphical elements with the current pen. Pen 1 is recommended for text and pens 2 through 9 for other graphical elements. Pen 0 is the eraser. You may change pens as often as you wish.

gph text $\#_r$ $\#_c$ $\#_{rotation}$ $\#_{alignment}$ *text* displays *text* (using the current pen). The text is displayed "at" $(r, c) = (\#_r, \#_c)$. What "at" means is determined by the rotation and alignment.

$\#_{rotation}$ is 0 or 1; 0 means the text is to be presented horizontally from left to right; 1 means vertically, from bottom to top.

$\#_{alignment}$ contains -1, 0, or 1, standing for left justified, centered, or right justified.

In left-justified text, $(\#_r, \#_c)$ specifies the left-most point; the text is to extend to the right of the specified point. (If the text is aligned vertically, the point is the bottom-most point and the text is to extend above it.)

In centered text, $(\#_r, \#_c)$ specifies the center point. The text is to extend to the left and right of the specified point. (If aligned vertically, the text is to extend below and above the specified point.)

In right-justified text, $(\#_r, \#_c)$ specifies the right-most point; the text is to extend to the left of the specified point. (If the text is aligned vertically, the point is the top-most point and the text is to extend below it.)

Regardless of alignment and justification, the appropriate element of $(\#_r, \#_c)$ defines the baseline of the text. The lowercase letter p extends below the baseline.

gph font $\#_{\Delta r}$ $\#_{\Delta c}$ specifies the font size for the text in units of height Δr and width Δc. This affects the size of the characters displayed by gph text. After gph open, the font size is $\Delta r = 923$ and $\Delta c = 444$. We recommend that whatever values you set for Δr and Δc their ratio be approximately 2. You may change the font size as often as you wish.

gph vtext $varname_r$ $varname_c$ $varname_{str}$ is a variation on gph text. It presents N lines of horizontal, centered text, the location and text itself being obtained from the specified variables.

gph line $\#_{r_1}$ $\#_{c_1}$ $\#_{r_2}$ $\#_{c_2}$ draws a line from $(\#_{r_1}, \#_{c_1})$ to $(\#_{r_2}, \#_{c_2})$.

gph vline $varname_r$ $varname_c$ is a variation on gph line. It draws one connected line through the N points contained in the specified variables.

gph vpoly $varname_{r_1}$ $varname_{c_1}$ $varname_{r_2}$ $varname_{c_2}$ ... $varname_{r_p}$ $varname_{c_p}$ is a variation on gph vline. It graphs N separate lines, each line connecting the p points in an observation. If your goal is to form closed polygons, the first point must be respecified as the last point in the variable list.

gph box $\#_{r_1}$ $\#_{c_1}$ $\#_{r_2}$ $\#_{c_2}$ $\#_{shade}$ displays a shaded rectangle $(\#_{r_1}, \#_{c_1}; \#_{r_2}, \#_{c_2})$, $0 \leq \#_{shade} \leq 4$. Shade 4 is the darkest shading.

gph point $\#_r$ $\#_c$ $\#_{\Delta c}$ $\#_{symbol}$ displays a point at $(\#_r, \#_c)$. The symbols are

0	dot
1	large circle
2	square
3	triangle
4	small circle
5	diamond
6	plus

The larger the size parameter $\#_{\Delta c}$, the larger the symbol. $\#_{\Delta c} = 275$ is recommended.

gph vpoint $varname_r$ $varname_c$ $\left[varname_{\Delta c} \; varname_{symbol} \right]$ is a variation on gph point; N points are displayed, their location obtained from the specified variables and their corresponding sizes and symbols from either variables or options.

gph arc $\#_r$ $\#_c$ $\#_{\Delta c}$ $\#_{\phi_1}$ $\#_{\phi_2}$ $\#_{shade}$ of $\#_{\phi_2}$ to 32,767, displays a shaded sector of a circle—a pie-shaped wedge. The center of the circle is $(\#_r, \#_c)$. The radius of the circle is $\#_{\Delta c}$. The arc of the wedge extends from angle $\#_{\phi_1}$ through angle $\#_{\phi_2}$ of the circle. Angles are measured on a scale of 0 to 32,767, corresponding to 0 to 360 degrees, and measured clockwise from 12:00. Allowed values of $\#_{shade}$ are from 0 to 4 where 4 is the darkest shading.

Use of the high-level graph command as a low-level component

The `graph` command can be used as a component of your program. For instance, the following program displays two graphs on top of each other:

```
program define mygph
        gph open
        graph mpg weight
        graph mpg
        gph close
end
```

That obviously is not very useful, but `graph`'s `bbox()` option allows you to specify where the graphs are to appear

```
program define mygph
        gph open
        graph mpg weight, bbox(1000,0, 13500,15000, 850,390, 0)
        graph mpg, bbox(9500,15000, 22800,31000, 850,390, 0)
        gph close
end
```

The result is

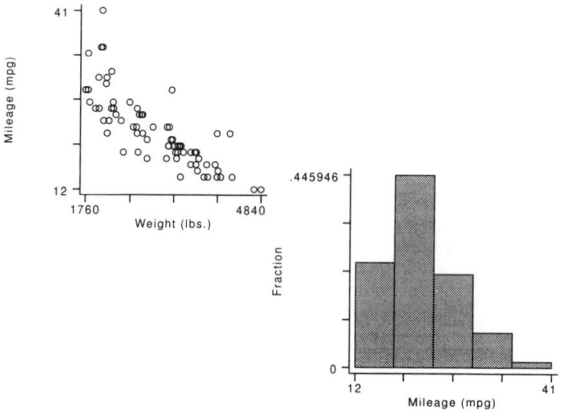

A bounding box contains 7 numbers

$$r_{top}, \quad c_{left}, \quad r_{bottom}, \quad c_{right}, \quad \text{text height } \Delta r, \quad \text{text width } \Delta c, \quad \text{rotation}$$

although the seventh, *rotation*, is not currently used and should be specified as 0.

The first four numbers specify the rectangle into which `graph` is to display its results.

The fifth and sixth numbers are the default text sizes from which `graph` derives all of its subsequent text sizes. Change these numbers and the text on the particular graph gets wider, longer, smaller, larger, etc.

In addition to accepting a bounding box, `graph` returns a bounding box, and this we can demonstrate interactively:

```
. graph mpg weight
  (output omitted)
. display "$S_G1"
0,0,22376,32000,923,444,0
```

In addition to the overall bounding box, `graph` returns the bounding box used by the data portion of the graph in $S_G2

```
. display "$S_G2"
1055,5425,19771,30945,443,213,0
```

and `graph` returns in `_result()` some other useful quantities:

```
. disp_res
   1.   12
   2.   41
   3.   1760
   4.   4840
   5.   -645.37931
   6.   27515.552
   7.   8.2857143
   8.   -9157.8571
```

See the *Saved Results* section for details. All of these results make it possible to add to a graph graphed by `graph`.

For instance, the following adds a triangle at the joint means of `mpg` and `weight` to a two-way scatterplot.

```
program define mygph
        gph open
        graph mpg weight
        local ay = _result(5)
        local by = _result(6)
        local ax = _result(7)
        local bx = _result(8)
        summarize mpg
        local y = _result(3)*`ay´ + `by´
        summarize weight
        local x = _result(3)*`ax´ + `bx´
        gph pen 3
        gph point `y´ `x´ 500 3
        gph close
end
```

The following program, which could be further developed, allows adding text to a two-way scatterplot after it has been drawn:

```
program define addtext
        local y = `1´
        local x = `2´
        mac shift 2
        local text "`*´"
        gph open                        /* begin low-level calls    */
        graph                           /* redisplay previous graph */
        local ay = _result(5)
        local by = _result(6)
        local ax = _result(7)
        local bx = _result(8)
        local r = `ay´*`y´ + `by´       /* convert data coordinates */
        local c = `ax´*`x´ + `bx´       /* to screen coordinates    */
        gph pen 1
        gph text `r´ `c´ 0 0 `text´     /* add to it                */
        gph close                       /* close graph              */
end
```

With the `addtext` command you could

```
. graph mpg weight
. addtext 39 2200 Outlier is diesel
```

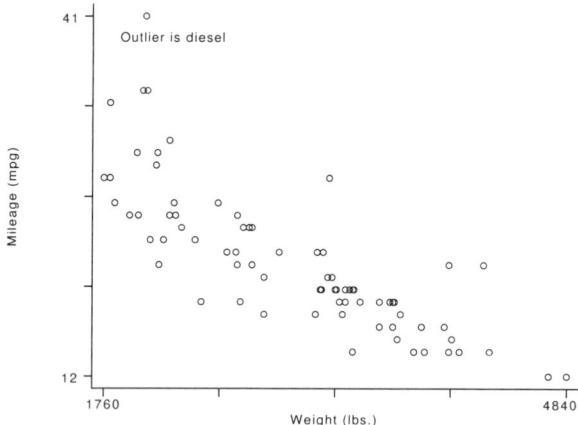

The numbers 39 and 2200 are in the data metric. The car yielding 41 mpg and weighing 2,040 pounds is the VW diesel.

Saved Results

The gph commands do not save any results, but the **graph** command saves in _result()

1.	y_{min}	5.	a_y
2.	y_{max}	6.	b_y, this and above used for $r = a_y y + b_y$
3.	x_{min}	7.	a_x
4.	x_{max}	8.	b_x, this and above used for $c = a_x x + b_x$

and saves in the global macro S_G1 the bounding box for the graphic and in S_G2 the bounding box of the data portion of the graph. The bounding box is a comma-separated list of seven values:

r_{top} , c_{left} , r_{bottom} , c_{right} , *text height* Δr , *text width* Δc , *rotation*

Also See

[R] **graph**

Title

> **graph** — Summary of graph command

Syntax

$$[\text{by } \textit{varlist}:] \ \underline{\text{gr}}\text{aph} \ [\textit{varlist}] \ [\textit{weight}] \ [\text{if } \textit{exp}] \ [\text{in } \textit{range}] \ [\text{, } \textit{options}]$$

$$\underline{\text{gr}}\text{aph using } \textit{filename} \ [\textit{filename} \ \ldots] \ [\text{, } \textit{options}]$$

$$\underline{\text{set}} \ \underline{\text{g}}\text{raphics} \ \{\text{on} \,|\, \text{off}\}$$

$$\underline{\text{set}} \ \underline{\text{t}}\text{extsize} \ \#$$

`aweights`, `fweights`, and `iweights` are allowed; see [U] **18.1.6 weight**. All are treated identically.

Description

graph draws graphs. **graph** typed without arguments redisplays the last graph drawn using the current data and loads the underlying **graph** command into the console review buffer; see [R] **graph redisplaying**.

set graphics determines whether graphs produced by **graph** are displayed on your monitor; see [R] **graph monitors**. The default is **on** if your monitor is capable of displaying graphs, otherwise it is **off**. Turning **graphics off** can be useful when you are using a do-file to save a series of graphs as .gph files; see [R] **graph monitors** for details. **set graphics on** restores the displaying of graphs after **set graphics off**. Unix windowing system users should also see [R] **xwindow**.

set textsize sets the overall size of text fonts used by **graph**; see [R] **graph textsize**.

Remarks

These remarks are not intended to fully explain **graph**. They provide only a brief overview. For further information, see *What to read* below. **graph** provides eight styles, specified as options in the first syntax:

Option	Meaning	Comment
histogram	Histogram	default when one variable is specified
twoway	Two-way scatterplot	default when more than one variable is specified. May be combined with oneway and box, but in that case you must specify twoway explicitly.
matrix	Two-way scatterplot matrix	up to 30 variables may be specified
oneway	One-way scatterplot	may be combined with box
box	Box-and-whisker plot	up to 6 variables may be specified
star	Star chart	up to 16 variables may be specified
bar	Bar chart	plot sums or means of variables
pie	Pie chart	plot sums of variables

29

Examples:

graph y x	plot y vs. x
graph y1 y2 x	plot y1 vs. x, y2 vs. x on the same graph
graph y x, twoway oneway box	plot y vs. x, draw a one-way & box on the same image
graph a b c, matrix	plot (a,b,c) vs. (a,b,c), arrange in matrix
graph a, oneway	produce a one-way scatterplot of a
graph a b, oneway	produce one-way scatterplots of a and b
graph a b, oneway box	produce two one-way scatterplots with boxes
graph a b, box	produce box-and-whisker for a and b
graph a b c d e, star	graph a, . . . , e as rays of star chart
graph a b c, bar	graph sums of a, b, and c as bars
graph a b c, bar means	graph means of a, b, and c as bars
graph a b c, pie	graph sums of a, b, and c as slices of pie

In addition to the eight basic styles, Figure 1 was made using Stata—it was *not* cut and pasted—so perhaps that makes a ninth style; see [R] **graph combining**.

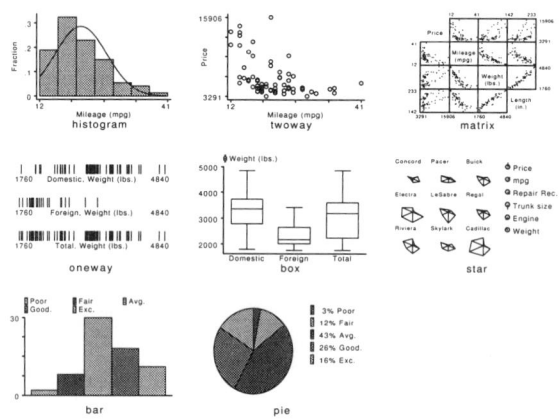

Figure 1.

Each of the eight basic styles corresponds to a *style option*, and we have titled each subimage above with the name of the option that drew it.

1. The histogram at the top left was made by typing graph mpg, histogram bin(7) normal. The histogram option was not strictly necessary because when we specify only one variable, graph assumes we want a histogram. The normal option overlaid a normal curve on our histogram. See [R] **graph histogram**.

2. The two-way scatterplot in the first row, second column, was drawn by typing graph price mpg, twoway. Again we did not have to bother with the twoway option because when we specify two or more variables, graph assumes we want a two-way scatterplot. See [R] **graph twoway**.

3. The scatterplot matrix in the upper-right corner was obtained by typing graph price mpg weight length, matrix. The matrix option was required in this case; had we omitted it, graph would have assumed we want a two-way scatterplot of price, mpg, and weight against length. See [R] **graph matrix**.

4. The one-way scatterplot on the far left of the second row was drawn by typing graph weight, oneway by(foreign) total. That's quite a few options, but the result was one graph for domestic cars, another for foreign cars, and a third for the combined total. See [R] **graph oneway**.

5. The box-and-whisker plot next to the one-way scatterplot was obtained by replacing oneway with the box option: graph weight, box by(foreign) total. See [R] **graph box**.

6. The star chart at the end of the second row was obtained by typing graph price mpg rep78 trunk displ weight in 1/9, star. See [R] **graph star**.

7. The bar chart was obtained by typing graph rep1-rep5, bar. See [R] **graph bar**.

8. The pie chart was obtained by typing graph rep1-rep5, pie. See [R] **graph pie**.

So how did we get the overall figure? In all the examples above, we typed two more options in addition to the ones we have already told you about. First, we specified a title() option to add a title underneath each graph. To obtain the histogram, we really typed graph mpg, bin(7) normal title("histogram"). To obtain the two-way scatterplot, we really typed graph price mpg, title("twoway"). You can specify better titles with the title() option, but these served our purposes. See [R] **graph titles**.

Finally, we specified the saving() option as well. When you draw a graph in Stata, you normally see it on the screen and that's it. Stata for Windows users can print at that point, but others must save the graph in a file—a .gph file—and then print. Windows users can also save graphs in files, and in this case we saved the graphs because we wanted to combine them into a single image—see [R] **graph combining**—which we then printed.

So, we drew the histogram by typing

```
. graph mpg, bin(7) normal title("histogram") saving(part1)
```

which drew the picture on our monitor *and* saved it in a file called part1.gph. We drew the two-way scatterplot by typing

```
. graph price mpg, title("twoway") saving(part2)
```

which created a file called part2.gph, and so on. When we were finished, we could review any of our graphs by typing graph using *filename*. We could, for instance, type

```
graph using part1
```

to see the histogram again. We flipped back through our graphs, satisfying ourselves that we had done everything right. Then we typed

```
. graph using part1 part2 part3 part4 part5 part6
          part7 part8, margin(15) saving(combined)
```

to make the combined graph and save it in a file called combined.gph. All that was left was to print it.

Remarks are presented under the headings

Common options

Most of the options are common across all of the graphic styles. We will review the common options first and then detail options unique to particular graphic styles.

Saving and printing the image

<u>sa</u>ving(*filename* [,replace])
              saves the graph in a file that can be reviewed by **graph using** and printed with the hard-copy drivers. If you do not specify an extension, .gph will be assumed.

              graph y x, saving(myfile) creates **myfile.gph** or refuses if **myfile.gph** already exists.

graph y x, `saving(myfile,replace)` creates or replaces
`myfile.gph`.

For instructions on subsequent printing, see [R] **graph printing DOS**,
[R] **graph printing Macintosh**, [R] **graph printing Unix**, or [R] **graph
printing Windows**.

Multiple-imaging options

by(*varname*) is allowed with all styles except `matrix` and `star`. It requests that graphs
be drawn separately for the groups defined by *varname* and be combined
into a single image. `graph y x, by(region)` would draw one graph for
each value of region and array them on the screen.

With `bar` and `box`, `by()` draws a single axis and then groups the bars or
boxes according to the *varname*. `graph y x, by(region) box` would draw
8 boxes if `region` took on 4 different values.

total may be specified only with `by()`. It requests that an additional group be
added to reflect all the data. If `region` takes on four values, `graph y x`,
`by(region) total` would draw five graphs in one image, one for each
region and one more for all four regions combined.

bsize(#) specifies the size of the text to be used to label the by-groups, with 100
(meaning 100% of normal) being the default. `bsize(150)` would increase
the size of the labels whereas `bsize(75)` would decrease them. `bsize()`
is also used with `star` to set the text size of the observation titles. Also see
`set textsize` below.

Rescale (note capitalization) is used only in combination with `by()`. It requests that
each by-group graph has its own scale. The default is to use the same scale
across all graphs in the by-group. (Do not confuse this option with `twoway`'s
`rescale`, which allows each variable on a graph to have its own scale.)

Specifying titles

title("*text*") adds a title in large letters at the bottom of the graph. Usually, the quotes
can be omitted if *text* contains no special characters. For example, `graph y`
`x, title(Figure 1. Raw Data)`.

t1title("*text*") are more titling options. There are two titles on every side of the figure.
t2title("*text*") The sides are referred to as `top`, `bottom`, `left`, and `right`. `b1title()` is
b1title("*text*") also known as simply the `title()`. These title options can always be
b2title("*text*") abbreviated by the first two characters of their name. `b2()` is the same
l1title("*text*") as `b2title()`. The first (#1) title on a side is always the title farther
l2title("*text*") from the figure. The second title is closer to the figure.
r1title("*text*")
r2title("*text*")

Setting the text size and gap

set textsize # is *not* an option but a separate command. You can control the text size used
in titles with the `set textsize` command. `textsize` is originally 100,
meaning 100% of "normal" size.

set `textsize` 125 will make the text 25% larger than normal.
set `textsize` 75 will make it smaller.

Example: `set textsize 125`
                    `graph y x, title("Figure 1")`

<u>gap</u>(#)   is an option. On any style that includes an axis, `gap()` sets the amount of space between the left title and the values along the axis. The default is 8 although it "should" be 9. If it were 9, the value labels could never run into the left title. In most cases, however, 8 is sufficient and 9 results in too much space to be aesthetically pleasing. You can close or widen the gap.

Labeling axes

<u>xlabel</u>[(#,...,#)]   `graph` usually labels just the minimums and maximums of the data.
<u>ylabel</u>[(#,...,#)]   These options request more aesthetically pleasing labels. On any style
<u>rlabel</u>[(#,...,#)]   that has a numeric x-axis, such as `histogram` or `twoway`, you can specify
<u>tlabel</u>[(#,...,#)]   `xlabel()`. Without arguments, `graph` will choose "round" values to be
                    labeled; with arguments, only the values that you choose will be labeled.
                    `ylabel()` works similarly.

`rlabel()` and `tlabel()` refer to the right- and top-axes, which `graph` does not typically label.

`graph y x, ylabel xlabel` plots y vs. x with round labeling of the axes.

`graph y x, ylabel xlabel(0,10,20,30,40)` does the same except the values 0, ..., 40 are labeled on the x-axis.

For the `matrix` style, the $\{x|y|r|t\}$`label()` options are not allowed. The `label` option, which allows no arguments, provides round labels.

Adding ticks and lines

<u>xtick</u>[(#,...,#)]   `graph` automatically places tick marks on axes anywhere they are labeled.
<u>ytick</u>[(#,...,#)]   These options allow you to specify additional ticking. They work the
<u>rtick</u>[(#,...,#)]   same way as $\{x|y|r|t\}$`label()`, described above.
<u>ttick</u>[(#,...,#)]

<u>xline</u>[(#,...,#)]   These options draw lines (using pen 1) across the graph. `yline()` and
<u>yline</u>[(#,...,#)]   `rline()` draw horizontal lines, `xline()` and `tline()` draw vertical
<u>rline</u>[(#,...,#)]   lines.
<u>tline</u>[(#,...,#)]

Setting the scale

<u>ys</u>cale(#,#)   These options attempt to widen the scale used for drawing a graph on
<u>xs</u>cale(#,#)   any style that has an axis (such as `twoway` or `histogram`). Left to its
<u>rs</u>cale(#,#)   own, `graph` chooses to scale each axis according to the minimum and maximum of all things that go on the axis. This includes the data and any labeling or ticking you specify.

$\{y|x|r\}$scale() adds two more numbers to the calculation. Thus, these options can widen the scale but never narrow it. The first number is the minimum and the second the maximum for the scale. Either can be specified as '.' to indicate that it is to be unchanged from what graph otherwise would have chosen.

Suppose x ranges from 1 to 9. graph y x, xscale(.,5) will have no effect on the scale: It will *not* graph solely the data for which x is between 1 and 5. graph y x if x<=5 will have the desired effect.

graph y x, xscale(0,.) would widen the x-scale to 0–9.
graph y x, xscale(.,10) would widen the x-scale to 1–10.
graph y x, xscale(0,10) would widen the x-scale to 0–10.

Setting the axes rendition

noaxis

graph typically draws an axis on any style that has an axis (such as twoway). noaxis requests that no axis be drawn. Axes are always drawn using pen 1.

[no]border

border requests that the axis be a complete border around the graph. On occasion, graph may decide by itself that a border would look better. On those occasions, noborder requests that only an axis be drawn.

graph y x, border requests a border rather than solely an axis.

border is also used in the matrix style to indicate that the diagonal entries are to be bordered.

Borders are always drawn using pen 1.

Creating log scales

log
ylog
xlog
rlog

specify log scales. log is used for histogram and the remaining options are used for twoway. rlog refers to the right scale and is allowed only on twoways with two vertical scales. The values of all labels, ticks, lines, etc., are specified in natural (unlogged) units.

Examples: graph y, log
               graph y x, ylog xlog
               graph y x, ylog
               graph y x, xlog
               graph y1 y2 x, rescale rlog

Specifying colors (pens)

pen(#...#)

specifies the pen to be used for each graphical element. All graphs are drawn with a theoretical concept called a *pen*. On color monitors, different pens are mapped to different colors. On monochrome monitors, all pens look alike (except pen 1 is sometimes dimmer than the others). When you print a graph on monochrome devices, the thicknesses of the pens can be altered. On color printers, different colors can be assigned.

Pens are numbered 1 through 9. graph uses pen 1 for labeling. Thereafter, each graphical element, corresponding to the variables in the *varlist*, is graphed using successively higher numbered pens, wrapping back to pen 2 after pen 9.

graph y1 y2 x graphs y1 vs. x using pen 2 and y2 vs. x using pen 3.

graph y1 y2 x, pen(23) does the same thing.

graph y1 y2 x, pen(22) graphs both series using the same pen.

Specifying shading

<u>shad</u>ing(#...#)

specifies the amount of shading on a scale of 1 to 4, with 1 being the lightest and 4 the darkest. shading() is allowed on histogram, bar, and pie. For histograms, only one number is specified, and the default value is 3.

For bar and pie, a shading value is specified for each variable. The default is 31423142....

Examples: graph x, hist shading(4)
graph a b c, bar shading(413)
graph a b c d e, pie shading(41324)

Specifying plotting symbols

<u>s</u>ymbol(s...s)

specifies the symbols used to draw points in twoway and matrix styles. symbol() may be abbreviated s(). Specify s as

O	large circle (default for twoway)
S	large square
T	large triangle
o	small circle (default for twoway with by, or matrix)
d	small diamond
p	small plus
.	dot
i	invisible
[*varname*]	variable to be used as text
[_n]	use obs. no. as symbol

When [*varname*] is the plotting symbol, the values of *varname* are used as the plotting symbol for each observation. *varname* may be either a string or a numeric variable. For instance, if *varname* were a string variable containing "Ca", "Wa", and "Or" in its first three observations, then the text Ca would be used as the plotting symbol for the first observation, Wa for the second, and Or for the third.

Examples: graph y x, symbol(o)
graph y x, s(.)
graph y1 y2 x, s(OS)
graph y1 y2 x, s(oo)
graph y x, s([state])
graph y x, s([_n])
graph y1 y2 x, s([state]o)
graph y1 y2 x, s([state][_n])
graph a b c d, matrix sy(.)

<u>tr</u>im(#)

is used only when one or more of the plotting symbols is [*varname*]. # specifies the maximum number of characters to be placed on the graph and defaults to 8. It may be set to numbers smaller or larger than 8. For instance, if *varname* were a string variable containing "California, " Washington", and "Oregon" in its first three observations, graph y x, s([*varname*]) trim(2) would use Ca as the plotting symbol for the first observation, Wa for the second, and Or for the third.

psize(#)   specifies the size of [*varname*] plotting symbols. The default is 100. For example, psize(150) uses larger and psize(75) uses smaller symbols.

Connecting points

connect(*c...c*)   specifies if points are to be connected in twoway and matrix plots. connect() may be abbreviated c(). Specify *c* as

.	do not connect (default)
l	draw straight lines between points
L	draw straight lines between ascending-x points
m	connect median bands using straight lines
s	connect median bands using cubic splines
J	connect rectilinearly, making steps
||	connect two variables vertically (high-low)
II	same as ||, but cap bottom and top of line

For twoway, l, L, and J mean connect points in order of the data. To connect in order of the *x*-axis, also specify the sort option. graph a b c, c(.l) sort plots a vs. c not connecting points and b vs. c connecting points with straight lines.

Specifying plotting symbols and connecting points

The invisible plotting symbol i and the connect() option can be usefully combined. To estimate and graph a regression line with the underlying data:

```
regress y x
predict hat
graph y hat x, c(.l) s(Oi) sort
```

Translating: y vs. x is not connected (.) and plotted with large circles (O); hat against x is connected (l) but the individual points are plotted invisibly (i); and sort requests the data be sorted into x-order before graphing.

One could also visually compare the regression fit with a cubic spline:

```
graph y hat x, c(sl) s(Oi) sort
```

High-low charts

Example: graph close high low time, s(oii) c(.\|\|)

Translating: Graph close against time using small circles; do not connect the points. Graph high and low against time, using the invisible symbol, seemingly adding nothing to the graph. Draw a vertical line between high and low at each time. If we wanted to cap the line, we would specify c(.II).

Result: Graph showing the closing price with overlaid vertical lines showing the day's high and low price.

Median bands used in connect(m) and connect(s)

<u>band</u>s(#)   specifies the number of bands along the x-axis in which data is summarized
                         and medians of x and y calculated. connect(m) then connects those cross-
                         medians whereas connect(s) uses the cross-medians to calculate a cubic
                         spline. Default is 200. Reducing the number to 12, for instance, results in
                         substantial smoothing.

                         Example: graph y x, s(o) c(s) bands(12)

Cubic spline rendition

<u>d</u>ensity(#)   specifies the number of points to be calculated between bands (knots) on the
                         cubic spline. Default is 5. Increasing density to 100, for instance, results in
                         a smoother-appearing image.

                         Example: graph y x, s(o) c(s) bands(12) density(100)

Options unique to histogram

<u>b</u>in(#)   specifies the number of intervals to use for accumulating the histogram.
                         Default is 5.

<u>freq</u>   labels the vertical axis in frequency units rather than fractional units.

<u>norma</u>l$\big[(\#,\#)\big]$ draws a normal density over the histogram. normal by itself will calculate
                         and use the observed mean and standard deviation. normal(1,2) would
                         overlay a normal with mean 1 and standard deviation 2.

<u>d</u>ensity(#)   is used only with normal. It specifies the number of points along the density
                         to be calculated. Default is 100.

Options unique to twoway

<u>j</u>itter(#)   adds spherical random noise to the point before graphing, where # represents
                         the magnitude of the noise as a percent of graphical area. The default is 0. 5
                         is a large amount. (This is useful to keep categorical data from overplotting.)
                         Also see *Weighted data*, below.

<u>r</u>escale   scales each y-variable independently. If there are two y-variables, the scale
                         for the first variable is presented on the left (x) axis and the scale for the
                         second on the right (r) axis. If there are more than two y-variables, no
                         vertical scale is labeled.

<u>r</u>box   places a rangefinder box plot on the graph.

{ <u>y</u>|<u>x</u>|<u>r</u> }<u>r</u>everse   reverses the indicated scale to run from high-to-low rather than low-to-high.

Options unique to oneway

<u>j</u>itter(#)   turns on # randomly selected points along the vertical line at the location of
                         the data, rather than display the entire line. Also see *Weighted data*, below.

Options unique to matrix

<u>h</u>alf	draws only the lower half of the matrix.
<u>j</u>itter(#)	is the same as for **twoway**. Also see *Weighted data*, below.

Options unique to box

[<u>no</u>]<u>alt</u>

graph automatically chooses whether all of the text labeling each box beneath the x-axis should be on the same line or if it should instead alternate between two lines. If you do not like **graph**'s choice, [no]alt allows you to enforce your preference. **alt** forces the staggered look whereas **noalt** forces the single-line approach.

<u>v</u>width

graph's **box** style produces variable-width box plots when you include the **vwidth** option. The width of the box is made proportional to the number of observations.

<u>r</u>oot

If you specify **vwidth** and add the **root** option, the width of the box is made proportional to the square root of the number of observations.

Options unique to bar

[<u>no</u>]<u>alt</u>

is the same as for **box**, above.

<u>means</u>

scales the bars according to the means of the variables rather than their sums. For example, **graph cost revenue, bar by(region)** graphs total cost and revenues for each region. **graph cost revenue, bar by(region) means** graphs average costs and revenues by region.

<u>stack</u>

stacks the bars for each variable rather than placing them side-by-side.

Options unique to pie

None.

Options unique to star

<u>label</u>(*varname*)

Star charts produce stars for each observation of the data. **graph** ordinarily labels each star with its corresponding observation number. **label()** uses the contents of the specified variable to label the observations. *varname* may be either a string or a numeric variable.

<u>select</u>(#,#)

The scaling of a star chart is a function of all the stars to be graphed. **select()** allows you to magnify a single or a few stars in the data while maintaining the same scaling. The first # specifies the first observation to be graphed and the second # specifies the last observation. **graph** still examines all of the data to set the scaling.

Example: graph a b c d, star label(name)
                 graph a b c d, star label(name) select(2,5)

Weighted data treatment by twoway and matrix

graph provides a number of options for dealing with weighted data. In twoway and matrix scatterplots, simply specifying a weight causes the symbols to be scaled so that their area is proportional to the weight of the observation. The scaling applies to text symbols as well as to the standard plotting symbols. The . symbol, however, always appears as a dot.

psize(#)   specifies the average size of the plotting symbols, where 100 means 100 percent of what graph otherwise would have chosen. psize(150) will increase the average size and psize(75) will decrease it.

graph scales symbols so that the sizes are a "fair" representation of population weights. To wit: If all the weights except one were 1,000 and the exception 999, the symbols will all be almost equal in size. The weight 999 observation will not be a dot and the weight 1,000 observations giant circles. That would be the result, however, if the exception had weight 1.

jitter(#)   offers an alternative. For each point, a circle of fixed radius is calculated and symbols are drawn randomly inside the circle, with the number of symbols proportional to the weight. This works best with the . symbol. # specifies the radius as a percent of graphical area. 5 is a large number.

Examples:

graph y x [w=pop]
  Plot y vs. x using a scaled circle to indicate the size of the population.

graph y x [w=pop], psize(150)
  Same as above, but make all the plotting symbols 50% larger.

graph y x [w=pop], s([name])
  Plot y vs. x using the observation's name as the plotting symbol. Make the text size proportional to the population.

graph y x [w=pop], symbol(.) jitter(4)
  Plot y vs. x, randomly turning on dots in a circle of radius 4% to indicate the size of the population.

graph y hat x [w=pop], s(Oi) c(.l) sort
  Plot y vs. x using a scaled circle to indicate the size of the population. Overlay hat vs. x, connecting the points with straight lines and suppressing the individual points. Perhaps hat was calculated by regress y x [w=pop] followed by predict hat.

Weighted data treatment by box

All statistics are correctly weighted. In addition,

vwidth   makes the width of the box proportional to the sum of the weights.

root   is used only with vwidth. It modifies the request to make the width proportional to the square root of the sum of the weights.

Weighted data treatment by oneway

Rather than a vertical line being drawn, points are randomly turned on along the line. The number turned on is proportional to the weight.

Weighted data treatment by bar and pie

Sums and means are correctly weighted.

graph using

The syntax is

$$\text{graph using } \textit{filename } \big[\textit{filename } [\dots] \big] \ \big[, \textit{options} \big]$$

where the options are

title("*text*")

{ t | b | l | r } { 1 | 2 }title("*text*")

margin(*#*)

saving(*filename*[,replace])

graph using not only allows you to review previously saved graphs but it also allows you to construct and save new images by combining previously saved graphs. The simplest use, however, is as follows:

. graph y x, saving(mypic)	(save the graph)
. *more Stata commands*	(do something else)
. graph using mypic	(find out what is in mypic)

Multiple imaging with graph using

If you specify more than one filename, all the images you specify will be placed on the screen simultaneously. The size of each of the images will, of course, be reduced so that they all fit, but there is no limit to the number of files that may be specified.

Unlike the optional Stata Graphics Editor (Stage), graph using provides little control over how the graphs are combined. You can obtain some control of the placement by creating a null graph and then including the null graph in the list of files to be displayed. graph using, saving(null) will create a null graph. graph using file1 file2 null file3 file4 null null null file5 would display five real graphs: four of them in a 2×2 array at the upper left of the image and the fifth at the lower right.

See [R] **graph combining**.

Adding titles with graph using

You can use any of the titling options to add titles to the combined graph. You can control the sizes of the titles just as you do with any other graph command, using set textsize (described above). For example:

```
. graph using hist hist2 twoway many, margin(5) t1(1980 CPS Data)
        title("Figure 1.  Summary of Data")
```

Saving new images with graph using

Finally, you might save the new image as combo.gph:

```
. graph using hist hist2 twoway many, margin(5) t1(1980 CPS Data)
        title("Figure 1.  Summary of Data") saving(combo)
```

Recombining images with graph using

Once `combo.gph` is saved, it can be reviewed by `graph using` and is as eligible as any other `.gph` file for subsequent inclusion in other combined graphs. A `.gph` file is a `.gph` file no matter how it is made.

A warning

Do not do the following:

```
. graph using myfile, title("A new title") saving(myfile,replace)
```

That is, *do not* attempt `graph using` and simultaneous `saving()` of the same file. Stata will attempt to catch this error, but it is not successful in all circumstances. This command will result in the contents of `myfile.gph` being lost.

What to read

The entries [R] **graph bar**, [R] **graph box**, [R] **graph histogram**, [R] **graph matrix**, [R] **graph oneway**, [R] **graph pie**, [R] **graph star**, and [R] **graph twoway** describe the use of the graphic style options.

[R] **graph saving** and [R] **graph printing**, read in that order, tell you everything you need to know to print graphs.

The remaining entries detail how to take control of the image and obtain various special effects. A suggested reading order is

[R] **graph redisplay**	Redisplay graphs
[R] **graph by**	Multiple imaging
[R] **graph titles**	Specify titles
[R] **graph textsize**	Control text size
[R] **graph axis labels**	Label axes
[R] **graph lines**	Add ticks and lines
[R] **graph axis scale**	Set the scale
[R] **graph axis rendition**	Set the axis rendition
[R] **graph log scales**	Create log scales
[R] **graph pens**	Specify colors and line thicknesses
[R] **graph shading**	Specify shadings for fill areas
[R] **graph symbol**	Specify plotting symbols
[R] **graph connect**	Connect points
[R] **graph combining**	Combine graphs into a single graph

Note that Stata's `graph` command can deal with weighted data; see [R] **graph weights**.

See [R] **graph monitors** for information on using Stata's graphics with various hardware and windowing systems.

There are other commands, besides `graph`, for drawing graphic images, too. Understanding `graph` is the basis for understanding the other commands. You may also wish to see

Entry	Type of graph
General:	
[R] **boxcox**	Box–Cox transform toward normality
[R] **cumul**	cumulative distributions
[R] **cusum**	binary-variable cumulative-sum plots
[R] **dotplot**	comparative scatterplots
[R] **factor**	greigen, graph eigenvalues after factor
[R] **fracpoly**	fracplot, fits fractional polynomial model
[R] **grmeanby**	graph means and medians by categorical variables
[R] **hilite**	highlight subset of observations in two-way scatter
[R] **hist**	histogram of categorical variable
[R] **kdensity**	kernel density
[R] **ksm**	locally weighted regression scatterplot
[R] **ladder**	ladder-of-powers histograms
[R] **logistic**	roc, logistic ROC curves after logistic
[R] **plot**	scatterplot using typewriter characters
[R] **serrbar**	standard error bar chart
[R] **stem**	stem-and-leaf plots
Diagnostic graphs:	
[R] **diagplots**	normal probability, chi-squared probability, quantile, quantile-normal, quantile-quantile, symmetry plots
[R] **fit**	regression diagnostics
[R] **logistic**	logistic regression diagnostics
Survival analysis:	
[R] **st sts graph**	graph Kaplan–Meier survival and failure curves both with and without Greenwood confidence bands
Quality control:	
[R] **qc**	cchart, graph number of nonconformities in a unit
	pchart, graph proportion of nonconformities in a subgroup
	rchart, graph R (dispersion) chart
	xchart, graph $\overline{X}$ (control line) chart
	shewhart, graph combined $\overline{X}$ and R chart

In addition, since Stata is programmable, users have implemented other useful graphs—see *References*.

References

Danuso, F. 1991. gr5: Triangle graphic for soil texture. *Stata Technical Bulletin* 2: 9–10. Reprinted in *Stata Technical Bulletin Reprints*, vol. 1, pp. 40–41.

Findley, T. 1991. sed3: Variable transformation and evaluation. *Stata Technical Bulletin* 2: 15. Reprinted in *Stata Technical Bulletin Reprints*, vol. 1, pp. 85–86.

Garrett, J. M. 1996. sg50: Graphical assessment of linear trend. *Stata Technical Bulletin* 30: 9–15. Reprinted in *Stata Technical Bulletin Reprints*, vol. 5, pp. 152–160.

Geiger, P. J. 1991. sbe3: Biomedical analysis with Stata: radioimmunoassay calculations. *Stata Technical Bulletin* 3: 12–15. Reprinted in *Stata Technical Bulletin Reprints*, vol. 1, pp. 68–73.

Goldstein, R. 1991. sg4: Confidence intervals for t-test. *Stata Technical Bulletin* 3: 25–26. Reprinted in *Stata Technical Bulletin Reprints*, vol. 1, pp. 116–118.

——. 1992. srd15: Restricted cubic spline functions. *Stata Technical Bulletin* 10: 29–32. Reprinted in *Stata Technical Bulletin Reprints*, vol. 2, pp. 185–189.

Gould, W. W. 1991. gr3: Crude 3-dimensional graphics. *Stata Technical Bulletin* 2: 6–8. Reprinted in *Stata Technical Bulletin Reprints*, vol. 1, pp. 35–38.

——. 1993a. gr3.1: Crude 3-dimensional graphics revisited. *Stata Technical Bulletin* 12: 12. Reprinted in *Stata Technical Bulletin Reprints*, vol. 2, p. 42.

——. 1993b. ssi5.1: Graphing functions. *Stata Technical Bulletin* 16: 23–26. Reprinted in *Stata Technical Bulletin Reprints*, vol. 3, pp. 188–193.

Gleason, J. R. 1996. gr18: Graphing high-dimensional data using parallel coordinates. *Stata Technical Bulletin* 29: 10–14. Reprinted in *Stata Technical Bulletin Reprints*, vol. 5, pp. 53–60.

Gray, J. P. and T. McGuire. 1995. gr16: Convex hull programs. *Stata Technical Bulletin* 23: 11–15. Reprinted in *Stata Technical Bulletin Reprints*, vol. 4, pp. 59–66.

Hamilton, L. C. 1992. *Regression with Graphics*, 128–129, 142. Pacific Grove, CA: Brooks/Cole Publishing Company. (This concerns constructing proportional added-variable (leverage) plots.)

Kuilen, G. van de. 1991. gr4: 3-dimensional contour plots using Stata and Stage. *Stata Technical Bulletin* 2: 8–9. Reprinted in *Stata Technical Bulletin Reprints*, vol. 1, pp. 39–40.

Salgado-Ugarte, I. H., M. Shimizu, and T. Taniuchi. 1994. sg23: Semi-graphical determination of Gaussian components in mixed distributions. *Stata Technical Bulletin* 18: 15–27. Reprinted in *Stata Technical Bulletin Reprints*, vol. 3, pp. 127–146.

Also See

[R] **query**

Title

graph axis labels — Label axes

Description

This entry discusses the `xlab` and `ylab` options to `graph`.

Remarks

In keeping with Stata's minimalist approach, `graph` typically labels just the minimums and maximums of the data, making the graphs more informative. For instance, using the `auto.dta`, typing `graph mpg weight` reveals not only the relationship but the range of the data, as well.

When analyzing data interactively, labeling just the minimums and maximums increases the information content of the graph. When making graphs for presentation, however, one often wants more and "rounder" labels. The `ylabel()`, `xlabel()`, `rlabel()`, and `tlabel()` options provide this.

On any style that has a numeric x-axis (such as `twoway` or `histogram`), you can specify `xlabel`. Without arguments, it requests that Stata choose round values to be labeled; with arguments, only the values you specify will be labeled. `ylabel`, `rlabel`, and `tlabel` work similarly for the y-axis, right-axis, and top-axis, respectively.

▷ Example

Let's graph `mpg` vs. `weight` in our `auto.dta` and include the `ylabel` and `xlabel` options. We will not bother to type out the whole words `ylabel` and `xlabel` since Stata always allows abbreviations; see [U] **18.2 Abbreviation rules**.

```
. graph mpg weight, ylab xlab
```

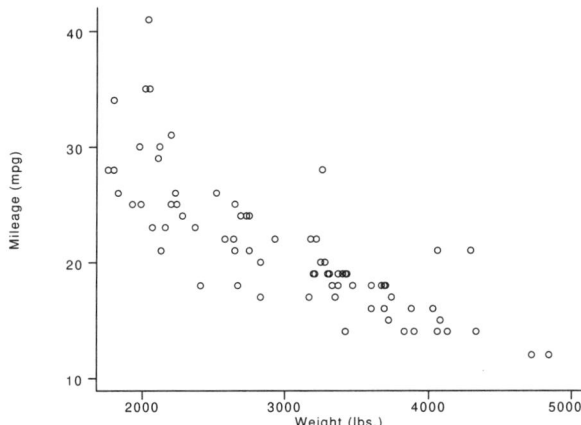

◁

▷ Example

The `tlabel` and `rlabel` options label the top and right scales, respectively. Stata normally suppresses these scales, but you can add one or both by specifying the appropriate option:

```
. graph mpg weight, ylab xlab tlab rlab
```

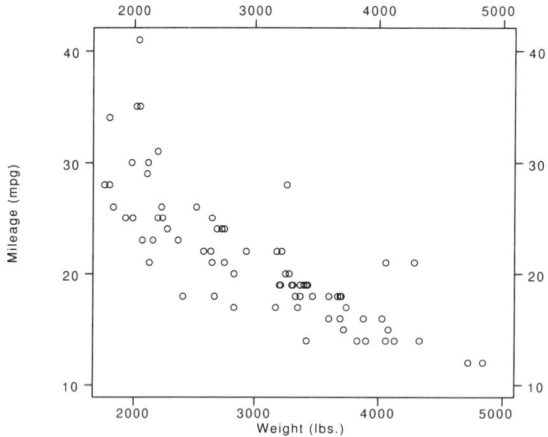

See [R] **graph twoway** for instructions on how to scale the left and right axes separately.

◁

▷ Example

Stata did a good job of choosing labels in the last example. That is not always the case. We tried graphing cooling degree days (`cooldd`) against average January temperature (`tempjan`) using our city data, and Stata chose to label the `cooldd` axis with the values 0, 2,000, and 4,000. That seemed a bit sparse, so now we take control and label the *y*-axis ourselves:

```
. graph cooldd tempjan, ylab(0,1000,2000,3000,4000) xlab by(region)
```

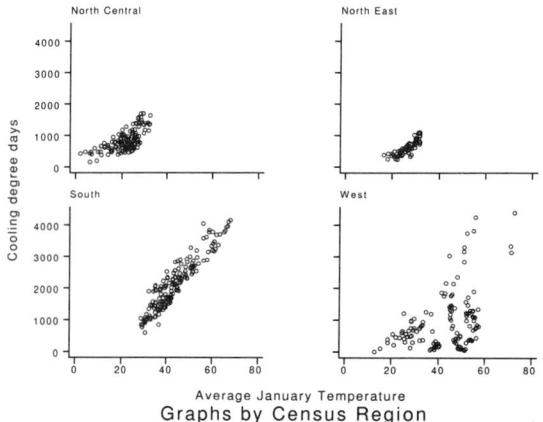

We included the `by()` option to show you how labeling works when an image consists of more than one graph; see [R] **graph by**.

◁

▷ Example

The `tlabel` and `rlabel` options can be quite effective when combined with `by()`. If you look at the graph in the previous example, you will note that Stata labels just the outside axes. Thus, the top-right graph has no values labeled at all since they are implied by the top-left and bottom-right graphs. Perhaps you might prefer

```
. graph cooldd tempjan, ylab(0,1000,2000,3000,4000) xlab by(region)
      rlab(1000,0,4000,2000,3000) tlab
```

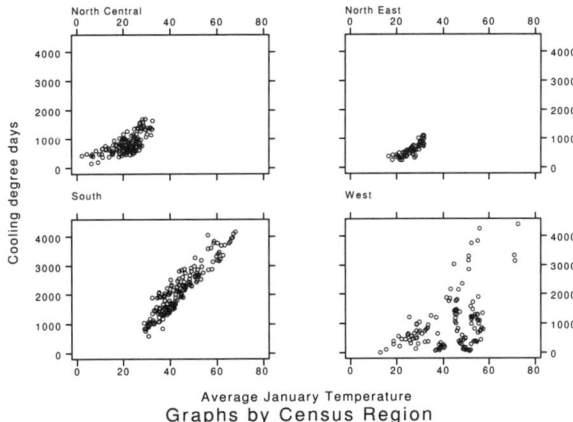

Notice that in the `rlabel()` option, we jumbled the order of the values to be labeled. Stata does not mind.

◁

□ Technical Note

Stata uses the *display format* of the variables for formatting the numbers; see [U] **19.5 Formats: controlling how data is displayed**. Thus, the January temperature of 20 degrees appeared as 20 and not 20.0 in the preceding image because `tempjan`'s format is the default `%9.0g`. If we had wanted all the temperatures to be displayed with one decimal place, we could have first typed `format tempjan %9.1f` and then issued our `graph` command.

□

□ Technical Note

For the scatterplot matrix, you label the axes with the `label` option. There is no option for labeling just the x- or y-axes. See [R] **graph matrix**.

□

References

Becketti, S. 1995. dm34: Constructing axis labels for dates. *Stata Technical Bulletin* 26: 8–11. Reprinted in *Stata Technical Bulletin Reprints*, vol. 5, pp. 32–36.

Hardin, J. 1995. dm28: Calculate nice numbers for labeling or drawing grid lines. *Stata Technical Bulletin* 25: 2–3. Reprinted in *Stata Technical Bulletin Reprints*, vol. 5, pp. 19–20.

Riley, A. 1995. dm26: Labeling graphs with date formats. *Stata Technical Bulletin* 24: 4–5. Reprinted in *Stata Technical Bulletin Reprints*, vol. 4, pp. 37–40.

Also See

[R] **graph**, [R] **graph lines**, [R] **graph titles**

Title

graph axis rendition — Set the axis rendition

Description

This entry discusses the `border` option to `graph`.

Remarks

Stata typically draws an axis on any style that has an axis (such as `twoway`). We say typically because Stata sometimes draws a complete border around the graph rather than an axis. Stata switches from an axis to a border whenever you tell it to label or tick something on the right or top axis; see [R] **graph axis labels** and [R] **graph lines**.

When Stata would normally draw an axis, specifying `border` forces it to draw a border instead. When Stata would draw a border, specifying `noborder` forces it to draw just an axis. You can suppress both the axis and the border by specifying `noaxis`.

▷ Example

Suppressing the axis can sometimes be remarkably effective. Suppose you have calculated values of the function $y = e^{-x/6} \sin x$ over the range $x = 0$ to 4π. This is how you would draw the graph:

```
. graph y x, noaxis yline(0) ylab ll(" ") t1("y = exp(-x/6) * sin(x)")
        symbol(i) connect(l)
```

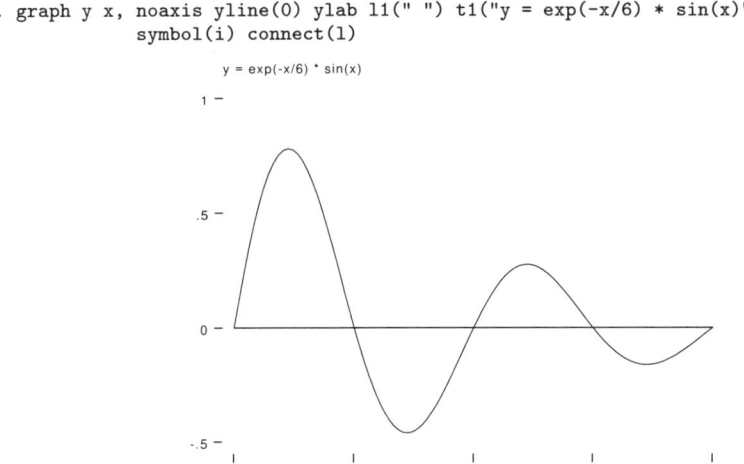

See [R] **graph symbol** and [R] **graph connect** for an explanation of the `symbol()` and `connect()` options. `symbol(i)` and `connect(l)` suppressed plotting the points and instead connected them with straight lines.

49

We suppressed the axis using the `noaxis` option and then, with `yline(0)`, we effectively drew our own x-axis; see [R] **graph lines**. We labeled the values on the invisible y-axis with `ylab` (see [R] **graph axis labels**), but suppressed the left title by specifying `ll(" ")` (see [R] **graph titles**). The blank inside the double quotes is important—`ll("")` would not have done the trick because then it would seem to Stata that we wanted the default `lltitle()`. Finally, we added a `t1title` identifying the function.

◁

▷ Example

Let's now go to the other extreme and put borders around our graphs. You can specify `border` even if you are unsure whether Stata would have supplied a border anyway:

```
. graph tempjan tempjuly, ylab xlab yline(32) rlab(32) border by(reg)
```

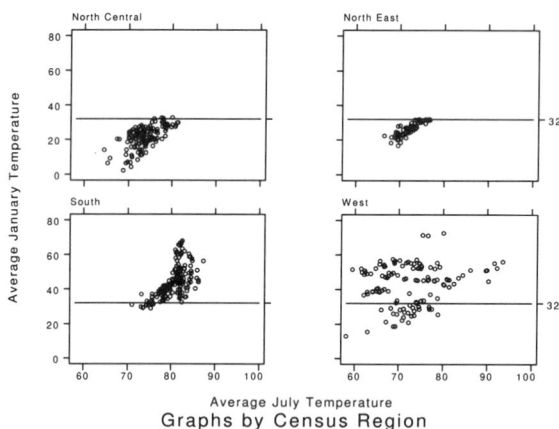

Graphs by Census Region

Specifying `border` was not really necessary in this case since the `rlabel()` option (see [R] **graph axis labels**) was enough to imply it. If we had not typed `rlab(32)`, however, Stata would still have drawn the borders because we requested them.

◁

Also See

[R] **graph**, [R] **graph axis labels**, [R] **graph axis scale**, [R] **graph log scales**

Title

graph axis scale — Set the scale

Description

This entry discusses the `xscale()`, `yscale()`, and `rscale()` options to `graph`.

Remarks

The `xscale()`, `yscale()`, and `rscale()` options allow you to widen, but not narrow, the scale used for drawing a graph on any style that has a numeric axis, such as `histogram` or `twoway`. (If using `by()`, the `Rescale` option allows different scales for each by-group; see [R] **graph by**. `twoway` allows up to two vertical scales, one on the left and the second on the right; see [R] **graph twoway**, but not before reading this entry.)

Left to its own, Stata chooses to scale each axis according to the minimum and maximum of all things that go on the axis. This includes the data and any labeling or ticking you specify. That is why, by default, the axes extend from the minimums to the maximums of the data.

Since `yscale()`, `xscale()`, and `rscale()` add two more numbers to this equation, these options can widen but never narrow the scale. The options require two arguments, a minimum and a maximum. Either can be specified as '.' (missing) to indicate that the scale is to be unchanged from what Stata otherwise would have chosen. In practice, these options are seldom specified.

▷ Example

Suppose x ranges from 1 to 9. Typing `graph y x, xscale(1,5)` will have no effect on the scale—Stata will *not* graph just the data for which x is between 1 and 5. None of the scaling options will ever cause Stata to omit data from the graph. If you want to graph just that subset of the data, type `graph y x if x<=5`.

Typing `graph y x, xscale(0,.)` would widen the x-scale from 1 to 9 to 0 to 9.

Typing `graph y x, xscale(.,10)` would widen the x-scale to 1 to 10.

Typing `graph y x, xscale(0,10)` would widen the x-scale to 0 to 10.

◁

Also See

[R] **graph**, [R] **graph axis labels**, [R] **graph axis rendition**, [R] **graph log scales**

Title

> **graph bar** — Graph bar charts

Description

This entry discusses the `bar` style option to `graph` and the options `means` and `stack`.

Remarks

Stata draws bar charts when you specify the `bar` option. The command `graph a b c, bar` produces a chart containing three bars with the height of each bar proportional to the *sum* of the respective variable.

To	Do
graph bars of **a**, **b**, and **c** with heights proportional to sums	`graph a b c, bar`
graph bars of **a**, **b**, and **c** with heights proportional to means	`graph a b c, bar means` see technical note below
graph bars of **a** by *category* with heights proportional to sums	`graph a, bar by(`*category*`)` see example below and [R] **graph by**
graph bars of **a** by *category* with heights proportional to means	`gr a, bar means by(`*category*`)`
graph bars of **a** and **b** by *category* with heights proportional to sums	`gr a b, bar by(`*category*`)` see example below and [R] **graph by**
graph stacked bars of **a** and **b** by *category* with heights proportional to sums	`gr a b, bar by(`*category*`) stack` see example below
control the shading of the bars	use `shading()`, see [R] **graph shading**
deal with weighted data	specify `fweight`, see [R] **graph weights**
force titling of by-groups to alternate between two lines	use `alt`, see technical note below
better control labeling of the *y*-axis	see [R] **graph axis labels**
add grid lines or tick marks to the *y*-axis	see [R] **graph lines**
suppress the axes	use `noaxis`, see [R] **graph axis rendition**
control the scaling (minimum and maximum of *y*-axis)	see [R] **graph axis scale**
add titles and annotations	see [R] **graph titles**
control the size of text	see [R] **graph textsize**
save or print the graph	see [R] **graph saving**, [R] **graph printing**

▷ Example

Suppose we have data recording the costs and profits of XYZ company where each observation reflects the financial information over a number of fiscal years. We wish to make a bar chart of labor costs, parts costs, advertising expenditures, and overhead, which we can obtain by typing `graph labor parts advert oh, bar`. The bar chart would contain four bars. If we want to break out the bar chart by year, we can add `by(year)` to the end of our command. We will add some other options to make the graph look prettier:

```
. graph labor parts advert oh, bar by(year) shading(3124) ylabel yline
        ti("Costs by Fiscal Year, XYZ Company")
        ll("(Thousands of Dollars)")
```

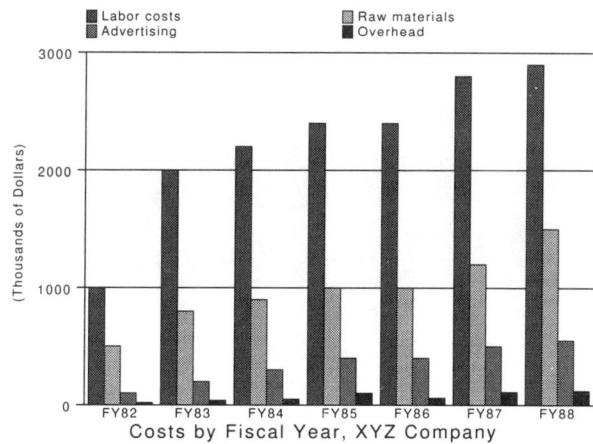

The resulting bar chart contains seven groups of four bars. The bars within the groups correspond to labor costs, parts cost, advertising, and overhead. The groups reflect the fiscal years 1982 through 1988.

See [R] **graph shading** for an explanation of the `shading()` option. See [R] **graph axis labels** for an explanation of the `ylabel` option—it added round value labels to the y-axis. See [R] **graph lines** for an explanation of the `yline` option—it added the horizontal grid lines across the graph. See [R] **graph titles** for an explanation of the `ti()` and `ll()` options—they added the titles.

We did not tell you a lot about the layout of our XYZ Company data because we did not need to. It does not matter whether observations reflect the costs for fiscal years or, say, fiscal months. Since Stata plots *sums* of variables, it will form the appropriate sum and make the chart automatically. All that is required is that the `year` variable mark observations that belong to the same year. In fact, our data is monthly.

◁

❏ Technical Note

Stata will also form bars whose heights are scaled to reflect *means* rather than sums when you include the `means` option. Now the organization of our data matters. If we specified `means`, the bars would reflect average *monthly* cost because our data is monthly. If our data were weekly, the bars would reflect average weekly cost.

❏

▷ Example

Stata is willing to stack the bars if we specify the **stack** option. Let's redraw our bar chart and try this feature:

```
. gr labor parts advert oh, bar by(year) sh(3124) ylabel yline
      ti("Costs by Fiscal Year, XYZ Company")
      ll("(Thousands of Dollars)") stack
```

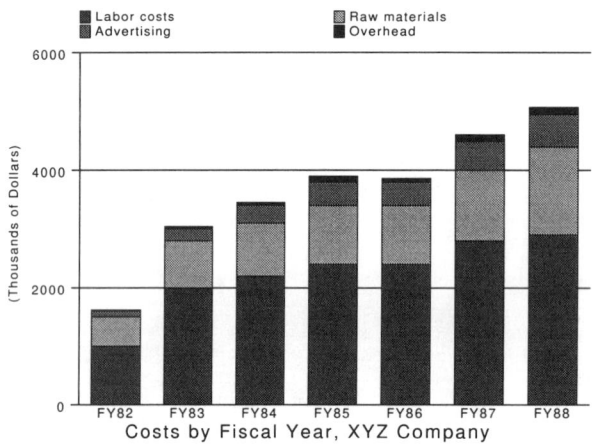

◁

▷ Example

Stata understands bars with negative heights. For instance, our XYZ Company data also includes profits, which were not so good in Fiscal-82:

```
. gr labor parts advert oh profit, bar by(year) sh(31241)
      ti("Costs and Profits by Fiscal Year, XYZ Company")
      ll("(Thousands of Dollars)") ylabel yline noaxis
```

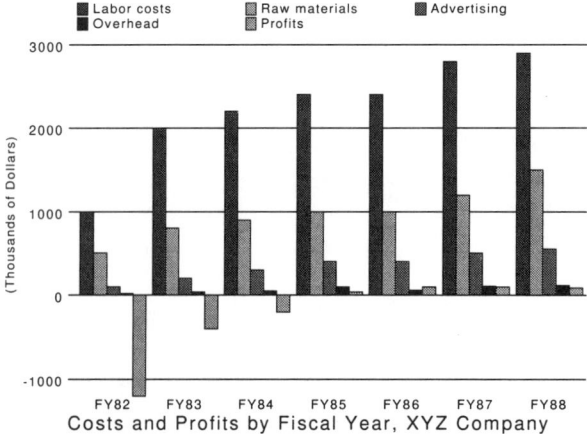

Even with the `stack` option, Stata can deal with negative bars:

```
. gr labor parts advert oh profit, bar by(year) sh(31241)
        ti("Costs and Profits by Fiscal Year, XYZ Company")
        ll("(Thousands of Dollars)") ylabel yline noaxis stack
```

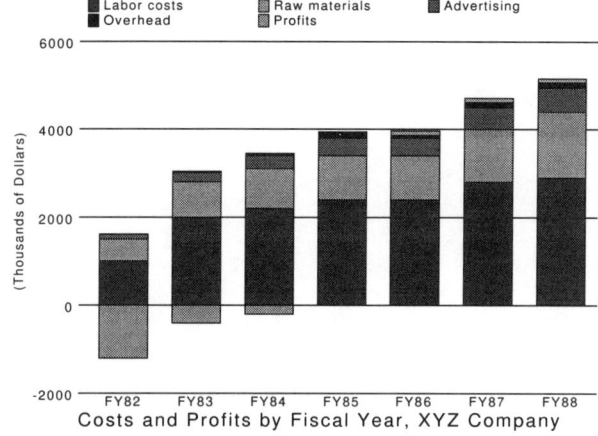

◁

□ Technical Note

You may specify up to six variables with the `bar` option. The maximum number of by-groups is 50, and the maximum number of bars (variables times by-groups) is 150.

□

□ Technical Note

Please see the last technical note in [R] **graph box**. What was said concerning the `alt` and `noalt` options applies here as well.

□

□ Technical Note

The first published bar chart appeared in William Playfair's *Commercial and Political Atlas* (1786). See Tufte (1983, 32–33) or Beniger and Robyn (1978) for additional historical information.

□

References

Beniger, J. R. and D. L. Robyn. 1978. Quantitative graphics in statistics: a brief history. *The American Statistician* 32: 1–11.

Playfair, W. 1786. *Commercial and Political Atlas.* London: Corry.

Tufte, E. R. 1983. *The Visual Display of Quantitative Information.* Cheshire, CT: Graphics Press.

Also See

[R] **graph**, [R] **graph axis labels**, [R] **graph axis scale**, [R] **graph by**, [R] **graph lines**, [R] **graph pens**, [R] **graph printing**, [R] **graph saving**, [R] **graph shading**, [R] **graph stage**, [R] **graph titles**, [R] **graph weights**, [R] **hist**

Title

graph box — Graph box-and-whisker plots

Description

This entry discusses the box style option and the [no]alt, vwidth, and root options.

Remarks

The box style option draws *box-and-whisker* plots, most often called simply box plots.

To	Do
graph box-and-whiskers for y and x	graph y x, box

graph box-and-whiskers for
  y by *category*
	graph y, box by(*category*)
	  see example below and [R] **graph by**

graph box-and-whiskers for
  y and x by *category*
	graph y x, box by(*category*)
	  see [R] **graph by**

force titling of by-groups to alternate between two lines	use alt, see technical note below
produce variable-width box plots	use vwidth, see technical note below
specify the plotting symbols for outside values	see [R] **graph symbol**
shorten a text plotting symbol	use trim(), see [R] **graph symbol**
deal with weighted data	specify fweight, aweight, or iweight, see [R] **graph weights**
better control labeling of the y-axis	see [R] **graph axis labels**
add grid lines or tick marks to the y-axis	see [R] **graph lines**
suppress the axes	use noaxis, see [R] **graph axis rendition**
control the scaling (minimum and maximum of the y-axis)	see [R] **graph axis scale**
add titles and annotations	see [R] **graph titles**
control the size of text	see [R] **graph textsize**
save or print the graph	see [R] **graph saving**, [R] **graph printing**

▷ Example

You have data on average temperatures for 956 U.S. cities. To draw a box plot comparing average July temperature across the four census regions, you could type

```
. gr tempjuly, box by(region) total ylabel s(o) ti(Temperatures by Region)
    ll(Temperature in Fahrenheit)
```

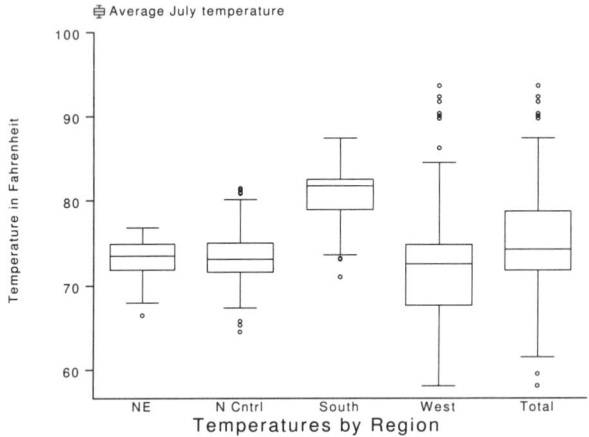

For a complete explanation of the by() option, see [R] **graph by**. The line in the middle of the box represents the median or 50th percentile of the data. The box extends from the 25th percentile ($x_{[25]}$) to the 75th percentile ($x_{[75]}$), the so-called interquartile range (IQ). The lines emerging from the box are called the *whiskers* and they extend to the upper and lower *adjacent values*. The upper adjacent value is defined as the largest data point less than or equal to $x_{[75]} + 1.5 \times IQ$. The lower adjacent value is defined as the smallest data point greater than or equal to $x_{[25]} - 1.5 \times IQ$. Observed points more extreme than the adjacent values, if any, are referred to as *outside values* and are individually plotted.

We specified a few options when we drew this picture, although they were not necessary. See [R] **graph by**, [R] **graph axis labels**, [R] **graph symbol**, and [R] **graph titles**.

◁

▷ Example

You may specify up to six variables when drawing box plots and, of course, you do not have to specify the by() option. You would type gr tempjan tempjuly, box, for instance, to draw box plots for tempjan and tempjuly.

You may combine more than one variable with the by() option. If you typed gr tempjan tempjuly, box by(region), Stata would produce a total of eight plots since there are two variables and four regions.

The maximum number of by-groups that can be displayed in a single image is 50. The maximum number of boxes (variables times by-groups) is 150.

◁

❏ Technical Note

Stata's `box` style produces *variable-width* box plots when you specify the `vwidth` option. The width of the box is then made proportional to the number of observations:

```
. gr tempjan, vw box by(div) sy(o) yline(32)
        ylabel(0,16,32,48,64,80) ti(Box Plots by Census Division)
        l1(January Temperature in Fahrenheit)
        t2("(Box width proportional to number of cities)")
```

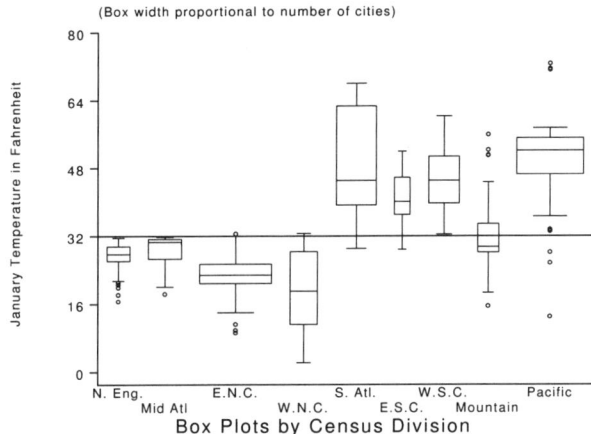

Among the many options we specified to dress up the image was `vw`, an abbreviation for `vwidth`. Notice that the box for New England is much narrower than, say, the box for Pacific.
❏

❏ Technical Note

When you specify the `vwidth` option, you can also add `root` to make the width of the box proportional to the square root of the number of observations (sum of the weights). You might want to do this if, rather than communicating sample size, you were trying to emphasize the precision of the calculated statistics. Standard errors are usually a function of the inverse square root of the sample size.
❏

❏ Technical Note

Compare the titling of the by-groups in the last two box plots. In our first example, the titles are all on one line, whereas in the second, the titles alternate between two lines. Stata decides which form to use and typically makes the right choice. There may be occasions, however, when you wish to force a different decision. The `alt` and `noalt` options do this. The `alt` option forces Stata to use the alternating scheme, as in the second example. The `noalt` option forces Stata to use the nonalternating scheme. If you specify neither of these options, Stata makes the decision for you.
❏

❏ Technical Note

Box plots have been used in geography and climatology, under the name "dispersion diagrams", since at least 1933; see Crowe (1933). His Figure 1 shows all data points, medians and quartiles and octiles, by month for monthly rainfalls for Glasgow, 1868–1917. His Figure 2, a map of Europe with several climatic stations, shows monthly medians, quartiles, and octiles.
❏

Methods and Formulas

For a description of box plots, see Cleveland (1993, 25–27).

Let x denote the variable for which we wish to calculate the summary statistics to be displayed as a box plot, and let x_i, $i = 1, \ldots, n$, denote the individual observations. Let v_i be the weight and, if no weight is specified, define $v_i = 1$ for all i. Define V as the sum of the weight $\sum v_i$ and w_i as the v_i normalized to sum to n, $w_i = v_i n / V$.

Let $x_{(i)}$ refer to the x in ascending order, and $w_{(i)}$ refer to the corresponding weights of $x_{(i)}$. The ordered sums of the normalized weights are

$$W_{(i)} = \sum_{j=1}^{i} w_{(j)}$$

To obtain the pth percentile, which we will denote as $x_{[p]}$, let $P = np/100$ and find the first index i such that $W_{(i)} > P$. The pth percentile is then

$$x_{[p]} = \begin{cases} \dfrac{x_{(i-1)} + x_{(i)}}{2} & \text{if } W_{(i-1)} = P \\ x_{(i)} & \text{otherwise} \end{cases}$$

The box extends from $x_{[25]}$ to $x_{[75]}$. A line is drawn through the "middle" at $x_{[50]}$.

The upper and lower adjacent values are as defined by Tukey (1977):

Define U as $x_{[75]} + \frac{3}{2}(x_{[75]} - x_{[25]})$. The upper adjacent value is defined as the $x_{(i)}$ such that $x_{(i)} \leq U$ and $x_{(i+1)} > U$.

Define L as $x_{[25]} - \frac{3}{2}(x_{[75]} - x_{[25]})$. The lower adjacent value is defined as the $x_{(i)}$ such that $x_{(i)} \geq L$ and $x_{(i-1)} < L$.

References

Chambers, J. M., W. S. Cleveland, B. Kleiner, and P. A. Tukey. 1983. *Graphical Methods for Data Analysis*. Belmont, CA: Wadsworth International Group.

Cleveland, W. S. 1993. *Visualizing Data*. Summit, NJ: Hobart Press.

———. 1994. *The Elements of Graphing Data*. Summit, NJ: Hobart Press.

Crowe, P. R. 1933. The analysis of rainfall probability. A graphical method and its application to European data. *Scottish Geographical Magazine* 49: 73–91.

Nash, J. C. 1996. gr19: Misleading or confusing boxplots. *Stata Technical Bulletin* 29: 14–17. Reprinted in *Stata Technical Bulletin Reprints*, vol. 5, pp. 60–64.

Tukey, J. W. 1977. *Exploratory Data Analysis*. Reading, MA: Addison-Wesley Publishing Company.

Also See

[R] **graph**, [R] **graph axis labels**, [R] **graph axis scale**, [R] **graph by**, [R] **graph lines**, [R] **graph pens**, [R] **graph printing**, [R] **graph saving**, [R] **graph stage**, [R] **graph symbol**, [R] **graph titles**, [R] **graph weights**, [R] **lv**

Title

graph by — Multiple imaging

Description

This entry discusses the by() option to graph.

Remarks

See [R] **graph combining** for instructions on making combined images of different graphic styles.

Many Stata commands can be by'd. For instance, the result of typing by x: summarize y is to produce separate summaries of y for each value of x. You can do the same thing with graph: You could type by x: graph y to obtain separate images for each value of x, but you can do better than that. If you type graph y, by(x), putting the by as an option *after* the command rather than as a prefix, you obtain a *single* image containing separate histograms of y. This works with all graphic styles except matrix and star.

▷ Example

We will use our favorite auto.dta. You may remember that our data has one variable (foreign) reflecting whether a car is of domestic or foreign manufacture and another (mpg) recording the mileage rating. If we were to type by foreign: graph mpg, we would be presented with two successive images, one for domestic and another for foreign cars.

That is not what we want. We want a single image containing both graphs, so we will type graph mpg, by(foreign). We will also add another option: total. total can be specified only with by(). It tells Stata to add one more graph reflecting all the data:

. graph mpg, by(foreign) total

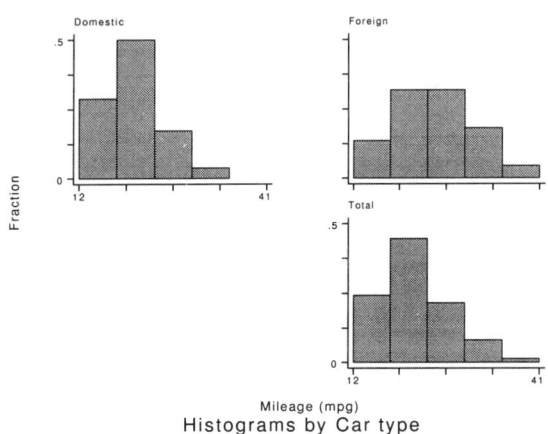

Histograms by Car type

Had we omitted the total option, the image would have consisted of only two graphs.

◁

❑ Technical Note

You are not limited to drawing just a few graphs in a single image. As you will discover, `graph` is willing to carry each of its concepts further than you would be willing to allow. For instance, we have another dataset on 956 cities of the United States:

. graph gaspc, by(state) total

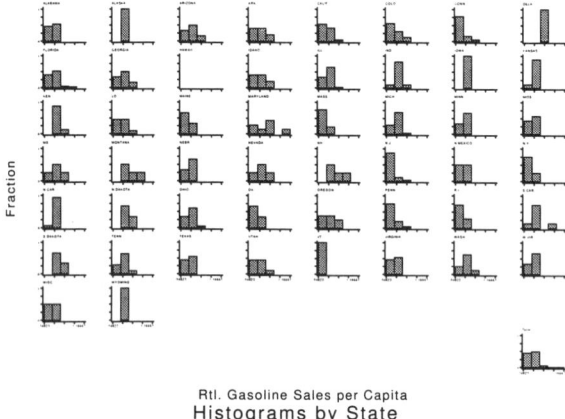

Rtl. Gasoline Sales per Capita
Histograms by State

There are "only" 51 histograms in this image. Stata would be willing to place as many as 400 histograms in a single image.

❑

❑ Technical Note

The previous technical note suggests another option: `bsize()`. You probably observed that the names of the states in the above graph are unreadable—they are too small. Actually, they would have been perfectly readable if we had printed the image at full size, but our manual pages are small and we are printing our images at 52% of standard size. Quite often you will want to print graphs of this size or perhaps even smaller. We also admit that, even on our high-resolution monitor, the names could not be read. (Actually, they were readable on our 21-inch workstation monitor.)

`bsize()` specifies the relative size of the text for labeling the by-groups. Its default, 100, means 100% of what Stata would otherwise have chosen. When you do not specify `bsize()`, it is the same as specifying `bsize(100)`. Specifying `bsize(75)` would make the text *smaller* (75% of normal) and `bsize(150)` would make the text *larger* (150% of normal). This is one of three options Stata provides for setting the text size; see [R] **graph textsize**.

Let's try our newfound knowledge and make the text labeling the by-groups 149% of what it otherwise would have been. This time, we will use a two-way scatterplot:

. graph tempjan tempjuly, by(region) bsize(149)

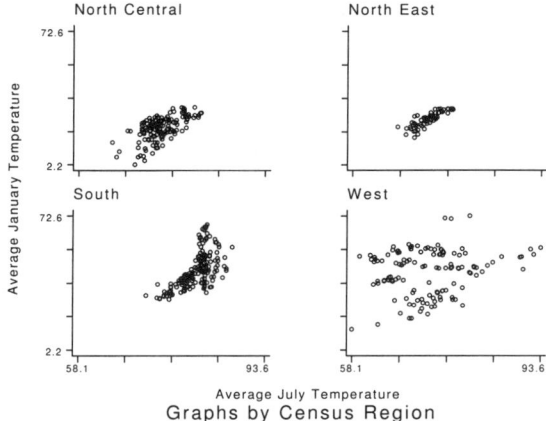

Graphs by Census Region

Had we included the `total` option, `graph` would have also added a fifth graph reflecting all the data.

❏

❏ Technical Note

When you specify `by()`, Stata goes to a lot of trouble to make sure that every graph in the image has the same scale. This makes them easier to read and compare. There may be rare instances, however, when you do not want Stata to do this. You want each graph to have its own scale. The `Rescale` option (not to be confused with `twoway`'s all-lowercase `rescale` option, see [R] **graph twoway**) does this.

. graph tempjan tempjuly, by(region) Rescale

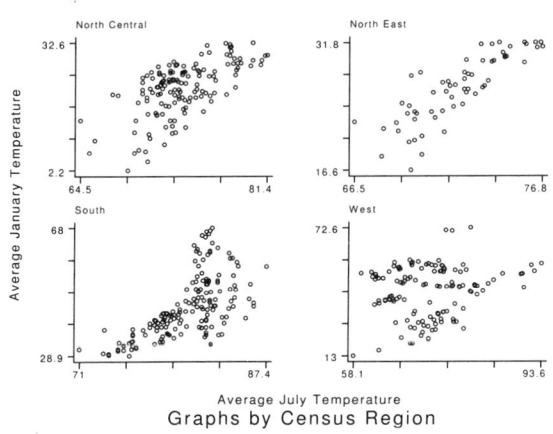

Graphs by Census Region

This is the same set of graphs as we drew in the previous technical note except that each graph now has its own scale and we did not specify the `bsize()` option, so you might want to compare the size of the text labeling the by-groups.

❏

❏ Technical Note

The two-way scatterplots produced with the by() option are similar to what are known as *casement displays* (see, for instance, Chambers et al. 1983, 141–145). To turn the graphs into real casement displays, however, we would have to edit the resulting image (say, with Stage; see [R] **graph stage**) and align all the graphs vertically or horizontally. This has the advantage that all the x- or y-axes are aligned, which is sometimes useful. However, if the point of the casement display is to allow us to see the relationship among the groups, as it most often is, the "square" alignment works as well and has the advantage that it better uses the display area of the monitor.

❏

References

Chambers, J. M., W. S. Cleveland, B. Kleiner, and P. A. Tukey. 1983. *Graphical Methods for Data Analysis*. Belmont, CA: Wadsworth International Group.

Also See

[R] **graph**, [R] **graph combining**, [R] **graph histogram**, [R] **graph twoway**

Title

graph combining — Combine graphs into a single graph

Description

This entry discusses `graph using` and the `margin()` option.

Remarks

Once an image has been saved in a `.gph` file (see [R] **graph saving**), it can be redisplayed using `graph using` *filename(s)*. If you specify more than one filename, all specified `.gph` files are redisplayed in a single image. You can use titling options to add titles to the combined image and the `saving()` option to create a new, combined `.gph` file.

Multiple imaging with graph using

▷ Example

In [R] **graph**, we combined eight separate `.gph` files into a single image, creating a new `.gph` file which we then printed. The image was created by the command:

```
graph using part1 part2 part3 part4 part5 part6 part7 part8,
          margin(15) saving(combined)
```

This command read the files `part1.gph`, `part2.gph`, and so on, creating a new file called `combined.gph`.

The only option unique to `graph using` is `margin()`, which specifies the margin to be placed around each graph as a percent of graphical area. The default is 0 and we asked for 15% margins, thus making each of the eight separate images a little smaller but increasing the separation between them. `margin(15)` is generally a good idea.

There is no limit to the number of files you can combine—you may combine an absurdly large number:

(*Continued on next page.*)

```
. gr using histcity star bigtxt bywl carhist exlbl exlbltr fcn histgas jjdif jjtwo
    jjtwors lbl lbltlbr mimage ss1way ss21box sshist ssmat sstext sstwobig
    sstwoby sstwoway title wgt0 wgt1 wl bar barstak pie hilitem symn make pig
    prwgt prwgt2 creg cregss raider cmess cclean m10 m30 s10 s30 pigts2 pigts1
    ksink rbox logsca logscaby famous owtemp minex9 owbtemp automat1 automat2
    owbjtemp boxtemp vw star9 barneg barnegs km bub bubtxt bubmtx, margin(15)
```

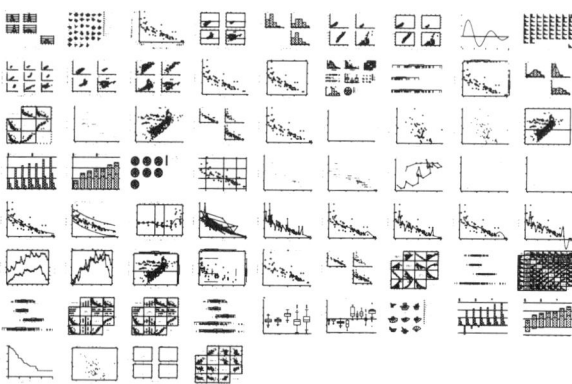

No, it is not readable, although printed very large it might be. We direct your attention to the sixth graph in the second row, which is Figure 1 from [R] **graph**, itself a creation of graph using. Once a graph has been saved in a .gph file, it can be combined and recombined.

◁

❑ Technical Note

Unlike the optional Stata Graphics Editor (Stage), graph using provides little control over how the graphs are combined. If you have Stage, it is best to wait and combine the graphs in the graphics editor; see [R] **graph stage**.

```
. graph x, saving(hist)
. graph y, saving(hist2)
. graph y x, saving(twoway)
. graph y x, by(region) saving
. graph using hist hist2 twoway many, saving(new)
```

In the graph using example above, the four graphs will be placed in a 2 × 2 array. The first graph (hist.gph) will appear at the top-left corner, the second (hist2.gph) at the top right, the third (twoway.gph) at the bottom left, and the fourth (many.gph) at the bottom right. In general, graph using displays the graphs in a $k \times k$ array. (Five graphs would appear in a 3 × 3 array, with the middle row containing two graphs and the bottom row being empty.)

You can obtain some control of the placement by creating a null graph and then including the null graph in the list of files to be displayed. graph using, saving(null) will create a null graph. graph using file1 file2 null file3 file4 null null null file5 would display five real graphs: four of them in a 2 × 2 array at the upper left of the image and the fifth at the lower right.

❑

Adding titles with graph using

▷ Example

graph using can also be used to add titles to a graph *ex post*. All the titling options described in [R] **graph titles** work with graph using. Suppose you drew a graph, saved it as mygph.gph, and now want to title it "Figure 1. The Big Picture" and add at the top of the graph "(Based on 1988 Data)". Type

```
graph using mygph, title("Figure 1. The Big Picture")
        t1("(Based on 1988 Data)") saving(gphwttl)
```

Notice that we used the saving() option to make a new .gph file. *Do not* attempt to replace the original file with the new one; that is, do not type saving(mygph,replace) when the original image is stored in mygph.gph. Stata attempts to catch this error, but it is not always successful. If it is not successful, the original contents of mygph.gph are lost and you will have to remake the original image.

Let's use four of our graphs from other parts of this manual along with the titling options to create a graph describing our temperature data:

```
. gr using wl bywl famous temp, marg(10)
        t1("(Based on 956 U.S. Cities)")
        ti(Summary of Temperature Data)
```

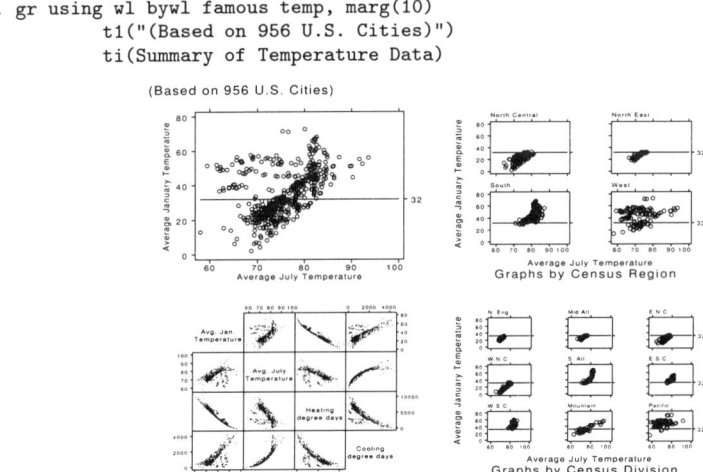

◁

□ Technical Note

When you know that you will be combining graphs, it is often a good idea to increase the text size before creating the original images. This way, even when the graphs are made smaller, the labels and titles will be readable. We did that in the above image. We set textsize 150, graphed each of the individual images, set textsize 100, and drew the combined image. We probably should have increased the text size even more; see [R] **graph textsize**.

□

Also See

[R] **graph**, [R] **graph printing**, [R] **graph redisplaying**, [R] **graph saving**, [R] **graph stage**

Title

> **graph connect** — Connect points

Description

This entry discusses the `connect()` option to `graph`.

Remarks

The `connect()` option specifies if and how points on a scatterplot are to be connected. The alternatives are

.	do not connect (default)
l	(letter ℓ) draw straight lines between points
m	connect median bands using straight lines
s	connect median bands using a cubic spline
J	connect in steps
L	connect x-ascending points
||	connect pairs of variables with vertical lines
II	same as || but cap the lines to make I's

▷ Example

If you do not specify the `connect()` option, the result is just as if you specified `connect(.)`; the points are not connected. Each argument of `connect()` corresponds to a variable in the *varlist*, so you would type `gr y1 y2 x, c(.l)` to connect y2 but not y1, and `gr y1 y2 x, c(l.)` to connect y1 but not y2. Note that `connect()` can be abbreviated as `c()`.

◁

▷ Example

`connect()` connects points in the order of the data, not the order of the x-axis, so you might end up with a picture like this:

```
. graph mpg weight, c(l)
```

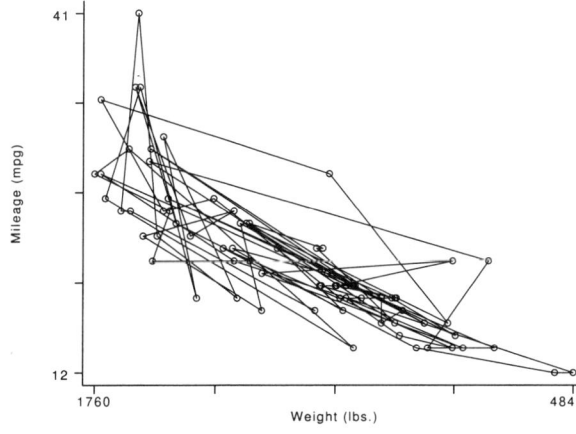

This is probably not what you wanted and you may even be tempted to view this "feature" as a bug. We assure you that it really is a feature and we will show you a use for it in a later example, but in the meantime, you will want to know how to avoid it.

One way would be to first `sort` your data, but you do not have to go to the trouble. `graph` includes a `sort` *option* that automatically sorts the data according to the x-axis before graphing. In addition, the `sort` option affects only the graph—it does not change the order of your data:

. `graph mpg weight, c(l) sort`

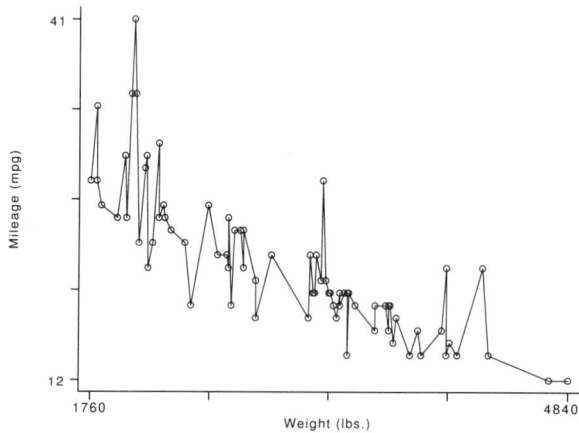

◁

▷ Example

Now that we know how to connect points with straight lines, we have everything we need to put, say, regression lines through our data. We simply graph two variables—the data and the regression predictions—using symbols for one and connecting the other with straight lines. We have to produce the regression predictions somehow, but that is easy. We estimate the regression and then use the `predict` command. In our example, we will use a quadratic to fit the data:

(Example continued on next page.)

```
. gen wgt2 = weight*weight
. regress mpg weight wgt2
(output omitted)
. predict hat
. graph mpg hat weight, c(.1) s(0i) sort
```

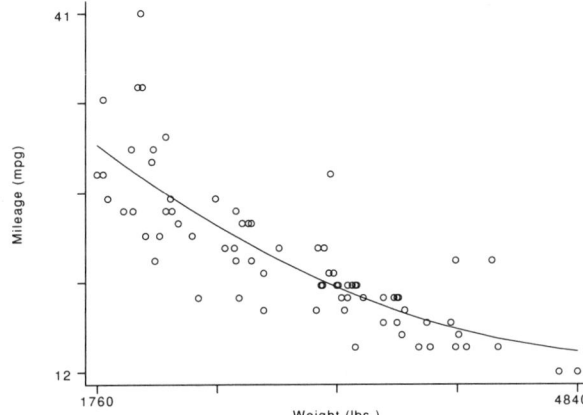

c(.1) says "do not connect mpg" and "do connect hat." Similarly, s(0i) says "use large circles for mpg" and "use an invisible symbol for hat"; see [R] **graph symbol**. Thus, we can see both our data and the regression line.

◁

▷ Example

Graphs may contain more than one line—we simply introduce additional variables and set their plotting symbols to i and connect them with l. For instance, we might redraw the graph above adding bands reflecting twice the standard error of the residuals. Being familiar with Stata, we know that predict will give us the standard error of the residuals, so we take that result and construct high and low bands:

```
. predict s, stdr
. gen lo = hat-2*s
. gen hi = hat+2*s
```

(Example continued on next page.)

```
. graph mpg hat hi lo weight, c(.lll) s(Oiii) sort ylab xlab
       t1(Regression of Mileage on Weight and Weight-squared)
       t2(Bands reflect 2 times the standard error of residuals)
```

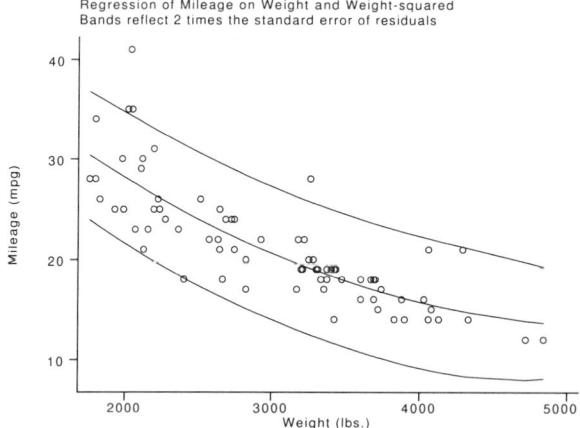

◁

▷ Example

Let's now combine all of our knowledge and also exploit Stata's "feature" of connecting points in the order of the data. We can put this feature to work with some time-series data, plotting one variable against another and connecting the points in time order.

We have quarterly data on pig production in the United Kingdom. Among the data are cln_sl, the number of clean pigs reared for meat production that are slaughtered during the quarter, and herd, a measure of the actual breeding herd size. First, let's draw our graph:

```
. gen tolbl = cln_sl if qtr==1
. gen rest = cln_sl if qtr~=1
. gr cln_sl tolbl rest herd, c(l..) s(i[year]O) ps(125) ylab xlab
       l1(Clean pig slaughter) t1(U.K. Pig Production)
       t2(Ministry of Agriculture, Fisheries and Food)
```

We created two new variables, tolbl—the points we intend to label with text showing the year—and rest—the remaining points. We decided to label the first quarter of each year. We graph cln_sl against herd, connecting the points with straight lines and suppressing the plotting symbol. We graph tolbl against herd, not connecting the points but using [year] as the plotting symbol, so the line has some of the points labeled. We finally graph rest against herd, also not connecting the points but using large circles as the symbol this time. The rest of the points are now marked.

We also decided to increase the text size used for the text plotting symbol to 125% of the ordinary size, to label the x- and y-axes, and to add some titles; see [R] **graph symbol**, [R] **graph textsize**, [R] **graph axis labels**, and [R] **graph titles**.

◁

❑ Technical Note

The previous graph can be improved considerably, but not with Stata. Using the Stata Graphics Editor (see [R] **graph stage**), however, we edited an image drawn similarly to the one above to make

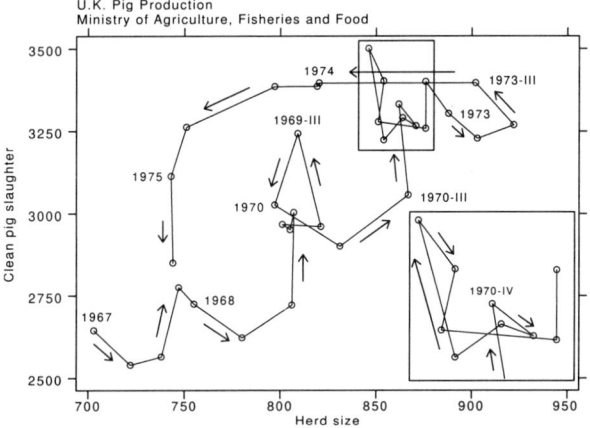

❑

▷ Example

connect() provides two other techniques for connecting points: median bands and cubic splines (also see [R] **ksm** for lowess smoothing). connect() divides the x-axis into n bands—the default is 200—and then calculates the cross-median of x and y within each band. The results are connected with straight lines in the median-band case or the points are used as the "knots" in a calculation of the cubic spline which is then graphed.

This sounds technical because it is, but the result is easily comprehended. Stata draws a curve through the data that reflects the data's tendencies and is reasonably resistant to outliers.

Let's try it with our automobile data:

. graph mpg weight, c(m) bands(10)

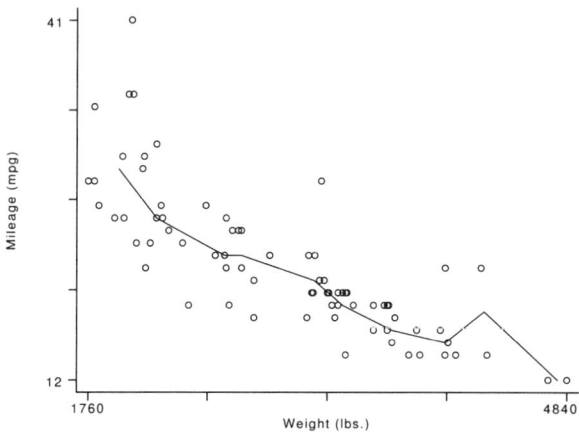

The **bands()** option specifies the number of bands on which the calculation is to be based. As we said, the default is 200, but that is usually too many since it results in little, if any, smoothing. How many bands should you use? It is an aesthetic judgment, but it partly depends on the number of observations. We have 74 automobiles in our data, so with 10 bands we will have roughly 7 cars per band, at least on average.

As a comparison, let's make the graph again but specify that we want 30 bands, yielding an average of only 2.5 cars per band:

. graph mpg weight, c(m) bands(30)

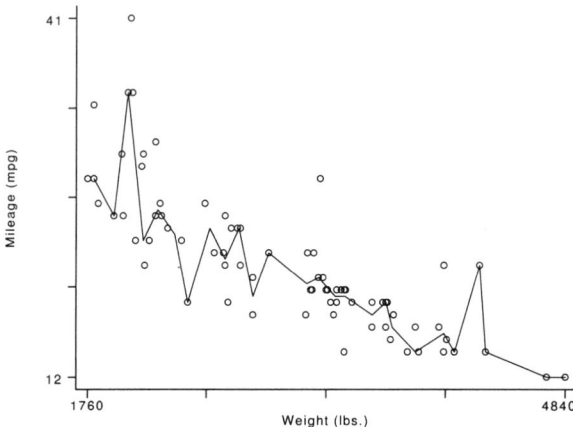

As expected, the amount of smoothing is minimal. In fact, the line begins to look like a line connecting the individual points.

◁

❑ Technical Note

Despite appearances to the contrary, neither of the graphs in the last example was drawn by the graph commands printed above them, although they could have been. We wanted to print the line with a slightly bolder pen than the rest of the image, so although we claimed to type graph mpg weight, c(m) bands(30), we actually typed graph mpg mpg weight, c(.m) s(0i) bands(30). We graphed mpg against weight twice—in the first case, displaying the points and in the second, adding the median band but suppressing the points. Thus, the points were drawn with pen 2 and the line with pen 3. When we printed the image, we then specified /t112, making pen 3 slightly bolder than pens 1 and 2. See [R] **graph pens**.

❑

▷ Example

The cubic spline option makes the median bands appear smoother by putting a smooth curve through them. In practice, one tends to use connect(m) for analysis work and connect(s) for presentation graphs. connect(m) is not as pretty, but it does reveal exactly where the median-band points are located. Let's redraw our last two graphs using splines:

. graph mpg weight, c(s) bands(10)

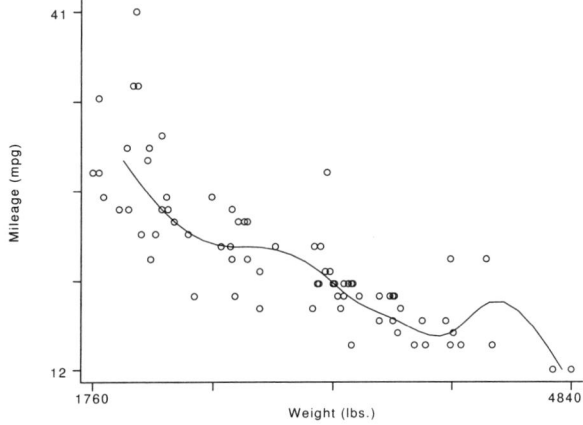

(Example continued on next page.)

. graph mpg weight, c(s) bands(30)

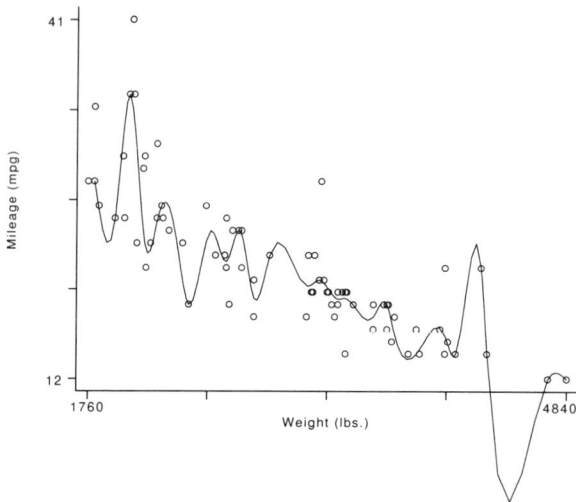

Our second example illustrates a common problem with splines when we specify too many bands:
The curve tends to oscillate.

◁

▷ Example

Let's now use splines to produce a graph suitable for publication. We have some NFL attendance
data, and wish to graph the home game attendance for the Los Angeles Raiders for ten seasons,
1977 through 1986. The variable att records attendance and time records date. For instance, the
first home game in our data was played in September 1976, and time records 76.66. The second
game was played in October, and time records 76.75.

Football games are played only during a short time of the year—September through early
December—so the time variable will divide the data into 10 bunches, one for each season. We
therefore elect to specify bands(10), creating a band for each season and thus forcing our curve
through the median attendance for each year:

(*Graph on next page.*)

```
. graph att time, c(s) bands(10) border ylabel
        xlabel(77,78,79,80,81,82,83,84,85,86) xline(80.25,82.25)
        t1(81 and 82 seasons played in Oakland after announcement)
        t2(83 and subsequent seasons played in L.A.)
        ti(Home Attendance at Raider Football Games)
```

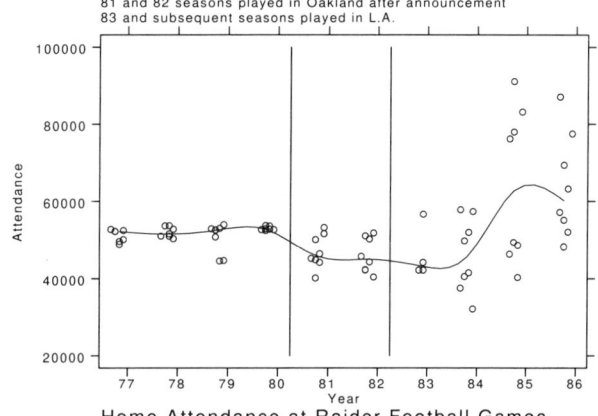

Home Attendance at Raider Football Games

◁

❏ Technical Note

When using connect(s), you can also specify the density() option. This sets the number of points calculated on the spline between median-band points. Straight lines are then used to connect each of the calculated points. The default is to calculate five points, although you can increase the number to as many as 300. density(50), for instance, would calculate 50 points between each median band. If you also specified bands(10), then a total of 500 points would be calculated along the curve.

❏

▷ Example

connect(||) works differently from the other connect options; it draws vertical lines connecting two variables *within each observation*, which is most useful for drawing high-low charts. If you had a dataset recording the high and low price of a stock, you might type graph high low time, c(||) to obtain a standard high-low chart. The || indicates that separate lines are to be drawn connecting the two corresponding variables high and low for each value of time.

In our case, we also have data on the closing price and we wish to dress the image, so we type

```
. graph close high low time, c(.||) s(Oii) border
        ylab(16,17,18,19,20,21) rlab(13,14,15,16) xlab(-40,-30,-20,-10,0,10)
        ttick(0) t2("              Black Monday")
        title("High, Low, and Close for XYZ Corp.")
```

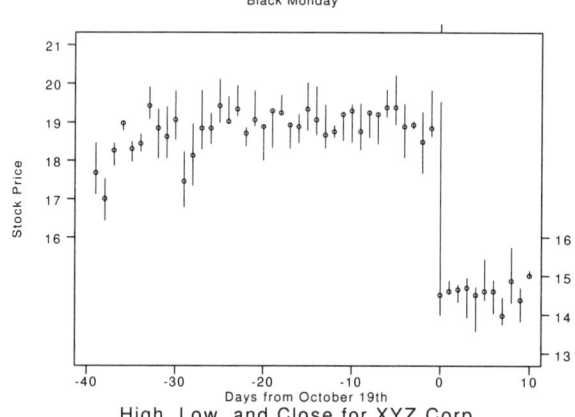

High, Low, and Close for XYZ Corp.

◁

▷ Example

connect(II) works the same as connect(||) except that the vertical lines are capped by short horizontal lines on the top and bottom and so look like I's. I's look better than |'s when there is less data. Going back to our U.K. pig production data:

```
. graph avg min max year, c(.II) s(Oii) ylab(700,750,800,850,900,950)
        xlab(1966,1968,1970,1972,1974,1976,1978) rlab(803,703,922)
        yline(803) t1("Range and Average Herd Size, 1968-1978")
        ti("U.K. Pig Production")
```

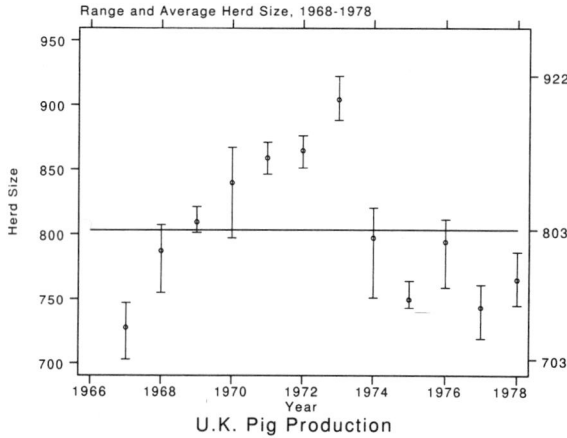

The length of the caps on the I's is proportional to psize(), so you could make them wider by specifying, for instance, psize(150).

◁

▷ Example

connect(J) is a variation on connect(l). Rather than drawing straight lines between points, J draws steps, traversing first the horizontal distance and then the vertical distance. Drawing step functions is often useful when dealing with empirical cumulative distributions.

Assume you have the results of an experiment that ran for 31 days and you now have data on the expected and observed number of failures. You might plot this data by typing

```
. graph actual exp t, c(Jl) s(Oi) rlab(22,37.41) ylab xlab
         t1("Expected and Observed Number of Failures")
```

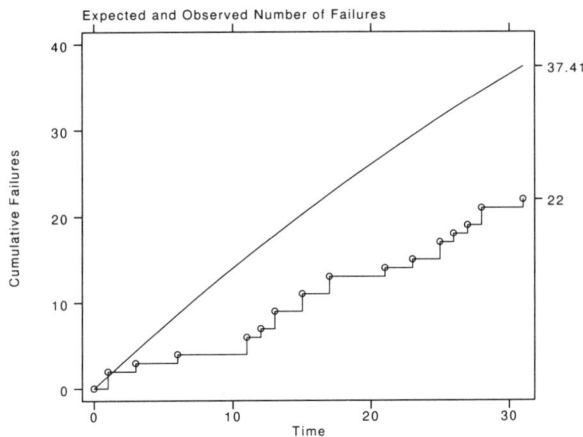

◁

▷ Example

connect(L) can be used to trick Stata into drawing lines connecting points within by-groups in a single graph. Imagine you wish to graph y against x, connecting the points separately for each value of *groupvar*. You might type

```
. graph y x, by(groupvar) c(l) sort
```

but that would create separate graphs (within the same image) for each value of *groupvar*. If *groupvar* took on three values—say 1, 2, and 3—you might

```
. gen y1 = y if groupvar==1
. gen y2 = y if groupvar==2
. gen y3 = y if groupvar==3
. graph y1 y2 y3 x, c(lll) sort
```

That would do what you want. Easier, however, is

```
. sort groupvar x
. graph y x, c(L)
```

Note that we sorted the data by *groupvar* and within *groupvar* by x. The L option will connect points only so long as x is ascending. For the first part of the dataset, where *groupvar* is 1, that will be true. When *groupvar* changes to 2, however, x will go back down, so the last point for *groupvar*==1 will not be connected with the first point for *groupvar*==2. The remaining points for *groupvar*==2 will be connected.

◁

Also See

[R] **graph**, [R] **graph matrix**, [R] **graph symbol**, [R] **graph twoway**, [R] **ksm**, [R] **serrbar**

Title

graph histogram — Graph histograms

Description

This entry discusses the `histogram` style option to `graph` and the options `bin()`, `freq`, `normal`, and `density()`.

Remarks

Histograms are drawn when you specify the `histogram` style option, although in practice you never bother to type the option since `graph` assumes `histogram` when you specify only one variable.

To	Do
draw a histogram of x	graph x
change the number of bins	use bin(), described below
label the y-axis in frequency units	use freq, described below
overlay a normal curve	use normal, described below
control shading of the bars	use shading(), see [R] graph shading
deal with weighted data	specify fweight or aweight, see [R] graph weights
draw histograms within category	see example below and [R] graph by
specify a different scale for each category	use Rescale, see [R] graph by
better control labeling of the axes	see [R] graph axis labels
add grid lines or tick marks to the axes	see [R] graph lines
control the style of the axes—for instance, to remove or change to a box	see [R] graph axis rendition
control the scaling (minimum and maximum of the axes)	see [R] graph axis scale
use log scale for x-axis	use log, see example below
add titles and annotations	see [R] graph titles
control the size of text	see [R] graph textsize
save or print the graph	see [R] graph saving, [R] graph printing

In addition to the standard options, `histogram` provides three unique options: `bin()`, `freq`, and `normal`.

The `bin()` option sets the number of bins or intervals used to accumulate the frequencies. The x-scale is divided into n intervals—five by default—and then the number of observations within each interval counted. Typing `gr x, bin(11)` would use 11 rather than 5 bins.

❏ Technical Note

The optimal number of bins for a histogram is a subject of debate. Various rules have been suggested. Emerson and Hoaglin (1983) compare three of these rules: $10\log_{10} n$; $2\sqrt{n}$; and $1 + \log_2 n$. They conclude "for exploration we would still prefer to begin a stem-and-leaf display or a histogram with roughly $10\log_{10} n$ lines or intervals" (Emerson and Hoaglin 1983, 29).

Using the $10\log_{10} n$ rule, if your data had 74 observations, you could

```
. display 10*log10(74)
18.692317
. graph x, bin(19)
```

In our judgment, 19 is too many bins for 74 observations, but the formula does seem to work well for $n > 800$. When n is "small", we prefer using $\sqrt{n}$. For 74 observations, this rule would tell us to use 8 or 9 bins. Therefore, our current favorite is

$$\min(\sqrt{n}, 10 \cdot \log_{10} n)$$

or equivalently, $\sqrt{n}$ for $n < 862$ and $10 \cdot \log_{10} n$ otherwise. In Stata, you can

```
. display min(sqrt(n), 10*log10(n))
```

❏

The **freq** option requests that the y-axis be labeled in frequency units rather than fractional units. If your data had 50 observations and one of the bins contained 20 observations, with the **freq** option it would be labeled as 20 rather than as 0.4.

The **normal** option overlays a normal curve on the histogram. **normal** specified without arguments calculates the mean and standard deviation of your data and bases the normal curve on that calculation. Alternatively, you may specify a mean and standard deviation, such as **normal(1,2)** which overlays a normal with mean 1 and standard deviation 2.

❏ Technical Note

The **density()** option specifies the number of points to be calculated along the normal. Those points are then connected with straight lines. If you do not specify this option, 100 points are used. You may increase the number up to 300.

❏

(Continued on next page.)

▷ Example

The common options that are relevant also work with histograms. For instance:

```
. gr tempjuly, bin(9) log normal xlabel noaxis yline ylabel xline(58,100)
    t1("(Based on 956 U.S. Cities)") by(region) total
```

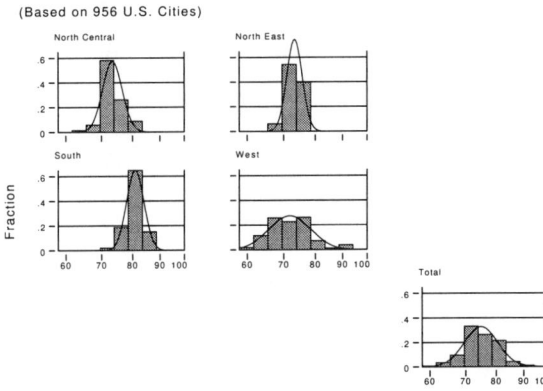

Average July Temperature
Histograms by Census Region

Note, in particular, the use of the `log` option to make histograms based on a log scale of temperature; see [R] **graph log scales**. Also see [R] **graph by** and [R] **graph titles**.

◁

❑ Technical Note

If we had added the option `pen(4)` to our `graph` command above, pen 4 would have been used to draw the bars. All text and lines would have been drawn, as always, with pen 1. In addition, `histogram` always uses pen 3 to draw the normal curve. See [R] **graph pens**.

❑

❑ Technical Note

Since we specified both the `normal` and the `log` options, `histogram` calculated the mean and standard deviation of the log of average July temperature. You might wonder what would happen if you specified `log` *and* `normal`(m,s), where m and s are two numbers. Stata would calculate $\mu = \log m$ and $\sigma = s/m$ and then use μ and σ as the parameters for the distribution.

❑

❑ Technical Note

According to Beniger and Robyn (1978, 4), although A. M. Guerry published a histogram in 1833, the word "histogram" was first used by Karl Pearson in 1895.

❑

References

Beniger, J. R. and D. L. Robyn. 1978. Quantitative graphics in statistics: a brief history. *The American Statistician* 32: 1–11.

Dixon, W. J. and R. A. Kronmal. 1965. The choice of origin and scale for graphs. *Journal of the Association for Computing Machinery* 12: 259–261.

Doane, D. P. 1976. Aesthetic frequency classifications. *The American Statistician* 30: 181–183.

Emerson, J. D. and D. C. Hoaglin. 1983. Stem-and-leaf displays. In *Understanding Robust and Exploratory Data Analysis*, ed. D. C. Hoaglin, F. Mosteller and J. W. Tukey, 7–30. New York: John Wiley & Sons.

Guerry, A. M. 1833. *Essai sur la Statistique Morale de la France.* Paris.

Pearson, K. 1895. Contributions to the mathematical theory of evolution.—II. Skew variation in homogeneous material. *Philosophical Transactions of the Royal Society of London*, A, 186: 343–414.

Scott, D. W. 1979. On optimal and data-based histograms. *Biometrika* 66: 605–610.

Sturges, H. A. 1926. The choice of a class interval. *Journal of the American Statistical Association* 21: 65–66.

Velleman, P. F. 1976. Interactive computing for exploratory data analysis I: display algorithms. *1975 Proceedings of the Statistical Computing Section.* Washington, D.C.: American Statistical Association.

Also See

[R] **cumul**, [R] **graph**, [R] **graph axis labels**, [R] **graph axis rendition**, [R] **graph axis scale**, [R] **graph by**, [R] **graph lines**, [R] **graph log scales**, [R] **graph pens**, [R] **graph printing**, [R] **graph saving**, [R] **graph shading**, [R] **graph stage**, [R] **graph titles**, [R] **graph weights**, [R] **hist**, [R] **stem**

Title

> **graph lines** — Add ticks and lines

Description

This entry discusses the xtick(), ytick(), rline(), and tline() options to graph.

Remarks

graph automatically places tick marks on axes anywhere they are labeled, but you can place additional ticks using the xtick(), ytick(), rtick(), and ttick() options. The ticking options work the same way as the labeling options—without arguments, they tick a few round values; with arguments, they tick where you say; see [R] **graph axis labels**.

A second set of options—yline(), xline(), rline(), and tline()—adds lines across the graph.

▷ Example

Let's plot tempjan against tempjuly, but include extra ticking between the labeled values and draw a line across the graph indicating the freezing point:

```
. graph tempjan tempjuly, ylab xlab yline(32) rlab(32)
                ytick(10,30,50,70) xtick(65,75,85,95)
```

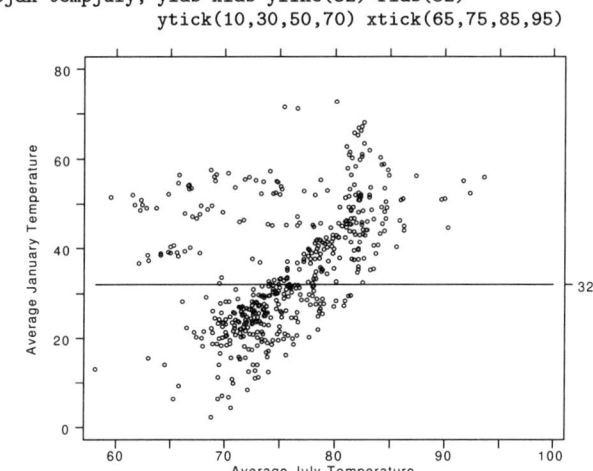

In our opinion, the extra ticking could just as well have been omitted, but putting aside aesthetic judgments, a few points are worth noting.

Specifying the xtick() option added ticking to both the bottom *and* the top axis, whereas specifying the ytick() option did not carry over to the right axis. Since we did not tell Stata what to put on the top axis, it assumed we wanted the same values ticked as for the bottom axis. Since we did tell Stata what we wanted on the right axis—rlab(32)—Stata took us at our word and stifled its automatic tendencies.

85

The `yline(32)` option drew a line across the graph corresponding to a y value of 32. We are not limited to drawing only one line. If we had typed `yline(32,45)`, lines would have been drawn across at both 32 and 45. If we had wanted a vertical line, we could have used the `xline()` option.

◁

❏ Technical Note

Stata is careful to obey Cleveland's (1994, 31) prescription to "Make the data rectangle slightly smaller than the scale-line rectangle. Tick marks should point outward." In the same rule, Cleveland also prescribes "Use a pair of scale lines for each variable", something Stata does not always do. You can, however, use the `border` option and so obey this rule as well; see [R] **graph axis rendition**.

❏

References

Cleveland, W. S. 1994. *The Elements of Graphing Data*. Summit, NJ: Hobart Press.

Hardin, J. W. 1995. dm28: Calculate nice numbers for labeling or drawing grid lines. *Stata Technical Bulletin* 25: 2–3. Reprinted in *Stata Technical Bulletin Reprints*, vol. 5, pp. 19–20.

Also See

[R] **graph**, [R] **graph axis labels**, [R] **graph axis rendition**, [R] **graph axis scale**, [R] **graph titles**

Title

graph log scales — Create log scales

Description

This entry discusses the `log`, `ylog`, `xlog`, and `rlog` options to `graph`.

Remarks

`log`, `ylog`, `xlog`, and `rlog` specify log scales. `log` is used with the `histogram` style and the remaining options are used with `twoway`. (`rlog` refers to the right scale and is allowed only on `twoway`s with two vertical scales; see [R] **graph twoway**.)

▷ Example

Let's graph the relationship between `mpg` and `weight` using our `auto.dta`, graphing `weight` on a log scale. We will draw separate graphs for foreign and domestic cars and include an overall total (see [R] **graph by**):

```
. graph mpg weight, by(foreign) total xlog ylab xlab
```

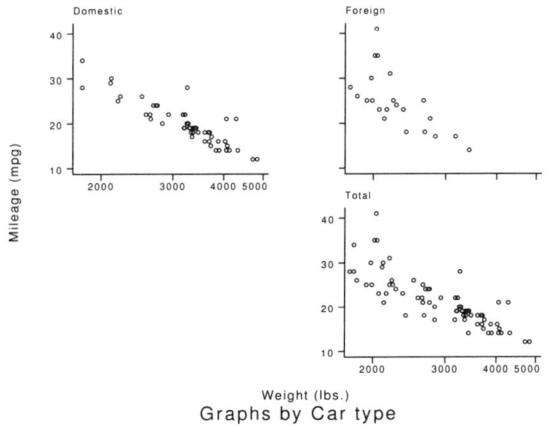

Graphs by Car type

Notice the log spacing of the x-axis.

◁

❏ Technical Note

You may specify any of the axis labeling or lines and ticks options with log scales; see [R] **graph axis labels** and [R] **graph lines**. When you specify values explicitly, they are specified in natural (unlogged) units even when you specify one of the log options. For instance, in the graph above, if we had wanted to label the weights 2,000, 2,500, 3,000, 4,000, and 5,000 in the previous example, we would have typed `xlabel(2000,2500,3000,4000,5000)`.

❏

Also See

[R] **graph**, [R] **graph axis labels**, [R] **graph axis rendition**, [R] **graph axis scale**

Title

> **graph matrix** — Graph scatterplot matrices

Description

This entry discusses the `matrix` style option to `graph`.

Remarks

The scatterplot matrix is just that—a set of two-way scatterplots arranged in a matrix. Stata draws a scatterplot matrix when you specify the `matrix` option. At the bottom of this page is the graph that appears on the cover of this manual.

To	Do
graph all possible two-way scatterplots between w, x, y, and z	`graph w x y z, matrix`
display only the lower triangle of the matrix	use `half`, see technical note below
include a border around the upper-left and lower-right graph	use `border`, see example below
add spherical random noise to your data before graphing	use `jitter()`, see technical note below and [R] **graph weights**
specify the plotting symbols	see [R] **graph symbol**
shorten a text plotting symbol	use `trim()`, see [R] **graph symbol**
connect points with lines and add curves	see [R] **graph connect**
deal with weighted data	specify `iweight`, see [R] **graph weights**
better control labeling of the axes	use `label`, see example below
add titles and annotations	see [R] **graph titles**
control the size of text	see [R] **graph textsize**
save or print the graph	see [R] **graph saving**, [R] **graph printing**

(Continued on next page.)

```
. graph tempjan tempjuly heatdd cooldd, matrix label sy(.)
```

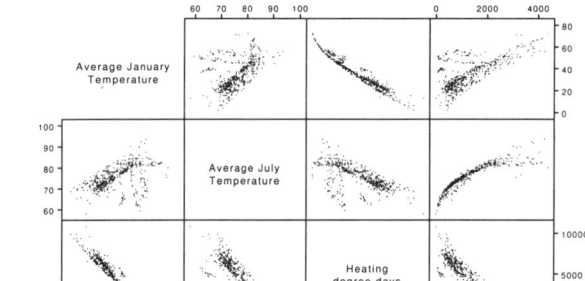

▷ Example

In the above graph, we specified the `label` and `symbol()` (abbreviated `sy`) options, but they were unnecessary. `label` labeled the axes; also see the next example. `symbol(.)` used dots as the plotting symbols; see [R] **graph symbol**. Here is the same graph, but this time we included the `border` option.

```
. graph tempjan tempjuly heatdd cooldd, matrix label sy(.) border
```

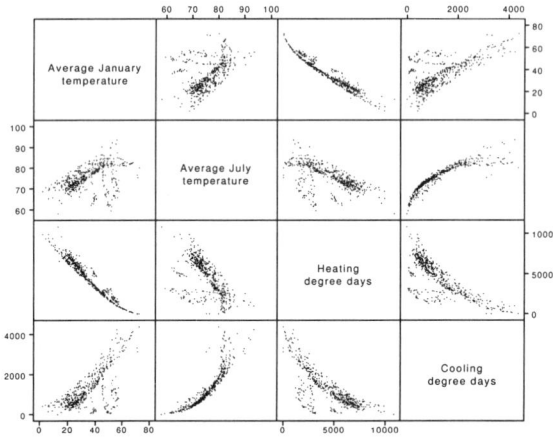

In our example, the top-left graph is January vs. July temperature; to the right of that is January temperature vs. heating degree days; and to the right of that is January temperature vs. cooling degree days. Starting at the second row, we have July vs. January temperature, which is just the transpose of the graph on the opposite side of the diagonal. In all, the image contains 11,472 points and is crammed with information.

◁

▷ Example

Your next question probably is, "How many variables can I graph simultaneously?" Answer: More than you will want—thirty, to be precise, with the resulting image containing 870 individual graphs. As a point of reference, here is a nine-by-nine scatterplot matrix:

. graph mpg-gratio, matrix nolabel sy(.)

There are "only" 72 graphs in this matrix, or about 8% of the upper limit. Matrices up to 8-by-8 tend to be quite readable on most monitors, and the 9-by-9 example above is easily read when printed on full-sized paper.

The `nolabel` option prevented Stata from adding numeric labels around the outside of the matrix and so made the graph a little larger. You could not have read the numeric labels, anyway.

◁

❑ Technical Note

We made the labels in the diagonal boxes (barely) readable by increasing the text size before graphing the image. In particular, we typed `set textsize 175` and then issued our `graph` command; see [R] **graph textsize**.

❑

▷ Example

Having now established our prowess, let's come back and tell you about the options, but first, let's see how a scatterplot matrix looks when we do not specify any options:

. graph mpg rep78 weight displ, matrix

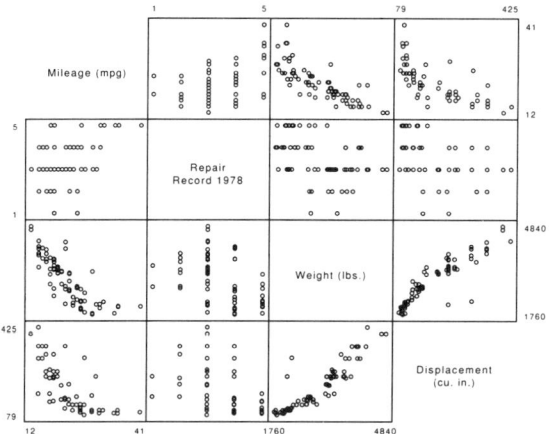

By default, Stata uses the small circle (symbol(o), see [R] **graph symbol**) as the plotting symbol and labels only the minimum and maximum of each axis. (In the previous example, we specified the nolabel option to prevent Stata from labeling the axes at all. In the example before that, we specified label to make Stata label a few round numbers along each axis. So now you know how label works.)

We want to emphasize the powerful interaction between the matrix style and the common options listed in the *Also See* at the end of this entry. For instance, here is another look at the scatterplot matrix we just drew:

. graph mpg rep78 weight displ, mat lab s(.) c(s) bands(9)

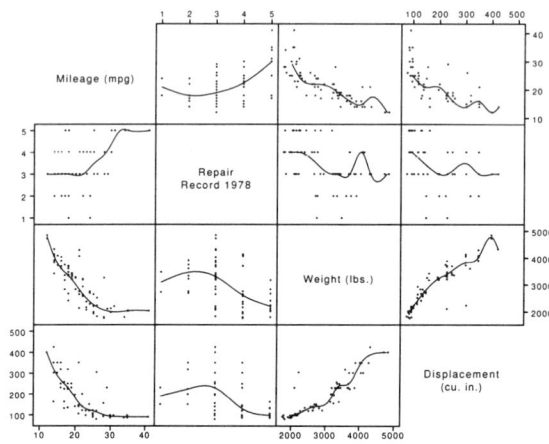

This time we labeled the outside of the matrix, changed the plotting symbol to a dot, and connected the points with cubic splines based on a nine-band calculation.

◁

❏ Technical Note

The command listed above the matrix in the previous example is not really the command we used, although we could have. We wanted to make the dots stand out a bit more than s(.) would achieve, so we left off the s(.) option with the result that Stata drew the image using small circles. Then, when we printed the graph, we specified the /so10 (-so10 for Unix users) option to gphdot, scaling the small circle down to 10% of its normal size; see [R] **graph printing**. This resulted in a rather bold-looking dot.

❏

❏ Technical Note

A potpourri: (1) You will notice that Stata does not box the diagonals of the matrix. If you prefer them boxed, specify the border option. (2) If you wish your graphs to contain only the lower triangle of the matrix, specify the half option. (3) The jitter option, described in a technical note in [R] **graph twoway**, may also be used with the matrix style. (4) The borders and titling are drawn with pen 1, the points with pen 2; you may not modify this.

❏

❏ Technical Note

The origin of the scatterplot matrix is unknown, although early written discussions may be found in Hartigan (1975), Tukey and Tukey (1981), and Chambers et al. (1983). The scatterplot matrix has also been called the *draftman's display* and *pairwise scatterplot*. Regardless of the name used, we believe the first "canned" implementation was by Becker and Chambers in a system called S; see Becker and Chambers (1984), although S predates 1984. We also believe that Stata provided the second implementation (and the first on DOS computers) in 1985. We followed Tufte's (1983, 114) advice and deleted the double outlines around the individual scatterplots drawn by S.

❏

References

Becker, R. A. and J. M. Chambers. 1984. *S: An Interactive Environment for Data Analysis and Graphics*. Belmont, CA: Wadsworth Advanced Book Program.

Chambers, J. M., W. S. Cleveland, B. Kleiner, and P. A. Tukey. 1983. *Graphical Methods for Data Analysis*. Belmont, CA: Wadsworth International Group.

Cleveland, W. S. 1993. *Visualizing Data*. Summit, NJ: Hobart Press.

———. 1994. *The Elements of Graphing Data*. Summit, NJ: Hobart Press.

Hartigan, J. A. 1975. Printer graphics for clustering. *Journal of Statistical Computing and Simulation* 4: 187–213.

Tufte, E. R. 1983. *The Visual Display of Quantitative Information*. Cheshire, CT: Graphics Press.

Tukey, P. A. and J. W. Tukey. 1981. Preparation; prechosen sequences of views. In *Interpreting Multivariate Data*, ed. V. Barnett, 189–213. Chichester, U.K.: John Wiley & Sons.

Also See

[R] **graph**, [R] **graph connect**, [R] **graph printing**, [R] **graph saving**, [R] **graph symbol**, [R] **graph textsize**, [R] **graph titles**, [R] **graph weights**

Title

graph monitors — Screen and monitor considerations

Remarks

Typing set graphics off will temporarily turn off the displaying of graphs. graph will still work but you will not see the result. This can be useful in do-files when you are automating the production of a large number of graphs using graph ..., saving(), gphdot, or gphpen. set graphics on will restore the displaying of graphs.

Stata for Windows and Stata for Macintosh

Stata for Windows and Stata for Macintosh users will likely never want to set graphics off. Other features of Stata related to graphs will not work if you have set graphics off, such as File–Print Graph, Edit–Copy Graph, and gphprint. The only reason Stata for Windows and Stata for Macintosh users would ever set graphics off is if they wanted to save a little time while generating large numbers of Stata .gph files from a do-file.

Stata for DOS

When you issue a graph command, and if graphics are on, Stata clears your screen, displays the graph, and then waits until you press any key. When you press a key, the screen clears and the original Stata session screen is restored.

Stata for DOS automatically turns graphics on for any PC with a graphics-capable monitor. With the saving() option, even people without graphics-capable monitors can use Stata's graphics. They just cannot see the image until they print it.

Stata supports the CGA, EGA, Hercules, and VGA graphic boards. If you have one of these types of boards and Stata does not automatically set graphics on—you can discover the setting with the query command—then your board is probably a clone of one of these boards and not a very good one at that. Do not panic; things can still work; see [R] stata. There are options you can specify when you start Stata to tell it the type of board you have. Stata's ability to automatically determine the type of board in your computer depends on the board exhibiting 100% compatibility with the original-label board.

We recommend that users with the (low-resolution) CGA board set textsize 125 or even set textsize 150. It will make the text on a graph far more readable. We also recommend that CGA users remember to set textsize 100 again before saving an image. The smaller letters look better when printed.

Stata for Unix

Stata for Unix supports the windowing systems on Unix systems, most importantly Sunview on Sun computers and X Windows on all computers including Sun. Read [R] xwindow—it will tell you how to create and manipulate graphic windows—and [U] **9.13 How Stata displays graphs (pipeline drivers)** or [U] **9.10 Using X Windows** for more advice. If you use X Windows, PCs running Windows can be connected to your network and display graphs using X terminal software for the PC.

Stata for Unix also supports remotely (meaning serially) connected PCs. The PC must be running Stata's Remote Graphics Support (RGS) program; see [U] **9.12 Remote Graphics Support (RGS)**. RGS is included with all Unix systems and may be copied freely.

Also See

[U] **9.10 Using X Windows**, [U] **9.11 Using X Windows remotely**, [U] **9.12 Remote Graphics Support (RGS)**, [U] **9.13 How Stata displays graphs (pipeline drivers)**

[R] **ansi**, [R] **stata**, [R] **xwindow**

Title

graph oneway — Graph one-way scatterplots

Description

This entry discusses the `oneway` style option to `graph` and the `jitter()` option.

Remarks

One-way scatterplots provide an effective alternative to histograms, especially when used for comparing distributions. The scheme is devilishly clever: Draw an axis or imagine one, then go through the data and draw a short vertical line along the axis everywhere there is an observation. When you are through, you have something that may remind you of a description of the spectrum from a distant star or a universal bar code, depending on your background. It is, however, a concise description of the distribution. There is an example of a one-way scatterplot at the bottom of this page.

To	Do
graph a one-way scatterplot of x	`graph x, oneway`
graph one-way scatterplots of x and y	`graph x y, oneway`
add spherical random noise to your data before graphing	use `jitter()`, see technical note below and [R] **graph weights**
combine `oneway` with `box`	see technical note below
deal with weighted data	specify `fweight` or `aweight`, see [R] **graph weights**
draw one-way scatterplots within category	see [R] **graph by** and examples below
specify a different scale for each category	use `Rescale`, see [R] **graph by**
add titles and annotations	see [R] **graph titles**
control the size of text	see [R] **graph textsize**
save or print the graph	see [R] **graph saving**, [R] **graph printing**

(Continued on next page.)

. graph tempjuly, by(region) oneway

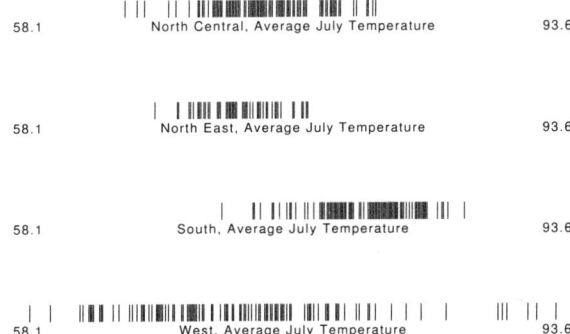

▷ Example

Since one-way scatterplots are intended for comparing distributions, one typically specifies more than one variable or the by() option or both. In the graph on the previous page, the July temperature in our data ranges from 58.1 to 93.6 degrees F, and we see that the West has the largest variation. Focusing on the two middle scatterplots, we note that there is little overlap in the distributions for the Northeast and South. Finally, since there is a mark for each observation in the data, we are able to infer something about the size as well as the distribution of the sample.

◁

▷ Example

You may specify up to twenty variables when drawing one-way scatterplots and, of course, you do not have to specify the by() option. You type graph tempjan tempjuly, oneway to draw one-way scatterplots for tempjan and tempjuly in a single image.

You may combine more than one variable with the by() option. If you type gr tempjan tempjuly, oneway by(region), Stata will produce a total of eight plots since there are two variables and four regions.

The maximum number of by-groups that can be displayed in a single image is 52. The maximum number of one-way scatterplots (variables times by-groups) is 60.

◁

(Continued on next page.)

❑ Technical Note

One-way scatterplots are often combined with box plots to make an even more informative image:

. graph tempjuly, by(region) oneway box

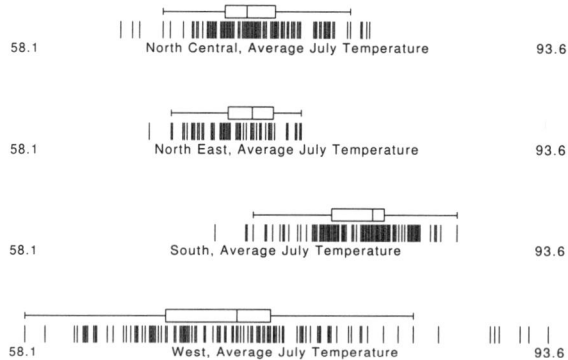

We can now see that the 25th percentile of temperature for the South is above the 75th percentile for the Northeast.

❑

❑ Technical Note

When dealing with reams of observations, drawing full lines for each observation can result in a scatterplot with solid black areas—adjacent lines are so close together that they merge into a single mass. We can avoid this by filling in a few randomly selected points on the line rather than filling in the whole line. The jitter(#) option does this, where # represents the number of points to be selected for each observation.

We opened this section by drawing a scatterplot for July temperature across the four regions of the U.S. Our data contains a total of 956 cities, distributed as 284 in the North Central, 166 in the Northeast, 250 in the South, and 256 in the West. We typed gr tempjuly, by(region) oneway to make the image. If we were to include the total option, Stata would add a fifth scatterplot representing all 956 cities. We try that and discover that the lines begin to merge into black masses, hiding the detail we seek. Thus, we redraw the image adding jitter(2), so that each city in the data is represented by two randomly chosen points on the line rather than by a whole line:

(Graph on next page.)

```
. graph tempjuly, by(region) total oneway box ji(2)
```

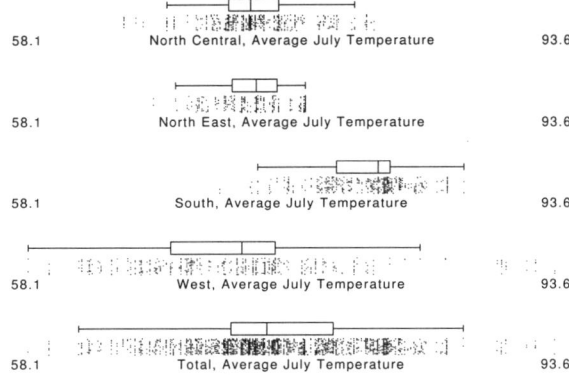

ji(2) is an abbreviation for jitter(2). We also overlaid our one-way with box plots.

◁

❏ Technical Note

An early discussion of the one-way scatterplot can be found in Chambers et al. (1983, 19–21); the term *one-dimensional scatterplot* is used rather than one-way scatterplot. In Chambers et al., small circles are plotted rather than lines and, in our opinion, this is less successful. Tufte (1983, 133) shows what he calls a *dot-dash plot* that uses lines rather than plotting symbols—the one-way scatters are substituted for the axes in a two-way scatterplot. Even earlier, examples of one-way scatterplots using short vertical lines can be found in Tufte (1974, pp. 10, 13, 28) and Smith (1937, 179). The earliest example, of which we have heard, of the one-way scatterplot can be found in Langren (1644). See [R] **graph twoway** for illustrations and instructions on how to draw such graphs. Stata implemented the one-way scatterplot in 1985.

❏

References

Chambers, J. M., W. S. Cleveland, B. Kleiner, and P. A. Tukey. 1983. *Graphical Methods for Data Analysis.* Belmont, CA: Wadsworth International Group.

Langren, Michael Florent van. 1644. *La Verdadera Longitud por Mar y Tierra.* Antwerp. p. 3.

Smith, H. Fairfield 1937. Contribution to the discussion of M. S. Bartlett: Some examples of statistical methods of research in agriculture and applied biology. *Journal of the Royal Statistical Society, Supplement* 4: 277–181.

Tufte, E. R. 1974. *Data Analysis for Politics and Policy.* Englewood Cliffs, NJ: Prentice-Hall.

——. 1983. *The Visual Display of Quantitative Information.* Cheshire, CT: Graphics Press.

Also See

Title

> **graph pens** — Specify colors and line thicknesses

Remarks

Graphs are drawn with a theoretical concept called a *pen*. The text is drawn using pen 1 and the graphical elements—which correspond to the variables in the *varlist*—are drawn with pens 2 through 9. On color monitors, different pens are mapped to different colors; on monochrome monitors, all pens look alike. When you print the graph, the thicknesses can be altered on monochrome devices, and the thicknesses can be altered and colors assigned on color printers.

▷ Example

Typing **graph y1 y2 x** plots **y1** vs. **x** using pen 2 and **y2** vs. **x** using pen 3. Pen 1 is used for the text. The **pen()** option allows you to vary the default. Typing **graph y1 y2 x, pen(22)** graphs both **y1** and **y2** using pen 2. Specifying **pen(32)** would draw **y1** using pen 3 and **y2** using pen 2.

In [R] **graph axis rendition**, we graphed the function $y = e^{-x/6} \sin x$ over the range 0 to 4π. Looking at that example, you now know that everything on the graph was drawn using pen 1 except for the y-curve itself, which was drawn using pen 2. Since we are printing on a monochrome device, all pens look alike, so there is no visual clue that the curve and the rest of the image were drawn using different pens.

We can, however, create dramatic effects when we print the graph. In the following graph, we set the thickness of pen 1 to 3 and the thickness of pen 2 to 8:

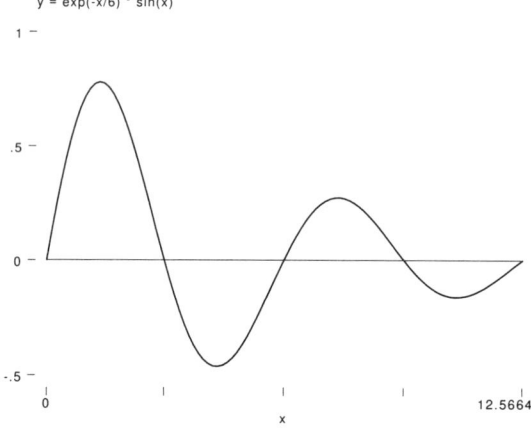

Stata for Windows and Stata for Macintosh users create this effect by pulling down **Prefs–Graph Preferences...**, choosing **Line Thicknesses**, and setting pen 1 to thickness 3 and pen 2 to thickness 8.

Stata for DOS and Stata for Unix users set pen 1 to thickness 3 and pen 2 to thickness 8 by specifying the **/t38** (or **-t38**) option with **gphdot** or **gphpen** when they print.

◁

❑ Technical Note

In addition to pens 1 through 9, there is pen 0. It is special in that it has no ink; anything drawn with it is invisible. Look at the opening figure in [R] **graph titles**. There is data in the center of the graph—you just cannot see it. When we made the graph, we added the option **pen(0)** so that what we plotted disappeared.

In addition to creating special effects, pen 0 can be useful to monochrome monitor users. Color monitor users can easily distinguish the different pens—they are different colors—but monochrome monitor users cannot. Suppose you plan to draw one of the graphical elements with a particularly bold pen when you print, but you are not sure that you have specified the **pen()** option correctly. Rather than waiting until you print the image to find out whether you made a mistake, you can issue the command assigning pen 0 to the element you hope to ultimately intensify. If it disappears from the image, you know you have the right graphical element, so you can reissue the command, replacing the zero with some other pen number.

❑

Choosing the line thickness requires experimentation; thicknesses vary across printers. If you are using a Lexmark, the following may help:

```
Pen thicknesses: Lexmark Optra R+, 1200 dpi

  Thickness 1     Thickness 1     Thickness 1    |__
  Thickness 2     Thickness 2     Thickness 2    |__
  Thickness 3     Thickness 3     Thickness 3    |__
  Thickness 4     Thickness 4     Thickness 4    |__
  Thickness 5     Thickness 5     Thickness 5    |__
  Thickness 6     Thickness 6     Thickness 6    |__
  Thickness 7     Thickness 7     Thickness 7    |__
  Thickness 8     Thickness 8     Thickness 8    |__
  Thickness 9     Thickness 9     Thickness 9    |__
```

The thickness at which text looks best depends mightily on its size. All the images in this manual are printed at 52% of standard sizes. Here is the same image printed at 92%:

(*Continued on next page.*)

```
Pen thicknesses: Lexmark Optra R+, 1200 dpi

   Thickness 1      Thickness 1      Thickness 1      ⌐

   Thickness 2      Thickness 2      Thickness 2      ⌐

   Thickness 3      Thickness 3      Thickness 3      ⌐

   Thickness 4      Thickness 4      Thickness 4      ⌐

   Thickness 5      Thickness 5      Thickness 5      ⌐

   Thickness 6      Thickness 6      Thickness 6      ⌐

   Thickness 7      Thickness 7      Thickness 7      ⌐

   Thickness 8      Thickness 8      Thickness 8      ⌐

   Thickness 9      Thickness 9      Thickness 9      ⌐
```

Among the materials supplied with Stata is a file called `penthick.gph`—you will find it in `\stata` (DOS and Windows), `/usr/local/stata` (Unix), or `~:Stata` (Macintosh). This is the same file we printed above, and you can print it as you would any other graph. The image uses all nine pens and when printed, each of the pens should be set to the same thickness as its pen number. You should print it *on your printer* at all sizes you typically use to produce graphs. Post the results on the wall near your computer. They will save you a lot of experimentation and time.

Stata for Windows and Stata for Macintosh users: The above two graphs were printed using the built-in Stata font. If you are not using this font, the pen thicknesses will not affect the text.

▷ Example

Stata for Windows users: Type `graph using c:\stata\penthick`. Pull down **Prefs–Graph Preferences...** and choose **Line Thicknesses**. Set pen 1 to thickness 1, pen 2 to thickness 2, ..., pen 9 to thickness 9. Click **OK**. Pull down **Prefs–Graph Preferences...**, choose **Magnifications**, and verify the overall is what you ordinarily use. Finally, pull down **File–Print Graph** to print the graph.

◁

▷ Example

Stata for Macintosh users: Open the `Stata` folder and double-click on `penthick.gph`. Pull down **Prefs–Graph Preferences...** and choose **Line Thicknesses**. Set pen 1 to thickness 1, pen 2 to thickness 2, . . . , pen 9 to thickness 9. Then choose **Magnifications**, and verify the overall is what you ordinarily use. Finally, pull down **File–Print Graph** to print the graph.

◁

▷ Example

Stata for DOS and Stata for Unix users: Pretend you ordinarily print graphs at 80% of standard size. Say you use DOS and `gphdot`. Type

```
> gphdot c:\stata\penthick /r80 /t123456789
```

If you instead use Unix with a PostScript printer, type

```
% gphpen -r80 -t123456789 penthick
```

Unix users will then have to use `lp(1)` or `lpr(1)` to send the resulting graph to their printer.

◁

❑ Technical Note

`penthick.gph` was created using the Stata Graphics Editor; see [R] **graph stage**.

❑

Also See

[R] **graph printing**, [R] **graph shading**, [R] **graph stage**

Title

graph pie — Graph pie charts

Description

This entry discusses the `pie` style option to `graph`.

Remarks

Stata draws pie charts when you specify the `pie` option. The command `graph a b c, pie` produces a pie chart containing three slices. The width of each slice is proportional to the sum of the respective variable.

To	Do
graph a pie chart of a, b, and c with slices proportional to sums	`graph a b c, pie`
graph a pie chart of a, b, and c by *category* with slices proportional to sums	`gr a b c, pie by(`*category*`)`
control the shading of the pie	use `shading()`, see [R] **graph shading**
deal with weighted data	specify `fweight` or `iweight`, see [R] **graph weights**
add titles and annotations	see [R] **graph titles**
control the size of text	see [R] **graph textsize**
save or print the graph	see [R] **graph saving**, [R] **graph printing**

▷ Example

If you have not yet read the first example of [R] **graph bar**, please do. In that example, we discuss the implications—all of them positive—of plotting *sums* of variables. We also introduce you to the XYZ Company data which we will use here.

The data contains the monthly costs of XYZ Company for the fiscal years 1982 through 1988. In [R] **graph bar**, we produce bar charts displaying those costs. Let's now regraph the data using a pie chart, completely masking the amounts and revealing only the relative shares:

(Continued on next page.)

```
. gr dlabor ilabor parts advert oh, pie by(year) sh(31324)
        title("Distribution of Costs, XYZ Company")
```

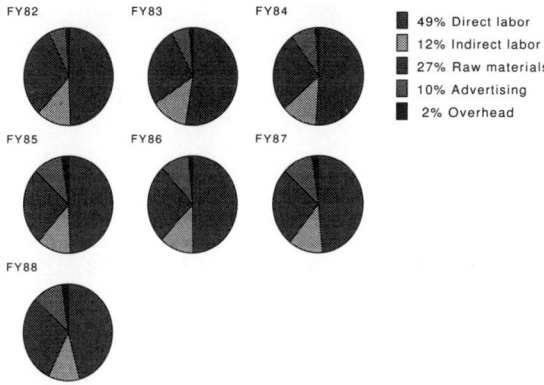

Distribution of Costs, XYZ Company

If we had not specified the by() option, Stata would have drawn a single pie chart reflecting the distribution of costs across all years.

◁

❑ Technical Note

Stata is willing to place up to 64 pie charts in a single image. You may specify up to 16 variables when you draw a pie chart.

❑

❑ Technical Note

The first pie chart is credited to William Playfair (1801). See Beniger and Robyn (1978), Funkhouser (1937, 283–285), or Tufte (1983, 44–45) for further historical details.

❑

References

Beniger, J. R. and D. L. Robyn. 1978. Quantitative graphics in statistics: a brief history. *The American Statistician* 32: 1–11.

Funkhouser, H. G. 1937. Historical development of the graphical representation of statistical data. *Osiris* 3: 269–404.

Playfair, W. 1801. *The Statistical Breviary; Shewing on a Principle Entirely New, the Resources of Every State and Kingdom in Europe.* London.

Tufte, E. R. 1983. *The Visual Display of Quantitative Information.* Cheshire, CT: Graphics Press.

Also See

[R] **graph**, [R] **graph by**, [R] **graph pens**, [R] **graph printing**, [R] **graph saving**, [R] **graph shading**, [R] **graph stage**, [R] **graph titles**, [R] **graph weights**

Title

graph printing — Print graphs in Stata

Description

Information on printing graphs is found in the entries listed in the following table. Please skip to the appropriate entry.

References common across the [R] **graph printing** ... entries are also given below.

Stata for Windows users	See [R] **graph printing Windows**
Stata for DOS users	See [R] **graph printing DOS**
Stata for Macintosh users	See [R] **graph printing Macintosh**
Stata for Unix users	See [R] **graph printing Unix**

References

Becketti, S. 1993. gr13.1: \special{} effects with Stata graphs in TeX documents. *Stata Technical Bulletin* 15: 12–13. Reprinted in *Stata Technical Bulletin Reprints*, vol. 3, p. 56.

——. 1994. gr15: Incorporating Stata graphs in TeX documents using an HP printer. *Stata Technical Bulletin* 19: 11–14. Reprinted in *Stata Technical Bulletin Reprints*, vol. 4, pp. 54–59.

Reese, R. A. 1991a. os1: Gphpen and colour PostScript. *Stata Technical Bulletin* 1: 10. Reprinted in *Stata Technical Bulletin Reprints*, vol. 1, p. 54.

——. 1991b. os1.1: Update on Gphpen and colour PostScript use. *Stata Technical Bulletin* 3: 10–11. Reprinted in *Stata Technical Bulletin Reprints*, vol. 1, p. 55.

Soon, T. W. and S. L. C. Saw. 1993. gr13: Incorporating Stata-created PostScript files into TeX/LaTeX documents. *Stata Technical Bulletin* 15: 7–12. Reprinted in *Stata Technical Bulletin Reprints*, vol. 3, pp. 49–56.

Tufte, E. R. 1983. *The Visual Display of Quantitative Information.* Cheshire, CT: Graphics Press.

Tukey, J. W. 1977. *Exploratory Data Analysis.* Reading, MA: Addison-Wesley Publishing Company.

Also See

[U] **A. Installation of Stata for Windows 95,** [U] **B. Installation of Stata for Windows 3.1,** [U] **C. Installation of Stata for Macintosh,** [U] **D. Installation of Stata for DOS,** [U] **E. Installation of Stata for Unix**

[R] **graph pens,** [R] **graph printing DOS,** [R] **graph printing Macintosh,** [R] **graph printing Unix,** [R] **graph printing Windows,** [R] **graph redisplaying,** [R] **graph saving**

Title

---

graph printing DOS — Print graphs in Stata for DOS

Description

This entry describes how you print graphs in Stata for DOS. Stata for Windows users, please see [R] **graph printing Windows**; Stata for Macintosh users, see [R] **graph printing Macintosh**; and Stata for Unix users, see [R] **graph printing Unix**.

Remarks

Remarks are presented under the headings

> *gphdot and gphpen*
> *Using gphdot*
> *Using gphpen*
> *Incorporating Stata graphs into documents*
> *Creating HP-GL files*
> *Creating PostScript files*
> *Creating Lotus .PIC files*
> *Special effects and aspect ratio*
> *Common questions*

After you have created a `.gph` file with the `saving()` option (see [R] **graph saving**), you can print the graph on a variety of devices. The discussion below assumes that Stata's hard-copy drivers have been installed according to the instructions in [U] **D. Installation of Stata for DOS** and that the appropriate defaults were set at that time.

gphdot and gphpen

`gphdot` and `gphpen` are the programs that print `.gph` files. These are not Stata commands but are separate programs which you can use outside of Stata. You can also use them from inside Stata. You may, however, have to `exit` Stata to use the programs if they do not have sufficient memory.

`gphdot` supports pixel-oriented devices such as dot-matrix and HP laser printers, whereas `gphpen` supports vector-oriented devices such as pen-plotters and PostScript printers. `gphpen` can also convert `.gph` files into Lotus `.PIC` format. Tables 1 and 2 below provide a list of printers supported by each of these commands along with some additional information. The tables printed in this manual are probably not up to date. If you cannot find your printer, look in your printer manual; your printer probably emulates one of the printers that are listed.

The syntax of `gphdot` and `gphpen` is

$$\{\text{gphdot} \mid \text{gphpen}\}\ \textit{filename}\ \left[\textit{/option /option} \ldots\right]$$

If *filename* is specified without an extension, `.gph` is assumed.

Here is what happens when you type one of these commands. First, the command looks for a file that describes your printer. These files have names like `fx80.dot` and `hp7475.pen`. Since `gphdot` and `gphpen` cannot divine which file to read, you have to tell them. One way is through an option which we will explain later. If you do not specify that option, `gphdot` looks for `default.dot` and `gphpen` looks for `default.pen`. Most users copy or rename one of the description files to the default filename at installation time and thus avoid having to deal with the option. Many users also delete all the irrelevant description files and save some disk space. Column two of Tables 1 and 2 names the description file for each printer.

Table 1. gphdot Input and Output Files

Printer Name	Printer File	output
AT&T 570	fx80.dot	prn:
Brother M-1309	fx80.dot	prn:
Brother M-1324	epsonlq.dot	prn:
Brother HL Series		
at 75 dpi	hpl.dot	prn:
at 150 dpi	hplp.dot	prn:
at 300 dpi	hplphr.dot	prn:
Canon BJ-300, -330	epsonlq.dot	prn:
Citizen 200GX	fx80.dot	prn:
Citizen GSX-130, -140, -145	epsonlq.dot	prn:
Citizen PN48	epsonlq.dot	prn:
C. Itoh 5000	ibmg.dot	prn:
Digital LN03 Laser	ln03.dot	prn:
Epson EPL		
at 75 dpi	hpl.dot	prn:
at 150 dpi	hplp.dot	prn:
at 300 dpi	hplphr.dot	prn:
Epson FX, LX, RX	fx80.dot	prn:
Epson LQ, SQ	epsonlq.dot	prn:
Epson MX-80 w/ GrafTrax	mx80.dot	prn:
Fujitsu DL3600	epsonlq.dot	prn:
Fujitsu RX		
at 75 dpi	hpl.dot	prn:
at 150 dpi	hplp.dot	prn:
at 300 dpi	hplphr.dot	prn:
HP LaserJet and DeskJet		
at 75 dpi	hpl.dot	prn:
at 150 dpi	hplp.dot	prn:
at 300 dpi	hplphr.dot	prn:
HP ThinkJet	hpt.dot	prn:
Hyundai HDP Series	fx80.dot	prn:
IBM ExecJet	epsonlq.dot	prn:
IBM Graphics printer	ibmg.dot	prn:
IBM Proprinter	ibmg.dot	prn:
Kodak Diconix	fx80.dot	prn:

(*Table continued on next page.*)

Table 1. **gphdot** Input and Output Files

Printer Name	Printer File	output
Mannesmann Tally 900 series		
at 75 dpi	hpl.dot	prn:
at 150 dpi	hplp.dot	prn:
at 300 dpi	hplphr.dot	prn:
NEC PC-8023A-C	nec8023.dot	prn:
NEC P6 and P7	necp6.dot	prn:
NEC Pinwriter	epsonlq.dot	prn:
Okidata Microline printers		
100 series	ibmg.dot	prn:
300 series	epsonlq.dot	prn:
non-IBM compatible	ml92.dot	prn:
Panasonic KX		
P1695	fx80.dot	prn:
P1123, P1124, P1624, P2624	epsonlq.dot	prn:
Ricoh PC Laser 6000		
at 75 dpi	hpl.dot	prn:
at 150 dpi	hplp.dot	prn:
at 300 dpi	hplphr.dot	prn:
Seikosha SL-90	epsonlq.dot	prn:
Seikosha SP-2000	fx80.dot	prn:
Star Micronics XB, NX-2420	epsonlq.dot	prn:
Star Micronics XR, NX-1020	fx80.dot	prn:
Tandy DMP	rsdmp.dot	prn:
Toshiba ExpressWriter	epsonlq.dot	prn:
Toshiba 3-in-1	p351.dot	prn:

Table 2. **gphpen** Input and Output Files

Printer Name	Printer File	output
HP-GL files	hpgl.pen	*filename*.hpg
HP 7550 *or*		
HP 7440 ColorPro		
Portrait	hp7440.pen	com1:
Landscape	hp7440ls.pen	com1:
HP 7470	hp7470ls.pen	com1:
HP 7475		
Portrait	hp7475.pen	com1:
Landscape	hp7475ls.pen	com1:
Oversize	hp7475w.pen	com1:
Houston Instruments	hi.pen	com1:
QMS Lasergrafix		
Portrait	qms.pen	com1:
Landscape	qmsls.pen	com1:
PostScript		
monochrome portrait	ps.pen	*filename*.ps
monochrome landscape	psls.pen	*filename*.ps
color portrait	psc.pen	*filename*.ps
color landscape	pscls.pen	*filename*.ps
Encapsulated PostScript		
monochrome	eps.pen	*filename*.eps
color	epsc.pen	*filename*.eps
Lotus .PIC		
Stata drawn font	pic.pen	*filename*.pic
Lotus built-in font	picpt.pen	*filename*.pic

Whether you explicitly specify the description file or go for the default, the description file does not have to be in the current directory. gphdot and gphpen look in the current directory first, but if the description file is not there, they look along your path and, if they still cannot find it, they look in \stata. If the programs still cannot find the file, they complain and stop.

Once the program has learned about your printer, it looks for *filename*—your .gph file. You do not have to type the .gph on the end of the filename because the programs will add it for you if necessary. They then read a little bit of the file to determine if it really is a .gph file and not some file that just happens to have a .gph suffix. If the programs do not like what they see, they complain and stop.

Having done all of this, the programs begin reading the file and converting it into a form suitable for your printer. On PCs running DOS, gphdot sends its output to prn: and gphpen *typically* sends its output to com1:. We say typically because if the output is PostScript, gphpen sends it to *filename*.ps and if it is Lotus .PIC format, to *filename*.pic. In any case, there is an option (/o*filename*, see below) to control where the output goes, so you can send it anywhere you wish.

❏ Technical Note

When using gphpen to send the output directly to the communication port, it is your responsibility to initialize the port correctly. We recommend that you configure your plotter/printer to operate at 9600 baud, no parity, 8 data bits, and 1 stop bit. If you follow our suggestion, then before using gphpen, type

```
MODE COM1:9600,N,8,1,P
```

The P at the end of the command indicates that the asynchronous adapter is being used for a serial interface printer or plotter.

❏

All that is left to understand are the options. We will refer to them as /*ltr*.

/o*device*:
/o*filename*
Tables 1 and 2 tell you where gphdot and gphpen normally send their output. The /o option allows you to override that default. Specifying /omyfile.prt, for instance, would send the output to the file myfile.prt. Notice that there is no space between the option letter and the filename. *Do not* type /o myfile.prt. This is true of all options that take arguments. The argument is placed right up against the option letter.

Returning to our example, you may find the /o option especially convenient. By saving the image in a file, you can print it later. If you are using gphdot, be warned that the resulting file is typically binary so you must specify the /B option to the DOS COPY command. To print the file on a printer attached to the parallel port, type COPY /B MYFILE.PRT PRN. Files created by gphpen are ASCII format, so you can dispense with COPY's /B option or even use DOS's PRINT command.

/d*filename*
specifies the name of the file describing your printer. If you do not specify this option, gphdot assumes the file is default.dot and gphpen assumes default.pen. For gphdot, specifying /dhplphr would specify the file hplphr.dot which corresponds to an HP LaserJet in its highest resolution mode, 300 dots-per-inch (see Table 1). For /gphpen, specifying /dhp7440ls would specify the file hp7440ls.pen which corresponds to an HP ColorPro pen-plotter in landscape mode (see Table 2).

/l{l|p}

(gphdot only) specifies landscape or portrait mode. Default is /lp: you type /ll for landscape mode. For gphpen, the landscape/portrait selection is made in the file describing the printer. See /d above and Table 2.

/-

suppresses the normal page ejection at the conclusion of the graph.

/+

ejects a page before starting the graph.

/c#

specifies the number of copies of the graph to be made. Default is /c1. The /c option is ignored by plotters.

/n

suppresses the Stata logo.

/r#

resizes the image to # percent of normal. Default is /r100.

/rx#

resizes the image horizontally to # percent of normal.

/ry#

resizes the image vertically to # percent of normal.

/s#

specifies the sizes of all plotting symbols. Default is /s100, meaning 100% of normal, where normal is defined after any adjustment made by the /r options. /s50 reduces the size of the plotting symbols to 50% of normal size. /s200 doubles the size.

/s{O|S|T|o|d|p|.}#

specifies the size of just the specified plotting symbol. /sO50 would make large circles 50% of their normal size. /so200 would make small circles twice their normal size. Only one symbol may be specified, but you may include the option more than once. For instance, to rescale both the small and the large circles, specify /sO50 /so200.

/i *filename*

specifies the name of an injection file—a file to be sent to the printer before any of the graph. This option is rarely used. For PostScript devices, the CRC-supplied file ps.plf (psls.plf, psc.plf, or pscls.pen) is automatically injected. For Lotus .PIC files, pic.plf is automatically injected.

/x

(gphpen *only*) slows down the pen motion on real pen-plotters to prevent ink from smearing on transparencies.

/p#...#

remaps the pens. The default is /p123456789, meaning pen 1 is pen 1, pen 2 is pen 2, and so on. /p122 would make both pen 2 and pen 3 equivalent to pen 2.

/t#...#

specifies the thicknesses of the *pens*. For pixel devices, the default is to make each pen one pixel wide. If you are using a 300-dpi device such as a laser printer, the image will probably look better if the pens have thickness four. Typing /t144 makes pen 1 one pixel and pens 2 and 3 four pixels wide. Typing /t444 would make the text pen thicker, too. See [R] **graph pens** for printed examples of the effects. For real pen-plotters, /t merely informs gphpen as to the width, in millimeters, of the actual pens in the carriage. gphpen can do a better job when it knows the widths. /t affects thicknesses *after* any remapping by /p. For instance, /p122 /t12 would make the original pens 2 and 3 have thickness 2.

Using gphdot

▷ Example

You have an HP LaserJet printer attached to the parallel port of your computer. You do not want to do anything special except print a graph which you have saved as mypic.gph. You still have to decide at what resolution you want to print the graph. You decide on the highest resolution, 300 dots-per-inch, so you type

    gphdot mypic

If you have followed our installation instructions, this will work. If you did not, you will see the message "file default.dot not found". In that case, you can type

    gphdot mypic /dhplphr

When you left off the /d option, gphdot attempted to use the description contained in default.dot. If all the pictures you want to print are going to be for an HP printer in high-resolution mode, you might want to rename hplphr.dot to default.dot; then you will not have to specify the /d option.

◁

▷ Example

You have the same LaserJet printer, but this time you want the output to go into a file that you will subsequently print. You type

    gphdot mypic /omypic.hp

to send the output to mypic.hp. Later it comes time to print the graph. You now type

    COPY /B MYPIC.HP PRN

to print the graph. You must specify COPY's /B option because the file is binary.

◁

Using gphpen

▷ Example

You have an HP 7440 pen-plotter. As in our previous three examples, you have a file called `mypic.gph` which you now wish to print. Since the pen-plotter is connected to the serial port of your PC, you must first initialize the serial port. You type

```
MODE COM1:9600,N,8,1,P
```

You only have to type this command once anytime after booting your computer or running another software package which resets the port. Your serial port is now initialized. You decide to print your graph in standard portrait mode:

```
gphpen mypic /dhp7440
```

although perhaps you omit the `/dhp7440` option. If you do omit it, **gphpen** will use the description contained in `default.pen`. If all the pictures you want to print are going to be for an HP plotter in portrait mode, you might want to rename `hp7440.pen` to `default.pen`.

◁

▷ Example

You have the same HP plotter, but this time you want the output to go into a file that you will subsequently print. You type

```
gphpen mypic /dhp7440 /omypic.hp
```

to send the output to `mypic.hp`, although you may omit the `/d` option if you have renamed `hp7440.pen` to `default.pen`.

When you want to print the graph, you must make sure the communication port has been properly initialized. If you have not already done so, you type

```
MODE COM1:9600,N,8,1,P
```

That out of the way, you type

```
COPY MYPIC.HP PRN
```

to print the graph. Since **gphpen** produces straight ASCII files, you could instead type `PRINT MYPIC.HP`. This has the advantage that you can continue working on your PC while the picture is being made.

◁

Incorporating Stata graphs into documents

You wish to incorporate a Stata graph into a document created by your favorite word processor or editor. How you do this depends on the other software that you are using. Instructions for creating HP-GL files, PostScript files, encapsulated PostScript files, and Lotus `.PIC` files are given below. See the references at the end of [R] **graph printing** for articles discussing incorporating Stata graphs into TEX documents.

Creating HP-GL files

▷ Example

You want to copy a graph produced by Stata into your word processor or graphics editor. Many programs read HP-GL files, but also see *Creating PostScript files* below. You type

```
gphpen mypic /dhpgl
```

This creates the file `mypic.hpg` in HP-GL format for importing into your other software.

◁

Creating PostScript files

▷ Example

If you wish to create an encapsulated PostScript file suitable for embedding in a document (such as a document created with WordPerfect), see *Creating encapsulated PostScript files* below. This example assumes that you want to print the file `mypic.gph` on your PostScript printer. You type

```
gphpen mypic /dps
```

to create the file `mypic.ps`, although you may omit the `/dps` if you have already renamed `ps.pen` to `default.pen`. For this command to work, you must also have the file `ps.plf` in the current directory, or along your path, or in the `\stata` directory. That file contains some additional information that `gphpen` will need to make the PostScript file. You must now print the file; use `COPY` or `PRINT`.

◁

Creating encapsulated PostScript files

▷ Example

If you wish to create PostScript files suitable for printing on a PostScript printer, see *Creating Postscript files* above. This example assumes that you wish to include the file `mypic.gph` in another document. You type

```
gphpen mypic /deps
```

to create the file `mypic.eps`, although you may omit the `/deps` if you have already renamed `eps.pen` to `default.pen`. For this command to work, you must also have the file `eps.plf` in the current directory, or along your path, or in the `\stata` directory. That file contains some additional information that `gphpen` will need to make the PostScript file.

◁

Creating Lotus .PIC files

▷ Example

You want to convert a .gph file into .PIC format so that you can edit it using Lotus Freelance. You must make a choice: Do you want the text in the graph to be drawn using the Stata font or the Lotus font? The Stata font looks better but it is literally drawn whereas the Lotus font is built into their package. Using the Stata font makes the .PIC files larger. You decide to use the Stata font, so you type

```
gphpen mypic /dpic.pen
```

to convert the file mypic.gph into mypic.pic. For this command to work, you must also have the file pic.plf in the current directory, or along your path, or in the \stata directory. That file contains some additional information that gphpen will need to make the .PIC file.

◁

Special effects and aspect ratio

▷ Example

By now you should understand where the output is going, so let's put aside that problem and focus on the other options. For instance, all the pictures in this manual were printed with the command

```
gphdot filename /r52
```

which rescaled the image to 52% of the normal size. Let's consider another, more complicated command. We will use gphdot in our example, but we could just as well use gphpen.

```
gphdot mypic /r80 /s50 /s025 /so110 /t122 /c10
```

prints mypic.gph. The image is rescaled to 80% of the ordinary size. All the symbols are rescaled to 50% of their ordinary size after the 80% rescaling, making the symbols 40% of their ordinary size. The large circle symbol, however, is scaled to 25% of 80%, that is, 20%, of its ordinary size. In addition, the small circle is scaled to 110% of 80%, or 88%, of its ordinary size. Pens 2 and 3 are made slightly bolder than the text pen 1, and finally we specify that we want 10 copies of the graph.

◁

❑ Technical Note

You can rescale images in the horizontal (x) and vertical (y) dimensions separately using the /rx and /ry options. For instance, under DOS

```
gphdot mypic /rx84 /ry110
```

would create a graph that is almost square, while

```
gphdot mypic /rx84 /ry130
```

would create a graph that is considerably taller than it is wide. The first graph will look "good", but the second will look "bad". This is not because graphs that are taller than they are wide are inherently bad; it is because as you change the aspect, you change the aspect of Stata's text font, as well. In the first case, you have not changed the aspect too much and the font, while looking different, will not appear odd. In the second case, the change is so drastic that the font will no longer look reasonable.

The best way to change aspect is to use Stage; see [R] **graph stage**. That is because as you change the aspect, Stage automatically corrects the font to maintain true aspect. To change the aspect, edit the graph in Stage, make one of the dimensions smaller, and then print the graph. If you want to make the overall graph bigger after editing, specify, perhaps, /r110 or even /r200, but do not attempt to make the graph bigger while in the Stage editor. Overall size is controlled at time of printing.

What aspect ratio should you choose? The one used by Stata is probably best in most circumstances. Tukey (1977, 129) and Tufte (1983, 186–190) suggest that, although there are exceptions, graphs should be greater in length than in height. The exceptions, of course, depend on the data, and you should choose the aspect that best reveals your data.

❑

Common questions

"I tried to print a graph using gphdot or gphpen and got the message 'Bad command or filename'." Either you have not installed gphdot.exe or gphpen.exe or, more likely, you have not added c:\stata to your DOS PATH; see [U] **D. Installation of Stata for DOS**.

"I tried to print a graph and gphdot is just sitting there, doing nothing." Your printer is not on-line. Press the on-line button on your printer. If the printer is on-line, check the cables between your computer and printer.

"I tried to print myfile.gph by typing gphdot myfile (or gphpen myfile) and got the message 'Unable to input file myfile.gph'." gphdot (gphpen) could not find your graph file, probably because it is in a different directory.

"I tried to print myfile.gph by typing gphdot myfile (or gphpen myfile) and got the message 'Unable to open device file default.dot'." gphdot (gphpen) could not find the printer description file. Either you have not installed a default description file (see [U] **D. Installation of Stata for DOS**) or you have not added c:\stata to your path (see [U] **D. Installation of Stata for DOS**).

"I tried to print myfile.gph and everything seemed to work, except what my printer produced looks like gibberish." You are using the wrong printer description file. See Tables 1 and 2 above, determine the right description file, and install it as described in [U] **D. Installation of Stata for DOS**.

"My printer is not listed in either Table 1 or 2." Look at your printer manual; your printer probably emulates one of the printers that are listed in the tables. Pretend your printer is that model printer and install the description file for it; see [U] **D. Installation of Stata for DOS**. In addition, consult the *Stata Technical Bulletin* for printer support added since the release of Stata 5.0; see [U] **2.4 The Stata Technical Bulletin**.

"I need to increase the size of the printed graph, how do I do this?" See the /r gphdot and gphpen option above.

Also See

[U] **D. Installation of Stata for DOS**

[R] **graph pens**, [R] **graph redisplaying**, [R] **graph saving**

Title

> **graph printing Macintosh** — Print graphs in Stata for Macintosh

Description

This entry describes how to print graphs in Stata for Macintosh. There is also a way to automate the printing of many graphs in Stata for Macintosh. See the *Automated printing—gphprint* section at the end of this entry.

Stata for Windows users, please see [R] **graph printing Windows**; Stata for DOS users, see [R] **graph printing DOS**; and Stata for Unix users, see [R] **graph printing Unix**.

Remarks

Remarks are presented under the headings

> *Overview*
> *Preferences*
> *Appearance preferences*
> *Line Thicknesses preferences*
> *Magnifications preference*
> *Colors preference*
> *Load Graph and Save Graph preferences*
> *Automated printing—gphprint*

Overview

To print a graph:

1. Display the graph. Either

    a. Draw it using the `graph` command, or

    b. Redisplay your last graph by pressing the **Graph** or **Regraph** button, or

    c. Pull down **File** and choose **Open Graph**, or

    d. Retrieve a previously saved graph by typing `graph using` *myfile*. (You previously saved the graph *myfile*.`gph`.)

2. Optionally pull down **Prefs** and choose **Graph Preferences**. This will allow you to set options specifying how the graph is displayed and printed.

3. Pull down **File** and choose **Print Graph**.

To copy a graph to the Clipboard:

1. Display the graph.

2. Optionally pull down **Prefs** and choose **Graph Preferences**. The same options which affect how a graph is printed also affect how it is copied.

3. Pull down **Edit** and choose **Copy**.

Preferences

Prefs–Graph Preferences affect how the graph is printed and copied. Some of the preferences affect what you see on the screen when Stata displays the graph, some do not, but all affect printing and copying. The preferences are divided into the dialog tabs

Appearance	various output options for graphs
Line Thicknesses	thicknesses of pens
Magnifications	symbols and overall scaling
Colors	foreground and background colors

Further options include

Load Graph Preferences	load prior set of graph preferences
Save Graph Preferences	save set of graph preferences
Restore Defaults	restore all preferences to initial settings

Appearance preferences

You can set various output options for graphs when printing, displaying or copying on the **Appearance** preference tab. The options are described below.

Use Macintosh Fonts in Graph

By default, Stata uses a Macintosh font for the text in graphs. If you uncheck this preference, Stata will use its own built-in font to draw the text in graphs. This built-in font is the same as the font that Stata for DOS and Stata for Unix users see in their graphs. The font typeface and style affects the entire graph; you cannot set the font typeface and style for individual text items. You can copy and paste the graph to a drawing application if you wish to change the font typeface and style for individual text items.

Macintosh users will generally prefer to use a Macintosh font for the text in their graphs. There are several advantages to using a native Macintosh font over Stata's built-in font:

1. You have a wide range of typefaces available to you when you use Macintosh fonts for the text in your graphs. Do you want to use a bold font? Pull down the **Font Style** popup on the **Appearance** tab and choose the bold style.

   Note: You cannot set the size of the font for the graph window. Stata sets the size of each element of text in the graph window separately. If you wish to set an overall size for the text in Stata's graphs, see [R] **graph textsize**.

2. Graphs drawn using a Macintosh font for the text are more easily edited in another Macintosh drawing application. When you copy and paste a Stata graph to a drawing application, that application will be able to recognize any text in the graph that has been drawn with a Macintosh font as text. This means that you can directly edit the text.

   Only Stata sees its built-in font as text. Other Macintosh applications see this font as a collection of lines and points, making it impossible to edit as text.

3. Graphs drawn using a Macintosh font for the text will draw (and redraw) faster than those drawn in Stata's built-in font. They will also consume less memory. This is because it takes one call to draw a line of text using a Macintosh font, while it takes many calls to draw the lines and points required for a single line of text in Stata's built-in font.

Note: The Macintosh has no built-in facility for drawing vertical text. Stata for Macintosh circumvents this limitation by drawing text horizontally as a bitmap, and then rotating the bitmap 90°. Because of this, vertical text may not print at as high of quality as horizontal text and the text cannot be directly edited.

Graph Font and Font Style options

When **Use Macintosh Fonts in Graph** is checked, you may choose the Graph's font and style with the **Graph Font** popup and the **Font Style** popup.

Ignore Pen Colors and Ignore Background Color options

The colors you choose affect the screen. They also affect what is sent to your printer if you uncheck **Ignore Pen Colors** and **Ignore Background Color**. With these two items checked, Stata will send the graph to your printer as a monochrome image on a null background (which will be white because the paper is white).

If you use a color printer, you will probably want to uncheck **Ignore Pen Colors** but leave **Ignore Background Color**. This will send color graphs but with a null background. If you want the background color as well, uncheck **Ignore Background Color**.

When Stata copies a graph to the Clipboard, it also ignores or honors the foreground and background colors according to your preferences.

Include Logo on Print option

When Stata prints a graph it places a small Stata logo at the bottom-right corner. You can suppress this by unchecking **Include Logo on Print**.

Line Thicknesses

The default **Line Thicknesses** settings are

Pen 1	1	Pen 6	1
Pen 2	1	Pen 7	1
Pen 3	1	Pen 8	1
Pen 4	1	Pen 9	1
Pen 5	1		

Pen thicknesses are discussed in [R] **graph pens**. These thicknesses have a dramatic effect on how a graph looks when printed and you will want to set them according to what looks best on your printer. Thicknesses range from 1 to 9.

Display Thicknesses on Screen

The **Display Thicknesses on Screen** option determines whether Stata's Graph window respects the pen thicknesses you have set. Respecting thicknesses tends to look bad because the screen has less resolution than your printer. Checking **Display Thicknesses on Screen** can be useful, however, for verifying relative thicknesses before printing.

Magnifications preference

The default **Magnifications** are

Overall	100	Symbol S	100
Horiz.	100	Symbol T	100
Vert.	100	Symbol o	100
All Sym.	100	Symbol d	100
Symbol O	100	Symbol p	100
		Symbol .	100

Overall magnification determines how big the graph is when printed. All magnifications are stated in percent—100 means 100% of the size Stata would ordinarily choose, and you may choose percentages smaller or larger than that.

Horiz. and Vert. magnifications allow you to separately set the horizontal and vertical magnifications. You could set Overall 52 and leave Horiz. 100 and Vert. 100, or you could leave Overall 100 and set Horiz. 52 and Vert. 52 and have the same effect. Magnifications are applied sequentially. Thus, if you set Overall 52 and Horiz. 125, the effective horizontal magnification is $52 \times 1.25 = 65\%$.

All Sym. affects all symbols within the graph. Again, magnifications are applied sequentially, so if Overall is 52, All Sym. 100 means the symbols are scaled appropriately for the overall size—to 52% of their normal size. Specifying All Sym. 110 would make all symbols 10% larger relative to the overall size of the graph.

In addition or instead, you can set the symbol magnifications individually. This allows you to change sizes of symbols relative to each other. Magnifications, as always, are interpreted as relative to Overall, so 110 means 10% larger after all other rescalings. Magnifications are also interpreted relative to All Sym., so you can set All Sym. 110 and Symbol O 110 and that means 10% larger than the remaining symbols.

The Overall, Horiz., and Vert. magnifications affect printing only. The Stata Graph window is resized by moving its borders. The Clipboard has no physical size—that will be determined by the receiving application.

The other magnifications affect printing, the Stata Graph window, and the Clipboard because they are sizes relative to the overall size of the graph.

Colors preference

The **Colors** preference tab allows you to change the color for Pen 1, Pen 2, ..., Pen 9, and the Background. Colors are settable separately via a standard Macintosh color dialog. The colors affect the colors you see in Stata's Graph window.

By default, we set the colors as follows:

Pen 1	cyan	Pen 6	blue
Pen 2	yellow	Pen 7	dark blue
Pen 3	red	Pen 8	gray
Pen 4	green	Pen 9	white
Pen 5	purple	Background	black

The most controversial of our defaults is black for the background. We think graphs look best on the screen with a black background, but you may disagree. Change it if you wish. If you change the background color, you will probably need to change the foreground colors—the colors of pens—as well. Colors that look good on black do not look good, and sometimes are not even visible, on top of other colors. If you use a monochrome monitor, you will want to change the colors. For CRT monitors, we think a black background looks best, but on LCD screens, white backgrounds look better. Unfortunately, white backgrounds shorten the life of LCD screens.

Load Graph, Save Graph preferences and Restore Defaults

There are a lot of graph preferences, and you may develop more than one set that you like. For instance, the thicknesses that look good when graphs are printed at 52% of normal size (as they are in this manual) are different from those for 100%.

You can save up to 8 sets of graph preferences.

Preferences–Save Graph Preferences saves the current set. You specify which of the 8 slots to use, but you also get to specify a short name to help you remember which are which.

Preferences–Load Graph Preferences allows you to reload a prior set of preferences.

Preferences–Restore Defaults resets all of the general and graph preferences to their initial settings. It also repositions and resizes all of Stata's windows to their initial settings.

Automated printing—gphprint

Stata for Macintosh users can automate the printing of many graphs. Imagine that you have created 100 graphs and need to print them all. It would be very tiresome to type graph using *myfile*.gph, pull down **File–Print Graph**, and click **OK** 100 times.

We face that problem here at Stata. The *Stata Reference Manual* contains literally hundreds of graphs. Each of those graphs was created using Stata for Windows. To help us create those graphs (and to help our users who may need to automate the production of many graphs), we created the gphprint command. The gphprint command prints whatever graph is currently showing in the Graph window to the default printer, bypassing the standard Macintosh print dialog. (Note: It is very important that you do not set graphics off, as gphprint requires that the Graph window exist before it will print a graph.) gphprint has options for controlling the appearance of the graph.

Syntax

gphprint [, copies(#) nologo statafonts shading(#) thickness(*thickstr*)

resize(#) rx(#) ry(#) symbols(#) s0(#) sS(#) sT(#) so(#) sd(#) sp(#) s.(#)

leftmargin(#) topmargin(#) saving(*filename* [, replace])]

Options

saving(*filename*) instructs Stata to save the graph as a Macintosh PICT file. If *filename* already exists, you will need to type saving(*filename*, replace) to overwrite the existing file. Note that some of the options below do not apply to graphs saved as a PICT file.

copies(#) specifies the number of copies of the graph to print. This option is not useful when the saving() option is also specified, since only one copy of the graph will be saved in *filename*.

nologo suppresses the Stata logo on the printed graph. When saving the graph as a PICT file, the logo is not saved with the graph regardless of the nologo option.

statafonts will cause the graph to be printed with Stata's built-in font for text. The default is to use a Macintosh font in the graph.

`shading(#)` overrides the default shading for all boxes drawn in the graph. You may specify a number from 1 to 4. See [R] **graph shading** for more details on shading. This option should probably not be used when printing bar charts with more than one color bar, as it will make all bars in the final output on a monochrome printer appear to be the same color.

`thickness(`*thickstr*`)` overrides the thickness of each pen used to draw the graph. *thickstr* is a string of 1 to 9 numbers between 1 and 9. For example, `gphprint, thickness(412)` tells Stata to print the current graph with a thickness of 4 for the first pen, a thickness of 1 for the second pen, and a thickness of 2 for the third pen.

`resize(#)` sets the overall magnification for the graph. You may specify a percent of the original size at which to print the graph. For example, most of the graphs in this manual were printed with `resize(52)`, or 52% of their original size. `resize(100)` would tell Stata to print the graph at 100% of its original size—in other words, it would have no effect on the size of the graph.

`rx(#)` sets the horizontal magnification for the graph. As with the `resize()` option above, you may specify a percent of the original horizontal size at which to print the graph. This percentage is applied after the `resize()` option, if any, has been applied. That is, if you specify both `resize(50)` and `rx(120)`, the entire graph will first be scaled to 50% of its original size, and then the resulting graph will be magnified horizontally by 120%.

`ry(#)` sets the vertical magnification for the graph. As with with the `resize()` option above, you may specify a percent of the original vertical size at which to print the graph. This percentage is applied after the `resize()` option, if any, has been applied. That is, if you specify both `resize(50)` and `rx(120)`, the entire graph will first be scaled to 50% of its original size, and then the resulting graph will be magnified horizontally by 120%. Most of the graphs in this manual were printed with a `resize(52)` option and a `ry(115)` option.

`symbols(#)` sets the overall magnification for all symbols on the graph. You may specify a percent of the original size for all symbols. `gphprint, symbols(200)` would print all symbols on the graph at twice their normal size.

`s0(#)`, `sS(#)`, ..., `s.(#)` set the magnification for each type of symbol on the graph. These magnifications are applied after the overall `symbol()` option, if also specified. For example, if you used `symbol(200)` and `s0(50)`, all symbols on the graph would first be magnified to twice their original size, and then the 0 symbol would be reduced to half of that size—back to its original size. See [R] **graph symbol** for more information on symbols.

`leftmargin(#)` sets the left margin of the graph in hundredths of inches. The default is 125, or 1.25 inches. For example, if you wanted a left margin of one-half of an inch, you could use `leftmargin(50)`. You can set any left margin from 0 to 800 hundredths of an inch—i.e., 0 to 8 inches. `leftmargin()` is ignored when saving the graph as a PICT file.

`topmargin(#)` sets the top margin of the graph in hundredths of inches. The default is 100, or 1 inch. You can set any top margin from 0 to 1100 hundredths of an inch—i.e., 0 to 11 inches. `leftmargin()` is ignored when saving the graph as a PICT file.

❑ Technical Note

The `gphprint` command is a good way to convert Stata graphs to the Macintosh PICT format. For example, most all Macintosh drawing applications will import PICT files. You can then write a do-file which loads each of your graphs with `graph using` commands and then saves them to a file with the `gphprint` command.

❑

▷ Example

```
. graph using matrix
. gphprint, left(0) top(0) resize(52) ry(115) thickness(75) nologo saving(matrix.pict)
```

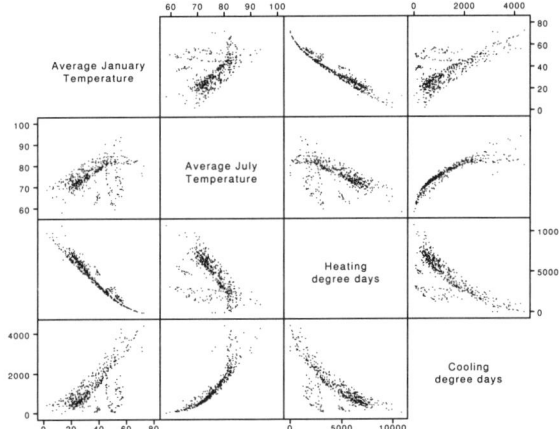

◁

❑ Technical Note

When you print a graph, the Macintosh first sends the output for the printer to a spool file. The information from that file is then sent to the printer. If you are printing complex graphs, or if your printer is slow, Stata may send several graphs to the Macintosh before it can spool all of the graphs to the printer. This can cause the spool folder to fill up. For example, if you were to write a do-file that created and printed 200 graphs, your printer probably would not be able to print graphs as fast as Stata can send them to the Macintosh.

There are two ways around this problem. The first way is to print all of your graphs to files with the `saving()` option. Then, you can print the files one at a time from another application.

The other way around the problem requires a little experimentation. First, try running your do-file. If you never see a message about the spool folder being full, then you don't need to worry. If you do receive such a message, you need to slow down Stata to give your printer a chance to catch up with the do-file. There is a `sleep` command which lets you make Stata "go to sleep" for a specified number of milliseconds. For example, `sleep 10000` would make Stata wait for 10 seconds before going on to the next command.

You can put a `sleep` command after each `gphprint` command in your do-file to make Stata wait a little bit before going on to the next graph. You can experiment with the `sleep` time to find the appropriate delay. You can get a good initial guess by timing how long it takes from the time you issue a single `gphprint` command until the printer is completely finished with the graph. Take that number of seconds, multiply by 1000 to get milliseconds, and use the resulting number after each `sleep` command.

❑

Also See

[U] C. Installation of Stata for Macintosh

[R] graph pens, [R] graph redisplaying, [R] graph saving, [R] sleep, [R] window manage

Title

> **graph printing Unix** — Print graphs in Stata for Unix

Description

This entry describes how you print graphs in Stata for Unix. Stata for Windows users, please see [R] **graph printing Windows**; Stata for DOS users, see [R] **graph printing DOS**; and Stata for Macintosh users, see [R] **graph printing Macintosh**.

Remarks

Remarks are presented under the headings

> gphdot and gphpen
> Using gphdot
> Using gphpen
> Incorporating Stata graphs into documents
> Creating HP-GL files
> Creating PostScript files
> Creating Lotus .PIC files
> Special effects and aspect ratio
> Common questions

After you have created a .gph file with the saving() option (see [R] **graph saving**), you can print the graph on a variety of devices. The discussion below assumes that Stata's hard-copy drivers have been installed according to the instructions in [U] **E. Installation of Stata for Unix** and that the appropriate defaults were set at that time.

gphdot and gphpen

gphdot and gphpen are the programs that print .gph files. These are not Stata commands but are separate programs which you could use outside of Stata. You, however, will probably find it more convenient to use them from inside Stata.

gphdot supports pixel-oriented devices such as dot-matrix and HP laser printers, whereas gphpen supports vector-oriented devices such as pen-plotters and PostScript printers. gphpen can also convert .gph files into Lotus .PIC format. Tables 1 and 2 below provide a list of printers supported by each of these commands along with some additional information. The tables printed in this manual are probably not up to date. If you cannot find your printer, look in your printer manual; your printer probably emulates one of the printers that are listed.

The syntax for gphdot and gphpen is

$$\{\text{gphdot}\,|\,\text{gphpen}\}\ \left[-\text{option}\ -\text{option}\ \ldots\right]\ \text{filename}$$

If *filename* is specified without an extension, .gph is assumed.

Here is what happens when you type one of these commands. First, the command looks for a file that describes your printer. These files have names like fx80.dot and hp7475.pen. Since gphdot and gphpen cannot divine which file to read, you have to tell them. One way is through an option which we will explain later. If you do not specify that option, gphdot looks for default.dot and gphpen looks for default.pen. Most users copy or rename one of the description files to the default filename at installation time and thus avoid having to deal with the option. Many users also delete all the irrelevant description files and save some disk space. Column two of Tables 1 and 2 names the description file for each printer.

Table 1. gphdot Input and Output Files

Printer Name	Printer File	output
AT&T 570	fx80.dot	*filename*.fxg
Brother M-1309	fx80.dot	*filename*.fxg
Brother M-1324	epsonlq.dot	*filename*.lsq
Brother HL Series		
at 75 dpi	hpl.dot	*filename*.hpl
at 150 dpi	hplp.dot	*filename*.hpl
at 300 dpi	hplphr.dot	*filename*.hpl
Canon BJ-300, -330	epsonlq.dot	*filename*.lsq
Citizen 200GX	fx80.dot	*filename*.fxg
Citizen GSX-130, -140, -145	epsonlq.dot	*filename*.lsq
Citizen PN48	epsonlq.dot	*filename*.lsq
C. Itoh 5000	ibmg.dot	*filename*.ibg
Digital LN03 Laser	ln03.dot	*filename*.dec
Epson EPL		
at 75 dpi	hpl.dot	*filename*.hpl
at 150 dpi	hplp.dot	*filename*.hpl
at 300 dpi	hplphr.dot	*filename*.hpl
Epson FX, LX, RX	fx80.dot	*filename*.fxg
Epson LQ, SQ	epsonlq.dot	*filename*.lsq
Epson MX-80 w/ GrafTrax	mx80.dot	*filename*.mxg
Fujitsu DL3600	epsonlq.dot	*filename*.lsq
Fujitsu RX		
at 75 dpi	hpl.dot	*filename*.hpl
at 150 dpi	hplp.dot	*filename*.hpl
at 300 dpi	hplphr.dot	*filename*.hpl
HP LaserJet and DeskJet		
at 75 dpi	hpl.dot	*filename*.hpl
at 150 dpi	hplp.dot	*filename*.hpl
at 300 dpi	hplphr.dot	*filename*.hpl
HP ThinkJet	hpt.dot	*filename*.hpt
Hyundai HDP Series	fx80.dot	*filename*.fxg
IBM ExecJet	epsonlq.dot	*filename*.lsq
IBM Graphics printer	ibmg.dot	*filename*.ibg
IBM Proprinter	ibmg.dot	*filename*.ibg
Kodak Diconix	fx80.dot	*filename*.fxg

(Table continued on next page.)

Table 1. `gphdot` Input and Output Files

Printer Name	Printer File	output
Mannesmann Tally 900 series		
at 75 dpi	`hpl.dot`	*filename*.`hpl`
at 150 dpi	`hplp.dot`	*filename*.`hpl`
at 300 dpi	`hplphr.dot`	*filename*.`hpl`
NEC PC-8023A-C	`nec8023.dot`	*filename*.`nec`
NEC P6 and P7	`necp6.dot`	*filename*.`p67`
NEC Pinwriter	`epsonlq.dot`	*filename*.`lsq`
Okidata Microline printers		
100 series	`ibmg.dot`	*filename*.`ibg`
300 series	`epsonlq.dot`	*filename*.`lsq`
non-IBM compatible	`ml92.dot`	*filename*.`okm`
Panasonic KX		
P1695	`fx80.dot`	*filename*.`fxg`
P1123, P1124, P1624, P2624	`epsonlq.dot`	*filename*.`lsq`
Ricoh PC Laser 6000		
at 75 dpi	`hpl.dot`	*filename*.`hpl`
at 150 dpi	`hplp.dot`	*filename*.`hpl`
at 300 dpi	`hplphr.dot`	*filename*.`hpl`
Seikosha SL-90	`epsonlq.dot`	*filename*.`lsq`
Seikosha SP-2000	`fx80.dot`	*filename*.`fxg`
Star Micronics XB, NX-2420	`epsonlq.dot`	*filename*.`lsq`
Star Micronics XR, NX-1020	`fx80.dot`	*filename*.`fxg`
Tandy DMP	`rsdmp.dot`	*filename*.`dmp`
Toshiba ExpressWriter	`epsonlq.dot`	*filename*.`lsq`
Toshiba 3-in-1	`p351.dot`	*filename*.`351`

Table 2. `gphpen` Input and Output Files

Printer Name	Printer File	output
HP-GL files	`hpgl.pen`	*filename*.`hpg`
HP 7550 *or*		
HP 7440 ColorPro		
Portrait	`hp7440.pen`	*filename*.`hp0`
Landscape	`hp7440ls.pen`	*filename*.`hp0`
HP 7470	`hp7470ls.pen`	*filename*.`hp0`
HP 7475		
Portrait	`hp7475.pen`	*filename*.`hpa`
Landscape	`hp7475ls.pen`	*filename*.`hpa`
Oversize	`hp7475w.pen`	*filename*.`hpb`
Houston Instruments	`hi.pen`	*filename*.`hip`
QMS Lasergrafix		
Portrait	`qms.pen`	*filename*.`qms`
Landscape	`qmsls.pen`	*filename*.`qms`
PostScript		
monochrome portrait	`ps.pen`	*filename*.`ps`
monochrome landscape	`psls.pen`	*filename*.`ps`
color portrait	`psc.pen`	*filename*.`ps`
color landscape	`pscls.pen`	*filename*.`ps`
Encapsulated PostScript		
monochrome	`eps.pen`	*filename*.`eps`
color	`epsc.pen`	*filename*.`eps`
Lotus `.PIC`		
Stata drawn font	`pic.pen`	*filename*.`pic`
Lotus built-in font	`picpt.pen`	*filename*.`pic`

Whether you explicitly specify the description file or go for the default, the description file does not have to be in the current directory. gphdot and gphpen look in the current directory first, but if the description file is not there, they look along your path and, if they still cannot find it, they look in /usr/local/stata. If the programs still cannot find the file, they complain and stop.

Once the program has learned about your printer, it looks for *filename*—your .gph file. You do not have to type the .gph on the end of the filename because the programs will add it for you if necessary. They then read a little bit of the file to determine if it really is a .gph file and not some file that just happens to have a .gph suffix. If the programs do not like what they see, they complain and stop.

Having done all of this, the programs begin reading the file and converting it into a form suitable for your printer. Both gphdot and gphpen send their output to *filename . brandname*. The last column of Tables 1 and 2 tells you which *brandname* goes with which printer.

All that is left to understand are the options.

−o*device*:
−o *filename*

    Tables 1 and 2 tell you where gphdot and gphpen normally send their output. The −o option allows you to override that default. Specifying −omyfile.prt, for instance, would send the output to the file myfile.prt. Notice that there is no space between the option letter and the filename. *Do not* type −o myfile.prt. This is true of all options that take arguments. The argument is placed right up against the option letter.

    You probably will find little use for −o since gphdot and gphpen always send their output to a reasonably named file and you must explicitly ask Unix to print the file, say by using lp(1) or lpr(1). On the other hand, you can specify −ostdout to route the output to stdout.

−d*filename*

    specifies the name of the file describing your printer. If you do not specify this option, gphdot assumes the file is default.dot and gphpen assumes default.pen. For gphdot, specifying −dhplphr would specify the file hplphr.dot which corresponds to an HP LaserJet in its highest resolution mode, 300 dots-per-inch (see Table 1). For gphpen, specifying −dhp7440ls would specify the file hp7440ls.pen which corresponds to an HP ColorPro pen-plotter in landscape mode (see Table 2).

−l$\{$l|p$\}$

    (gphdot only) specifies landscape or portrait mode. Default is −lp: you type −ll for landscape mode. For gphpen, the landscape/portrait selection is made in the file describing the printer. See −d above and Table 2.

−−

    suppresses the normal page ejection at the conclusion of the graph.

−+

    ejects a page before starting the graph.

−c#

    specifies the number of copies of the graph to be made. Default is −c1. The −c option is ignored by plotters.

−n

    suppresses the Stata logo.

−r#

    resizes the image to # percent of normal. Default is −r100.

-rx#
> resizes the image horizontally to # percent of normal.

-ry#
> resizes the image vertically to # percent of normal.

-s#
> specifies the sizes of all plotting symbols. Default is -s100, meaning 100% of normal, where normal is defined after any adjustment made by the -r options. -s50 reduces the size of the plotting symbols to 50% of normal size. -s200 doubles the size.

-y{O|S|T|o|d|p|.}#
> specifies the size of just the specified plotting symbol. -s050 would make large circles 50% of their normal size. -so200 would make small circles twice their normal size. Only one symbol may be specified, but you may include the option more than once. For instance, to rescale both the small and the large circles, specify -s050 -so200.

-i*filename*
> specifies the name of an injection file—a file to be sent to the printer before any of the graph. This option is rarely used. For PostScript devices, the StataCorp-supplied file ps.plf (psls.plf, psc.plf, or pscls.pen) is automatically injected. For Lotus .PIC files, pic.plf is automatically injected.

-x

> (gphpen *only)* slows down the pen motion on real pen-plotters to prevent ink from smearing on transparencies.

/p#...#
> remaps the pens. The default is -p123456789, meaning pen 1 is pen 1, pen 2 is pen 2, and so on. -p122 would make both pen 2 and pen 3 equivalent to pen 2.

-t#...#
> specifies the thicknesses of the *pens.* For pixel devices, the default is to make each pen one pixel wide. If you are using a 300-dpi device such as a laser printer, the image will probably look better if the pens have thickness four. Typing -t144 makes pen 1 one pixel and pens 2 and 3 four pixels wide. Typing -t444 would make the text pen thicker, too. See [R] **graph pens** for printed examples of the effects. For real pen-plotters, -t merely informs gphpen as to the width, in millimeters, of the actual pens in the carriage. gphpen can do a better job when it knows the widths. -t affects thicknesses *after* any remapping by -p. For instance, -p122 -t12 would make the original pens 2 and 3 have thickness 2.

Using gphdot

▷ Example

   You wish to print your graph on an HP LaserJet printer. Please read the example directly above, except note that rather than the result going directly to the printer, it goes into a file called mypic.hpl in the current directory. You must now use some Unix command, such as lp(1) or lpr(1), to send that file to the printer.

◁

Using gphpen

▷ Example

You wish to print your graph on an HP 7440 pen-plotter. Please read the example directly above, except note that rather than the result going directly to the printer, it goes into a file called `mypic.hp0`. You must now use some Unix command, such as `lp(1)` or `lpr(1)`, to send the file to the plotter.

◁

Incorporating Stata graphs into documents

You wish to incorporate a Stata graph into a document created by your favorite word processor or editor. How you do this depends on the other software that you are using. Instructions for creating HP-GL files, PostScript files, encapsulated PostScript files, and Lotus `.PIC` files are given below. See the references at the end of [R] **graph printing** articles discussing incorporating Stata graphs into TeX documents.

Creating HP-GL files

▷ Example

You want to copy a graph produced by Stata into your word processor or graphics editor. Many programs read HP-GL files, but also see *Creating PostScript files* below.

You type

```
gphpen -dhpgl mypic
```

◁

Creating PostScript files

▷ Example

If you wish to create an encapsulated PostScript file suitable for embedding in a document (such as a document created with WordPerfect), see *Creating encapsulated PostScript files* below. This example assumes that you want to print the file `mypic.gph` on your PostScript printer. You type

```
gphpen mypic -dps
```

to create the file `mypic.ps`, although you may omit the `-dps` if you have already renamed `ps.pen` to `default.pen`. For this command to work, you must also have the file `ps.plf` in the current directory, or along your path, or in the `/usr/local/stata` directory. That file contains some additional information that `gphpen` will need to make the PostScript file. You must now print the file; you probably use `lp(1)` or `lpr(1)`.

◁

Creating encapsulated PostScript files

▷ Example

If you wish to create PostScript files suitable for printing on a PostScript printer, see *Creating Postscript files* above. This example assumes that you wish to include the file `mypic.gph` in another document. You type

```
gphpen mypic -deps
```

to create the file `mypic.eps`, although you may omit the `-deps` if you have already renamed `eps.pen` to `default.pen`. For this command to work, you must also have the file `eps.plf` in the current directory, or along your path, or in the `/usr/local/stata` directory. That file contains some additional information that **gphpen** will need to make the PostScript file.

◁

Creating Lotus .PIC files

▷ Example

You are a PC user and want to convert a `.gph` file into `.PIC` format so that you can edit it using Lotus Freelance. You must make a choice: Do you want the text in the graph to be drawn using the Stata font or the Lotus font? The Stata font looks better but it is literally drawn whereas the Lotus font is built into their package. Using the Stata font makes the `.PIC` files larger. You decide to use the Stata font, so you type

```
gphpen mypic -dpic.pen
```

to convert the file `mypic.gph` into `mypic.pic`. For this command to work, you must also have the file `pic.plf` in the current directory, or along your path, or in the `/usr/local/stata` directory. That file contains some additional information that **gphpen** will need to make the `.PIC` file.

◁

Special effects and aspect ratio

▷ Example

By now you should understand where the output is going, so let's put aside that problem and focus on the other options. For instance, all the pictures in this manual were printed with the command

```
gphdot filename -r52
```

which rescaled the image to 52% of the normal size. Let's consider another, more complicated command. We will use **gphdot** in our example, but we could just as well use **gphpen**.

```
gphdot mypic -r80 -s50 -s025 -so110 -t122 -c10
```

prints `mypic.gph`. The image is rescaled to 80% of the ordinary size. All the symbols are rescaled to 50% of their ordinary size after the 80% rescaling, making the symbols 40% of their ordinary size. The large circle symbol, however, is scaled to 25% of 80%, that is, 20%, of its ordinary size. In addition, the small circle is scaled to 110% of 80%, or 88%, of its ordinary size. Pens 2 and 3 are made slightly bolder than the text pen 1, and finally we specify that we want 10 copies of the graph.

◁

❑ Technical Note

You can rescale images in the horizontal (x) and vertical (y) dimensions separately using the `-rx` and `-ry` options. For instance,

        gphdot mypic -rx84 -ry110

would create a graph that is almost square, while

        gphdot mypic -rx84 -ry130

would create a graph that is considerably taller than it is wide. The first graph will look "good", but the second will look "bad". This is not because graphs that are taller than they are wide are inherently bad; it is because as you change the aspect, you change the aspect of Stata's text font, as well. In the first case, you have not changed the aspect too much and the font, while looking different, will not appear odd. In the second case, the change is so drastic that the font will no longer look reasonable.

The best way to change aspect is to use Stage; see [R] **graph stage**. That is because as you change the aspect, Stage automatically corrects the font to maintain true aspect. To change the aspect, edit the graph in Stage, make one of the dimensions smaller, and then print the graph. If you want to make the overall graph bigger after editing, specify, perhaps, `-r110` or even `-r200`, but do not attempt to make the graph bigger while in the Stage editor. Overall size is controlled at time of printing.

What aspect ratio should you choose? The one used by Stata is probably best in most circumstances. Tukey (1977, 129) and Tufte (1983, 186–190) suggest that, although there are exceptions, graphs should be greater in length than in height. The exceptions, of course, depend on the data, and you should choose the aspect that best reveals your data.

❑

Common questions

"I tried to print a graph and gphdot is just sitting there, doing nothing." Your printer is not on-line. Press the on-line button on your printer. If the printer is on-line, check the cables between your computer and printer.

"I tried to print `myfile.gph` by typing `gphdot myfile` (or `gphpen myfile`) and got the message 'Unable to input file myfile.gph'." gphdot (gphpen) could not find your graph file, probably because it is in a different directory.

"I tried to print `myfile.gph` by typing `gphdot myfile` (or `gphpen myfile`) and got the message 'Unable to open device file default.dot'." gphdot (gphpen) could not find the printer description file. You have not installed a default description file; see [U] **E. Installation of Stata for Unix**.

"I tried to print `myfile.gph` and everything seemed to work, except what my printer produced looks like gibberish." You are using the wrong printer description file. See Tables 1 and 2 above, determine the right description file, and install it as described in [U] **E. Installation of Stata for Unix**.

"My printer is not listed in either Table 1 or 2." Look at your printer manual; your printer probably emulates one of the printers that are listed in the tables. Pretend your printer is that model printer and install the description file for it; see [U] **E. Installation of Stata for Unix**. In addition, consult the *Stata Technical Bulletin* for printer support added since the release of Stata 5.0; see [U] **2.4 The Stata Technical Bulletin**.

"I need to increase the size of the printed graph, how do I do this?" See the `-r gphdot` and `gphpen` option above.

Also See

[U] **E. Installation of Stata for Unix**

[R] **graph pens**, [R] **graph redisplaying**, [R] **graph saving**

Title

> **graph printing Windows** — Print graphs in Stata for Windows

Description

This entry describes how you print graphs interactively in Stata for Windows. There is also a way to automate the printing of many graphs in Stata for Windows. See the *Automated printing—gphprint* section at the end of this entry.

Stata for DOS users, please see [R] **graph printing DOS**; Stata for Macintosh users, see [R] **graph printing Macintosh**; and Stata for Unix users, see [R] **graph printing Unix**.

Remarks

Remarks are presented under the headings

> *Overview*
> *Preferences*
> *Line Thicknesses and Display Thicknesses on Screen preferences*
> *Magnifications preference*
> *Colors preference*
> *Ignore Pen Colors on Print and Ignore Back Color on Print preferences*
> *Include Logo on Print preference*
> *Use Windows fonts preference*
> *Load Graph and Save Graph preferences*
> *Automated printing—gphprint*

Overview

To print a graph:

1. Display the graph. Either

   a. Draw it using the `graph` command, or

   b. Redisplay your last graph by pressing the **Graph** or **Regraph** button, or

   c. Retrieve a previously saved graph by typing `graph using` *myfile*. (You previously saved the graph *myfile*.`gph`.) If you are using Stata for Windows 95, and the name of *myfile*.`gph` contains spaces, enclose *myfile*.`gph` in double-quotes.

2. Optionally pull down **Prefs** and choose **Graph Preferences**. This will allow you to set options specifying how the graph is printed.

3. Pull down **File** and choose **Print Graph**.

Note: If you are using Windows 95 and have not installed your printer, go outside of Stata and click on **Start–Settings–Printers**. If you are using Windows 3.1, click on the Control Panel, and then on the Printer icon. See your Microsoft documentation.

To copy a graph to the clipboard:

1. Display the graph.

2. Optionally pull down **Prefs** and choose **Graph Preferences**. The same options which affect how a graph is printed also affect how it is copied.

3. Pull down **Edit** and choose **Copy**.

Preferences

Prefs–Graph Preferences affect how the graph is printed and copied. Some of the preferences affect what you see on the screen when Stata displays the graph, some do not, but all affect printing and copying. The preferences that you can set are

Line Thicknesses	thicknesses of pens
Display Thicknesses on Screen	whether the Graph window honors thicknesses
Magnifications	sizes and relative sizes
Colors	foreground and background colors
Ignore Pen Colors on Print	whether to print/copy in specified colors
Ignore Back Color on Print	whether to print/copy with background color
Include Logo on Print	whether to print Stata logo on graph
Use Windows fonts	whether to use Windows fonts or Stata's built-in font for text
Load Graph Preferences	load prior set of graph preferences
Save Graph Preferences	save set of graph preferences

Line Thicknesses and Display Thicknesses on Screen preferences

The default **Line Thicknesses** settings are

Pen 1	1	Pen 6	1
Pen 2	1	Pen 7	1
Pen 3	1	Pen 8	1
Pen 4	1	Pen 9	1
Pen 5	1		

Pen thicknesses are discussed in [R] **graph pens**. These thicknesses have a dramatic effect on how a graph looks when printed and you will want to set them according to what looks best on your printer. Thicknesses range from 1 to 9.

The **Display Thicknesses on Screen** preference determines whether Stata's Graph window respects the pen thicknesses you have set. Respecting thicknesses tends to look bad because the screen has less resolution than your printer. Checking **Display Thicknesses on Screen** can be useful, however, for verifying relative thicknesses before printing.

Magnifications preference

The default **Magnifications** are

Overall	100	Symbol S	100
Horiz.	100	Symbol T	100
Vert.	100	Symbol o	100
All Sym.	100	Symbol d	100
Symbol O	100	Symbol p	100
		Symbol .	100

Overall magnification determines how big the graph is when printed. All magnifications are stated in percent—100 means 100% of the size Stata would ordinarily choose, and you may choose percentages smaller or larger than that.

Horiz. and Vert. magnifications allow you to separately set the horizontal and vertical magnifications. You could set Overall 52 and leave Horiz. 100 and Vert. 100, or you could leave Overall 100 and set Horiz. 52 and Vert. 52 and have the same effect. Magnifications are applied sequentially. Thus, if you set Overall 52 and Horiz. 125, the effective horizontal magnification is $52 \times 1.25 = 65\%$.

All Sym. affects all symbols within the graph. Again, magnifications are applied sequentially, so if Overall is 52, All Sym. 100 means the symbols are scaled appropriately for the overall size—to 52% of their normal size. Specifying All Sym. 110 would make all symbols 10% larger relative to the overall size of the graph.

In addition or instead, you can set the symbol magnifications individually. This allows you to change sizes of symbols relative to each other. Magnifications, as always, are interpreted as relative to Overall, so 110 means 10% larger after all other rescalings. Magnifications are also interpreted relative to All Sym., so you can set All Sym. 110 and Symbol O 110 and that means 10% larger than the remaining symbols.

The Overall, Horiz., and Vert. magnifications affect printing only. The Stata Graph window is resized by moving its borders. The clipboard has no physical size—that will be determined by the receiving application.

The other magnifications affect printing, the Stata Graph window, and the clipboard because they are sizes relative to the overall size of the graph.

Colors preference

You can set the colors for Pens 1 through 9 and the Background of the Stata graph. If you use Stata for Windows 95, you will see all ten colors displayed in a tabbed dialog box. You can click on a button next to each color to change it. If you use Stata for Windows 3.1, you can choose **Pen 1**, **Pen 2**, ..., **Pen 9**, and **Background** from the **Graph Preferences** menu and set the color for each.

The colors affect the colors you see in Stata's Graph window. Some of the colors in the dialog box, however, are dithered—that is, a mixture of pixels of different colors. Others are pure. Dithered colors work fine for filling and backgrounds, but their color changes when used to draw lines and such. Dithered colors will not be what you expect when Stata draws lines and symbols with them.

In the color dialog, you can find out how the color will appear by choosing a color and clicking on **Define Custom Colors**. A box will appear showing, among other things, the dithered color and the corresponding solid color. It is the solid color that Stata uses to draw lines and symbols on the screen.

By default, we set the colors as follows:

Pen 1	cyan	Pen 6	blue
Pen 2	yellow	Pen 7	dark blue
Pen 3	red	Pen 8	gray
Pen 4	green	Pen 9	white
Pen 5	purple	Background	black

The most controversial of our defaults is black for the background. We think graphs look best on the screen with a black background, but you may disagree. Change it if you wish. If you change the background color, you will probably need to change the foreground colors—the colors of pens—as well. Colors that look good on black do not look good, and sometimes are not even visible, on top of other colors. If you use a monochrome monitor, you will want to change the colors. For CRT monitors, we think a black background looks best, but on LCD screens, white backgrounds look better. Unfortunately, white backgrounds shorten the life of LCD screens.

Ignore Pen Colors on Print, and Ignore Back Color on Print preferences

The colors you choose affect the screen. They also affect what is sent to your printer if you uncheck **Ignore Pen Colors on Print** and **Ignore Back Color on Print**. With these two items checked, when Stata sends the graph to your printer, it sends a monochrome image on a null background (which will be white because the paper is white).

If you use a color printer, you will probably want to uncheck **Ignore Pen Colors on Print** but leave **Ignore Back Color on Print**. This will send color graphs but with a null background. If you want the background color as well, uncheck **Ignore Back Color on Print**.

When Stata copies a graph to the clipboard, it also ignores or honors the foreground and background colors according to your preferences. Most receiving applications do not care.

Include Logo on Print preference

When Stata prints a graph it places a small Stata logo at the bottom-right corner. You can suppress this by unchecking **Include Logo on Print**.

When Stata copies to the clipboard, it omits the logo even if **Include Logo on Print** is checked.

Use Windows fonts preference

By default, Stata uses a Windows TrueType font for the text in graphs. If you uncheck this preference, Stata will use its own built-in font to draw the text in graphs. This built-in font is the same as the font that Stata for DOS and Stata for Unix users see in their graphs.

Windows users will generally prefer to use a TrueType font for the text in their graphs. The font typeface and style affects the entire graph; you can not set the font typeface and style for individual text items. You can copy and paste the graph to a drawing application if you wish to change the font typeface or style for individual text items.

There are several advantages to using a native Windows font over Stata's built-in font:

1. You have a wide range of typefaces available to you when you use TrueType fonts for the text in your graphs. Do you want to use a bold font? Pull down the system menu box on the Graph window (the little box at the left of the Graph window's title bar), and choose **Fonts**. You can select any TrueType typeface or style you wish.

   Note: The size field in the font dialog box for the Graph window has no effect. Stata sets the size of each element of text in the graph window separately. If you wish to set an overall size for the text in Stata's graphs, see [R] **graph textsize**.

2. Graphs drawn using a TrueType font for the text are more easily edited in another Windows drawing program. When you copy and paste a Stata graph to a Windows drawing program, that program will be able to recognize any text in the graph that has been drawn with a TrueType font as text. This means that the drawing program will be able to edit this text.

   Only Stata sees its built-in font as text. Other Windows programs see this font as a collection of lines and points, making it impossible to edit as text.

3. Graphs drawn using a TrueType font for the text will draw (and redraw) faster than those drawn in Stata's built-in font. They will also consume less memory. This is because it takes one call to the Windows GDI (Graphics Device Interface) to draw a line of text using a TrueType font, while it takes many calls to draw the lines and points required for a single line of text in Stata's built-in font.

Load Graph and Save Graph preferences

There are a lot of graph preferences, and you may develop more than one set that you like. For instance, the thicknesses that look good when graphs are printed at 52% of normal size (as they are in this manual) are different from those for 100%.

You can save up to 8 sets of graph preferences. **Prefs–Save Graph Preferences** saves the current set. You specify which of the 8 slots to use, but you also get to specify a short name to help you remember which are which.

Prefs–Load Graph Preferences allows you to reload a prior set of preferences.

Automated printing—gphprint

Stata for Windows users can automate the printing of many graphs. Imagine that you have created 100 graphs and need to print them all. It would be very tiresome to type graph using *myfile*.gph, pull down **File–Print Graph**, and click **OK** 100 times.

We face that problem here at Stata. The *Stata Reference Manual* contains literally hundreds of graphs. Each of those graphs was created using Stata for Windows. To help us create those graphs (and to help our users who may need to automate the production of many graphs), we created the gphprint command. The gphprint command prints whatever graph is currently showing in the Graph window to the default printer, bypassing the standard Windows print dialog. gphprint can also save the current graph as a Windows Metafile (WMF). (Note: It is very important that you do not set graphics off, as gphprint requires that the Graph window exist before it will print a graph.) gphprint has options for controlling the appearance of the graph.

Syntax

gphprint [, <u>c</u>opies(#) <u>no</u>logo <u>s</u>tatafonts <u>sh</u>ading(#) <u>t</u>hickness(*thickstr*)

   <u>r</u>esize(#) rx(#) ry(#) <u>s</u>ymbols(#) sO(#) sS(#) sT(#) so(#) sd(#) sp(#) <u>s</u>.(#)

   <u>le</u>ftmargin(#) <u>to</u>pmargin(#) <u>sa</u>ving(*filename* [, replace])]

Options

saving(*filename*) instructs Stata to redirect the printed output to *filename*. If *filename* already exists, you will need to type saving(*filename*, replace) to overwrite the existing file. gphprint will save the graph as a Windows Metafile (WMF) if *filename* has the extension '.wmf'. Note that some of the options below apply only to graphs printed or saved through the default print driver, not to graphs saved as metafiles.

copies(#) specifies the number of copies of the graph to print. This option is not useful when the saving() option is also specified, since only one copy of the graph will be saved in *filename*.

nologo suppresses the Stata logo on the printed graph. This option is ignored when saving the graph as a metafile.

statafonts will cause the graph to be printed with Stata's built-in font for text. The default is to use a Windows font in the graph.

shading(#) overrides the default shading for all boxes drawn in the graph. You may specify a number from 1 to 4. See [R] **graph shading** for more details on shading. This option should probably not be used when printing bar charts with more than one color bar, as it will make all bars in the final output on a monochrome printer appear to be the same color.

thickness(*thickstr*) overrides the thickness of each pen used to draw the graph. *thickstr* is a string of 1 to 9 numbers between 1 and 9. For example, gphprint, thickness(412) tells Stata to print the current graph with a thickness of 4 for the first pen, a thickness of 1 for the second pen, and a thickness of 2 for the third pen.

resize(#) sets the overall magnification for the graph. You may specify a percent of the original size at which to print the graph. For example, most of the graphs in this manual were printed with resize(52), or 52% of their original size. resize(100) would tell Stata to print the graph at 100% of its original size—in other words, it would have no effect on the size of the graph.

rx(#) sets the horizontal magnification for the graph. As with the resize() option above, you may specify a percent of the original horizontal size at which to print the graph. This percentage is applied after the resize() option, if any, has been applied. That is, if you specify both resize(50) and rx(120), the entire graph will first be scaled to 50% of its original size, and then the resulting graph will be magnified horizontally by 120%.

ry(#) sets the vertical magnification for the graph. As with with the resize() option above, you may specify a percent of the original vertical size at which to print the graph. This percentage is applied after the resize() option, if any, has been applied. That is, if you specify both resize(50) and rx(120), the entire graph will first be scaled to 50% of its original size, and then the resulting graph will be magnified horizontally by 120%. Most of the graphs in this manual were printed with a resize(52) option and a ry(115) option.

symbols(#) sets the overall magnification for all symbols on the graph. You may specify a percent of the original size for all symbols. gphprint, symbols(200) would print all symbols on the graph at twice their normal size.

s0(#), sS(#), ..., s.(#) set the magnification for each type of symbol on the graph. These magnifications are applied after the overall symbol() option, if also specified. For example, if you used symbol(200) and s0(50), all symbols on the graph would first be magnified to twice their original size, and then the 0 symbol would be reduced to half of that size—back to its original size. See [R] **graph symbol** for more information on symbols.

leftmargin(#) sets the left margin of the graph in hundredths of inches. The default is 125, or 1.25 inches. For example, if you wanted a left margin of one-half of an inch, you could use leftmargin(50). You can set any left margin from 0 to 800 hundredths of an inch—i.e., 0 to 8 inches. leftmargin() is ignored when saving the graph to a metafile because metafiles have no size—that is determined by the application importing a metafile.

topmargin(#) sets the top margin of the graph in hundredths of inches. The default is 100, or 1 inch. You can set any top margin from 0 to 1100 hundredths of an inch—i.e., 0 to 11 inches. topmargin() is ignored when saving the graph to a metafile.

❑ Technical Note

The gphprint command is a good way to convert Stata graphs to another format. For example, many drawing programs will import encapsulated PostScript (EPS) files. If you want to convert many Stata graphs to EPS files, you can install a PostScript printer driver on your Windows computer even if you do not have a PostScript printer. Then, from the Windows Control Panel, you can set this printer driver as your default printer and modify its settings to create encapsulated PostScript.

You can then write a do-file which loads each of your graphs with **graph using** commands and then prints them to a file with the **gphprint** command. Since you have set up your default printer driver to create encapsulated PostScript, the files created by **gphprint** will all be EPS files. Note that Windows PostScript printer drivers do not save a preview of the graph in the EPS file. If you import the EPS files into a word processor, you may not be able to see the actual image until you print. ❑

▷ Example

```
. graph using matrix
. gphprint, left(0) top(0) resize(52) ry(115) thickness(75) nologo saving(matrix.eps)
```

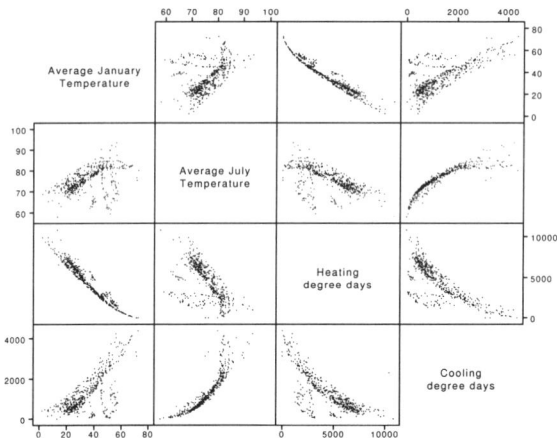

◁

❑ Technical Note

When you print a graph, Windows first sends the output for the printer to a spool file. The information from that file is then sent to the printer. If you are printing complex graphs, or if your printer is slow, Stata may send several graphs to Windows before Windows can spool all of the graphs to the printer. This can cause the spool directory to fill up. For example, if you were to write a do-file that created and printed 200 graphs, your printer probably would not be able to print graphs as fast as Stata can send them to Windows.

There are two ways around this problem. The first way is to print all of your graphs to files with the **saving()** option. Then, you can print these files one at a time.

The other way around the problem requires a little experimentation. First, try running your do-file. If you never see a message about the spool directory being full, then you don't need to worry. If you do receive such a message, you need to slow down Stata to give your printer a chance to catch up with the do-file. There is a **sleep** command which lets you make Stata "go to sleep" for a specified number of milliseconds. For example, **sleep 10000** would make Stata wait for 10 seconds before going on to the next command.

You can put a **sleep** command after each **gphprint** command in your do-file to make Stata wait a little bit before going on to the next graph. You can experiment with the **sleep** time to find the appropriate delay. You can get a good initial guess by timing how long it takes from the time you issue a single `gphprint` command until the printer is completely finished with the graph. Take that number of seconds, multiply by 1000 to get milliseconds, and use the resulting number after each `sleep` command.

❏

Also See

[U] **A. Installation of Stata for Windows 95**, [U] **B. Installation of Stata for Windows 3.1**

[R] **graph pens**, [R] **graph redisplaying**, [R] **graph saving**, [R] **sleep**, [R] **window manage**

Title

graph redisplaying — Redisplay graphs

Remarks

graph, typed without arguments, recalculates and redisplays the last graph. For instance, you type

```
. graph mpg weight, s(o)
```

during your session. Later, if you type graph, the results are the same as if you typed graph mpg weight, s(o). If the mpg or weight data has changed, the redisplayed graph will correctly reflect the new data.

graph without arguments also puts the underlying graph command in the console review buffer—if you pressed *PrevLine* (see [U] **17 Keyboard use**), you would not see graph but graph mpg weight, s(o) or whatever it was you previously typed to draw the graph. Thus, you can edit the line. If you wish to permanently save the graph, you might add the option saving(mygph); see [R] **graph saving** and [R] **graph printing**.

A graph that has been saved using the saving() option can be redisplayed by typing graph using *filename*; see [R] **graph combining**. In this case, the graph is not recalculated but is redisplayed from the copy preserved on disk.

Stata for Windows and Stata for Macintosh

If you bury the Graph window, pressing the **Graph** button brings it to the top. The **Regraph** button does the same, but it also redraws the graph; so if the data has changed, those changes will be reflected in the Graph window. Pressing **Regraph** is the same as typing graph without arguments.

If you close the Graph window, you can only reopen it by using the **Regraph** button or by issuing a graph command.

Also See

[R] **graph**, [R] **graph combining**, [R] **graph printing**, [R] **graph saving**

Title

graph saving — Save images for printing or editing

Description

This entry discusses the saving() option to graph.

Remarks

There are three reasons to save an image. You save it because (1) you think you might want to look at it again and you do not want to have to redraw it; (2) you want to print it and you are not using Stata for Windows or Stata for Macintosh; or (3) you want to combine it with other images (or edit it with Stage) and then print it.

To	Do
graph y vs. x, view it on the screen, but save no permanent copy	graph y x
graph y vs. x, view it on the screen, and save a copy of the graph	graph y x, saving(*mypic*)
graph y vs. x, view it on the screen, and save a copy of the graph by replacing a previously saved graph	graph y x, saving(*mypic*,replace)
review a previously saved graph	graph using *mypic*
print a previously saved graph	see [R] **graph printing**
combine two previously saved graphs	see [R] **graph combining** and [R] **graph stage**
edit a previously saved graph	see [R] **graph stage**

You specify the saving() option to save an image. The syntax of saving() is

$$saving(\textit{filename}\,[,\texttt{replace}])$$

▷ Example

Typing graph y x graphs y against x but saves no permanent copy of the image. Typing graph y x, saving(mypic) produces the same picture and simultaneously creates a file called mypic.gph containing the image.

If later you forget what is in mypic.gph, you can type graph using mypic and the image will appear once again on your monitor. graph using does not disturb the data in memory. It simply replays the .gph file.

Once a file has been saved, you can print it (see [R] **graph printing**), edit the image with Stage (see [R] **graph stage**), or combine the image with other saved images (see [R] **graph combining**).

143

Stata for Windows users and Stata for Macintosh users need not save a graph before printing. Users of other operating systems must first save the graph.

◁

▷ Example

If you later try to make another graph and add `saving(mypic)`, Stata will refuse, claiming "file mypic.gph already exists". And so it does since we created it in the last example.

You can add the `replace` option if it's okay to overwrite the file. You would type `graph y x, saving(mypic,replace)`.

◁

❏ Technical Note

The standard rules for specifying filenames apply to `saving()`. If you do not specify an extension, the default extension—in this case, `.gph`—will be added for you. As always, you may prefix the filename with an explicit path. See [U] **18.6 File-naming conventions**.

❏

❏ Technical Note

Stata for Windows and Stata for Macintosh users have another way of saving the graph: Use the `saving()` option or, once the graph is drawn, pull down **File** and select **Save Graph**. The advantage of this method is that you need not plan ahead.

❏

Also See

[U] **18.6 File-naming conventions**

[R] **graph**, [R] **graph printing**, [R] **graph redisplaying**, [R] **graph stage**

Title

graph shading — Specify shadings for fill areas

Description

This entry discusses the `shading()` option to `graph`.

Remarks

Whenever `graph` draws bars, such as in a histogram or bar chart, or whenever it draws a pie chart, it shades certain areas. `graph` provides four levels of shading, numbered 1 through 4, lightest to darkest. The exact rendition of the shadings varies across hardware. On dot-matrix devices, the shadings usually correspond to dot-fill patterns or a gray scale. On vector devices, the shadings usually refer to hatching patterns.

▷ Example

`graph` uses a shading of 2 for filling the bars of histograms, although you can vary this with the `shading()` option. For instance, `graph y, shading(4)` draws a histogram and shades the bars as darkly as possible.

◁

▷ Example

The default shading for bar and pie charts is 3. `graph` repeats the shading pattern 3, 1, 4, 2 for filling the areas of bar and pie charts. Suppose we have a dataset recording the costs and profits of XYZ Company where each observation reflects the costs and profits for a particular fiscal year. We wish to make a bar chart of labor costs, parts cost, advertising expenditures, and overhead. By default, the labor costs bar will be filled with shading 3, the parts bar with shading 1, and so on. We look at the graph and think it would look better if we interchanged the shading of the last two bars. We also add some options to dress up the image:

```
. graph labor parts advert oh, bar by(year) sh(3124) ylabel yline
         ti("Costs by Fiscal Year, XYZ Company")
         l1("(Thousands of Dollars)")
```

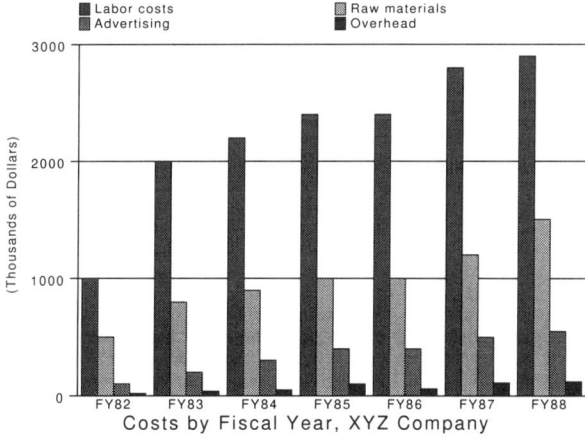

145

sh(3124) is the shading() option: we just abbreviated it. Similarly, ti is an abbreviation for title and ll an abbreviation for lltitle.

sh(3124) means fill the bar for the first variable with shading 3, the bar for the second with shading 1, the third with 2, and the fourth with 4. If our graph contained five bars and we did not like the default shading, then we would have specified five numbers in the shading() option.

Shading can also be used with pie charts and histograms.

◁

❑ Technical Note

Shadings were first used by Homo Erectus (c. −200,000) to decorate cave walls, and the drawings so produced bear a remarkable resemblance to the bar and pie charts now so popular with middle management.

❑

References

Erectus, H. −200,000 (date approximate). (There is no title to this as it predates written language and quite possibly verbal language as well. Experts disagree on what the ape creature was attempting to draw—if he was attempting to draw anything at all—and divide into two schools: those who believe the title would have been "Mom" and those who believe it would have been "Fractional shares of food consumed, by family member"). Euphrates Valley.

Also See

[R] **graph**, [R] **graph bar**, [R] **graph histogram**, [R] **graph pens**, [R] **graph pie**

Title

---

graph stage — Stata Graphics Editor

Remarks

The Stata Graphics Editor, informally known as Stage, is a separate product from Stata, which may be purchased separately. It is available for both DOS and Unix.

Stage edits .gph files. It is full-screen, what-you-see-is-what-you-get (WYSIWYG), and interactive.

Unlike other graphic editors, which are adept at editing pictures because they adopt the artist's point of view—an image is seen only as lines, shadings, and fill patterns—Stage *understands* statistical graphs. To Stage, an image is composed of point clouds, connected lines, connected lines with interspersed points, and all the other graphic elements that statisticians—and Stata—use to describe a graph.

Stage allows combining graphs, inserting text, boxes, and lines; drawing arrows and dashed lines; and magnifying, moving, and deleting objects.

You load a graph drawn with Stata into Stage, edit it, and save it. When you are editing, the screen looks something like this:

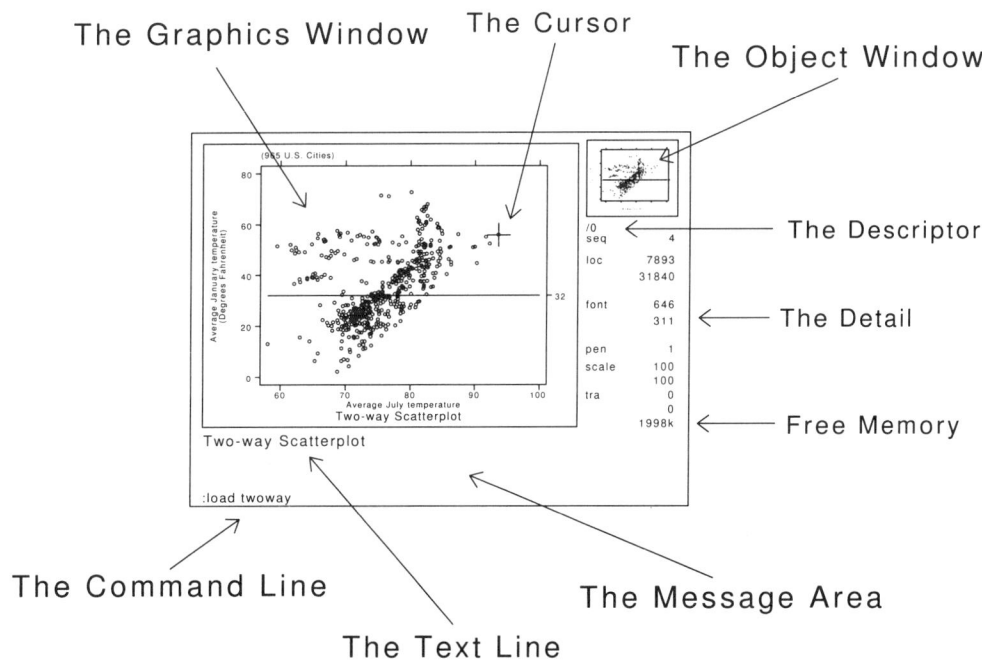

With Stage, you can start with a graph that looks like this (which is not the best that Stata can do even without Stage):

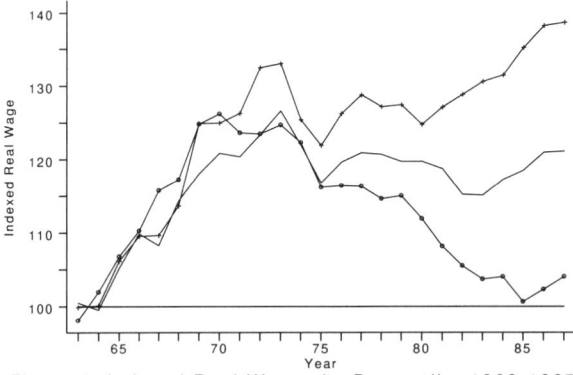

Figure 1. Indexed Real Wages by Percentile, 1963-1987

and create this:

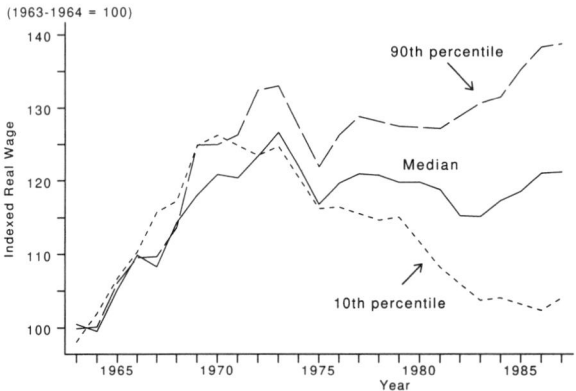

Figure 1. Indexed Real Wages by Percentile, 1963-1987

Complete instructions can be found in the *Stata Graphics Editor Reference Manual.* Here are some more examples of graphs after editing by Stage:

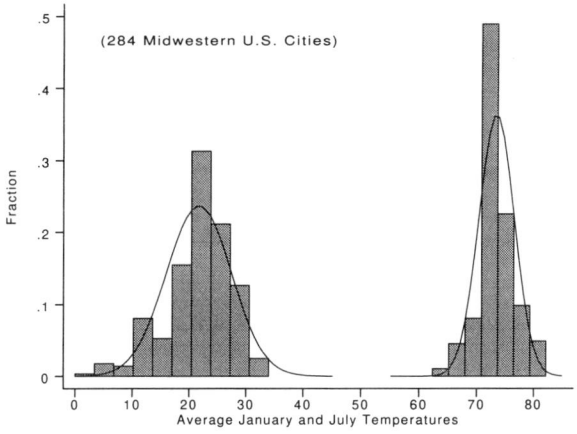

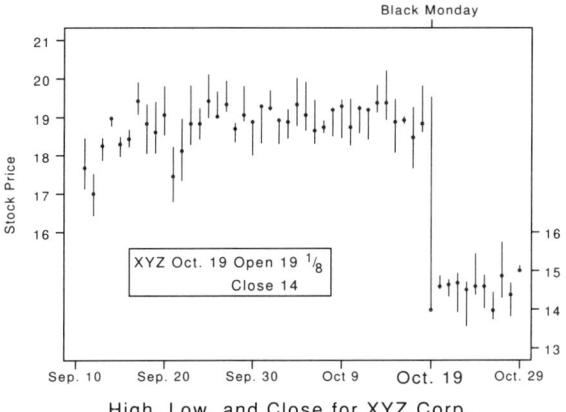

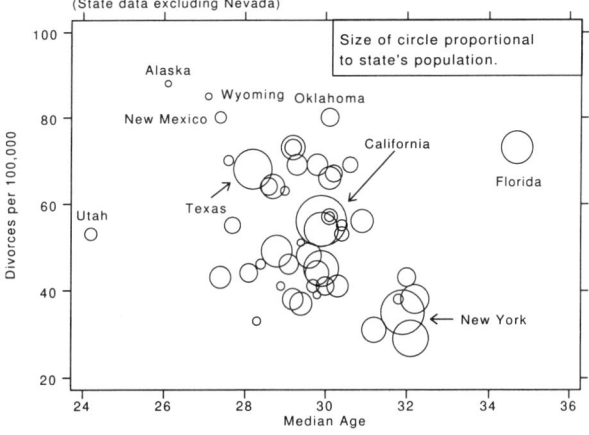

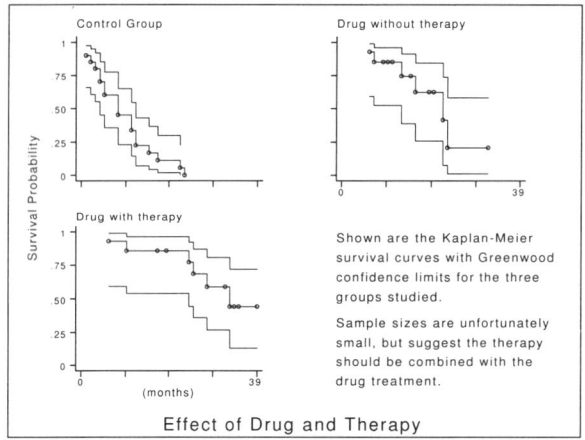

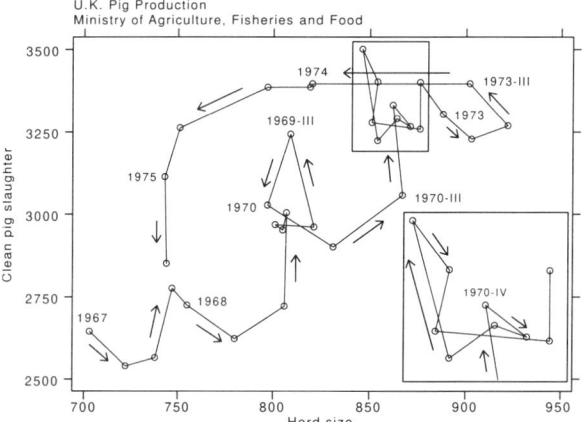

References

Stata Corporation. 1993 (originally published 1989). *Stata Graphics Editor Reference Manual*. College Station, TX: Stata Corporation.

Also See

[R] **graph**

Title

graph star — Graph star charts

Description

This entry discusses the `star` style option to `graph` and the `label()` and `select()` options.

Remarks

Stata draws star charts when you specify the `star` option. The command `graph a b c, star` draws a three-ray star for every observation in the data. The lengths of the rays are proportional to the relative magnitudes of the respective variables.

To	Do
graph characteristics x1, x2, x3, and x4	`graph x1 x2 x3 x4, star`
better control labeling of each star	use `label()`, see example below
graph a subset of stars so as to make them larger	use `select()`, see technical note below
add titles and annotations	see [R] **graph titles**
control the size of text	see [R] **graph textsize**
save or print the graph	see [R] **graph saving**, [R] **graph printing**

▷ Example

The above may not be quite enough explanation, so let's begin again, starting with a picture. We will use a subset of our automobile data and graph each car according to twelve of its characteristics:

```
. gr rep78 rep77 ntd ngr displ length weight trunk rseat hdroom mpg
      nprice, star bsize(125) label(make)
```

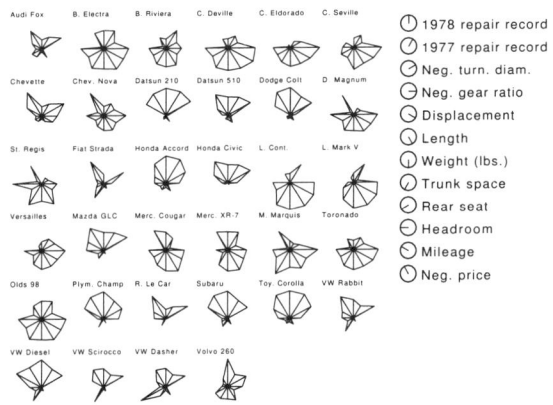

151

We produced an image containing 34 stars, one for each of the 34 cars. (You may remember that our data contains 74 cars. Stata could have drawn stars for all 74 in a single image, but since we are reducing the images to fit on the pages of the manual, you probably could not have read it. We are using a subset of the data.)

For each car, Stata drew a twelve-ray star, with each ray corresponding to a variable. There is a key along the right-side of the diagram, and we see that the ray pointing straight up corresponds to the 1978 repair record (which in turn corresponds to the variable `rep78`), the ray at one o'clock corresponds to the 1977 repair record, and so on. The length of each ray is set according to the value of the variable for the car. The car that has the smallest value of the variable gets a ray with length zero, the car with the largest value gets a ray of maximum length, and the other cars get rays scaled accordingly.

Our `rep78` variable is coded 1 to 5, with 1 reflecting a poor frequency-of-repair record and 5 corresponding to a good record. Thus, if you get out your magnifying glass, you can see that the Audi Fox has an about-average repair record.

You should not, however, get out your magnifying glass. The point of a star chart is to generate distinct shapes so that you can quickly see which observations are similar to other observations in the data. We see, for instance, that the Datsun 210 is a lot like the Dodge Colt which is a lot like the Toyota Corolla. We see that the Lincoln Continental is a lot like the Cadillac Deville. We see that the Datsun/Dodge/Toyota is not at all like the Lincoln/Cadillac. If you have lived all your life in New York City, you might find this information useful before making a trip to Los Angeles.

Now let's turn to the command that created this image. We specified twelve variables—one for each ray of the star—and added two options in addition to `star`: `bsize(125)` and `label(make)`.

The `bsize(125)` sets the size of the by-group labeling text. Although we did not specify the `by()` option—we cannot with this style—`bsize()` is still used to specify the text size. Finally, `label(make)` told Stata what text to use. If we did not specify this option, Stata would have labeled each star with its observation number.

◁

❑ Technical Note

You may specify up to 16 variables (characteristics) with the `star` style; you must specify at least 2 variables. Stata can graph up to 81 stars in the same image.

❑

❑ Technical Note

There may be occasions when you wish to extract a few of the stars and make them larger. For instance, if you were seriously interested in the 34 cars we just graphed above, you might want to make the stars bigger and print, say, nine to a page. Your graph would then take four pages, but it would be readable. You could then take the four pages and put them in a technical appendix.

Your first guess on how to do this is probably wrong. You think, printing the first nine graphs will be easy, I'll just add `in 1/9` to the `graph` command. Then I'll print the second nine by saying `in 10/18`, and so on. It is true that this procedure will generate nine stars per page, but they will not be the same stars we generated in the preceding image.

Adding `in 1/9` to the `graph` command will create stars for the first nine observations comparing these observations with themselves. The rays will be scaled so that the shortest rays correspond to the smallest values of the characteristics *in the first nine observations* and the longest rays will correspond to the largest values *in the first nine observations*. That is not what we want. We want the stars scaled using the smallest and largest values across all the observations in our data, but we want to graph only the first nine of them.

The `select(#₁,#₂)` option does this. $\#_1$ specifies the first observation to be graphed and $\#_2$ specifies the last.

```
. gr rep78 rep77 ntd ngr displ length weight trunk rseat hdroom mpg
     nprice, star bsize(125) label(make) select(1,9)
```

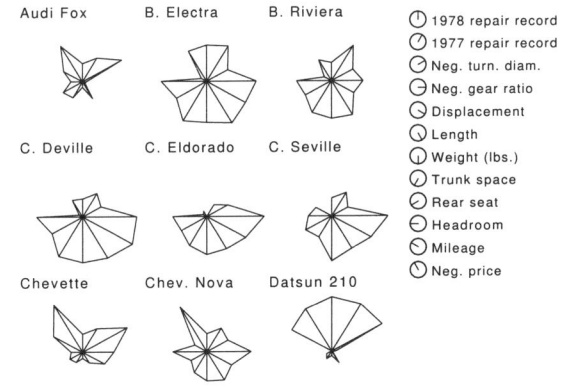

The graph above contains only nine stars, but the scaling is based on all the data.

❑ Technical Note

Labels and titles are graphed using pen 1, the stars themselves are drawn using pen 2. You may specify `pen(#)`, e.g., `pen(3)`, to specify that the stars are to be drawn with pen 3. See [R] **graph pens**, but understand that a separate pen is not specified for each variable in this case.

❑ Technical Note

Star charts (Siegel, Goldwyn, and Friedman 1971, 237) are one type of compound character used for displaying multivariate data. Tukey and Tukey (1981) and Chambers et al. (1983) discuss several other choices and the problems of using compound characters. Displays are sensitive to the order in which variables are assigned to the individual elements of the compound characters. Kleiner and Hartigan tree symbols (Kleiner and Hartigan 1981) are an attempt to avoid this problem by using hierarchical clustering of the variables.

References

Chambers, J. M., W. S. Cleveland, B. Kleiner, and P. A. Tukey. 1983. *Graphical Methods for Data Analysis*. Belmont, CA: Wadsworth International Group.

Kleiner, B. and J. A. Hartigan. 1981. Representing points in many dimensions by trees and castles. *Journal of the American Statistical Association* 76: 260–269.

Siegel, J. H., R. M. Goldwyn, and H. P. Friedman. 1971. Pattern and process in the evolution of human septic shock. *Surgery* 70: 232–245.

Tukey, P. A. and J. W. Tukey. 1981. Summarization; smoothing; supplemented views. In *Interpreting Multivariate Data*, ed. V. Barnett, 245–275. Chichester, U.K.: John Wiley & Sons.

Also See

[R] **graph**, [R] **graph pens**, [R] **graph printing**, [R] **graph saving**, [R] **graph stage**, [R] **graph titles**

Title

> **graph symbol** — Specify plotting symbols

Description

This entry discusses the `symbol()` option to `graph`.

Remarks

Plotting symbols mark the location of a point on a scatterplot. Although **graph** attempts to make intelligent choices as to which plotting symbols to use, you can enforce your preferences by using the `symbol()` option.

The plotting symbols are

O	large circle	o	small circle
T	large triangle	p	small plus
S	large square	d	small diamond
[_n]	use obs. no. as symbol	.	dot
[*varname*]	use *varname* as symbol	i	invisible

▷ Example

If we type **gr y1 y2 x**, Stata plots y1 and y2 against x, using O for y1 and T for y2. It is just as if we specified the option **s(OT)**.

Overprinting to create compound symbols can sometimes make quite effective graphs. For example:

```
. gen mpgfor = mpg if foreign
(52 missing values generated)
. graph mpg mpgfor weight, s(Op) xlog l1("Mileage (mpg)")
          t1("Foreign Cars Highlighted")
          noaxis yline xline
```

155

Since foreign cars are a subset of all cars, they are plotted twice. We explicitly specify the symbols, using O for mpg and p for mpgfor, so foreign cars will be plotted with a circle first and then additionally with a plus, effectively highlighting their points. (Also see [R] **hilite** for an alternative way to achieve highlighting.)

We specify the t1title() because we do not want Stata's default; see [R] **graph titles**. Finally, we give the graph a different look by specifying noaxis yline xline, creating a grid that emphasizes the logged x-scale; see [R] **graph axis rendition**, [R] **graph lines**, and [R] **graph log scales**.

◁

By default, twoway chooses the symbols O, T, S, and the remainder . when you do not specify the symbol() option. Had we not specified the symbol() option, Stata would have graphed mpg using large circles (O) and mpgfor using triangles (T). When twoway is combined with by(), however, it chooses the smaller o, p, d, and the remainder . by default.

▷ Example

If we do not like Stata's choice, we can modify it. Typing **graph y x** graphs y against x using the O plotting symbol. If we have a lot of data, small circles might look better. In that case, we would type **graph y x, symbol(o)**.

Actually, we would probably type **gr y x, s(o)**, abbreviating **graph** as **gr** and **symbol** as **s**.

◁

▷ Example

In addition to the built-in plotting symbols, Stata provides text symbols. A text symbol is always enclosed in square brackets []. [_n] plots each point with its observation number. When you look at a graph, you will sometimes discover an outlier and wonder what that point is. The symbol [_n] provides an easy way to find out. We will not bother to dress up the following image since it is not something you would ever want to print—it is something you would use while analyzing data:

```
. graph mpg weight, s([_n]) xlog
```

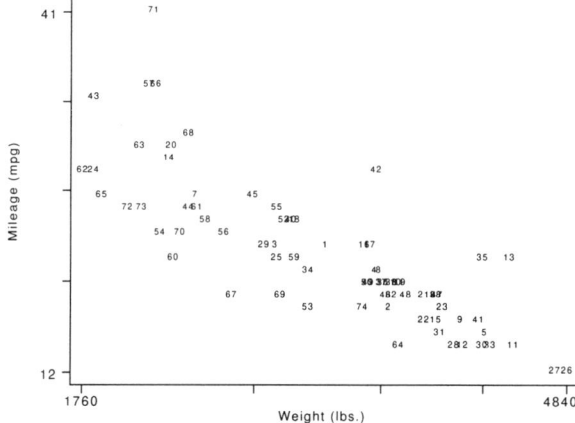

We see that four points stand out from the rest, observations 71, 42, 35, and 13. When we look back at our data, we discover that they are, respectively, the VW Diesel, Plymouth Arrow, Olds 98, and Cadillac Seville. We make some checks and discover that our information on the Plymouth Arrow is in error.

◁

▷ Example

If all we wanted to know was the make of the cars, we could have specified that we wanted [make] as the plotting symbol, since make is a string variable in our data recording the manufacturer and make of the car.

. graph mpg weight, s([make]) xlog

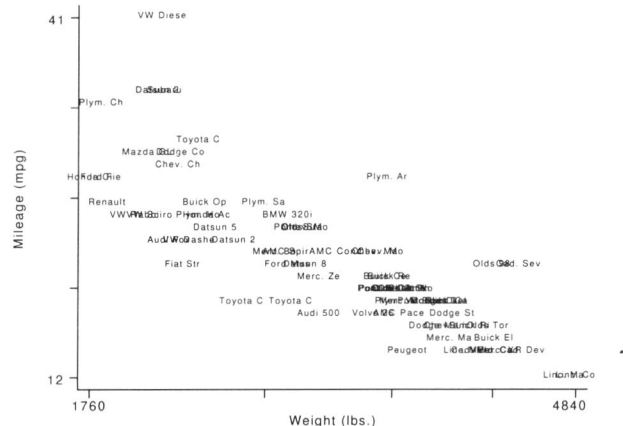

Identifying the VW Diesel and Plymouth Arrow is easy, but identifying the Olds 98 and Cadillac Seville is more problematic due to the overprinting.

Although make is a string variable, it does not have to be. If make were a numeric variable with an associated value label, Stata would have used the text recorded in the value label; see [U] **19.6.3 Value labels**. If make had no value label, Stata would use actual numeric values as the plotting symbol.

◁

▷ Example

The preceding graph is an excellent example of Stata's analysis graphics because it is informative and easy to make. On the other hand, it is unlikely that we would ever want to print it.

Did you notice that the VW Diesel was labeled as VW Diese—that the final *l* was missing? Or that the Plymouth Arrow became a Plym. Ar? Unless we tell Stata otherwise, it uses only the first eight letters of the string in an attempt to reduce the overprinting. The trim() option varies this. If we specified trim(2), only the first two letters of the names would be used. If we said trim(32), Stata would use the first 32 characters. In fact, none of our strings is that long (the variable is only a str18), so trim(32) would guarantee that we used the full string.

Remaking the above graph and specifying trim(32), however, is not going to produce a better-looking image. The names will be spelled out, but that will increase the already substantial amount of overprinting.

For presentation graphics, text symbols work best when the amount of data is small, for instance:

```
. graph price weight if foreign, s([make]) trim(32) xlog ylog
     ylab(4000,8000,12000,16000) xlab(1750,2250,2750,3250,3750)
```

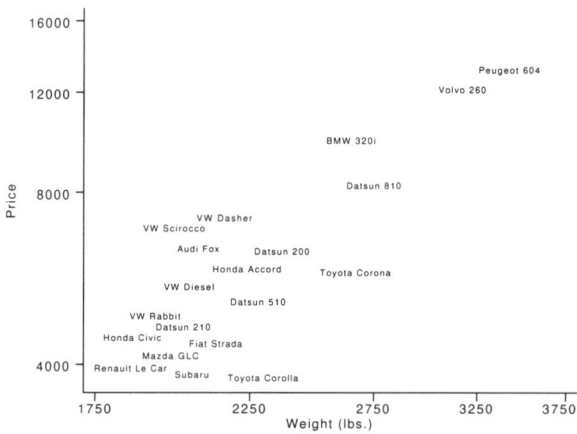

▷ Example

You can increase the size of the font used for the text plotting symbols with the **psize()** option. As with the other two text size options, **bsize()** (see [R] **graph by**) and **set textsize** (see [R] **graph textsize**), the default 100 means 100% of what Stata would otherwise have chosen. The symbols in our previous example were about the right size—if they had been any larger, some points would have been printed on top of others. To demonstrate **psize()**, we will omit a few cars from our data and then draw the graph again:

```
. graph price weight if foreign, s([make]) tr(32) ps(125) xlog ylog
     ylab(4000,8000,12000,16000) xlab(1750,2250,2750,3250,3750)
```

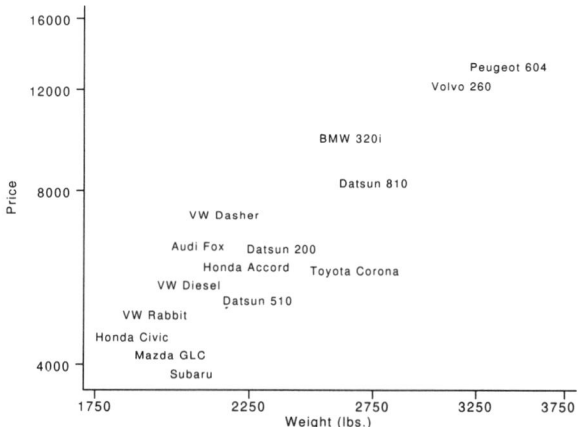

❏ Technical Note

You can combine text and nontext plotting symbols in the same command. For instance, gr y1 y2 x, s(o[txt]) graphs y1 using small circles and y2 using the contents of the variable txt as the symbols. Similarly, we could turn things around and type gr y1 y2 x, s([txt]o).

This gives you another way to use text symbols even with large amounts of data. Suppose you wish to plot y against x and identify just a few of the outlying points. You could create a variable called y1 equal to y for the nonoutlying points and a variable y2 equal to y for the outlying points. Then you could type gr y1 y2 x, s(o[txt]). See [R] **regress** for an example.

❏

❏ Technical Note

You may also specify the symbol option, including text symbols, with the matrix style. By default, matrix uses the o symbol.

❏

Also See

[R] **graph connect**, [R] **graph matrix**, [R] **graph twoway**, [R] **hilite**

Title

graph textsize — Control text size

Description

This entry discusses the `bsize()` and `psize()` options to `graph` and the `set textsize` command.

Remarks

There are one command—`set textsize`—and two options—`bsize()` and `psize()`—that control the size of the text that appears on a graph.

`set textsize` controls the size of the text used in graphs. Its initial value, 100, means 100% of what Stata would ordinarily decide to use. If you type `set textsize 125`, all future graphs will have text that is 25% larger than normal. You can make the `textsize` smaller or larger.

Stata's graphs are What-You-See-Is-What-You-Get (WYSIWYG). If you change `textsize` and specify the `saving()` option, when you print the graph, the text will be larger or smaller, too.

Although we think that the value of 100 looks good on most monitors and printers, the choice is yours. If you are a PC user with a CGA monitor, Stata's text is barely readable. We recommend that you `set textsize 125`. When you make a graph for printing, however, we also recommend that you `set` the `textsize` back to 100. The smaller font size looks better on most printers.

▷ Example

You can make the font as small as 1% of normal or as large as 400% of normal. These extremes are well beyond reasonable. For example:

```
. set textsize 250
. graph mpg weight
```

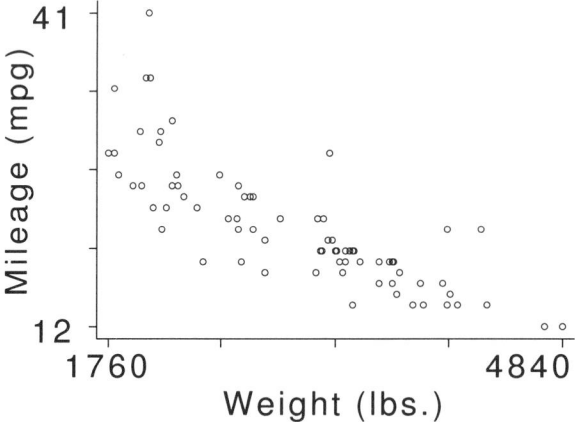

Try other values of `textsize`. When you are through experimenting, type `set textsize 100` to reestablish the original default. Note that changing the `textsize` is only effective at the time you draw the graph, not when you redisplay it using `graph using`.   ◁

In this entry, we will just mention the two `graph` options—`bsize(#)` and `psize(#)`—that also control the size of text. Both options are demonstrated in other entries in this manual.

The `bsize(#)` option affects the size of the text that is used to label by-groups and the individual stars of the star plot—text which tends to be the smallest that appears on a graph; see [R] **graph by** and [R] **graph star**. As with `set textsize`, 100 means 100% of the size Stata otherwise would have chosen, and that is after any adjustment due to `set textsize`. `bsize()` is a useful option since quite often the only text on the graph that needs to be larger is the text affected by `bsize()`. If the text is too small when using the `by()` option, or when drawing star charts, it is always best to try `bsize()` before taking the more drastic measures of `set textsize`.

The `psize(#)` option affects the size of text that is used within the graph to mark the location of points; see [R] **graph symbol**. Again, 100 means 100% of the size Stata otherwise would have chosen after any adjustment due to `set textsize`, so the option works like `bsize()`. This option has an effect, however, only if you are using a text plotting symbol—a symbol specified in square brackets with the `symbol()` option—which is to say, not often. `psize()` also affects the size of nontext plotting symbols when you draw weighted scatterplots; see [R] **graph weights**.

Stata for Windows and Stata for Macintosh

Stata for Windows and Stata for Macintosh users can use either fonts native to their operating system or Stata's built-in font for the text in graphs. If you use one of these two operating systems, you will probably prefer to use your operating system's native fonts.

Assuming you are not using Stata's built-in font in the Graph window, you may want to change the font typeface or size. Stata for Windows users can change this font by pulling down the system menu box on the Graph window (the little box at the left of the Graph window's title bar) and choosing **Fonts**. You can select any TrueType typeface or style you wish. You will notice a size setting in the font dialog box—you should ignore this. The size setting in the font dialog box is ignored by Stata. `set textsize` is the only way to change the font size in Stata for Windows.

Stata for Macintosh users can change the font in the Graph window with the *Graph Font* popup in the **Appearance** preference tab of the **Graph Preferences** dialog box. There is no size setting for the font available on this tab—`set textsize` is the only way to change the font size in Stata for Macintosh.

Also See

[R] **graph**, [R] **graph by**, [R] **graph star**, [R] **graph symbol**, [R] **graph titles**, [R] **graph weights**

Title

Description

This entry discusses the t1title(), t2title(), l1title(), l2title(), b1title(), b2title(), r1title(), and r2title() options to graph.

Remarks

graph allows up to two titles on every side of the image—top, left, bottom, and right—referred to as t1title(), t2title(), l1title(), l2title(), b1title(), b2title(), r1title(), and r2title(). The first title (b1title(), l1title(), etc.) is always the title farther from the figure, the second is closer to the figure.

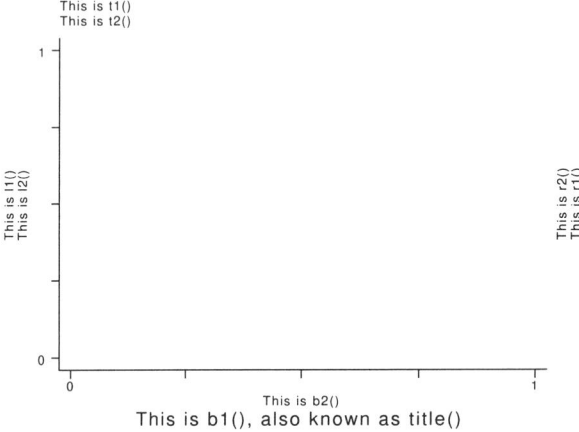

The title options are usually abbreviated by their first two letters, such as l1 for l1title, but you can spell them out if you wish. The b1title() is larger than the other titles and is therefore also known as simply the title() and typically abbreviated ti, although b1 also works.

Stata for Windows and Stata for Macintosh users can use either Stata's built-in font or fonts native to their operating system for text in graphs. See [R] **graph printing Windows**, [R] **graph printing Macintosh**, and [R] **graph textsize** for more information.

▷ Example

Sometimes titles are filled in automatically, but you can always specify the title explicitly and override any default Stata might provide. Here Stata comes up with its own titles:

(Continued on next page.)

. graph tempjan tempjuly, by(region)

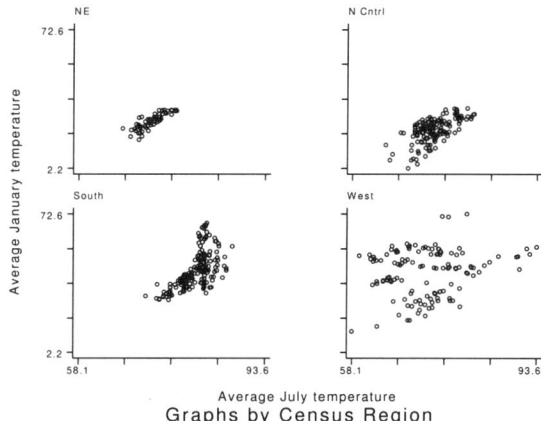

Graphs by Census Region

The l1title() is "Average January Temperature"; the b2title() is "Average July Temperature"; and the b1title() (or just title()) is "Graphs by Census Region". Stata came up with those titles on its own.

How? We said to graph tempjan against tempjuly. Stata looked at the variable tempjan and found that it had a *variable label* (see [U] **19.6.3 Value labels**) of Average January Temperature, so it used the label to title the y-axis. If tempjan had no variable label, Stata would have used the variable's name—tempjan—for the l1title(). Stata went through similar logic for the title on the x-axis, b2title(). Labeling your data is one way to get your graphs titled correctly. The advantage of this approach is that whenever you use a labeled variable, the corresponding axis or graphical element will be properly titled.

Stata also composed a title() for this graph, although that is the exception rather than the rule. It was really the by() option that provided the title. Whenever you use by(), Stata wants to put an explanation of what the separate images mean, so it adds a title at the bottom saying "Graphs by . . .". It fills in the dots with (preferably) the variable label of the by variable or, if no such label exists, with the name of the variable. Evidently, we had previously typed label variable region "Census Region" since the title was "Graphs by Census Region" rather than "Graphs by region".

◁

▷ Example

You do not have to accept the titles Stata automatically supplies; you can specify the titles you prefer. For instance, if we wanted the title to be "Figure 2. Breakdown by Region", we could have typed graph tempjan tempjuly, by(region) title("Figure 2. Breakdown by Region").

You can eliminate any title Stata automatically generates by specifying the title as " ", i.e., a single blank. For instance, graph tempjan tempjuly, by(region) title(" ") would do away with the overall title. You must specify the single blank—do not type title("").

◁

▷ Example

We can add more titles to our graphs, too. Let's remake our image, this time drawing separate graphs for each Census division rather than region (there are nine divisions and four regions), adding a top title describing the data, and overriding one of Stata's automatically defined titles:

```
. graph tempjan tempjuly, by(division)
          t1("(1980 U.S. Census Data for 956 Cities)")
          title("Breakdown by Census Division")
```

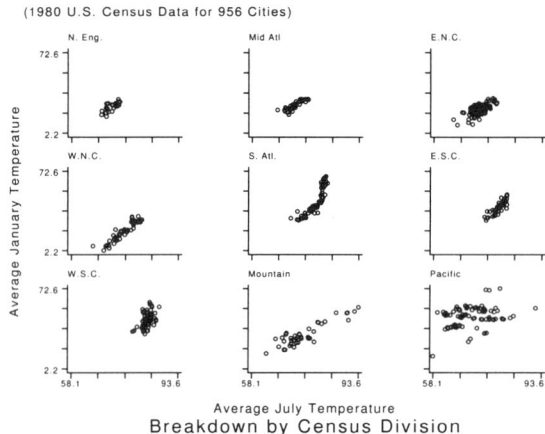

◁

❏ Technical Note

On any style that includes an axis, `gap()` sets the amount of space between the left title and the values along the axis. The default is 8 although it "should" be 9. If it were 9, the values could never run into the left title. In most cases, however, 8 is sufficient and 9 results in too much space. In rare instances the values labeled on the left axis may completely disappear. If they do, it is because they have run off the left edge of the screen and Stata has suppressed displaying them completely. To get them back, widen the gap. Try specifying, for instance, `gap(9)`.

In addition, the text size may be controlled with `set textsize`; see [R] **graph textsize**.

❏

Also See

[R] **graph**, [R] **graph axis labels**, [R] **graph lines**, [R] **graph textsize**, [R] **graph stage**

Title

graph twoway — Graph two-way scatterplots

Description

This entry discusses the `twoway` style option to `graph` and the options `jitter()`, `rescale`, `rbox`, `yreverse`, `xreverse`, and `rreverse`.

Remarks

Stata draws two-way scatterplots whenever you specify the `twoway` style option, although in practice you seldom type the option since `graph` assumes `twoway` whenever you include two or more variables. Examples of the `twoway` style can be found throughout the [R] **graph** ... entries.

To	Do
graph y against x	`graph y x`
graph y1 and y2 against x	`graph y1 y2 x`
draw graphs with separate left- and right-hand scales	use `rescale`, see example below
reverse scales to run from high-to-low	see technical note below
add spherical random noise to your data before graphing	use `jitter()`, see technical note below and [R] **graph weights**
overlay a rangefinder box plot	use `rbox`, see technical note below
combine `twoway` with `oneway` and `box`	see technical note below
specify the plotting symbols	see [R] **graph symbol**
shorten a text plotting symbol	use `trim()`, see [R] **graph symbol**
connect points with lines and add curves	see [R] **graph connect**
deal with weighted data	specify `iweight`, see [R] **graph weights**
draw scatterplots within category	see [R] **graph by**
specify a different scale for each category	use `Rescale`, see [R] **graph by**
better control labeling of the axes	see [R] **graph axis labels**
add grid lines or tick marks to the axes	see [R] **graph lines**
control the style of the axes—for instance, to remove or change to a box	see [R] **graph axis rendition**
control the scaling (minimum and maximum of the axis)	see [R] **graph axis scale**
use log scales	see [R] **graph log scales**
add titles and annotations	see [R] **graph titles**
control the size of text	see [R] **graph textsize**
save or print the graph	see [R] **graph saving**, [R] **graph printing**

▷ Example

There are so many examples of simple two-way scatterplots in this manual that it would be silly to add one more. So let's make this problem more complex, by overlaying the graph of domestic and foreign cars using different plotting symbols to denote the origin of manufacture. Our data contains `mpg`, the mileage rating; `weight`, the weight; and `foreign`, an indicator variable that is 1 if the car is manufactured outside the U.S. The solution is to create two new variables, `mpgfor` for cars manufactured outside and `mpgdom` for cars manufactured inside the U.S.:

```
. gen mpgfor = mpg if foreign
(52 missing values generated)
. gen mpgdom = mpg if ~foreign
(22 missing values generated)
. label var mpgfor "Foreign manufacture"
. label var mpgdom "Domestic manufacture"
. gr mpgfor mpgdom weight, xlog ylab xlab l1("Mileage (mpg)")
```

See [R] **graph log scales** for an explanation of the `xlog` option, [R] **graph axis labels** for an explanation of the `ylab` and `xlab` options, and [R] **graph titles** for an explanation of the `l1()` option.

◁

Among the few options unique to `twoway`, the most important is `rescale`. With this option, you can draw graphs with separate left- and right-hand scales.

▷ Example

We have data on U.K. pig production for 1967 through 1975, and among the variables are `cln_sl`, the clean pig slaughter, and `herd`, the breeding herd size. The slaughter variable ranges from 2,540 to 3,501, whereas the herd-size variable ranges from 703 to 922. If we were to graph both series against time in the same graph, the herd-size variable would hardly move off the bottom axis. `rescale` solves this problem:

. gr cln_sl herd time, c(ll) rescale

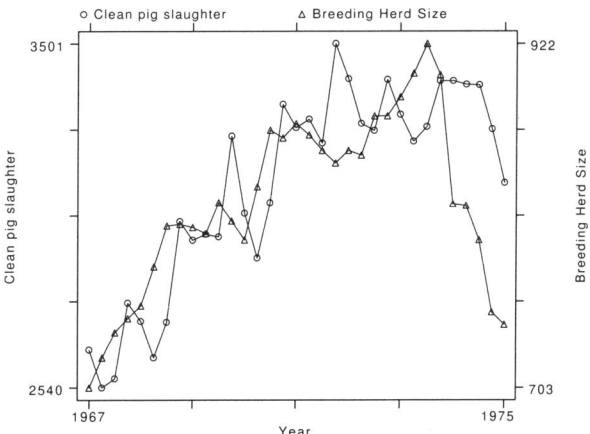

> ◁

▷ Example

We can make the graph look better by adding some separation between the two curves. We can do this by specifying the yscale() option for the first variable and the rscale() option for the second variable. Suppose we wish to move the slaughter series up and the herd size down. Then we wish to decrease the minimum of the left scale to leave some extra white space and simultaneously increase the maximum of the right scale. We will take this opportunity to dress up the image, too:

```
. gr cln_sl herd time, c(ll) resca ysca(2000,3500) rsca(700,1100)
        ylab(2500,2750,3000,3250,3500)
        rlab(700,750,800,850,900) t1(U.K. Pig Production)
        xlab(1967,1968,1969,1970,1971,1972,1973,1974,1975)
```

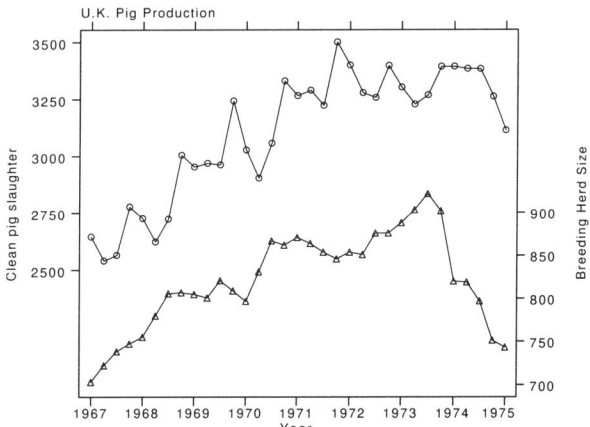

Notice our use of ylabel and xlabel—which we abbreviated ylab and xlab—to label explicitly each scale separately; see [R] **graph axis labels**.

You should compare this graph with the one made in [R] **graph connect**. Both graph the same data; we leave it to you to decide which is more effective.

◁

❏ **Technical Note**

If you specify `rescale` and more than two y-variables, Stata gives up all attempts at labeling the vertical scales and draws a single, unlabeled y-axis. Such pictures are seldom suitable for presentation but can still be useful in analysis.

❏

❏ **Technical Note**

The maximum number of y-variables that you may specify with `twoway` is 20.

❏

❏ **Technical Note**

Stata will allow you to reverse scales to run from high-to-low rather than low-to-high with the `yreverse`, `xreverse`, and `rreverse` options.

❏

❏ **Technical Note**

Stata will add spherical random noise to your data before graphing if you specify the `jitter(#)` option, where # represents the magnitude of the noise as a percent of the graphical area. This can be useful for creating graphs of categorical data when, were the data not jittered, many of the points would be on top of one another making it impossible to tell whether a plotted point represented one or 1,000 observations. `jitter(5)` is a large amount of jittering.

❏

❏ **Technical Note**

Stata is willing to combine its `twoway`, `oneway`, and `box` styles, in any combination, into a single image. We will focus on combinations that include `twoway`. If you specify the options `twoway oneway`, Stata will draw the two-way scatterplot and add one-way scatterplots on the top and right of the graph. If you specify `twoway box`, Stata draws the scatterplot and adds box plots along the outside edges. If you specify all three, you get all three. For instance:

(Continued on next page.)

```
. gr tempjan tempjuly, two one box sy(o) yline(32)
      ylab(2.2,32,72.6) rlab(31.3)
      xlab(58.1,67,76,86,93.6) tlab(74.25)
      t1(Data for 956 U.S. Cities)
```

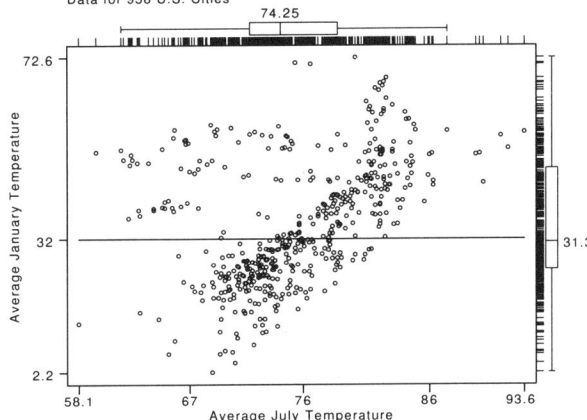

All those options were not necessary; we just wanted to make the image look as good as possible. You might wonder how we knew the values to label for the medians. We used `summarize, detail`; see [R] **summarize**.

❏

❏ Technical Note

Stata has one more capability, the ability to overlay a rangefinder box plot over the scatterplot. The rangefinder box plot is a two-dimensional analog of the box plot. Here we will add the rangefinder box and the regular boxes to the graph, so you get the idea:

```
. gr mpg displ, two box rbox ylab xlab border
```

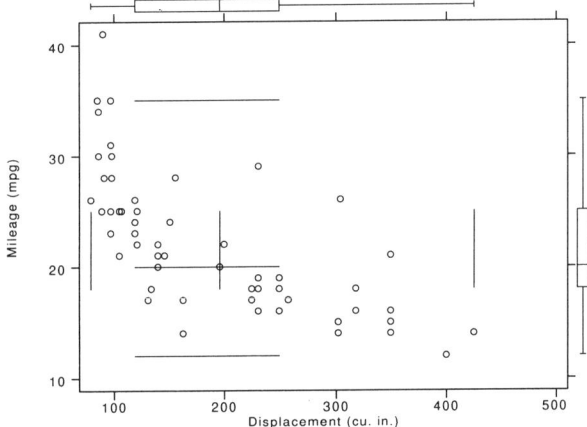

The crosshairs meet at the cross-median. The length of the crosshairs is the interquartile range. Outside lines are drawn at the upper- and lower-adjacent values.

❏

References

Becketti, S. 1988. Reply [to Lenth]. *The American Statistician* 42: 87–88.

Becketti, S. and W. W. Gould. 1987. Rangefinder box plots. *The American Statistician* 41: 149.

Chambers, J. M., W. S. Cleveland, B. Kleiner, and P. A. Tukey. 1983. *Graphical Methods for Data Analysis.* Belmont, CA: Wadsworth International Group.

Lenth, R. V. 1988. Comment on Becketti and Gould. *The American Statistician* 42: 87.

Tufte, E. R. 1983. *The Visual Display of Quantitative Information.* Cheshire, CT: Graphics Press.

Also See

[R] **diagplots**, [R] **graph**, [R] **graph axis labels**, [R] **graph axis rendition**, [R] **graph axis scale**, [R] **graph by**, [R] **graph connect**, [R] **graph lines**, [R] **graph log scales**, [R] **graph pens**, [R] **graph printing**, [R] **graph saving**, [R] **graph stage**, [R] **graph symbol**, [R] **graph titles**, [R] **graph weights**

Title

> **graph weights** — Weighted data

Remarks

All of Stata's graphic styles except `star` can be weighted. `graph` allows `aweights`, `fweights`, and `iweights`, but treats all the same. See [U] **18.1.6 weight** for an explanation of weights and how they are specified.

▷ Example

When you make a weighted two-way scatterplot, the area of the plotting symbols is proportional to the weight. For instance, if you had Census data on the fifty states and among the variables was pop, the population of each state, you might type

```
. gr dvc medage [w=pop] if state~="NV", ylab xlab border
     t1(State Data excluding Nevada)
     t2("Area of symbol proportional to state's population")
```

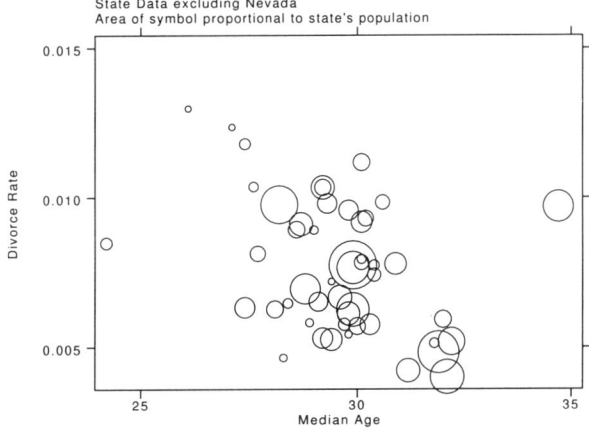

◁

❑ Technical Note

Stata's sizing of the plotting symbols is designed to be a "fair" representation for weighted data. Our graph above, for instance, is a visually fair representation for the purposes of weighted regression and other statistical techniques. There is nothing stopping you, however, from using Stata's scaled symbols to illustrate the value of a third variable that has nothing to do with issues of statistical weighting. Using the automobile data, for instance, you could graph mileage against engine displacement and make the plotting symbols proportional to the *car's* weight. You would type `graph mpg displ [w=weight]`.

You should first, however, understand how Stata determines the size of the symbols. Stata does *not* examine the weights, find the minimum and maximum, and then adopt a scaling so that the minimum weight corresponds to the smallest symbol and the maximum to the largest. To see the problem with that technique, imagine a dataset where every observation except one is a mean based on 1,000 observations and the one exception is based on 1,001 observations. You would not want a graph with $n - 1$ tiny symbols and one giant symbol, because the statistical importance of one observation more or less in a sample of size 1,000 is virtually zero.

Stata scans the data to find the minimum and maximum weight. It then considers assigning the minimum weight to the smallest symbol it can draw and calculates how big the symbol corresponding to the maximum weight would be. If that symbol is smaller than the largest symbol it can draw, it uses that scaling. So in our example, Stata would draw n very small symbols, with one of them being just a little bigger than the rest.

Now imagine that our exception is based on two instead of 1,001 observations. Stata would consider assigning the two-observation point the smallest symbol. Let's imagine that the smallest symbol has a diameter of one-eighth of an inch. The remaining points should have areas 500 times larger than the smallest symbol, which means the diameter must increase by $\sqrt{500} \approx 22.36$, making it roughly 2.8 inches. Stata decides that this symbol is too big, so it instead assigns the largest symbol it is willing to draw to the maximum weight and scales the remaining weights appropriately. This means the two-observation point will effectively vanish from the picture. Rather than let this happen, Stata plots points with radii below the threshold as dots.

All of this is exactly what you would want to happen when the weighting variable reflects population weights. When the weighting variable has nothing to do with statistical weights, however, these issues of fair representation do not apply. What happens when Stata applies these rules? The heaviest car in our automobile data weighs 4,840 pounds whereas the lightest weighs 1,760 pounds. The ratio of those two numbers, 2.75, means that the largest symbol will have an area 2.75 times as large as the smallest symbol. That may sound like a lot, but it is not. If the smallest symbol is one-eighth of an inch in diameter, then the largest symbol will have a diameter of $\frac{1}{8}\sqrt{2.75} \approx \frac{1}{5}$ of an inch. The symbols will appear nearly equal in size.

Stata's scaled symbols have a dynamic range (the area of the largest symbol divided by the area of the smallest symbol) of approximately 100. If you have an arbitrary variable that you want to use to weight the symbols, and you want the smallest symbol to be associated with the smallest value and the largest with the largest value, you want to scale that variable to have the same dynamic range. A formula for doing this is

$$\frac{99}{M - m}(x - m) + 1$$

where m is the minimum and M is the maximum of x.

Thus, you might type

```
. gen new=(99/(4840-1760))*(weight-1760)+1
. graph mpg weight [w=new]
```

❏

▷ Example

Stata can scale all of its symbols (see [R] **graph symbol**), including the text symbols. In the case of text, Stata scales the symbol so that a text string of length eight would have the same width as the diameter of the circles we just drew above. Let's make our last graph again and identify the states. In order to reduce the amount of overprinting, we will make the graphs by region:

```
. gr dvc medage [w=pop] if state~="NV", ylab xlab border
    by(region) s([state]) psize(400)
```

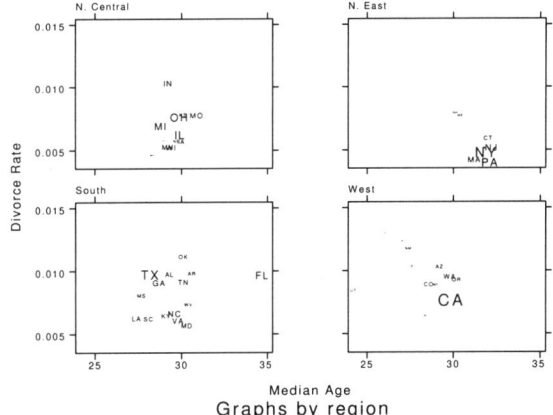

When you are using scaled symbols, psize() sets the *average* size of the symbols. In weighted scatterplots, psize() can be used with both text and nontext symbols.

◁

▷ Example

Stata has one more way of showing weighted data. When you specify the jitter() option, Stata takes a circle of *fixed* radius and then randomly selects points to plot within the circle. The number of points it selects is proportional to the weight. The argument to jitter() specifies the radius of the circle as a percent of graphical area. The resulting graph is sometimes called a *smudge plot*:

```
. gr dvc mrg drate medage [w=pop] if state~="NV", mat label s(.) j(3)
```

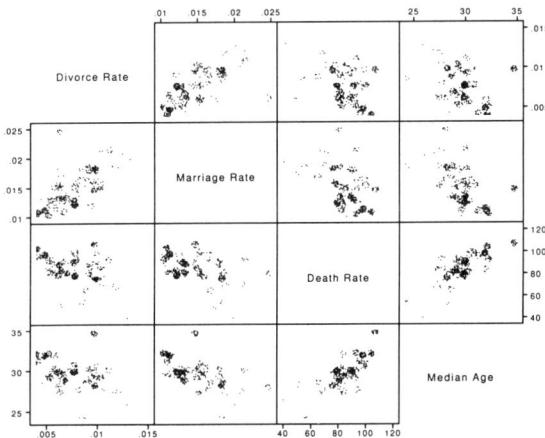

j(3) is an abbreviation for jitter(3), and mat indicates that we want a scatterplot matrix. The jitter option and scaled symbols work equally well with scatterplot matrices and two-way scatterplots.

◁

▷ Example

Let's consider how weighted data is handled by Stata's other styles. The one-way scatterplot works like the smudge plot just illustrated, although you do not have to specify the `jitter` option. `graph a b [w=pop]` draws two weighted one-way scatterplots, turning on an average of three points along the line for each observation in the data. (The number of points actually turned on is proportional to the weight.) You may specify the `jitter(#)` option to vary this. Adding `jitter(4)` would display, on average, four points per observation.

When you specify weights with a histogram, you obtain a weighted histogram. The height of the bars reflects the distribution of the sums of the weights.

`graph a b [w=pop], box` draws two weighted box-and-whisker plots on the same graph. The medians, etc., are all correctly weighted. If you also specify the `vwidth` option, the widths of the boxes are proportional to the sums of the weights.

When you draw weighted bar and pie charts, the areas are proportional to the weighted sums of the variables.

◁

Also See

[R] **graph**, [R] **graph bar**, [R] **graph box**, [R] **graph matrix**, [R] **graph oneway**, [R] **graph pie**, [R] **graph twoway**, [R] **graph weights**

Title

> **grmeanby** — Graph means and medians by categorical variables

Syntax

> grmeanby [*varlist*] [*weight*] [if *exp*] [in *range*], <u>summarize</u>(*varname*) [<u>median</u>
>
> *graph_options*]

aweights and fweights are allowed; see [U] **18.1.6 weight**.

Description

> grmeanby graphs the (optionally weighted) means or medians of *varname* according to the values of the variables in *varlist*. The variables in *varlist* may be string or numerical and, if numerical, may be labeled.

Options

> <u>summarize</u>(*varname*) is not optional; it specifies the name of the variable whose mean or median is to be graphed.
>
> <u>median</u> is optional; it specifies the graph is to be of medians, not means.
>
> *graph_options* are any of the options allowed with **graph, twoway**; see [R] **graph twoway**.

Remarks

> The idea of graphing means of categorical variables was shown in Chambers and Hastie (1992, 3). Since this was shown in the context of an S function for making such graphs, it doubtless has roots going back further than that. grmeanby is, in any case, another implementation of what we will assume is their idea.

▷ Example

> Using the auto.dta, we graph the mean of mpg by foreign, rep77, rep78, and make:

(Continued on next page.)

. grmeanby foreign rep77 rep78 make, sum(mpg) ylab

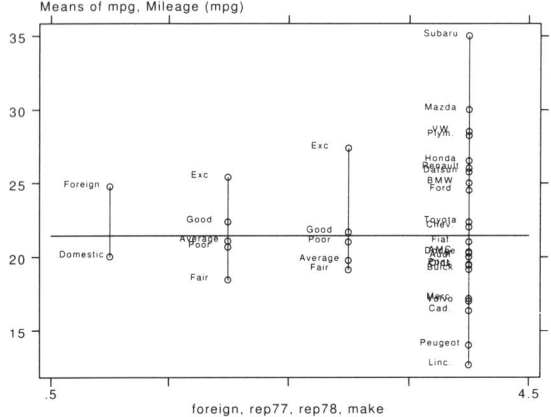

Had we wanted a graph of medians rather than means, we could have typed

. grmeanby foreign rep77 rep78 make, sum(mpg) ylab median

◁

▷ Example

Using a 29,650-observation subsample of men with labor force experience (and other restrictions) from the 1991 Current Population Survey (CPS), we graph the mean of wage:

. grmeanby race hhrel imputed marstat reltohd ftpt, sum(wage) ylab

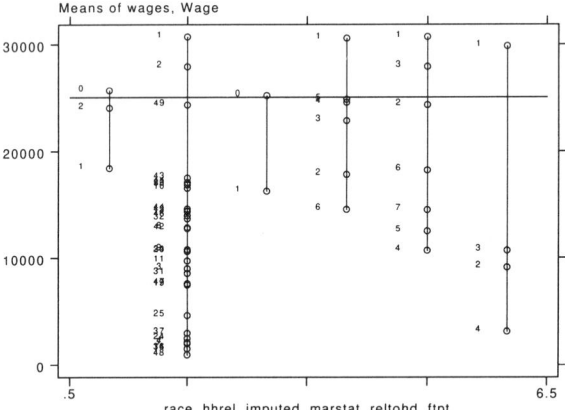

◁

Methods and Formulas

grmeanby is implemented as an ado-file.

References

Chambers, J. M. and T. J. Hastie. 1992. *Statistical Models in S*. Pacific Grove, CA: Wadsworth and Brooks/Cole.

Gould, W. W. 1993. gr12: Graphs of means and medians by categorical variables. *Stata Technical Bulletin* 12: 13. Reprinted in *Stata Technical Bulletin Reprints*, vol. 2, pp. 44–45.

Also See

[R] **graph**

Title

> **gsort** — Ascending and descending sort

Syntax

> gsort [+|-] *varname* [[+|-] *varname* ...] [, generate(*newvar*) mfirst]

Description

gsort arranges observations to be in ascending or descending order of the specified variables and so differs from sort in that sort produces ascending-order arrangements only; see [R] **sort**.

Each *varname* can be numeric or string.

The observations are placed in ascending order of *varname* if + or nothing is typed in front of the name and in descending order if - is typed.

Options

generate(*newvar*) creates *newvar* containing 1, 2, 3, ..., for each group denoted by the ordered data. This is useful when using the ordering in a subsequent by; see [U] **18.5 by varlist: construct** and examples below.

mfirst specifies that missing values are to be placed first in descending orderings rather than last. With mfirst, descending sorts are in some sense more logically arranged but are, in fact, less useful. They are more logical because Stata treats missing values as $+\infty$; therefore, in an arrangement from high to low values, the missing values ought to be first. Missing-values-first orderings are less useful in programming situations because one can no longer be certain that the largest real value is the first observation. They are less useful in interactive situations because, if one lists the data, one must wade through the missing, noninformative observations first.

Remarks

gsort is almost a plug-compatible replacement for sort, the only difference being that you cannot specify a general *varlist* with gsort. For instance, sort alpha-gamma means to sort the data in ascending order of alpha, within equal values of alpha, sort on the next variable in the data (presumably beta), within equal values of alpha and beta, etc. gsort alpha-gamma would be interpreted as gsort alpha -gamma, meaning sort the data in ascending order of alpha and, within equal values of alpha, descending order of gamma.

▷ Example

The difference in *varlist* interpretation aside, gsort can be used in place of sort. To list the ten smallest incomes in the data,

```
. gsort income
. list name income in 1/10
```

or, if you prefer,

```
. gsort +income
. list name income in 1/10
```

To list the 10 largest incomes in the data:

```
. gsort -income
. list name income in 1/10
```

gsort can also be used with string variables. To list all the names in reverse alphabetical order:

```
. gsort -name
. list name
```

◁

▷ Example

gsort can be used with multiple variables. Given a dataset on hospital patients with multiple observations per patient,

```
. gsort id time
. list id time bp
```

lists each patient's blood pressures in the order the measurements were taken.

```
. gsort id -time
. list id time bp
```

lists each patient's blood pressures in reverse-time order.

◁

❑ Technical Note

Say one wished to attach to each patient's records the lowest and highest blood pressures observed during the hospital stay (let's ignore the easier way to achieve this result, egen's min() and max() functions):

```
. egen lo_bp = min(bp), by(id)
. egen hi_bp = max(bp), by(id)
```

(see [R] egen). Here is how you could do it using gsort:

```
. gsort id bp
. quietly by id: gen lo_bp = bp[1]
. gsort id -bp
. quietly by id: gen hi_bp = bp[1]
```

This works even in the presence of missing values of bp because such missing values are placed last within arrangements regardless of the direction of the sort.

❑

❑ Technical Note

Assume a dataset containing x for which we wish to obtain the forward and reverse cumulatives. The forward cumulative is defined as $F(X) =$ the fraction of observations such that $x \leq X$. Again, let's ignore the easier way to obtain the forward cumulative, which would be to use Stata's cumul command

```
. cumul x, gen(cum)
```

(see [R] **cumul**). Eschewing `cumul`, we could type

```
. sort x
. quietly by x: gen cum = _N if _n==1
. replace cum = sum(cum)
. replace cum = cum/cum[_N]
```

That is, we first place the data in ascending order of x; we used `sort` but could have used `gsort`. Next, for each observed value of x, we generated `cum` containing the number of observations that take on that value (you can think of this as the discrete density). We summed the density, obtaining the distribution, and finally normalized it to sum to 1.

The reverse cumulative $G(X)$ is defined as the fraction of data such that $x \geq X$. To obtain it, one might try simply reversing the sort:

```
. gsort -x
. quietly by x: gen rcum = _N if _n==1
. replace rcum = sum(rcum)
. replace rcum = rcum/rcum[_N]
```

This would work except for one detail: Stata will complain that the data are not sorted in the second line. Stata complains because it does not understand descending sorts (`gsort` is an ado-file). To remedy this problem, `gsort`'s `generate()` option will create a new grouping variable that is in ascending order (thus satisfying Stata's narrow definition) and that is, in terms of the groups it defines, identical to that of the true sort variables:

```
. gsort -x, gen(revx)
. quietly by revx: gen rcum = _N if _n==1
. replace rcum = sum(rcum)
. replace rcum = rcum/rcum[_N]
```

❑

Methods and Formulas

`gsort` is implemented as an ado-file.

Also See

[R] **sort**

Title

hadimvo — Identify multivariate outliers

Syntax

hadimvo *varname* [if *exp*] [in *range*], generate(*newvar₁* [*newvar₂*]) [p(#)]

Description

hadimvo identifies multiple outliers in multivariate data using the method of Hadi (1992, 1994), creating *newvar₁* equal to 1 if an observation is an "outlier" and 0 otherwise. Optionally, *newvar₂* can also be created containing the distances from the basic subset.

Options

generate(*newvar₁* [*newvar₂*]) is not optional; it identifies the new variable(s) to be created. Whether you specify two variables or one, however, is optional. *newvar₁*—which is required—will create *newvar₁* containing 1 if the observation is an outlier in the Hadi sense and 0 otherwise. Specifying gen(odd) would call this variable odd. *newvar₂*, if specified, will also create *newvar₂* containing the distances (not the distances squared) from the basic subset. Specifying gen(odd dist) creates odd and also creates dist containing the Hadi distances.

p(#) specifies the "significance" level for outlier cutoff; $0 < \# < 1$. The default is p(.05). Larger numbers identify a larger proportion of the sample as outliers. If # is specified greater than 1, it is interpreted as a percent. Thus, p(5) is the same as p(.05).

Remarks

Multivariate analysis techniques are commonly used to analyze data from many fields of study. The data often contains outliers. The search for subsets of the data which, if deleted, would change results markedly is known as the search for outliers. hadimvo provides one, computer-intensive but practical method for identifying such observations.

Classical outlier detection methods (e.g., Mahalanobis distance and Wilks' test) are powerful when the data contain only one outlier, but the power of these methods decreases drastically when more than one outlying observation is present. The loss of power is usually due to what are known as masking and swamping problems (false negative and false positive decisions) but in addition, these methods often fail simply because they are affected by the very observations they are supposed to identify.

Solutions to these problems often involve an unreasonable amount of calculation and therefore computer time. (Solutions involving hundreds of millions of calculations for samples as small as 30 have been suggested.) The method developed by Hadi (1992, 1994) attempts to surmount these problems and produce an answer, albeit second best, in finite time.

A basic outline of the procedure is as follows: A measure of distance from an observation to a cluster of points is defined. A base cluster of r points is selected and then that cluster is continually redefined by taking the $r + 1$ points "closest" to the cluster as the new base cluster. This continues until some rule stops the redefinition of the cluster.

Ignoring many of the fine details, given k variables, the initial base cluster is defined as $r = k + 1$ points. The distance that is minimized in selecting these $k + 1$ points is a covariance-matrix distance on the variables with their medians removed. (We will use the language loosely; if we were being more precise, we would have said the distance is based on a matrix of second moments, but remember, the medians of the variables have been removed. We would also discuss how the $k + 1$ points must be of full column rank and how they would be expanded to include additional points if they are not.)

Given the base cluster, a more standard mean-based center of the r-observation cluster is defined and the $r + 1$ observations closest in the covariance-matrix sense are chosen as a new base cluster. This is then repeated until the base cluster has $r = \text{int}\big((n + k + 1)/2\big)$ points.

At this point, the method continues in much the same way, except a stopping rule based on the distance of the additional point, and the user specified p(), is introduced.

Simulation results are presented in Hadi (1994).

Examples

```
. hadimvo price weight, gen(odd)
. list if odd                         /* list the outliers          */
. summ price weight if ~odd           /* summary stats for clean data */

. drop odd
. hadimvo price weight, gen(odd D)
. gen id=_n                           /* make an index variable     */
. graph D id                          /* index plot of D            */
. graph price weight [w=D]            /* 2-way scatter, outliers big */
. graph price weight [w=1/D]          /* same, outliers small       */
. summarize D, detail
. sort D
. list make price weight D odd

. hadimvo price weight mpg, gen(odd2 D2) p(.01)
. fit ... if ~odd2
```

Identifying outliers

You have a theory about $x_1, x_2, \ldots, x_k$ which we will write as $F(x_1, x_2, \ldots, x_k)$. Your theory might be that $x_1, x_2, \ldots, x_k$ are jointly distributed normally, perhaps with a particular mean and covariance matrix; or your theory might be that

$$x_1 = \beta_1 + \beta_2 x_2 + \ldots + \beta_k x_k + u$$

where $u \sim N(0, \sigma^2)$; or your theory might be

$$x_1 = \beta_{10} + \beta_{12} x_2 + \beta_{14} x_4 + u_1$$
$$x_2 = \beta_{20} + \beta_{21} x_1 + \beta_{23} x_3 + u_2$$

or your theory might be anything else—it does not matter. You have some data on $x_1, x_2, \ldots, x_k$, which you will assume is generated by $F(\cdot)$, and from that data you plan to estimate the parameters (if any) of your theory and then test your theory in the sense of how well it explains the observed data.

What if, however, some of your data is generated not by $F(\cdot)$ but by $G(\cdot)$, a different process? For example, you have a theory on how wages are assigned to employees in a firm and, for the bulk of employees, that theory is correct. There are, however, six employees at the top of the hierarchy for whom wages are set by a completely different process. Or, you have a theory on how individuals select different health insurance options except that, for a handful of individuals already diagnosed with serious illness, a different process controls the selection process. Or, you are testing a drug that reduces trauma after surgery except that, for a few patients with a high level of a particular protein, the drug has no effect. Or, in another drug experiment, some of the historical data is simply misrecorded.

The data generated by $G(\cdot)$ rather than $F(\cdot)$ are called contaminant observations. Of course, the analysis should be based only on the observations generated by $F(\cdot)$, but in practice we do not know which observations those are. In addition, if it happened by chance that some of the observations are within a reasonable distance from the center of $F(\cdot)$, it becomes impossible to determine whether they are contaminants. Accordingly, we adopt the following operational definition: Outliers are observations that do not conform to the pattern suggested by the majority of the observations in a dataset. Accordingly, observations generated by $F(\cdot)$ but located at the tail of $F(\cdot)$ are considered outliers. On the other hand, contaminants that are within a statistically reasonable distance from the center of $F(\cdot)$ are not considered outliers.

It is well worth noting that outliership is strongly related to the completeness of the theory—a grand unified theory would have no outliers because it would explain all processes (including, one supposes, errors in recording the data). Grand unified theories, however, are difficult to come by and are most often developed by synthesizing the results of many special theories.

Theoretical work has tended to focus on one special case: the data contain only one outlier. As mentioned above, the single-outlier techniques often fail to identify multiple outliers, even if applied recursively. One of the classic examples is the star cluster data (a.k.a. Hertzsprung–Russell diagram) shown in the figure below (Rousseeuw and Leroy 1987, 27). For 47 stars, the data contains the (log) light intensity and the (log) effective temperature at the star's surface. (For the sake of illustration, we treat the data here as bivariate data—not as regression data—i.e., the two variables are treated similarly with no distinction between which variable is dependent and which is independent.)

This graph presents a scatter of the data along with two ellipses expected to contain 95% of the data. The larger ellipse is based on the mean and covariance matrix of the full data. All 47 stars are inside the larger ellipse, indicating that classical single-case analysis fails to identify any outliers. The smaller ellipse is based on the mean and covariance matrix of the data without the five stars identified by `hadimvo` as outliers. These observations are located outside the smaller ellipse. The dramatic effects of the outliers can be seen by comparing the two ellipses. The volume of the larger ellipse is much greater than that of the smaller one and the two ellipses have completely different orientations. In fact, their major axes are nearly orthogonal to each other; the larger ellipse indicates a negative correlation ($r = -0.2$) whereas the smaller ellipse indicates a positive correlation ($r = 0.7$). (Theory would suggest a positive correlation: hot things glow.)

(Graph on next page.)

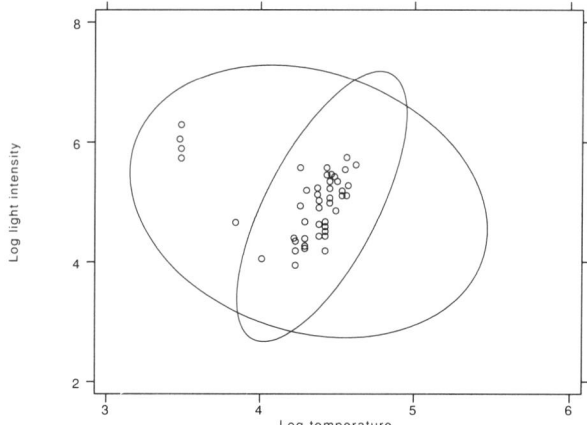

The single-outlier techniques make calculations for each observation under the assumption that it is the only outlier—and the remaining $n - 1$ observations are generated by $F(\cdot)$—producing a statistic for each of the n observations. Thinking about multiple outliers is no more difficult. In the case of two outliers, consider all possible pairs of observations (there are $n(n - 1)/2$ of them) and, for each pair, make a calculation assuming the remaining $n - 2$ observations are generated by $F(\cdot)$. For the three-outlier case, consider all possible triples of observations (there are $n(n - 1)(n - 2)/(3 \times 2)$ of them) and, for each triple, make a calculation assuming the remaining $n - 3$ observations are generated by $F(\cdot)$.

Conceptually, this is easy but practically, it is difficult because of the rapidly increasing number of calculations required (there are also theoretical problems in determining how many outliers to test simultaneously). Techniques designed for detecting multiple outliers, therefore, make various simplifying assumptions to reduce the calculation burden and, along the way, lose some of the theoretical foundation. This loss, however, is no reason for ignoring the problem and the (admittedly second best) solutions available today. It is unreasonable to assume that outliers do not occur in real data.

If outliers exist in the data, they can distort parameter estimation, invalidate test statistics, and lead to incorrect statistical inference. The search for outliers is not merely to improve the estimates of the current model but also to provide valuable insight into the shortcomings of the current model. In addition, outliers themselves can sometimes provide valuable clues as to where more effort should be expended. In a drug experiment, for example, the patients excluded as outliers might well be further researched to understand why they do not fit the theory.

Multivariate, multiple outliers

hadimvo is an example of a multivariate, multiple outlier technique. The multivariate aspect deserves some attention. In the single-equation regression techniques for identifying outliers, such as residuals and leverage, an important distinction is drawn between the dependent and independent variables—the y and the $\mathbf{x}$'s in $y = \mathbf{x}\boldsymbol{\beta} + u$. The notion that the y is a linear function of $\mathbf{x}$ can be exploited and, moreover, the fact that some point $(y_i, \mathbf{x}_i)$ is "far" from the bulk of the other points has different meanings if that "farness" is due to y_i or $\mathbf{x}_i$. A point that is far due to $\mathbf{x}_i$ but, despite that, still close in the y_i given $\mathbf{x}_i$ metric, adds precision to the measurements of the coefficients and may not indicate a problem at all. In fact, if we have the luxury of designing the experiment, which means choosing the values of $\mathbf{x}$ a priori, we attempt to maximize the distance between the $\mathbf{x}$'s (within the bounds of $\mathbf{x}$ we believe are covered by our linear model) to maximize that precision. In that extreme case, the distance of $\mathbf{x}_i$ carries no information as we set it prior to running the experiment. More recently, Hadi and Simonoff (1993) exploit the structure of the linear model and suggest two methods for identifying multiple outliers when the model is fitted to the data (also see [R] **fit**).

In the multivariate case, we do not know the structure of the model, so $(y_i, \mathbf{x}_i)$ is just a point and the y is treated no differently from any of the $\mathbf{x}$'s—a fact which we emphasize by writing the point as $(x_{1i}, \mathbf{x}_{2i})$ or simply $(\mathbf{X}_i)$. The technique does assume, however, that the $\mathbf{X}$'s are multivariate normal or at least elliptically symmetric. This leads to a problem if some of the $\mathbf{X}$'s are functionally related to the other $\mathbf{X}$'s, such as the inclusion of x and x^2, interactions such as $x_1 x_2$, or even dummy variables for multiple categories (in which one of the dummies being 1 means the other dummies must be 0). There is no good solution to this problem. One idea, however, is to perform the analysis with and without the functionally related variables and to subject all observations identified for further study (see *What to do with outliers* below).

An implication of `hadimvo` being a multivariate technique is that it would be inappropriate to apply it to $(y, \mathbf{x})$ when $\mathbf{x}$ is the result of experimental design. The technique would know nothing of our design of $\mathbf{x}$ and would inappropriately treat "distance" in the $\mathbf{x}$-metric the same as distance in the y-metric. Even when $\mathbf{x}$ is multivariate normal, unless y and $\mathbf{x}$ are treated similarly it may still be inappropriate to apply `hadimvo` to $(y, \mathbf{x})$ because of the different roles that y and $\mathbf{x}$ play in regression. However, one may apply `hadimvo` on $\mathbf{x}$ to identify outliers which, in this case, are called leverage points. (We should also mention here that if `hadimvo` is applied to $\mathbf{x}$ when it contains constants or any collinear variables, those variables will be correctly ignored, allowing the analysis to continue.)

It is also inappropriate to use `hadimvo` (and other outlier detection techniques) when the sample size is too small. `hadimvo` uses a small-sample correction factor to adjust the covariance matrix of the "clean" subset. Because the quantity $n - (3k + 1)$ appears in the denominator of the correction factor, the sample size must be larger than $3k + 1$. Some authors would require the sample size to be at least $5k$, i.e., at least five observations per variable.

With these warnings, it is difficult to misapply this tool assuming that you do not take the results as more than suggestive. `hadimvo` has a `p()` option that is a "significance level" for the outliers that are chosen. We quote the term significance level because, although great effort has been expended to really make a significance level, approximations are involved and it will not have that interpretation in all cases. It can be thought of as an index between 0 and 1, with increasing values resulting in the labeling of more observations as outliers and with the suggestion that you select a number much as you would a significance level—it is roughly the probability of identifying any given point as an outlier if the data truly were multivariate normal. Nevertheless, the terms significance level or critical values should be taken with a grain of salt. It is suggested that one examine a graphical display (e.g., an index plot) of the distance with perhaps different values of `p()`. The graphs give more information than a simple yes/no answer. For example, the graph may indicate that some of the observations (inliers or outliers) are only marginally so.

What to do with outliers

After a reading of the literature on outlier detection, many people are left with the incorrect impression that once outliers are identified, they should be deleted from the data and analysis continued. Automatic deletion (or even automatic down-weighting) of outliers is not always correct because outliers are not necessarily bad observations. On the contrary, if they are correct, they may be the most informative points in the data. For example, they may indicate that the data did not come from a normally distributed population as is commonly assumed by almost all multivariate techniques.

The proper use of this tool is to label outliers and then subject the outliers to further study, not simply to discard them and continue the analysis with the rest of the data. After further study, it may indeed turn out to be reasonable to discard the outliers, but some mention of the outliers must certainly be made in the presentation of the final results. Other corrective actions may include correction of errors in the data, deletion or down-weighting of outliers, redesigning the experiment or sample survey, collecting more data, etc.

Methods and Formulas

`hadimvo` is implemented as an ado-file. Formulas are given in Hadi (1992, 1994).

Acknowledgments

We would like to thank Ali S. Hadi of Cornell University for his assistance in writing `hadimvo`.

References

Gould, W. W. and A. S. Hadi. 1993. smv6: Identifying multivariate outliers. *Stata Technical Bulletin* 11: 28–32. Reprinted in *Stata Technical Bulletin Reprints*, vol. 2, pp. 163–168.

Hadi, A. S. 1992. Identifying multiple outliers in multivariate data. *Journal of the Royal Statistical Society*, Series B 54: 761–771.

——. 1994. A modification of a method for the detection of outliers in multivariate samples. *Journal of the Royal Statistical Society*, Series B 56: 393–396.

Hadi, A. S. and J. S. Simonoff. 1993. Procedures for the identification of multiple outliers in linear models. *Journal of the American Statistical Association* 88: 1264–1272.

Rousseeuw, P. J. and A. M. Leroy. 1987. *Robust Regression and Outlier Detection*. New York: John Wiley & Sons.

Also See

[R] **fit**, [R] **mvreg**, [R] **sureg**

Title

> **heckman** — Heckman selection model

Syntax

heckman *eqname*$_1$ *eqname*$_2$ [*weight*] [if *exp*] [in *range*] [, <u>noc</u>onstant <u>holdrho</u>

<u>l</u>evel(#) <u>iter</u>ate(#) <u>trac</u>e *maximize_options*]

aweights and fweights are allowed; see [U] **18.1.6 weight**.

heckman shares the features of all estimation commands; see [U] **26 Estimation and post-estimation commands**.

To reset problem-size limits, see [R] **matsize**.

Description

heckman performs full maximum-likelihood estimation of Heckman selection models.

eqname$_1$ is the name of the regression equation to be estimated. *eqname*$_2$ is the name of an "equation" containing the variables thought to determine whether the dependent variable in *eqname*$_1$ is defined or missing '.'.

You are warned that heckman can be quite slow; be patient.

heckman typed without arguments redisplays the previous estimates.

Options

noconstant omits the constant term from the estimation. The default is to include a constant. If a constant term is desired in only one of the equations, create a variable that is one everywhere (gen c=1) and include it explicitly in the equation where it is wanted.

holdrho causes the solution to be found conditional on the value of rho estimated in the Mills' ratio solution.

level(#) specifies the confidence level, in percent, for confidence intervals. The default is level(95) or as set by set level; see [U] **26.4 Specifying the width of confidence intervals**.

iterate(#) is one of the *maximize_options*; see [R] **maximize**. iterate(0), however, produces Heckman's (1979) two-step procedure estimates with full-information standard errors.

trace is one of the *maximize_options*; see [R] **maximize**. In addition to displaying the details of the maximum-likelihood iterations, trace displays the initial probit and regression used to determine the initial Mills' ratio coefficient estimate.

maximize_options control the maximization process; see [R] **maximize**. With the exception of iterate(#) and trace, you should never have to specify them.

Remarks

The Heckman selection model (Gronau 1974, Lewis 1974, Heckman 1976) assumes that a potential observation j is observed if

$$\mathbf{z}_j\boldsymbol{\gamma} + u_{1j} > 0$$

where u_{1j} has a standard normal distribution. Simultaneously, there is another regression equation

$$y_j = \mathbf{x}_j\boldsymbol{\beta} + \sigma u_{2j}$$

where u_{2j} also has a standard normal distribution, but u_{2j} is potentially correlated with u_{1j} with correlation ρ. When $\rho \neq 0$, standard regression techniques applied to the second equation yield biased results. heckman provides consistent, asymptotically efficient estimates for such models.

In the classic example, the second equation describes the wages of women. Women choose whether to work and thus, from our point of view as researchers, whether we observe their wages in our data. If women made this decision randomly, we could ignore the fact that not all wages are observed and use ordinary regression to estimate a wage model. Such a random-participation-in-the-labor-force assumption, however, is unlikely to be true; women who would have low wages may be unlikely to choose to work and thus the sample of observed wages is biased upward. In the jargon of economics, women choose not to work when their personal reservation wage is greater than the wage offered by employers. Thus, it is possible that women who choose not to work could have even higher offer wages than those who do work—they may have high offer wages, but they have even higher reservation wages. One could tell a story that competency is related to wages, but competency is rewarded more at home than in the labor force.

In any case, in this problem—which is the paradigm for all such problems—a solution can be found if there are some variables that strongly affect the chances for observation (the reservation wage) but not the outcome under study (the offer wage). Such a variable might be the number of children in the home. (Actually, one theoretically does not need such identifying variables, but without them, one is depending on functional form to identify the model. It would be difficult for anyone to take such results seriously since the functional-form assumptions have no firm basis in economic theory.)

▷ Example

To use Stata's heckman procedure, you specify two equations: the regression equation of interest and a second list of variables thought to determine whether the dependent variable in the regression equation is observed or missing. In our female wage example, number of children at home would be included in the second list. We have a (fictional) dataset on 2,000 women, of whom 1,471 work:

```
. summarize

    Variable |       Obs        Mean    Std. Dev.       Min        Max
-------------+--------------------------------------------------------
         age |      2000     40.0095     11.7359         20         60
        educ |      2000      14.406    2.844505         10         20
     married |      2000       .6015    .4897118          0          1
    children |      2000       1.445    1.394972          0          4
        wage |      1471    29.02968    6.743488   6.022012   48.57617
```

We will assume that the hourly wage is a function of education and age whereas the likelihood of working (the likelihood of the wage being observed) is a function of marital status, number of children at home, and (implicitly) the wage (via the inclusion of age and education which we think determine the wage):

```
. eq wage educ age
. eq probit: married children educ age
. heckman wage probit
Iteration 0:  Log Likelihood = -5609.784
Iteration 1:  Log Likelihood = -5605.3495
Iteration 2:  Log Likelihood = -5605.3199
Iteration 3:  Log Likelihood = -5605.3199
Iteration 4:  Log Likelihood = -5605.3199
```

Heckman selection model

		Number of obs	=	2000
		Model chi2(7)	=	446.99
		Prob > chi2	=	0.0000

Log Likelihood = -5605.3198732

wage	Coef.	Std. Err.	z	P>|z|	[95% Conf. Interval]
wage					
educ	.9844541	.0565015	17.423	0.000	.8737132 1.095195
age	.2015654	.0131992	15.271	0.000	.1756954 .2274353
_cons	5.500916	1.096162	5.018	0.000	3.352479 7.649354
probit					
married	-.6440935	.0730464	-8.818	0.000	-.7872619 -.5009252
children	-.4458327	.0253535	-17.585	0.000	-.4955245 -.3961408
educ	.0852276	.0123257	6.915	0.000	.0610697 .1093855
age	.0114021	.0028215	4.041	0.000	.0058721 .016932
_cons	.1095977	.2197041	0.499	0.618	-.3210144 .5402098
_athrho					
_cons	.4270231	.0975642	4.377	0.000	.2358008 .6182455
_lnsigma					
_cons	1.784616	.0224788	79.391	0.000	1.740559 1.828674

rho	0.40283		[_athrho]_cons = atanh(rho)
sigma	5.957293		[_lnsigma]_cons = ln(sigma)
lambda	2.3997793	.5197669	

We began by specifying our equations; see [R] **eq**. To review, you can specify a name for an equation by typing a name followed by a colon, or you can omit specifying the name and colon, in which case the first variable listed will be interpreted as both the name and part of the contents of the equation. We typed

```
. eq wage educ age
. eq probit: married children educ age
```

Our first equation is named **wage** and contains **wage educ age**. Our second equation is named **probit** and contains **married children educ age**. When we type

```
. heckman wage probit
```

heckman assumes that the first-named equation is the regression equation and the second-named equation contains a list of variables that determines whether the dependent variable in the first equation is observed or missing. Thus, we estimated the model

$$\mathtt{wage} = \beta_0 + \beta_1 \mathtt{educ} + \beta_2 \mathtt{age} + \sigma u_2$$

and we assumed that **wage** is not missing if

$$\gamma_0 + \gamma_1 \mathtt{married} + \gamma_2 \mathtt{children} + \gamma_3 \mathtt{educ} + \gamma_4 \mathtt{age} + u_1 > 0$$

where u_1 and u_2 have correlation ρ.

The reported results, at least for `wage` and `probit`, should be self-explanatory. The other results do require some explanation. `heckman` does not directly estimate ρ; it estimates the inverse hyperbolic tangent of ρ:

$$\text{atanh}\, \rho = \frac{1}{2} \ln\left(\frac{1+\rho}{1-\rho}\right)$$

This estimate is reported under _cons for _athrho. At the end of the output, `heckman` undoes this transformation for you: the estimated value of ρ is .40283.

Similarly, σ—the standard error of the residual in the wage equation—is not directly estimated; `heckman` instead estimates $\ln\sigma$. The untransformed `sigma` is reported at the end of the output: 5.96.

Finally, some researchers—especially economists—are used to the selectivity effect summarized not by ρ but by $\lambda = \rho\sigma$. `heckman` reports this, too, along with an estimate of the standard error.

◁

❑ Technical Note

`heckman` uses Mills' ratio estimates for starting values. In the iterative maximization routine, derivatives of the likelihood are computed numerically. The χ^2 test reported is a comparison with the null probit/regression model, which is generally not an interesting comparison. `heckman` is an estimation command, however, so you can use `test`, `testnl`, or `lrtest` to perform tests against whatever more basic model you wish to choose; see [R] **test**, [R] **testnl**, and [R] **lrtest**.

The estimation of ρ and σ in the form atanh ρ and $\ln\sigma$ extends the range of these parameters to infinity in both directions, thus avoiding boundary problems during the maximization. Tests of ρ must be made in the transformed units. However, since $\text{atanh}(0) = 0$, the reported test for atanh $\rho = 0$ is equivalent to the test for $\rho = 0$. The $z = 4.377$, significantly different from zero, justifies the Heckman selection equation with this data.

❑

❑ Technical Note

Since `heckman` is a standard estimation command, after estimation, we can obtain the predicted wage from the `wage` equation using `predict`:

    . predict hswage

`heckman` estimates a multiple-equation model, and those of you are familiar with the syntax of the `predict` command know that you are supposed to specify the appropriate equation for the prediction. That is, you would type

    . predict hswage, eq(wage)

However, by default, `predict` assumes the first equation when no equation is specified, so both of the above commands give the same results. If you want predicted values of $\mathbf{Z}\gamma$ for the second equation, you must specify the equation name when using `predict`.

It is instructive to compare these predicted values for the wage equation with an ordinary regression model—a model without the selection adjustments:

    . regress wage educ age

Source	SS	df	MS		Number of obs =	1471
					F(2, 1468) =	258.46
Model	17408.7935	2	8704.39674		Prob > F =	0.0000
Residual	49438.9066	1468	33.6777293		R-squared =	0.2604
					Adj R-squared =	0.2594
Total	66847.7001	1470	45.4746259		Root MSE =	5.8033

```
   wage |      Coef.   Std. Err.       t    P>|t|     [95% Conf. Interval]
--------+----------------------------------------------------------------
   educ |   .9011685   .0526744    17.108   0.000     .7978434   1.004494
    age |   .1931489   .0128991    14.974   0.000     .1678463    .2184515
  _cons |   7.929087   .9475446     8.368   0.000     6.070401   9.787773
------------------------------------------------------------------------

. predict regwage
. summarize hswage regwage
Variable |      Obs       Mean   Std. Dev.        Min        Max
---------+------------------------------------------------------------
  hswage |     2000   27.74749   3.685432   19.37676   37.28392
 regwage |     2000   28.63911   3.440401   20.80375   37.54139
```

Since we in writing this manual concocted the data, we know the true coefficients to be 1, 0.2, and 5, respectively. The regression equation is significantly off, but gives the right sense. Ordinary regression yields predictions that are about a dollar per hour too high due to the selection effect.

❑

❑ Technical Note

The heckman command is slow. Heckman (1979) developed a two-step procedure for estimating selection models that involves estimating a maximum-likelihood probit model and then a regression including Mills' ratio. Those are the starting values used by heckman. Therefore, you can obtain the two-step estimates, with full-information standard errors, by including the iterate(0) option:

```
. eq wage educ age
. eq probit : married children educ age
. heckman wage probit, iterate(0)
Iteration 0:  Log Likelihood = -5609.784
Heckman selection model                   Number of obs   =     2000
                                          Model chi2(7)   =   438.06
                                          Prob > chi2     =   0.0000
Log Likelihood = -5609.7839544

    wage |      Coef.   Std. Err.       z    P>|z|     [95% Conf. Interval]
---------+----------------------------------------------------------------
wage     |
    educ |   1.000159   .0534945    18.696   0.000     .8953118   1.105006
     age |   .2034312    .012645    16.088   0.000     .1786474    .228215
   _cons |   5.033971   1.013426     4.967   0.000     3.047692    7.02025
---------+----------------------------------------------------------------
probit   |
 married |  -.6260646   .0718386    -8.715   0.000    -.7668657   -.4852634
children |  -.4444517    .025061   -17.735   0.000    -.4935703    -.395333
    educ |   .0848365   .0123009     6.897   0.000     .0607272    .1089459
     age |    .010928   .0028117     3.887   0.000     .0054172    .0164389
   _cons |   .1213606   .2191906     0.554   0.580     -.308245    .5509662
---------+----------------------------------------------------------------
_athrho  |
   _cons |   .5397222   .0838106     6.440   0.000     .3754565    .7039879
---------+----------------------------------------------------------------
_lnsigma |
   _cons |   1.751985   .0220205    79.561   0.000     1.708825    1.795144
---------+----------------------------------------------------------------
     rho    0.49278                 [_athrho]_cons = atanh(rho)
   sigma    5.7660346               [_lnsigma]_cons = ln(sigma)
  lambda    2.8413732    .406852
```

In addition, if you decide to go for the maximum-likelihood solution and then tire of waiting, you can press *Break*. The computer will respond by typing "maximization aborted, computing standard errors". It will then resume thinking and, after a pause, display the interim results. If you do not want to see the results at all, after seeing the message, press *Break* again.

❑

❑ Technical Note

The Heckman selection model depends strongly on model correctness—more so than for ordinary regression. Running a separate probit or logit for sample inclusion followed by a regression, referred to in the literature as the two-part model (Manning, Duan, and Rogers 1987)—not to be confused with Heckman's two-step procedure—is an especially attractive alternative if the regression part of the model arose because of taking a logarithm of zero values. When the goal is to predict the value of the dependent variable that would have been observed, however, the Heckman selection model is more appropriate. When the goal is to predict an actual response, the two-part model is usually the better choice.

The Heckman selection model is infamous for instability when the model is not properly specified. For example, consider the following selection model output from a nonsense model. In order to explore the convergence properties of this model, we specify the **trace** option to watch the convergence process more completely:

```
. replace price=. if foreign
(22 real changes made, 22 to missing)

. eq price mpg weight

. eq probit: displ

. heckman price probit, trace
```

Probit Estimates   Number of obs =   74
                                                    chi2(1)   =   44.06
                                                    Prob > chi2   = 0.0000
Log Likelihood = -23.004215   Pseudo R2   = 0.4892

__0000MT	Coef.	Std. Err.	z	P>|z|	[95% Conf. Interval]	
displ	.0231829	.0059231	3.914	0.000	.011574	.0347919
_cons	-2.999473	.787286	-3.810	0.000	-4.542525	-1.456421

Note: 0 failures and 3 successes completely determined.

Mills´ ratio coefficient estimate from regression

Source	SS	df	MS		Number of obs =	52
					F(3, 48) =	18.17
Model	260157662	3	86719220.6		Prob > F =	0.0000
Residual	229037139	48	4771607.06		R-squared =	0.5318
					Adj R-squared =	0.5025
Total	489194801	51	9592054.92		Root MSE =	2184.4

price	Coef.	Std. Err.	t	P>|t|	[95% Conf. Interval]	
__0000MV	2557.997	1143.039	2.238	0.030	259.7625	4856.231
mpg	162.7514	137.8043	1.181	0.243	-114.3226	439.8254
weight	5.120607	.9647999	5.307	0.000	3.180747	7.060467
_cons	-14778.32	5545.562	-2.665	0.010	-25928.42	-3628.217

```
Coefficient of Mills' ratio  2557.997
Initial estimate of rho      1.171029
Initial rho set to           0.99
Heckman model may be inappropriate since initial |rho| > 0.9

ML computation begins ...
    162.75137   5.120607   -14778.316   .02318294   -2.9994732   2.6466524
    7.6890969
Iteration 0:  Log Likelihood = -494.74219
(nonconcave function encountered)
    162.75022   5.1034113  -14778.316   .02354183   -2.9708743   2.5616013
    7.7699959
Iteration 1:  Log Likelihood = -493.06855
(nonconcave function encountered)
    162.75453   5.1096936  -14778.316   .0234526    -3.0047829   2.5266472
    7.818037
Iteration 2:  Log Likelihood = -492.76383
(nonconcave function encountered)
    162.75857   5.1008661  -14778.316   .02355732   -3.0270295   2.4242647
    7.8411641
Iteration 3:  Log Likelihood = -492.67548
(nonconcave function encountered)
    162.76278   5.1066643  -14778.316   .02349328   -3.0584798   2.369032
    7.8318013
Iteration 4:  Log Likelihood = -492.60578
(nonconcave function encountered)
    162.76725   5.1011696  -14778.315   .02368485   -3.070343    2.2448216
    7.8297245
  (output omitted)
Iteration 12:  Log Likelihood = -490.83493
    105.5897    4.1791758  -10449.21    .0262556    -3.3591755   2.2028686
    7.7478327
Iteration 13:  Log Likelihood = -490.83493
```

```
Heckman selection model                    Number of obs  =      74
                                           Model chi2(4)  =   58.71
                                           Prob > chi2    =  0.0000

Log Likelihood =   -490.8349341
```

price	Coef.	Std. Err.	z	P>|z|	[95% Conf. Interval]
price					
mpg	105.5897	77.37173	1.365	0.172	-46.0561 257.2355
weight	4.179176	.6291039	6.643	0.000	2.946155 5.412197
_cons	-10449.21	3376.82	-3.094	0.002	-17067.66 -3830.765
probit					
displ	.0262556	.0067118	3.912	0.000	.0131007 .0394105
_cons	-3.359176	.855216	-3.928	0.000	-5.035368 -1.682983
_athrho					
_cons	2.202869	.892738	2.468	0.014	.4531342 3.952603
_lnsigma					
_cons	7.747833	.1010999	76.635	0.000	7.549681 7.945985

```
      rho     0.97588              [_athrho]_cons  = atanh(rho)
    sigma  2316.5463              [_lnsigma]_cons = ln(sigma)
   lambda  2260.6717   269.7547
```

The output after the initial regression indicates that the initial estimate of ρ is 1.17. Whenever the initial ρ is greater than 1 (or less than -1), it is set to 0.99 (or -0.99). The final estimated value of ρ is 0.976. It is so large that we do not believe this model is appropriate.   □

Saved Results

heckman saves in the S_E_ macros:

S_E_cmd	heckman
S_E_nobs	number of observations
S_E_chi2	chi-squared value
S_E_ll	log-likelihood value
S_E_tdf	missing value
S_E_mdf	model degrees of freedom (counts rho as a parameter)
S_E_depv	dependent variable

In addition, heckman saves in the global S_# macros:

S_1	ρ	S_3	λ
S_2	σ	S_4	standard error of λ

Methods and Formulas

heckman is implemented as an ado-file. Greene (1993, 708–713) provides an introduction to the Heckman selection model.

heckman uses the ml maximizer with the lf linear-form method, a technique that uses numerical derivatives; see [R] ml. Mills' ratio estimates (Heckman 1979) are used as starting values.

The participation equation is

$$\mathbf{z}_j \boldsymbol{\gamma} + u_{1j} > 0$$

where $u_{1j} \sim N(0, 1)$. The regression equation is

$$y_j = \mathbf{x}_j \boldsymbol{\beta} + \sigma u_{2j}$$

where $u_{2j} \sim N(0, 1)$, but u_2 is potentially correlated with u_1 with correlation ρ.

The log-likelihood for observation j is

$$l_j = \begin{cases} \ln \Phi \left(\dfrac{\mathbf{z}_j \boldsymbol{\gamma} + (y_j - \mathbf{x}_j \boldsymbol{\beta})\rho/\sigma}{\sqrt{1 - \rho^2}} \right) - \dfrac{1}{2} \left(\dfrac{y_j - \mathbf{x}_j \boldsymbol{\beta}}{\sigma} \right)^2 & \text{if } y_j \text{ is observed} \\ \ln \Phi(-\mathbf{z}_j \boldsymbol{\gamma}) & \text{if } y_j \text{ is not observed} \end{cases}$$

where Φ is the standard cumulative normal.

In the maximum-likelihood estimation, σ and ρ are not directly estimated. Directly estimated are $\ln \sigma$ and atanh ρ:

$$\text{atanh } \rho = \frac{1}{2} \ln \left(\frac{1 + \rho}{1 - \rho} \right)$$

The standard error of $\lambda = \rho\sigma$ is approximated through propagation of error methods; that is,

$$\text{Var}(\lambda) \doteq \mathbf{D} \, \text{Var}\big([\text{atanh } \rho \quad \ln \sigma]\big) \, \mathbf{D}'$$

where $\mathbf{D}$ is the Jacobian of λ with respect to atanh ρ and $\ln \sigma$.

References

Greene, W. H. 1993. *Econometric Analysis*. 2d ed. New York: Macmillan.

Gronau, R. 1974. Wage comparisons: A selectivity bias. *Journal of Political Economy* 82: 1119–1155.

Heckman, J. 1976. The common structure of statistical models of truncation, sample selection, and limited dependent variables and a simple estimator for such models. *The Annals of Economic and Social Measurement* 5: 475–492.

——. 1979. Sample selection bias as a specification error. *Econometrica* 47: 153–161.

Lewis, H. 1974. Comments on selectivity biases in wage comparisons. *Journal of Political Economy* 82: 1119–1155.

Manning, W. G., N. Duan, and W. H. Rogers. 1987. Monte Carlo evidence on the choice between sample selection and two-part models. *Journal of Econometrics* 35: 59–82.

Also See

[U] **20.5 Accessing coefficients and standard errors**, [U] **26 Estimation and post-estimation commands**

[R] **cnreg**, [R] **eq**, [R] **lincom**, [R] **lrtest**, [R] **predict**, [R] **regress**, [R] **test**, [R] **testnl**, [R] **vce**

Title

help — Obtain on-line help

Syntax

Windows and Macintosh:	h̲elp [*command or topic name*]
	whelp [*command or topic name*]
DOS:	h̲elp [*command or topic name*]
Unix:	{h̲elp	man} [*command or topic name*]
All:	s̲et h̲elp *filename*

Description

The `help` command displays help information on the specified command or topic. If `help` is not followed by a command or a topic name, the topics for which help is available are listed. Stata for Unix users may type `help` or `man`—they mean the same thing.

Stata for Windows and Stata for Macintosh users may click on the **Help** button. They may also type `whelp` *something* to display the help topic for *something* in Stata's Help window.

`set help` specifies the name of the file containing the help information for Stata's built-in commands.

Remarks

See [U] **12 Stata's on-line help and lookup facilities** for a complete description of how to use `help`.

❏ Technical Note

When you type `help` *something*, Stata first looks along the S_ADO path for *something*.hlp; see [U] **23.5 Where does Stata look for ado-files?**. If nothing is found, it then looks in stata.hlp for the topic. Unless you have previously given the command `set help` *filename*, the file stata.hlp must be in your current directory, somewhere along your path, or in the directory \stata (Windows and DOS), /usr/local/stata (Unix), or ~:Stata (Macintosh). If it is not, you will see the following when you request help:

```
. help
file stata.hlp not found
r(601);
```

If you store the stata.hlp somewhere other than where Stata expects, use the `set help` command to tell Stata where the file is. It is difficult to imagine why you would want to do this.

❏

Also See

[U] **12 Stata's on-line help and lookup facilities**

[R] **ado**, [R] **lookup**

Title

hilite — Highlight a subset of points in a two-way scatterplot

Syntax

hilite *yvar xvar* [if *exp*] [in *range*], <u>h</u>ilite(*exp₂*) [*graph_options*]

Description

The hilite command draws a two-way scatterplot highlighting the observations selected by exp_2.

Options

hilite(exp_2) is not optional. It specifies an expression identifying the observations to be highlighted.

graph_options are any of the options allowed with **graph, twoway**; see [R] **graph twoway**.

Remarks

▷ Example

You have data on 956 U.S. cities, including average January temperature, average July temperature, and region. The region variable is coded 1, 2, 3, and 4, with 4 standing for the West. You wish to make a graph showing the relationship between January and July temperatures, highlighting the fourth region:

```
. hilite tempjan tempjuly, hilite(region==4) ylabel xlabel
```

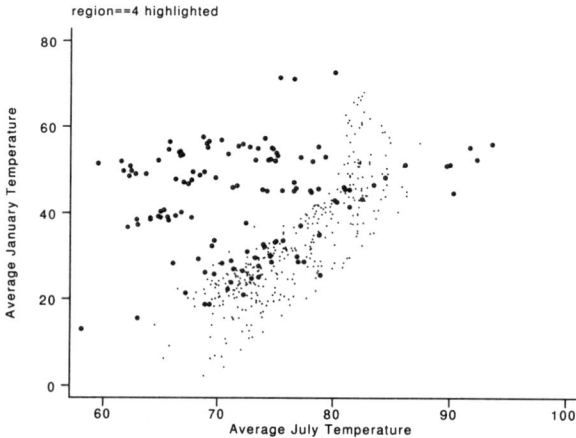

In [R] **graph symbol**, we showed you how to produce graphs like this yourself. Although it is not difficult, `hilite` is often more convenient.

◁

❏ Technical Note

By default, `hilite` uses '.' for the plotting symbol and additionally highlights using the o symbol. Its default is equivalent to specifying `symbol(.o)` as one of the *graph_options*. You can vary the symbols used, but you must specify exactly two symbols. The first is used to plot all the data and the second is used for overplotting the highlighted subset.

❏

Methods and Formulas

`hilite` is implemented as an ado-file.

Also See

[R] **graph twoway**

Title

> **hist** — Categorical variable histogram

Syntax

$$\texttt{hist } varname \; [weight] \; [\texttt{if } exp] \; [\texttt{in } range] \; [, \; \underline{\texttt{incr}}(\#) \; graph\_options]$$

`fweights` are allowed; see [U] **18.1.6 weight**.

Description

hist graphs a histogram of *varname*, the result being quite similar to **graph** *varname*, **histogram**. **hist**, however, is intended for use with integer-coded categorical variables.

hist determines the number of bins automatically, the x-axis is automatically labeled, and the labels are centered below the corresponding bar.

hist may only be used with categorical variables with a range of less than 50; i.e., maximum(*varname*) − minimum(*varname*) < 50.

Options

incr(#) specifies how the x-axis is to be labeled. **incr**(1), the default if *varname* reflects 25 or fewer categories, labels the minimum, minimum + 1, minimum + 2, ..., maximum. **incr**(2), the default if there are more than 25 categories, would label the minimum, minimum + 2, ..., etc.

graph_options refers to any of the options allowed with **graph**'s **histogram** style excluding **bin()**, **xlabel()**, and **xscale()**. These do include, for instance, **freq**, **ylabel()**, **by()**, **total**, and **saving()**.

Remarks

▷ Example

You have a categorical variable **rep78** reflecting the repair records of automobiles. It is coded 1 = Poor, 2 = Fair, 3 = Average, 4 = Good, and 5 = Excellent. You could type

(Continued on next page.)

200

. graph rep78, histogram bin(5)

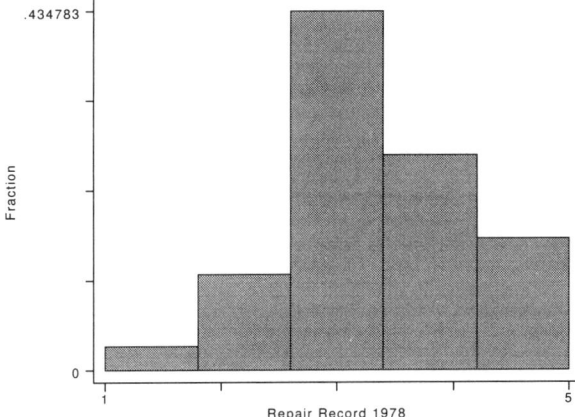

to obtain a histogram. You should specify bin(5) because your categorical variable takes on 5 values and you want one bar per value. (You could omit the option in this case, but only because the default value of bin() is 5; if you had 4 or 6 bars, you would have to specify it; see [R] **graph histogram**.) In any case, the resulting graph, while technically correct, is aesthetically displeasing because the numeric code 1 is on the left edge of the first bar while the numeric code 5 is on the right edge of the last bar.

Using hist is better:

. hist rep78

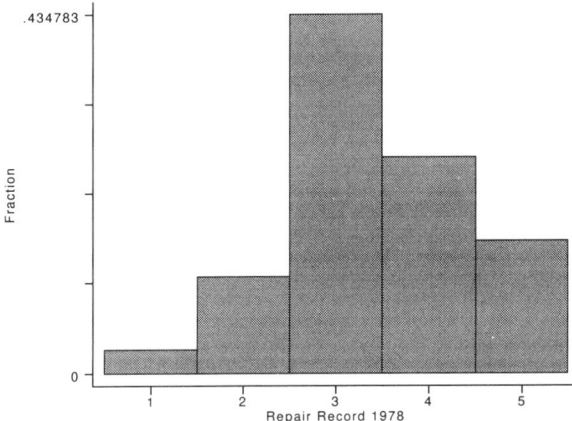

hist not only centers the numeric codes underneath the corresponding bar, it also automatically labels all the bars.

You are cautioned: hist is not a general replacement for **graph, histogram**. hist is intended for use with categorical data only, which is to say, noncontinuous data. If you wanted a histogram of automobile prices, for instance, you would still want to use the more general **graph, histogram** command.   ◁

▷ Example

You may use any of the options you would with **graph**, `histogram`. Using data collected by Voter Research and Surveys based on questionnaires completed by 15,490 voters from 300 polling places on election day—data originally printed in the *New York Times*, November 5, 1992 and reprinted in Lipset (1993)—you draw the following graph:

```
. hist candi [freq=pop], by(inc) total ylab yline noaxis
                title(Exit Polling By Family Income)
```

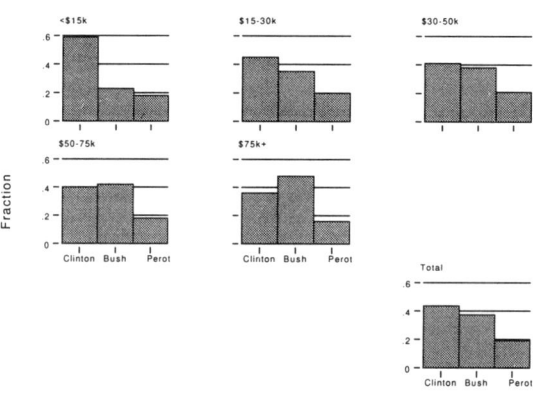

Exit Polling by Family Income

◁

❑ Technical Note

In both of these examples, each bar is labeled; if your categorical variable takes on many values, you may not want to label them all. Typing

```
. hist myvar, incr(2)
```

would label every other bar. Specifying `incr(3)` would label every third bar, and so on.

❑

Methods and Formulas

`hist` is implemented as an ado-file.

References

Lipset, S. M. 1993. The significance of the 1992 election. *Political Science and Politics* 26(1): 7–16.

Also See

[R] **graph histogram**

Title

> **hlu** — Hildreth–Lu regression

Syntax

> hlu *depvar* [*varlist*] [if *exp*] [in *range*] [, t(*varname_t*) force level(#) nolog nodw
>
> tol(#) iterate(#)]

hlu shares the features of all estimation commands; see [U] **26 Estimation and post-estimation commands**, but note that to use predict, you must first type gen _inter=1.

To reset problem-size limits, see [R] **matsize**.

Description

hlu estimates a linear regression of *depvar* on *varlist* that is corrected for serially correlated residuals using the Hildreth–Lu (1960) estimator. This estimator has been shown to work better than the Cochrane–Orcutt (1949) estimator for small samples.

Options

t(*varname_t*) specifies the variable name that contains the time at which the observation was recorded. This must be specified once as the variable named here is used to determine the order of the observations in the estimation. Once specified, however, it need not be specified again except to change the variable's identity. Note that the data must be equally spaced in time unless you specify the force option.

force specifies that estimation is to be forced even though t() is not equally spaced. If you specify a t() variable that indicates observations are not equally spaced, hlu will refuse to estimate the model. But if you also specify force, hlu will estimate the model and assume that the lags based on the data ordered by t() are appropriate.

level(#) specifies the confidence level, in percent, for confidence intervals. The default is level(95) or as set by set level; see [U] **26.4 Specifying the width of confidence intervals**.

nolog prevents the iteration log from printing.

nodw prevents the Durbin–Watson statistic from being included in the output.

tol(#) specifies the minimum change in the estimated autocorrelation parameter between iterations before convergence can be declared and defaults to 0.001.

iterate(#) specifies the maximum number of iterations and defaults to 100, a number close enough to infinity to be nonbinding. You should never have to specify this option.

Remarks

The two principal remedial measures for dealing with serially correlated data in regression are to add one or more independent variables to the model or to use transformed variables. Stata already includes the means for transforming the variables using the Cochrane–Orcutt or Prais–Winsten procedures; see [R] **corc** and [R] **prais** for details.

The Hildreth—Lu procedure (Neter, et al., 1989, 500) is closely related to both the Cochrane—Orcutt procedure and the Prais—Winsten procedure. All must estimate the autocorrelation parameter ρ. Cochrane—Orcutt estimates this by assuming a functional form for the error term in the proposed model. Hildreth—Lu uses an iterative technique that guarantees that the error sum of squares for the transformed model

$$\text{SSE} = \sum_t \left(Y_t' - \widehat{Y}_t' \right)^2$$

is minimized.

The motivation for using the Hildreth—Lu procedure rather than the Cochrane—Orcutt procedure is that Cochrane—Orcutt tends to underestimate the parameter ρ. When this bias is serious, it can significantly reduce the effectiveness of the Cochrane—Orcutt procedure. The Hildreth—Lu procedure does not require any iterations once the autocorrelation parameter is estimated.

▷ Example

We have data on quarterly sales, in millions of dollars, for five years, and we would like to use this information to model sales for company X.

```
. regress csales isales

Source |       SS       df       MS              Number of obs =      20
-------+------------------------------            F( 1,   18) =14888.15
 Model | 110.256901     1  110.256901            Prob > F      = 0.0000
Residual| .133302302   18  .007405683            R-squared     = 0.9988
-------+------------------------------            Adj R-squared = 0.9987
 Total | 110.390204    19  5.81001072            Root MSE      = .08606

------------------------------------------------------------------------
 csales |    Coef.   Std. Err.      t     P>|t|    [95% Conf. Interval]
--------+---------------------------------------------------------------
 isales |  .1762828   .0014447   122.017   0.000    .1732475    .1793181
  _cons | -1.454753   .2141461    -6.793   0.000   -1.904657   -1.004849
------------------------------------------------------------------------
```

Noting that we have serial correlation in the errors, we first attempt to correct for this using the Cochrane—Orcutt procedure.

```
. corc csales isales, t(t) nolog

(Cochrane-Orcutt regression)

Source |       SS       df       MS              Number of obs =      19
-------+------------------------------            F( 1,   17) =  596.10
 Model | 2.51740536     1  2.51740536            Prob > F      = 0.0000
Residual| .071793235   17  .004223131            R-squared     = 0.9723
-------+------------------------------            Adj R-squared = 0.9706
 Total | 2.5891986     18  .143844367            Root MSE      = .06499

------------------------------------------------------------------------
 csales |    Coef.   Std. Err.      t     P>|t|    [95% Conf. Interval]
--------+---------------------------------------------------------------
 isales |  .1615211   .0066156    24.415   0.000    .1475634    .1754788
 _inter |  1.307525   1.267446     1.032   0.317   -1.366553    3.981602
--------+---------------------------------------------------------------
    rho |  0.9441     0.0229      41.316   0.000    0.8961      0.9921
------------------------------------------------------------------------

Durbin-Watson statistic (original)      0.734728
Durbin-Watson statistic (transformed)   1.712389
```

Since the Cochrane—Orcutt procedure tends to underestimate the correlation and we know that the correlation is very high in this problem, we will also look at the Hildreth—Lu approach:

```
. hlu csales isales, t(t) nolog

(Hildreth-Lu regression)
      Source |       SS       df       MS              Number of obs =      19
-------------+------------------------------           F(  1,    17) =  482.30
       Model |  2.0652403        1  2.0652403          Prob > F      =  0.0000
    Residual |  .072794656      17  .004282039         R-squared     =  0.9660
-------------+------------------------------           Adj R-squared =  0.9639
       Total |  2.13803495      18  .11877972          Root MSE      =  .06544

------------------------------------------------------------------------------
      csales |      Coef.   Std. Err.       t    P>|t|     [95% Conf. Interval]
-------------+----------------------------------------------------------------
      isales |   .1588276   .0072321    21.961   0.000     .1435692    .1740861
      _inter |   20.79255   11.82342     1.759   0.097    -4.152699    45.73779
-------------+----------------------------------------------------------------
         rho |     0.9989     0.0007  1348.318   0.000       0.9974      1.0005
------------------------------------------------------------------------------

Durbin-Watson statistic (original)     0.734728
Durbin-Watson statistic (transformed)  1.748792
```

◁

A comparison of the Hildreth—Lu, Cochrane—Orcutt, and Prais—Winsten methods for dealing with regression with autocorrelated error terms essentially provide the same estimate of σ^2 (the variance of the disturbance terms). The estimated standard error of the β parameters from ordinary least squares regression may be seriously underestimated when positive autocorrelation is present.

Saved Results

hlu saves in the S_E_ macros:

S_E_cmd	hlu
S_E_nobs	number of observations
S_E_rho	autocorrelation parameter ρ
S_E_srho	standard error of ρ
S_E_tdf	residual degrees of freedom
S_E_depv	dependent variable name
S_E_vl	variable list
S_E_if	if expression
S_E_in	in expression
S_E_dw	Durbin—Watson statistic for transformed model
S_E_dwo	Durbin—Watson statistic for original model

Methods and Formulas

hlu is implemented as an ado-file.

The procedure for calculating the correlation parameter for use in the regression transformations is similar to the search for the parameter λ in the power transformation of Box—Cox. The value chosen for ρ is the one which minimizes the error sum of squares for the transformed regression model. The transformation of the regression model is given by

$$Y'_t = Y_t - \rho Y_{t-1}$$
$$X'_t = X_t - \rho X_{t-1}$$

The algorithm for finding the parameter ρ is a simple bisection search that continues until the estimate does not differ until the fifth decimal place (meaning there is a maximum of 15 iterations).

References

Hildreth, C. and J. Y. Lu. 1960. Demand relations with autocorrelated disturbances. *Agricultural Experiment Station Technical Bulletin* 276. East Lansing, MI: Michigan State University.

Maddala, G. S. 1992. *Introduction to Econometrics.* 2d ed. New York: Macmillan.

Neter, J., W. Wasserman, and M. H. Kutner. 1989. *Applied Regression Models.* Homewood, IL: Irwin.

Also See

[U] **20.5 Accessing coefficients and standard errors**, [U] **26 Estimation and post-estimation commands**

[R] **corc**, [R] **lincom**, [R] **linktest**, [R] **prais**, [R] **predict**, [R] **test**, [R] **testnl**, [R] **vce**, [R] **xi**

Title

hotel — Hotelling's T-squared generalized means test

Syntax

hotel *varlist* [*weight*] [**if** *exp*] [**in** *range*] [**, by**(*varname*) <u>nota</u>ble]

aweights and **fweights** are allowed; see [U] **18.1.6 weight**.

To reset problem-size limits, see [R] **matsize**.

Description

hotel performs Hotelling's T-squared test for testing whether a set of means is zero or, alternatively, equal between two groups.

Options

by(*varname*) specifies a variable identifying two groups; the test of equality of means between groups is performed. If **by()** is not specified, a test of means being jointly zero is performed.

notable suppresses printing a table of the means being compared.

Remarks

hotel performs Hotelling's T-squared test of whether a set of means is zero, or two sets of means are equal. It is a multivariate test that reduces to a standard t test if only one variable is specified.

▷ Example

You wish to test whether a new fuel additive improves gas mileage in both stop-and-go and highway situations. Taking twelve cars, you fill them with gas and run them on a highway-style track, recording their gas mileage. You then refill them and run them on a stop-and-go style track. Finally, you repeat the two runs but this time use fuel with the additive. Your data is

```
. describe
Contains data from gasexp.dta
  obs:            12
  vars:            5                          24 May 1996 10:13
  size:          288 (99.9% of memory free)
-----------------------------------------------------------------------------
  1. id          float  %9.0g                 car id
  2. bmpg1       float  %9.0g                 track 1 before additive
  3. ampg1       float  %9.0g                 track 1 after additive
  4. bmpg2       float  %9.0g                 track 2 before additive
  5. ampg2       float  %9.0g                 track 2 after additive
-----------------------------------------------------------------------------
Sorted by:
```

To perform the statistical test, you jointly test whether the differences in before-and-after results are zero:

```
. gen diff1 = ampg1 - bmpg1
. gen diff2 = ampg2 - bmpg2
. hotel diff1 diff2
Variable |     Obs       Mean    Std. Dev.        Min        Max
---------+-----------------------------------------------------
   diff1 |      12       1.75    2.70101           -3          5
   diff2 |      12   2.083333   2.906367         -3.5        5.5
1-group Hotelling´s T-squared = 9.6980676
F test statistic: ((12-2)/(12-1)(2)) x 9.6980676 = 4.4082126

HO: Vector of means is equal to a vector of zeros
             F(2,10) =      4.4082
        Pr > F(2,10) =      0.0424
```

The means are different at the 4.24% significance level.

◁

❏ Technical Note

We used Hotelling's T-squared test because we were testing two differences jointly. Had there been only one difference, we could have used a standard t test; it would have yielded the same results as Hotelling's test:

```
* We could have performed the test like this:
. ttest ampg1 = bmpg1
Paired t-test                                  Number of obs =        12
------------------------------------------------------------------------
Variable |    Mean    Std. Err.       t     P>|t|    [95% Conf. Interval]
---------+--------------------------------------------------------------
   ampg1 |   22.75    .9384465   24.2422   0.0000    20.68449    24.81551
   bmpg1 |      21    .7881701   26.644    0.0000    19.26525    22.73475
---------+--------------------------------------------------------------
    diff |    1.75    .7797144   2.24441   0.0463    .0338602     3.46614
------------------------------------------------------------------------
Degrees of freedom: 11
                        Ho: mean diff = 0
      Ha: diff < 0           Ha: diff ~= 0           Ha: diff > 0
        t =  2.244             t =  2.244             t =  2.244
    P < t = 0.9768         P > |t| = 0.0463       P > t = 0.0232
* Or like this:
. ttest diff1 = 0
One-sample t-test                              Number of obs =        12
------------------------------------------------------------------------
Variable |    Mean    Std. Err.       t     P>|t|    [95% Conf. Interval]
---------+--------------------------------------------------------------
   diff1 |    1.75    .7797144   2.24441   0.0463    .0338602     3.46614
------------------------------------------------------------------------
Degrees of freedom: 11
                       Ho: mean(diff1) = 0
     Ha: mean < 0          Ha: mean ~= 0           Ha: mean > 0
        t =  2.244             t =  2.244             t =  2.244
    P < t = 0.9768         P > |t| = 0.0463       P > t = 0.0232
```

```
* Or like this:
. hotel diff1

Variable |     Obs        Mean    Std. Dev.        Min         Max
---------+-----------------------------------------------------------
   diff1 |      12        1.75      2.70101         -3           5

1-group Hotelling's T-squared = 5.0373832
F test statistic: ((12-1)/(12-1)(1)) x 5.0373832 = 5.0373832

H0: Vector of means is equal to a vector of zeros
              F(1,11) =      5.0374
         Pr > F(1,11) =      0.0463
```

▷ Example

Now consider a variation on the experiment: rather than using 12 cars and running each car with and without the fuel additive, you run 24 cars, 12 with the additive and 12 without. You have the following data:

```
. describe
Contains data from gasexp2.dta
  obs:           24
  vars:           4                       24 May 1996 10:14
  size:         480 (98.9% of memory free)
-------------------------------------------------------------------------
   1. id          float   %9.0g                    car id
   2. mpg1        float   %9.0g                    track 1
   3. mpg2        float   %9.0g                    track 2
   4. additive    float   %9.0g        yesno       additive?
-------------------------------------------------------------------------
Sorted by:

. tab additive

 additive? |      Freq.      Percent        Cum.
-----------+-----------------------------------
       no  |        12        50.00        50.00
      yes  |        12        50.00       100.00
-----------+-----------------------------------
     Total |        24       100.00
```

This is an unpaired experiment because there is no natural pairing of the cars; we want to test that the means of mpg1 are equal for the two groups specified by additive as are the means of mpg2:

```
. hotel mpg1 mpg2, by(additive)
-> additive=         no
Variable |     Obs        Mean    Std. Dev.        Min         Max
---------+-----------------------------------------------------------
    mpg1 |      12          21     2.730301         17          25
    mpg2 |      12    19.91667     2.644319         16          24

-> additive=        yes
Variable |     Obs        Mean    Std. Dev.        Min         Max
---------+-----------------------------------------------------------
    mpg1 |      12       22.75     3.250874         17          28
    mpg2 |      12          22     3.316625       16.5        27.5

2-group Hotelling's T-squared = 7.1347584
F test statistic: ((24-2-1)/(24-2)(2)) x 7.1347584 = 3.4052256

H0: Vectors of means are equal for the two groups
              F(2,21) =      3.4052
         Pr > F(2,21) =      0.0524
```

◁

❏ Technical Note

As in the paired experiment, had there been only one test track, the t test would have yielded the same results as Hotelling's test:

```
. hotel mpg1, by(additive)

-> additive=      no
Variable |     Obs        Mean    Std. Dev.        Min         Max
---------+-----------------------------------------------------------
   mpg1 |      12          21     2.730301          17          25

-> additive=     yes
Variable |     Obs        Mean    Std. Dev.        Min         Max
---------+-----------------------------------------------------------
   mpg1 |      12       22.75     3.250874          17          28

2-group Hotelling's T-squared = 2.0390921
F test statistic: ((24-1-1)/(24-2)(1)) x 2.0390921 = 2.0390921

H0: Vectors of means are equal for the two groups
         F(1,22) =      2.0391
     Pr > F(1,22) =     0.1673

. ttest mpg1, by(additive)
Two-sample t-test with equal variances              no: Number of obs =        12
                                                   yes: Number of obs =        12

------------------------------------------------------------------------------
Variable |     Mean    Std. Err.        t     P>|t|      [95% Conf. Interval]
---------+--------------------------------------------------------------------
     no |       21    .7881701    26.644    0.0000      19.26525    22.73475
    yes |    22.75    .9384465    24.2422   0.0000      20.68449    24.81551
---------+--------------------------------------------------------------------
   diff |    -1.75    1.225518   -1.42797   0.1673      -4.291568   .7915684
------------------------------------------------------------------------------
Degrees of freedom: 22
                    Ho: mean(no) - mean(yes) = diff = 0

Ha: diff < 0                Ha: diff ~= 0                Ha: diff > 0
   t = -1.428                 t = -1.428                   t = -1.428
  P < t = 0.0837           P > |t| = 0.1673             P > t = 0.9163
```

With more than one pair of means, however, there is no t test equivalent to Hotelling's test although there are other logically (but not practically) equivalent solutions. One is the discriminant function: if the means of mpg1 and mpg2 are different, the discriminant function should separate the groups along that dimension.

```
. regress additive mpg1 mpg2
   Source |      SS        df        MS                Number of obs =        24
---------+------------------------------              F( 2,    21) =      3.41
   Model | 1.46932917      2    .734664585            Prob > F      =    0.0524
Residual | 4.53067083     21    .21574623             R-squared     =    0.2449
---------+------------------------------              Adj R-squared =    0.1730
   Total |     6.00       23    .260869565            Root MSE      =    .46448

------------------------------------------------------------------------------
additive |    Coef.    Std. Err.        t     P>|t|      [95% Conf. Interval]
---------+--------------------------------------------------------------------
   mpg1 | -.4570407    .2416657    -1.891    0.072      -.959612     .0455306
   mpg2 |  .5014605    .2376762     2.110    0.047       .0071859    .9957352
  _cons | -.0120115    .7437049    -0.016    0.987      -1.55863     1.534607
------------------------------------------------------------------------------
```

This test would declare the means different at the 5.24% level. Alternatively, we could have estimated this model using logistic regression:

```
. logit additive mpg1 mpg2

Iteration 0:  Log Likelihood =-16.635532
Iteration 1:  Log Likelihood =-13.471421
Iteration 2:  Log Likelihood =-13.371971
Iteration 3:  Log Likelihood =-13.371143
Iteration 4:  Log Likelihood =-13.371143

Logit Estimates                              Number of obs =      24
                                             chi2(2)       =    6.53
                                             Prob > chi2   =  0.0382
Log Likelihood = -13.371143                  Pseudo R2     =  0.1962

------------------------------------------------------------------------------
additive |    Coef.   Std. Err.       z     P>|z|    [95% Conf. Interval]
---------+--------------------------------------------------------------------
    mpg1 | -2.306844   1.36139    -1.694    0.090    -4.975119    .3614307
    mpg2 |  2.524477   1.367373    1.846    0.065    -.1555257    5.20448
   _cons | -2.446527   3.689821   -0.663    0.507    -9.678443    4.78539
------------------------------------------------------------------------------
```

This test would have declared the means different at the 3.82% level.

Are the means different? The three methods yield different answers. Hotelling's T-squared rejects equality at the 5.15% level; the discriminant function, at the 5.24% level; and the logistic regression, at the 3.82% level. It is not uncommon for the Hotelling test results to be more similar to the discriminant-function results than to the logistic-regression results.   ❏

Saved Results

hotel saves in the S_# macros:

S_1	number of observations	S_3	degrees of freedom
S_2	number of variables	S_4	Hotelling's T-squared

Methods and Formulas

hotel is implemented as an ado-file.

See Wilks (1962, 556–561) for a general discussion. The original formulation was by Hotelling (1931) and Mahalanobis (1930, 1936).

For the test of the means of k variables being 0, let $\overline{\mathbf{x}}$ be a $1 \times k$ matrix of the means and $\mathbf{S}$ be the estimated covariance matrix. Then $T^2 = \overline{\mathbf{x}}\mathbf{S}^{-1}\overline{\mathbf{x}}'$.

In the case of two groups, the test of equality is $T^2 = (\overline{\mathbf{x}}_1 - \overline{\mathbf{x}}_2)\mathbf{S}^{-1}(\overline{\mathbf{x}}_1 - \overline{\mathbf{x}}_2)'$.

References

Hotelling, H. 1931. The generalization of Student's ratio. *Annals of Mathematical Statistics* 2: 360–378.

Mahalanobis, P. C. 1930. On tests and measures of group divergence. *Journal Asiatic Soc. of Bengal* 26: 541–588.

——. 1936. On the generalized distance in statistics. *Proc. Nat. Inst. Sci. Calcutta* 12: 49–55.

Wilks, S. S. 1962. *Mathematical Statistics.* New York: John Wiley & Sons.

Also See

[R] **regress**, [R] **ttest**

Title

┌───┐
│ **if** — if programming command   │
└───┘

Syntax

```
if exp {
        stata_commands
}
else    stata_commands
```

Description

The `if` command (not to be confused with the `if` qualifier) evaluates *exp*. If the result is *true* (nonzero), the commands inside the braces are executed. If the result is *false* (zero), those statements are ignored.

Remarks

The `if` command is intended for use inside programs and do-files. See [U] **24.3.4 Macros and expressions** for examples of its use.

▷ Example

Do not confuse the `if` command with the `if` qualifier. Typing `if age>21 {summarize age}` will summarize *all* the observations on `age` if the first observation on `age` is greater than 21. Otherwise, it will do nothing. Typing `summarize age if age>21`, on the other hand, summarizes all the observations on `age` that are greater than 21.

◁

▷ Example

`if` is typically used in do-files and programs. For instance, let's write a program to calculate the Tukey (1977, 90–91) "power" function of a variable x:

```
. program define power
        if `2´>0 {
                generate z=`1´^`2´
                label variable z "`1´^`2´"
        }
        else if `2´==0 {
                generate z=log(`1´)
                label variable z "log(`1´)"
        }
        else {
                generate z=-(`1´^(`2´))
                label variable z "-`1´^(`2´)"
        }
        end
```

This program takes two arguments. The first argument is the name of an existing variable, x. The second argument is a number, which we will call n. The program creates a new variable z. If $n > 0$, z is x^n; if $n = 0$, z is $\log x$; if $n < 0$, z is $-x^n$. No matter which path the program follows through the code, it labels the variable appropriately:

```
. power age 2
. describe z
   7. z              float   %9.0g              age^2
```

◁

❏ Technical Note

If the expression refers to any variables, their values in the first observation are used unless explicit subscripts are specified.

❏

References

Tukey, J. W. 1977. *Exploratory Data Analysis*. Reading, MA: Addison-Wesley Publishing Company.

Also See

[U] **24 Programming Stata**

Title

> **impute** — Predict missing values

Syntax

> impute *depvar* *varlist* [*weight*] [if *exp*] [in *range*] , generate(*newvar₁*)
>
> [varp(*newvar₂*)]

aweights and fweights are allowed; see [U] **18.1.6 weight**.

Description

impute fills in missing values; *depvar* is the variable whose missing values are to be imputed. *varlist* is the list of variables on which the imputations are to be based and *newvar₁* is the new variable to contain the imputations.

impute organizes the cases by patterns of missing data so the missing-value regressions can be conducted efficiently; this necessitates a limit of 31 variables in *varlist*.

Options

generate(*newvar₁*) specifies the name of the new variable to be created and is not optional.

varp(*newvar₂*) specifies the name of a new variable to contain the variance (*not* the standard error) of the prediction.

Remarks

In observations where *depvar* is not equal to missing, *newvar₁* is set equal to *depvar* and *newvar₂* (if specified) is set to zero. Where *depvar* is missing, *newvar₁* is imputed using the prediction from the best available subset of otherwise present data. *newvar₂* (if specified) is set to the variance of the prediction. This variance is in the sense of predict's stdp option, although squared; see [R] **predict**. It is an estimate of how far the prediction of the mean would differ from the actual data point were it known.

This is not the only method for coping with missing data, but it is often much better than deleting cases with any missing data, which is the default. For a discussion of different methods of imputation, see, for example, Little and Rubin (1987).

▷ Example

impute may be used in conjunction with, for instance, regression (or any estimation technique) to avoid the loss of an unacceptable number of cases due to missing data. Bear in mind, however, that the subsequent estimates may be biased because any variable imputed by impute is only an estimate of the unknown, true value. In the case of linear regression, a reasonable bound (in fractional terms) for the bias is given by the ratio of the mean of *newvar₂* to the variance of *newvar₁*. Usually, the bias is toward zero, meaning that the effect of the variable will be underestimated.

You have been hired by the restaurant industry to study expenditures on eating and drinking. You have data on 898 U.S. cities:

```
. describe

Contains data from edm.dta
   obs:            898                         1980 City Data
  vars:              9                         24 May 1996 11:42
  size:         34,124 (96.7% of memory free)
----------------------------------------------------------------------------
   1. fips        long    %12.0g              state/place code
   2. ln_eat      float   %9.0g               ln(Dining sales per capita)
   3. mincpc      int     %8.0g               Per capita money income
   4. ln_rtl      float   %9.0g               ln(retail sales per capita)
   5. jantemp     float   %9.0g               Median Jan. temp. (F)
   6. precip      float   %9.0g               Annual precipitation (in.)
   7. ln_inc      float   %9.0g               ln(median per capita income)
   8. medage      float   %9.0g               Median age
   9. hhsize      float   %9.0g               Persons per household
----------------------------------------------------------------------------
Sorted by:
Note:  data has changed since last save
```

You begin by running the regression:

```
. regress ln_eat ln_rtl jantemp precip ln_inc medage hhsize

   Source |      SS        df        MS              Number of obs =     664
----------+-----------------------------           F(  6,   657) =  212.55
    Model | 87.7285014       6  14.6214169          Prob > F      =  0.0000
 Residual | 45.1948678     657  .068789753          R-squared     =  0.6600
----------+-----------------------------           Adj R-squared =  0.6569
    Total | 132.923369     663  .200487736          Root MSE      =  .26228

----------------------------------------------------------------------------
   ln_eat |     Coef.   Std. Err.       t      P>|t|    [95% Conf. Interval]
----------+-----------------------------------------------------------------
   ln_rtl |  .6611241    .026623     24.833   0.000    .6088476    .7134006
  jantemp |  .0019624   .0007601      2.582   0.010    .0004698     .003455
   precip | -.0014311   .0008433     -1.697   0.090   -.0030869    .0002247
   ln_inc |  .1158486    .056352      2.056   0.040    .0051969    .2265003
   medage | -.0010863   .0002823     -3.847   0.000   -.0016407   -.0005319
   hhsize | -.0050407   .0004243    -11.880   0.000   -.0058739   -.0042076
    _cons | -1.377592   .4777641     -2.883   0.004    -2.31572    -.439463
----------------------------------------------------------------------------
```

Despite having data on 898 cities, your regression was estimated on only 664 cities—74% of the original 898. Some 234 observations were unused due to missing data. In this case, when you type `summarize`, you discover that each of the independent variables has missing values, so the problem is not that one variable is missing in 26% of the observations, but that each of the variables is missing in some observations. In fact, `summarize` revealed that each of the variables is missing in roughly 5% of the observations. We lost 26% of our data because, in aggregate, 26% of the observations have one or more missing variables.

Thus, we impute each independent variable on the basis of the other independent variables:

```
. impute ln_rtl  jantemp precip ln_inc medage hhsize, gen(i_ln_rtl)
  4.90% (44) observations imputed
. impute jantemp  ln_rtl precip ln_inc medage hhsize, gen(i_jantmp)
  5.90% (53) observations imputed
. impute precip  ln_rtl jantemp ln_inc medage hhsize, gen(i_precip)
  4.56% (41) observations imputed
. impute ln_inc  ln_rtl jantemp precip medage hhsize, gen(i_ln_inc)
  4.34% (39) observations imputed
. impute medage  ln_rtl jantemp precip ln_inc hhsize, gen(i_medage)
  4.45% (40) observations imputed
```

```
. impute hhsize  ln_rtl jantemp precip ln_inc medage, gen(i_hhsize)
  5.23% (47) observations imputed
```

That done, we can now reestimate the regression on the imputed variables:

```
. regress ln_eat i_ln_rtl i_jantmp i_precip i_ln_inc i_medage i_hhsize

    Source |       SS       df       MS                  Number of obs =     898
-----------+------------------------------               F(  6,    891) =  253.41
     Model | 108.85923        6  18.1432051              Prob > F      =  0.0000
  Residual | 63.7929145      891  .071596986             R-squared     =  0.6305
-----------+------------------------------               Adj R-squared =  0.6280
     Total | 172.652145      897  .192477308             Root MSE      =  .26758

------------------------------------------------------------------------------
    ln_eat |    Coef.   Std. Err.      t     P>|t|    [95% Conf. Interval]
-----------+------------------------------------------------------------------
  i_ln_rtl |   .660906   .0245827     26.885  0.000    .6126593    .7091528
  i_jantmp |   .0021019  .0006932      3.032  0.002    .0007414    .0034625
  i_precip |  -.0013268  .0007646     -1.735  0.083   -.0028275    .0001739
  i_ln_inc |   .095863   .0510231      1.879  0.060   -.0042764    .1960024
  i_medage |  -.0011234  .0002584     -4.348  0.000   -.0016304   -.0006163
  i_hhsize |  -.0052508  .0003953    -13.283  0.000   -.0060267    -.004475
     _cons |  -1.143142  .4304284     -2.656  0.008   -1.987914   -.2983702
------------------------------------------------------------------------------
```

Note that the regression is now estimated on all 898 observations.

◁

▷ Example

impute can also be used with **factor** to extend factor score estimates to cases with missing data. For instance, we have a variant of the automobile data (see [U] **13 Stata's on-line tutorials and sample datasets**) that contains a few additional variables. We will begin by factoring all but the price variable (see [R] **factor**):

```
. factor mpg-foreign, factors(4)
  (obs=66)
```

(principal factors; 4 factors retained)

Factor	Eigenvalue	Difference	Proportion	Cumulative
1	6.99066	5.59538	0.7596	0.7596
2	1.39528	0.80576	0.1516	0.9112
3	0.58952	0.29082	0.0640	0.9753
4	0.29870	0.05618	0.0324	1.0077
5	0.24252	0.11654	0.0264	1.0341
6	0.12598	0.08970	0.0137	1.0478
7	0.03628	0.05085	0.0039	1.0517
8	-0.01457	0.01275	-0.0016	1.0501
9	-0.02732	0.02860	-0.0030	1.0472
10	-0.05591	0.05736	-0.0061	1.0411
11	-0.11327	0.00564	-0.0123	1.0288
12	-0.11891	0.02714	-0.0129	1.0159
13	-0.14605	.	-0.0159	1.0000

Factor Loadings

Variable	1	2	3	4	Uniqueness
mpg	-0.78200	-0.02985	-0.06546	0.33951	0.26803
rep78	-0.51076	0.68322	-0.11181	-0.01428	0.25963
rep77	-0.27332	0.70653	-0.32005	0.04710	0.32145
hdroom	0.56480	0.26549	0.29651	0.16485	0.49542

```
  rseat |   0.66134    0.20472    0.36471    0.02062    0.38727
  trunk |   0.72934    0.37094    0.28176    0.12140    0.23633
 weight |   0.95127    0.10135   -0.18056   -0.09179    0.04378
 length |   0.94621    0.19595   -0.05372   -0.10325    0.05274
   turn |   0.88264   -0.05607   -0.08502    0.01169    0.21043
  displ |   0.92199    0.06333   -0.17349   -0.02554    0.11518
 gratio |  -0.82782    0.06672    0.24558   -0.10994    0.23787
  order |  -0.25907    0.15344    0.01622    0.14668    0.88756
foreign |  -0.75728    0.30756    0.19130   -0.29188    0.21014
```

There appear to be two factors here. Let's pretend that we have given the first two factors an interpretation—we might interpret the first factor as size. We now obtain the factor scores:

```
. score f1 f2
            (based on unrotated factors)
            (2 scorings not used)

            Scoring Coefficients
 Variable |      1          2
----------+----------------------
     mpg |  -0.02094    0.11106
   rep78 |  -0.03224    0.44562
   rep77 |  -0.11150    0.27942
  hdroom |   0.05530    0.10017
   rseat |   0.03355    0.02812
   trunk |   0.04603    0.20622
  weight |   0.12250   -0.13040
  length |   0.39996    0.60223
    turn |   0.04562   -0.12825
   displ |   0.19281    0.11611
  gratio |  -0.08534    0.03528
   order |   0.00638    0.06433
 foreign |  -0.06469    0.28292
```

Although it is not revealed by this output, in 8 cases the scores could not be calculated because of missing values (we would see that if we typed summarize). To impute the factor scores to all the observations:

```
. impute f1  mpg-foreign, gen(i_f1)
10.81% (8) observations imputed
. impute f2  mpg-foreign, gen(i_f2)
10.81% (8) observations imputed
```

And we might now run a regression of price in terms of the two factors:

```
. regress price i_f1 i_f2
    Source |      SS       df       MS                  Number of obs =      74
-----------+------------------------------             F(  2,    71) =   11.88
     Model |  159223103     2   79611551.5             Prob > F      =  0.0000
  Residual |  475842293    71   6702004.13             R-squared     =  0.2507
-----------+------------------------------             Adj R-squared =  0.2296
     Total |  635065396    73   8699525.97             Root MSE      =  2588.8

-------------------------------------------------------------------------------
     price |     Coef.   Std. Err.       t     P>|t|    [95% Conf. Interval]
-----------+-------------------------------------------------------------------
      i_f1 |  1225.347   315.7177      3.881   0.000    595.8234   1854.87
      i_f2 |  911.2878   339.9821      2.680   0.009    233.3827   1589.193
     _cons |  6262.285   301.7093     20.756   0.000    5660.694   6863.877
-------------------------------------------------------------------------------
```

◁

Methods and Formulas

impute is implemented as an ado-file.

Consider the command impute y x_1 x_2 ...x_k, gen($\widehat{y}$) varp($\widehat{v}$).

When y is not missing, $\widehat{y} = y$ and $\widehat{v} = 0$.

Let y_j be an observation for which y is missing. A regressor list is formed from x_1, x_2, ..., x_k containing all x's for which x_{ij} is not missing. If the resulting list is empty, $\widehat{y}_j$ and $\widehat{v}_j$ are set to missing. Otherwise a regression of y on the list is estimated (see [R] **regress**) and $\widehat{y}_j$ is defined as the predicted value of y_j (see [R] **predict**). $\widehat{v}_j$ is defined as the square of the standard error of the prediction, as calculated by predict, stdp; see [R] **predict**.

References

Little, R. J. A. and D. B. Rubin. 1987. *Statistical Analysis with Missing Data*. New York: John Wiley & Sons.

Also See

[R] **ipolate**, [R] **predict**, [R] **regress**

Title

> **infile** — Quick reference for reading data into Stata

Description

This entry provides a quick reference for determining which method to use for reading non-Stata data into memory. See [U] **27 Commands to input data** for another guide that provides more explanation.

Remarks

Summary of the different methods

insheet

- o `insheet` reads text (ASCII) files created by a spreadsheet or a database program.

- o The data must be tab-separated or comma-separated, but not both simultaneously, nor can it be space-separated.

- o A single observation must be on only one line.

- o The first line in the file can optionally contain the names of the variables.

infile (free format)—infile without a dictionary

- o The data can be space-separated, tab-separated, or comma-separated.

- o Strings with embedded spaces or commas must be enclosed in quotes (even if tab- or comma-separated).

- o A single observation can be on more than one line or there can even be multiple observations per line.

infix (fixed format)

- o The data must be in fixed-column format.

- o A single observation can be on more than one line.

- o `infix` has simpler syntax than `infile` (fixed format).

infile (fixed format)—infile with a dictionary

- o The data may be in fixed-column format.

- o A single observation can be on more than one line.

- o `infile` (fixed format) has the most capabilities for reading data.

Examples

▷ Example

———————————————— top of examp1.raw ————————————————

```
1       0       1       John Smith      m
0       0       1       Paul Lin        m
0       1       0       Jan Doe f
0       0       .       Julie McDonald  f
```
———————————————— end of examp1.raw ————————————————

contains tab-separated data. The `type` command with the `showtabs` option, shows the tabs:

```
. type examp1.raw, showtabs
```

```
1<T>0<T>1<T>John Smith<T>m
0<T>0<T>1<T>Paul Lin<T>m
0<T>1<T>0<T>Jan Doe<T>f
0<T>0<T>.<T>Julie McDonald<T>f
```

It could be read in by

```
. insheet a b c name gender using examp1
```
◁

▷ Example

———————————————— top of examp2.raw ————————————————

```
a,b,c,name,gender
1,0,1,John Smith,m
0,0,1,Paul Lin,m
0,1,0,Jan Doe,f
0,0,,Julie McDonald,f
```
———————————————— end of examp2.raw ————————————————

could be read in by

```
. insheet using examp2
```
◁

▷ Example

———————————————— top of examp3.raw ————————————————

```
1       0       1       "John Smith"    m
0       0       1       "Paul Lin"      m
0       1       0       "Jan Doe"       f
0       0       .       "Julie McDonald"        f
```
———————————————— end of examp3.raw ————————————————

contains tab-separated data with strings in double quotes.

```
. type examp3.raw, showtabs
```

```
1<T>0<T>1<T>"John Smith"<T>m
0<T>0<T>1<T>"Paul Lin"<T>m
0<T>1<T>0<T>"Jan Doe"<T>f
0<T>0<T>.<T>"Julie McDonald"<T>f
```

It could be read in by

```
. infile byte (a b c) str15 name str1 gender using examp3
```

or could be read in by

. insheet a b c name gender using examp3

or could be read in by

. infile using dict3

where the dictionary dict3.dct contains

── top of dict3.dct ──────────

```
infile dictionary using examp3 {
        byte    a
        byte    b
        byte    c
        str15   name
        str1    gender
}
```

────────────────────────────────────── end of dict3.dct ──────────
◁

▷ Example

────────────────────────────────────── top of examp4.raw ──────────

```
1 0 1 "John Smith" m
0 0 1 "Paul Lin" m
0 1 0 "Jan Doe" f
0 0 . "Julie McDonald" f
```

────────────────────────────────────── end of examp4.raw ──────────

could be read in by

. infile byte (a b c) str15 name str1 gender using examp4

or could be read in by

. infile using dict4

where the dictionary dict4.dct contains

────────────────────────────────────── top of dict4.dct ──────────

```
infile dictionary using examp4 {
        byte    a
        byte    b
        byte    c
        str15   name
        str1    gender
}
```

────────────────────────────────────── end of dict4.dct ──────────
◁

▷ Example

────────────────────────────────────── top of examp5.raw ──────────

```
101mJohn Smith
001mPaul Lin
010fJan Doe
00 fJulie McDonald
```

────────────────────────────────────── end of examp5.raw ──────────

could be read in by

. infix a 1 b 2 c 3 str gender 4 str name 5-19 using examp5

or could be read in by

. infix using dict5a

where dict5a.dct contains

```
——————————————————————————————————— top of dict5a.dct ———————
infix dictionary using examp5 {
                a       1
                b       2
                c       3
        str     gender  4
        str     name    5-19
}
——————————————————————————————————— end of dict5a.dct ———————
```

or could be read in by

. infile using dict5b

where dict5b.dct contains

```
——————————————————————————————————— top of dict5b.dct ———————
infile dictionary using examp5 {
        byte    a       %1f
        byte    b       %1f
        byte    c       %1f
        str1    gender  %1s
        str15   name    %15s
}
——————————————————————————————————— end of dict5b.dct ———————
```

◁

▷ Example

```
——————————————————————————————————— top of examp6.raw ———————
line 1 : a heading
There are a total of 4 lines of heading.
The next line contains a useful heading:
----+----1----+----2----+----3----+----4----+-
1       0       1       m       John Smith
0       0       1       m       Paul Lin
0       1       0       f       Jan Doe
0       0               f       Julie McDonald
——————————————————————————————————— end of examp6.raw ———————
```

could be read in by

. infile using dict6a

where dict6a.dct contains

```
——————————————————————————————————— top of dict6a.dct ———————
infile dictionary using examp6 {
_firstline(5)
                byte    a
                byte    b
_column(17)     byte    c       %1f
                str1    gender
_column(33)     str15   name    %15s
}
——————————————————————————————————— end of dict6a.dct ———————
```

or could be read in by

```
. infix 5 first a 1 b 9 c 17 str gender 25 str name 33-46 using examp6
```

or could be read in by

```
. infix using dict6b
```

where `dict6b.dct` contains

————————————————————————— top of dict6b.dct ———————

```
infix dictionary using examp6 {
5 first
            a       1
            b       9
            c       17
      str   gender  25
      str   name    33-46
}
```

————————————————————————— end of dict6b.dct ———————

◁

▷ Example

————————————————————————— top of examp7.raw ———————

```
a b c gender name
1 0 1
m
John Smith
0 0 1
m
Paul Lin
0 1 0
f
Jan Doe
0 0
f
Julie McDonald
```

————————————————————————— end of examp7.raw ———————

could be read in by

```
. infile using dict7a
```

where `dict7a.dct` contains

————————————————————————— top of dict7a.dct ———————

```
infile dictionary using examp7 {
_firstline(2)
            byte    a
            byte    b
            byte    c
_line(2)
            str1    gender
_line(3)
            str15   name    %15s
}
```

————————————————————————— end of dict7a.dct ———————

Or, if you wanted to include variable labels:

```
. infile using dict7b
```

where `dict7b.dct` contains

```
─────────────────────────────────────────── top of dict7b.dct ───────────
infile dictionary using examp7 {
_firstline(2)
            byte    a           "Question 1"
            byte    b           "Question 2"
            byte    c           "Question 3"
_line(2)
            str1    gender      "Gender of subject"
_line(3)
            str15   name    %15s
}
──────────────────────────────────────────── end of dict7b.dct ───────────
```

`infix` could also read this data:

. `infix 2 first 3 lines a 1 b 3 c 5 str gender 2:1 str name 3:1-15 using examp7`

or it could be read in by

. `infix using dict7c`

where `dict7c.dct` contains

```
─────────────────────────────────────────── top of dict7c.dct ───────────
infix dictionary using examp7 {
2 first
                a       1
                b       3
                c       5
        str     gender  2:1
        str     name    3:1-15
}
──────────────────────────────────────────── end of dict7c.dct ───────────
```

or it could be read in by

.`infix using dict7d`

where `dict7d.dct` contains

```
─────────────────────────────────────────── top of dict7d.dct ───────────
infix dictionary using examp7 {
2 first
                a       1
                b       3
                c       5
/
        str     gender  1
/
        str     name    1-15
}
──────────────────────────────────────────── end of dict7d.dct ───────────
```

◁

Also See

[U] **27 Commands to input data**

[R] **edit**, [R] **infile (fixed format)**, [R] **infile (free format)**, [R] **infix (fixed format)**, [R] **input**, [R] **insheet**

Title

---
infile (fixed format) — Read ASCII (text) data in fixed format with a dictionary
---

Syntax

infile using *dfilename* [if *exp*] [in *range*] [, automatic using(*filename₂*) clear]

If *dfilename* is specified without an extension, .dct is assumed.

If *filename₂* is specified without an extension, .raw is assumed.

The syntax for a dictionary, a file created with an editor or word processor outside of Stata, is

――――――――――――――――――――――――――――――――― top of dictionary file ―――――

```
[infile] dictionary [using filename] {
        * comments may be included freely
        _lrecl(#)
        _firstlineoffile(#)
        _lines(#)

        _line(#)
        _newline[(#)]
        _column(#)
        _skip[(#)]

        [type] varname [:lblname] [%infmt] ["variable label"]
}
(your data might appear here)
```

―――――――――――――――――――――――――――――――――――――― end of dictionary file ―――――

where %*infmt* is { %[#[.#]]{f|g|e} | %[#]s }

If using *filename* is not specified, the data is assumed to begin on the line following the close brace.

If using *filename* is specified, the data is assumed to be located in *filename*. If *filename* is specified without an extension, .raw is assumed.

Description

infile using reads data from a disk dataset that is not in Stata format. infile using does this by first reading *dfilename*, called a dictionary, that describes the format of the data file, and then reads the file containing the data. The dictionary is a file you create in an editor or word processor outside of Stata.

The data may be in the same file as the dictionary or in another file.

Another variation on infile omits the intermediate dictionary; see [R] **infile (free format)**. This variation is easier to use, but will not read fixed-format files. On the other hand, although infile using will read free-format files, the variation is even better at it.

An alternative to infile using for reading fixed-format files is infix; see [R] **infix (fixed format)**. infix provides fewer features than infile using but is easier to use.

Stata has other commands for reading data. If you are not certain that infile using is what you are looking for, see [R] **infile** and [U] **27 Commands to input data**.

Options

automatic causes Stata to create value labels from the nonnumeric data it reads.

using(*filename*₂) specifies the name of a file containing the data. If using() is not specified, the data is assumed to follow the dictionary in *dfilename* or, if the dictionary specifies the name of some other file, that file is assumed to contain the data. If using(*filename*₂) is specified, *filename*₂ is used to obtain the data even if the dictionary itself says otherwise.

clear specifies that it is okay for the new data to replace what is currently in memory. To ensure that you do not lose something important, infile using will refuse to read new data if data is already in memory. clear is one way you can tell infile using that it is okay. The other is to drop the data yourself by typing drop _all before reading new data.

Dictionary directives

* marks comment lines. Wherever you wish to place a comment, begin the line with a *. Comments can appear many times in the same dictionary.

_lrecl(#) is used only when reading datasets that do not have end-of-line delimiters (carriage return, linefeed, or some combination). Such files are often produced by mainframe computers and have been poorly translated from EBCDIC into ASCII. _lrecl() specifies the logical record length. _lrecl() requests that infile act as if a line ends every # characters.

_lrecl() appears only once, and typically not at all, in a dictionary.

_firstlineoffile(#) (abbreviation _first()) is also rarely specified. It states the line of the file where the data begins. _first() is not specified when the data follows the dictionary; Stata can figure that out for itself. first() is instead specified when reading data from another file and the first line of that file does not contain data because of headers or other markers.

_first() appears only once, and typically not at all, in a dictionary.

_lines(#) states the number of lines per observation in the file. Simple datasets typically have _lines(1). Large datasets often have many lines (sometimes called records) per observation. _lines() is optional even when there is more than one line per observation because infile can sometimes figure it out for itself. Still, if _lines(1) is not right for your data, it is best to specify the directive.

_lines() appears only once in a dictionary.

_line(#) tells infile to jump to line # of the observation. Distinguish _lines() from _line(), and consider a file with _lines(4), meaning four lines per observation. _line(2) says to go to the second line of the observation. _line(4) says to go to the fourth line of the observation. You may jump forward or backward, infile does not care nor is there any inefficiency in going forward to _line(3), reading a few variables, jumping back to _line(1), reading another variable, and jumping forward again to _line(3).

It is not your responsibility to ensure that, at the end of your dictionary, you are on the last line of the observation. infile knows how to get to the next observation because it knows where you are and it knows _lines(), the total number of lines per observation.

_line() may appear, and typically does, many times in a dictionary.

_newline[(#)] is an alternative to _line(). _newline(1), which may be abbreviated _newline, goes forward one line. _newline(2) goes forward two lines. We do not recommend the use of _newline() because _line() is better. If you are currently on line 2 of an observation and want to get to line 6, you could type _newline(4), but your meaning is clearer if you type _line(6).

_newline() may appear many times in a dictionary.

_column(#) jumps to column # on the current line. You may jump forward or backward within a line. _column() may appear many times in a dictionary.

_skip(#) jumps forward # columns on the current line. _skip() is just an alternative to _column(). _skip() may appear many times in a dictionary.

[*type*] *varname* [: *lblname*] [% *infmt*] ["*variable label*"] instructs infile to read a variable. The simplest form of this instruction is the variable name itself: *varname*.

First understand that at all times infile is on some column of some line of an observation. infile starts by being on column 1 of line 1, so pretend that is where we are. Given the simplest directive '*varname*', infile goes through the following logic:

Is the current column blank? If so, skip forward until there is a nonblank column (or until the end of the line). If we just skipped all the way to the end of the line, store a missing value in *varname*. If we skipped to a nonblank column, begin collecting what is there until we come to a blank column or the end of the line. That is the data for *varname*. Now set the current column to wherever we are.

The logic is a bit more complicated. For instance, when skipping forward to find the data, infile might encounter a quote. If so, it then collects the characters for the data by skipping forward until it finds the matching quote. If you specified a % *infmt*, infile skips the skipping-forward step and simply collects the specified number of characters. Nevertheless, the general logic is (optionally) skip, collect, and reset.

Remarks

infile using follows a two-step process to read your data. You type something like infile using descript and

1. infile using reads the file descript.dct, which tells infile about the format of the data; and

2. infile using then reads the data according to the instructions recorded in descript.dct.

descript.dct (the file could be named anything) is called a dictionary and descript.dct is just a text file you create with an editor or word processor outside of Stata.

As for the data themselves, they can be in the same file as the dictionary or in a different file. It does not matter.

Reading free-format files

There is another variation of infile for reading free-format files described in [R] **infile (free format)**. We will refer to the variation as infile without a dictionary. The distinction between the two variations is in the treatment of line breaks. infile without a dictionary does not consider them significant. infile with a dictionary does.

A line, also known as a record, physical record, or physical line (as opposed to observations, or logical records, or logical lines), is a string of characters followed by the line terminator. If you were to type the file, a line is what would appear on your screen if your screen were infinitely wide. Your screen would have to be infinitely wide so that there would be no possibility that a single line could take more than one line of your screen, thus fooling you into thinking there are multiple lines when there is only one.

A logical line, on the other hand, is a sequence of one or more physical lines that represents a single observation of your data. `infile` with a dictionary does not willy-nilly go to new physical lines; it goes to a new line between observations and it goes to a new line when you tell it to, but that is all. `infile` without a dictionary, on the other hand, goes to a new line whenever it needs to, which can be right in the middle of an observation. Thus, consider the following little bit of data which, we will tell you, is for three variables:

```
5 4
1 9 3
2
```

How do you interpret this data?

Here is one interpretation: There are three observations. The first is 5, 4, and missing. The second is 1, 9, and 3. The third is 2, missing, and missing. That is the interpretation that `infile` with a dictionary makes.

Here is another interpretation: There are two observations. The first is 5, 4, and 1. The second is 9, 3, and 2. That is the interpretation that `infile` without a dictionary makes.

Which is right? We would have to ask the person who entered this data. The question is, are the line breaks significant? Do they mean anything? If the line breaks are significant, we use `infile` with a dictionary. If the line breaks are not significant, we use `infile` without a dictionary.

The other distinction between the two `infile`s is that `infile` with a dictionary does not process comma-separated-value format. If your data is comma-separated, see [R] **infile (free format)** or [R] **insheet**.

▷ Example

Outside of Stata you have typed into the file `highway.dct` information on the accident rate per million vehicle miles along a stretch of highway, the speed limit on that highway, and the number of access points (on-ramps and off-ramps) per mile. Your file contains

```
─────────────────────────────────────────── top of highway.dct, example 1 ───────
infile dictionary {
        acc_rate  spdlimit acc_pts
}
4.58 55 4.6
2.86  60 4.4
1.61 . 2.2
3.02 60 4.7
─────────────────────────────────────────── end of highway.dct, example 1 ───────
```

This file can be read by typing `infile using highway`. Stata displays the dictionary and reads the data:

```
. infile using highway
infile dictionary {
        acc_rate  spdlimit acc_pts
}
(4 observations read)

. list
        acc_rate   spdlimit    acc_pts
   1.      4.58         55        4.6
   2.      2.86         60        4.4
   3.      1.61          .        2.2
   4.      3.02         60        4.7
```

◁

▷ Example

We can include variable labels in a dictionary so that after we `infile` the data it will be fully labeled. We could change `highway.dct` to read

```
———————————————————————————————————————— top of highway.dct, example 2 ————————
infile dictionary {
* This is a comment and will be ignored by Stata
* You might type the source of the data here.
        acc_rate   "Acc. Rate/Million Miles"
        spdlimit   "Speed Limit (mph)"
        acc_pts    "Access Pts/Mile"
}
4.58 55 4.6
2.86  60 4.4
1.61  . 2.2
3.02 60 4.7
———————————————————————————————————————— end of highway.dct, example 2 ————————
```

Now when we type `infile using highway`, Stata not only reads the data but labels the variables.

◁

▷ Example

We can indicate the variable types in the dictionary. For instance, if we wanted to store `acc_rate` as a `double` and `spdlimit` as a `byte`, we could change `highway.dct` to read

```
———————————————————————————————————————— top of highway.dct, example 3 ————————
infile dictionary {
* This is a comment and will be ignored by Stata
* You might type the source of the data here.
 double acc_rate  "Acc. Rate/Million Miles"
 byte   spdlimit   "Speed Limit (mph)"
        acc_pts    "Access Pts/Mile"
}
4.58 55 4.6
2.86  60 4.4
1.61  . 2.2
3.02 60 4.7
———————————————————————————————————————— end of highway.dct, example 3 ————————
```

Since we do not indicate the variable type for `acc_pts`, it is given the default variable type `float` (or the type specified by the `set type` command).

◁

▷ Example

By specifying the types, we can read string variables as well as numeric variables. For instance:

```
———————————————————————————————————————————————— top of emp.dct ————————
infile dictionary {
* data on employees
  str20 name        "Name"
        age         "Age"
      int sex       "Sex coded 0 male 1 female"
}
"Lisa Gilmore" 25 1
Branton 32 1
´Bill Ross´ 27 0
———————————————————————————————————————————————— end of emp.dct ————————
```

The strings can be delimited by single or double quotes and quotes may be omitted altogether if the string contains no blanks or other special characters.

◁

❑ Technical Note

You may attach value labels to variables in the dictionary using the colon notation:

```
————————————————————————————————————————— top of emp2.dct —————
infile dictionary {
* data on name, sex, and age
    str16 name        "Name"
          sex:sexlbl  "Sex"
    int age           "Age"
}
"Arthur Doyle" Male 22
"Mary Hope" Female 37
"Guy Fawkes" Male 48
"Sherry Crooks" Female 25
————————————————————————————————————————— end of emp2.dct —————
```

If you wish the value labels to be automatically created, you must specify the **automatic** option on the **infile** command. This data could be read by typing **infile using person2, automatic** assuming the dictionary and data are stored in the file **person2.dct**.

❑

▷ Example

The data need not be in the same file as the dictionary. We might leave the highway data in **highway.raw** and write a dictionary called **highway.dct** describing it:

```
————————————————————————————————————— top of highway.dct, example 4 —————
infile dictionary using highway {
* This dictionary reads the file highway.raw.  If the
* file were called highway.txt, the first line would
* read "dictionary using highway.txt"
        acc_rate  "Acc. Rate/Million Miles"
        spdlimit  "Speed Limit (mph)"
        acc_pts   "Access Pts/Mile"
}
————————————————————————————————————— end of highway.dct, example 4 —————
```

◁

▷ Example

The **firstlineoffile()** directive allows you to ignore lines at the top of the file. Consider the following raw dataset:

```
————————————————————————————————————————— top of mydata.raw —————
The following data was entered by Marsha Holliday.  It was checked by
Helen Troy.
id income educ sex age
1024 25000 HS Male 28
1025 27000 C Female 24
——————————————————            ——————————— end of mydata.raw —————
```

Your dictionary might read

——————————————————————————————— top of mydata.dct ———————

```
infile dictionary using mydata {
        _first(4)
        int id "Identification Number"
        income "Annual income"
        str2 educ "Highest educ level"
        str6 sex
        byte age
    }
```

——————————————————————————————— end of mydata.dct ———————

◁

▷ Example

The _line() and _lines() directives instruct Stata how to read your dataset when there are multiple records per observation. You have the following in **mydata2.raw**:

——————————————————————————————— top of mydata2.raw ———————

```
id income educ sex age
1024 25000 HS
Male
28
1025 27000 C
Female
24
1035 26000 HS
Male
32
1036 25000 C
Female
25
```

——————————————————————————————— end of mydata2.raw ———————

You can read this with a dictionary **mydata2.dct**, which we will just let Stata list as it simultaneously reads the data:

```
. infile using mydata2, clear
infile dictionary using mydata2 {
    _first(2)                        * Begin reading on line 2
    _lines(3)                        * Each observation takes 3 lines.
    int id "Identification Number"   * Since _line is not specified, Stata
    income "Annual income"           * assumes that it is 1.
    str2 educ "Highest educ level"
    _line(2)                         * Go to line 2 of the observation.
    str6 sex                         * (values for sex are located on line 2)
    _line(3)                         * Go to line 3 of the observation.
    int age                          * (values for age are located on line 3)
}
(4 observations read)
. list
```

	id	income	educ	sex	age
1.	1024	25000	HS	Male	28
2.	1025	27000	C	Female	24
3.	1035	26000	HS	Male	32
4.	1036	25000	C	Female	25

Now, here is the really good part: We read these variables in order but that was not necessary. We could just as well have used the dictionary:

```
                                                        ─── top of mydata2p.dct ───────
   infile dictionary using mydata2 {
         _first(2)
         _lines(3)
         _line(1)    int    id      "Identification number"
                            income  "Annual income"
                     str2   educ    "Highest educ level"
         _line(3)    int    age
         _line(2)    str6   sex
   }
                                                        ─── end of mydata2p.dct ───────
```

We would obtain the same results—and just as quickly—the only difference being that our variables in the final dataset would be in the order specified: id, income, educ, age, and sex.

◁

□ Technical Note

You can use _newline to specify where breaks occur, if you prefer:

```
                                                    ─── top of highway.dct, example 5 ───
   infile dictionary {
           acc_rate   "Acc. Rate/Million Miles"
           spdlimit   "Speed Limit (mph)"
   _newline acc_pts   "Access Pts/Mile"
   }
   4.58 55
   4.6
   2.86   60
    4.4
   1.61  .
   2.2
   3.02 60
    4.7
                                                    ─── end of highway.dct, example 5 ───
```

The line that reads '1.61 .' could have been read 1.61 (without the period), and the results would have been unchanged. Since dictionaries do not go to new lines automatically, a missing value is assumed for all values not found in the record.

□

Reading fixed-format files

Values in formatted data are sometimes packed one against the other with no intervening blanks. For instance, the highway data might appear as

```
                                                    ─── top of highway.raw, example 6 ───
   4.58554.6
   2.86604.4
   1.61  2.2
   3.02604.7
                                                    ─── end of highway.raw, example 6 ───
```

The first four columns of each record represent the accident rate; the next two columns, the speed limit; and the last three columns, the number of access points per mile.

To read this data, you must specify the % *infmt* in the dictionary. Numeric % *infmt*s are denoted by a leading percent sign (%) followed optionally by a string of the form w or $w.d$, where w and d stand for two integers. The first integer, w, specifies the width of the format. The second integer, d, specifies the number of digits that are to follow the decimal point. Logic requires that d be less than or equal to w. Finally, a character denoting the format type (f, g, or e) is appended. For example, %9.2f specifies an f format that is nine characters wide and has two digits following the decimal point.

Numeric formats

The f format indicates that `infile` is to attempt to read the data as a number. When you do not specify the % *infmt* in the dictionary, `infile` assumes the %f format. The missing width w means that `infile` is to attempt to read the data in free format.

At the start of each observation, `infile` reads a record into its buffer and sets a column pointer to 1, indicating that it is currently on the first column. When `infile` processes a %f format, it moves the column pointer forward through white space. It then collects the characters up to the next occurrence of white space and attempts to interpret those characters as a number. The column pointer is left at the first occurrence of white space following those characters. If the next variable is also free format, the logic repeats.

When you explicitly specify the field width w, as in %wf, `infile` does not skip leading white space. Instead, it collects the next w characters starting at the column pointer and attempts to interpret the result as a number. The column pointer is left at the old value of the column pointer plus w, that is, on the first character following the specified field.

▷ Example

If the data above is stored in file `highway.raw`, you could create the following dictionary to read it:

```
                                            ── top of highway.dct, example 6 ──────
   infile dictionary using highway {
           acc_rate   %4f  "Acc. Rate/Million Miles"
           spdlimit   %2f  "Speed Limit (mph)"
           acc_pts    %3f  "Access Pts/Mile
   }
                                            ── end of highway.dct, example 6 ──────
```

When you explicitly indicate the field width, `infile` does not skip intervening characters. The first four columns are used for the variable `acc_rate`, the next two for `spdlimit`, and the last three for `acc_pts`.

◁

❏ Technical Note

The d specification in the %$w.d$f indicates the number of *implied* decimal places in the data. For instance, the string 212 read in a %3.2f format represents the number 2.12. You should *not* specify d unless your data has elements of this form. The w alone is sufficient to tell `infile` how to read data in which the decimal point is explicitly indicated.

When you specify d, it is taken only as a suggestion. If the decimal point is explicitly indicated in the data, that decimal point always overrides the d specification. Decimal points are also not implied if the data contains an E, e, D, or d, indicating scientific notation.

Fields are right-justified before implying decimal points. Thus, '2 ', ' 2 ', and ' 2' are all read as 0.2 by the %3.1f format.

❏

❏ Technical Note

The g and e formats are the same as the f format. You can specify any of these letters interchangeably. The letters g and e are included as a convenience to those familiar with FORTRAN. In FORTRAN, the e format indicates scientific notation. For example, the number 250 could be indicated as 2.5E+02 or 2.5D+02. FORTRAN programmers would refer to this as an E7.5 format, and in Stata, this format would be indicated as %7.5e. In Stata, however, you need specify only the field width w, so you could read this number using %7f, %7g, or %7e.

The g format is really a FORTRAN output format that indicates a freer format than f. In Stata, the two formats are identical.

Throughout this section, you may freely substitute the g or e formats for the f format.

❏

❏ Technical Note

Be careful to distinguish % *fmts* and % *infmts*. % *fmts* are also known as *display* formats—they describe how a variable is to look when it is outputted; see [U] **19.5 Formats: controlling how data is displayed**. % *infmts* are also known as *input* formats—they describe how a variable looks when it is inputted. For instance, there is an output date format %d, but there is no corresponding input format. (See [U] **30 Commands for dealing with dates** for recommendations on how to read dates.) For the other formats, we have attempted to make the input and output definitions as similar as possible. Thus, we include g, e, and f % *infmts*, even though they all mean the same thing, since g, e, and f are also % *fmts*.

❏

String formats

The s format is for reading strings. The syntax is %*w*s where the w is optional. If you do not specify the field width, your strings must be enclosed in quotes (single or double) or they must not contain any characters other than letters, numbers, and '_'.

This may surprise you, but the s format can be used for reading numeric variables and the f format can be used for reading string variables! When you specify the field width w in the %*w*f format, all embedded blanks in the field are removed before the result is interpreted. They are not removed by the %*w*s format.

For instance, the %3f format would read '- 2', '-2 ', or ' -2' as the number −2. The %3s format would not be able to read '- 2' as a number, since the sign is separated from the digit, but it could read ' -2' or '-2 '. The %*w*f format removes blanks; datasets written by some FORTRAN programs separate the sign from the number.

There are, however, some side effects of this practice. The string '2 2' will be read as 22 by a %3f format. Most FORTRAN compilers would read this number as 202. The %3s format would issue a warning and store a *missing*.

Now consider reading the string 'a b' into a string variable. Using a %3s format, it will store as it appears: a b. Using a %3f format, however, it will be stored as ab—the middle blank will be removed.

Examples using the %s format are provided below, right after we discuss specifying column and line numbers.

❑ Technical Note

Quotes are always stripped, even when you read data using %*w*s. Of course, the quotes are not required when using %*w*s even if the string contains embedded blanks. Prior to Stata 3.0, infile had one odd behavior (read bug) when reading a field containing all blanks with %*w*s—it would store a single period rather than a null string. The idea was that an all blank input string represented missing and the fact that the string was missing would be encoded "." just as missing number is encoded '.'. This, however, violates the rules for missing values laid out in [U] **19 Data** where it is clearly stated that a missing value for a string is ""; i.e., null string.

This problem is fixed, but some old do-files may depend on the previous, incorrect behavior. Typing version 2.1 will restore the previous behavior; see [R] **version**.

❑

Specifying column and line numbers

_column() jumps to the specified column. For instance, the documentation of some dataset indicates that the variable age is recorded as a 2-digit number in column 47. You could read this by coding

```
_column(47) age %2f
```

After this, you are now at column 49, so if immediately following age were a 1-digit number recording sex as 0 or 1, you could code

```
_column(47) age %2f
            sex %1f
```

or, if you wanted to be explicit about it:

```
_column(47) age %2f
_column(49) sex %1f
```

It makes no difference. If at column 50 were a 1-digit code for race, and you wanted to read it but skip reading the sex code, you could code

```
_column(47) age %2f
_column(50) race %1f
```

You could equivalently skip forward using _skip():

```
_column(47) age %2f
_skip(1)    race %1f
```

One advantage of column() over _skip is that it let's you jump forward or backward in a record. If you wanted to read race and then age, you could code

```
_column(50) race %1f
_column(47) age %2f
```

If the dataset you are reading has multiple lines per observation (sometimes said as multiple records per observation), tell `infile` how many lines per record there are using `_lines()`:

```
_lines(4)
```

`_lines()` appears only once in a dictionary. Good style says it should be placed near the top of the dictionary, but Stata does not care.

When you want to go to a particular line, include the `_line()` directive. In our example, let's assume `race`, `sex`, and `age` are recorded on the second line of each observation:

```
_lines(4)
_line(2)
    _column(47) age %2f
    _column(50) race %1f
```

Let's assume `id` is recorded on line 1.

```
_lines(4)
_line(1)
    _column(1)  id  %4f
_line(2)
    _column(47) age %2f
    _column(50) race %1f
```

`_line()` works like `_column()` in that you can jump forward or backward, so this data could just as well be read by

```
_lines(4)
_line(2)
    _column(47) age %2f
    _column(50) race %1f
_line(1)
    _column(1)  id  %4f
```

Remember that this dataset has 4 lines per observation and yet we have never referred to `line(3)` or `line(4)`. That is okay. Also note that, at the end of our dictionary, we are on line 1, not 4. That is okay, too. `infile` will still get to the next observation correctly.

❑ Technical Note

Another way to move between records is `_newline()`. `_newline()` is to `_line()` as `_skip()` is to `_column()`, which is to say, `_newline()` can only go forward. There is one difference: `_skip()` has its uses; `_newline()` is useful only for backward capability with older versions of Stata.

`_skip()` has its uses because sometimes one is thinking in terms of columns and sometimes one is thinking in terms of widths. Some data documentation might very well include the sentence "At column 54 are recorded the answers to the 25 questions, one column alloted to each." If we wanted to read the answers to questions 1 and 5, it would indeed be natural to code

```
_column(54) q1 %1f
_skip(3)
            q5 %1f
```

Nobody has ever read data documentation with the statement, "Demographics are recorded on record 2 and, 2 records after that, are the income values." The documentation would instead say, "Record 2 contains the demographic information and record 5, income." The `_newline()` way of thinking is based on what is convenient for the computer which does, after all, have to eject a certain number of records. That, however, is no reason for making you think that way.

Before that thought occurred to us, Stata users specified _newline() to go forward records. They still can so their old dictionaries will work. When you use _newline() and do not specify _lines(), it is your responsibility to eject the right number of records so that, at the end of the dictionary, you are on the last record. In this mode, when Stata reexecutes the dictionary to process the next observation, it goes forward one record.

❏

Examples of reading fixed-format files

▷ Example

In this example, each observation occupies two lines. The first two observations in the dataset are

```
John Dunbar                      10001   101 North 42nd Street
1010111111
Sam K. Newey, Jr.                10002   15663 Roustabout Boulevard
0101000000
```

The first observation tells us that the name of the respondent is John Dunbar; his id is 10001; his address is 101 North 42nd Street; and his answers to questions 1 through 10 are yes, no, yes, no, yes, yes, yes, yes, yes, and yes.

The second observation tells us the name of the respondent is Sam K. Newey, Jr.; his id is 10002; his address is 15663 Roustabout Boulevard; and his answers to questions 1 through 10 were no, yes, no, yes, no, no, no, no, no, and no. (Probably John and Sam are not best friends.)

In order to see the layout within the file, we can temporarily add two rulers to help our eyes see the appropriate columns:

```
----+----1----+----2----+----3----+----4----+----5----+----6----+----7----+----8
John Dunbar                      10001   101 North 42nd Street
1010111111
Sam K. Newey, Jr.                10002   15663 Roustabout Boulevard
0101000000
----+----1----+----2----+----3----+----4----+----5----+----6----+----7----+----8
```

Each observation in the data appears in two physical lines within our text file. We had to check in our editor to be sure that there really were newline characters (i.e., "hard returns") after the address. This is important because some programs will wrap output for you and a single line may appear as many lines. The two seemingly identical files will differ in that one has a hard return and the other has a soft return added only for display purposes.

In our data, the name occupies columns 1 through 32; a person identifier occupies columns 33 through 37; and the address occupies columns 40 through 80. Our worksheet revealed that the widest address ended in column 80.

The text file containing this data is called fname.txt. Our dictionary file looks like this:

```
                                                  ──── top of fname.dct ────
     infile dictionary using fname.txt {
     *
     * Example reading in data where observations extend across more
     * than one line.  The next line tells infile there are 2 lines/obs:
     *
     _lines(2)
     *
                    str50    name    %32s      "Name of respondent"
     _column(33)    long     id      %5f       "Person id"
     _skip(2)       str50    addr    %41s      "Address"
     _line(2)
     _column(1)     byte     q1      %1f       "Question 1"
                    byte     q2      %1f       "Question 2"
                    byte     q3      %1f       "Question 3"
                    byte     q4      %1f       "Question 4"
                    byte     q5      %1f       "Question 5"
                    byte     q6      %1f       "Question 6"
                    byte     q7      %1f       "Question 7"
                    byte     q8      %1f       "Question 8"
                    byte     q9      %1f       "Question 9"
                    byte     q10     %1f       "Question 10"
     }
                                                  ──── end of fname.dct ────
```

Up to five pieces of information may be supplied in the dictionary for each variable: the location of the data, the storage type of the variable, the name of the variable, the input format, and the variable label.

Thus, the str50 line says that the first variable is to be given a storage type of str50, should be called **name**, and have the variable label "Name of respondent". The %32s is the input format—this tells Stata how to read the data. The s tells Stata not to remove any embedded blanks; the 32 tells Stata to go across 32 columns when reading the data.

The next line says that the second variable is to be assigned a storage type of long, named id, and labeled "Person id". Stata should start reading the information for this variable in column 33. The f tells Stata to remove any embedded blanks, and the 5 says to read across 5 columns.

The third variable is to be given a storage type of str50, called **addr**, and labeled "Address". The _skip(2) directs Stata to skip 2 columns before beginning to read the data for this variable, and the %41s instructs Stata to read across 41 columns and to not remove embedded blanks.

line(2) instructs Stata to go to line 2 of the observation.

The remainder of the data is 0/1 coded—the answers to the questions. It would be convenient if we could use a shorthand to specify this portion of the dictionary, but we must supply explicit directives.

◁

❑ Technical Note

In the preceding example, there were two pieces of information about location: where the data begins for each variable (the _column(), _skip(), _line()) and how many columns it spans (the %32s, %5f, %41s, %1f). In our dictionary, some of this information was redundant. After reading **name**, Stata had finished with 32 columns of information. Unless instructed otherwise, Stata would proceed to the next column—column 33—to begin reading information about id. The _column(33) was unnecessary.

The _skip(2) was not, however, unnecessary. Stata had read 37 columns of information and was ready to look at column 38. Although the address information does not begin until column 40, columns 38 and 39 contain blanks. Since these are leading blanks, instead of embedded blanks, Stata would just ignore them. There is no problem so far. The problem is with the %41s. If Stata begins reading the address information from column 38 and reads 41 columns, Stata would stop reading in column 78 ($78 - 41 + 1 = 38$), and the widest address ends in column 80. We could have omitted the _skip(2) if we had specified an input format of %43s.

The _line(2) was necessary although we could have gotten to the second line by coding _newline instead.

The _column(1) could have been omitted. After the _line(), Stata begins in column 1.

See the following example for a dataset where both pieces of location information are required.

❑

▷ Example

The following file contains six variables in a variety of formats. Note that in the dictionary we read the variables fifth and sixth out of order by forcing the column pointer.

```
───────────────────────────────────────────────── top of example.dct ─────────
infile dictionary {
                              first    %3f
                     double   second   %2.1f
                              third    %6f
         _skip(2)    str4     fourth   %4s
         _column(21)          sixth %4.1f
         _column(18)          fifth %2f
}
1.2125.7e+252abcd 1 .232
1.3135.7    52efgh2    5
1.41457     52abcd 3 100.
1.5155.7D+252efgh04 1.7
16 16 .57   52abcd 5 1.71
─────────────────────────────────────────────────── end of example.dct ──────────
```

Assuming the above is stored in a file called example.dct, it can be infiled and listed by typing

```
. infile using example
infile dictionary {
                              first    %3f
                     double   second   %2.1f
                              third    %6f
         _skip(2)    str4     fourth   %4s
         _column(21)          sixth %4.1f
         _column(18)          fifth %2f
}
(5 observations read)

. list

       first   second   third   fourth   sixth   fifth
  1.    1.2      1.2      570    abcd     .232      1
  2.    1.3      1.3      5.7    efgh      .5       2
  3.    1.4      1.4       57    abcd     100       3
  4.    1.5      1.5      570    efgh     1.7       4
  5.    16.      1.6      .57    abcd     1.71      5
```

◁

Reading fixed-block files

❑ Technical Note

The _lrecl(#) directive is for use in reading datasets that do not have end-of-line delimiters (carriage return, linefeed, or some combination). Such datasets are typical of IBM mainframes—where they are known as fixed block or FB. The word LRECL is IBM-mainframe jargon for logical record length.

Fixed-block datasets are datasets where each # characters are to be interpreted as a record. For instance, consider the data

```
1 21
2 42
3 63
```

In fixed-block format, this data might be recorded

```
————————————————————————————————————————— top of mydata.ibm ———————
1 212 423 63
————————————————————————————————————————— end of mydata.ibm ———————
```

and you would be told, on the side, that the LRECL is 4. If you then pass along that information to infile, it will be able to read the data:

```
———————————————————————————————————————————— top of mydata.dct ———————
infile dictionary using mydata.ibm {
        _lrecl(4)
        int     id
        int     age
}
———————————————————————————————————————————— end of mydata.dct ———————
```

When you do not specify the _lrecl(#) directive, infile assumes that each line ends with the standard ASCII delimiter (which can be linefeed or carriage return or linefeed followed by carriage return or carriage return followed by linefeed). When you do specify _lrecl(#), infile reads the data in blocks of # characters and then acts as if that is a line.

A common mistake in processing fixed-block datasets is to be incorrect about the LRECL value, for instance, thinking the LRECL is 160 when it is really 80. To understand what can happen, pretend we thought the LRECL in our data was 6 rather than 4. Taking the characters in groups of 6, the data appears as

```
1 212
423 63
```

Stata has no way of verifying that you have specified the correct LRECL so, if the data appears incorrect, verify you have the correct number.

The maximum LRECL infile allows is 18,998 with Stata for Unix, 7,998 with Stata for Windows and Stata for DOS, and 3,998 with Stata for Macintosh.

❑

References

Gould, W. W. 1992. dm10: Infiling data: Automatic dictionary creation. *Stata Technical Bulletin* 9: 4–8. Reprinted in *Stata Technical Bulletin Reprints*, vol. 2, pp. 28–34.

Nash, J. D. 1994. dm19: Merging raw data and dictionary files. *Stata Technical Bulletin* 20: 3–5. Reprinted in *Stata Technical Bulletin Reprints*, vol. 4, pp. 22–25.

Also See

[U] **27 Commands to input data**

[R] **infile**, [R] **infix (fixed format)**, [R] **outfile**, [R] **outsheet**, [R] **save**

Title

---

infile (free format) — Read unformatted ASCII (text) data

Syntax

$\underline{\text{inf}}\text{ile}$ *varlist* $\big[\,\_\text{skip}\big[(\#)\big]\ \big[\textit{varlist}\ \big[\_\text{skip}\big[(\#)\big]\ \ldots\big]\big]\big]$ using *filename* $\big[\text{if}\ \textit{exp}\big]\ \big[\text{in}\ \textit{range}\big]$

$\big[,\ \underline{\text{a}}\text{utomatic}\ \underline{\text{b}}\text{yvariable}(\#)\ \text{clear}\ \big]$

If *filename* is specified without an extension, `.raw` is assumed.

Description

`infile` reads into memory a disk dataset that is *not* in Stata format.

Here we discuss using `infile` to read free-format data, meaning datasets where the knowledge of the formatting information is not necessary to make sense of them. Another variation on `infile` allows reading fixed-format data and is discussed in [R] **infile (fixed format)**. Yet another alternative is `insheet`, which is easier to use if your data is tab- or comma-separated and contains one observation per line. Stata has other commands for reading data, too. If you are not certain that `infile` is what you are looking for, see [R] **infile** and [U] **27 Commands to input data**.

After the data is read into Stata, the data can be saved as a Stata-format dataset; see [R] **save**.

Options

`automatic` causes Stata to create value labels from the nonnumeric data it reads.

`byvariable`(#) specifies that the external data file is organized by variables rather than by observations. All the observations on the first variable appear, followed by all the observations on the second variable, and so on. Time-series datasets sometimes come in this format.

`clear` specifies that it is okay for the new data to replace what is currently in memory. To ensure that you do not lose something important, `infile` will refuse to read new data if data is already in memory. `clear` is one way you can tell `infile` that it is okay. The other is to drop the data yourself by typing `drop _all` before reading new data.

Remarks

`infile`—or, at least, the `infile` features discussed here—reads data in free or comma-separated-value format.

Remarks are presented under the headings

> *Reading free format data*
> *Reading comma-separated data*
> *Specifying variable types*
> *Reading string variables*
> *Skipping variables*
> *Skipping observations*
> *Reading time-series data*

Reading free format data

In free format, data are separated by one or more white-space characters. White-space characters are blanks, tabs, and newlines (carriage return, linefeed, or carriage-return/linefeed combinations). Thus, a single observation may span any number of lines.

Numeric missing values are indicated by single periods ('.').

▷ Example

In the file `highway.raw`, you have information on the accident rate per million vehicle miles along a stretch of highway, the speed limit on that highway, and the number of access points (on-ramps and off-ramps) per mile. Your file contains

```
                                         ─── top of highway.raw, example 1 ───
    4.58 55 4.6
    2.86  60 4.4
    1.61 . 2.2
    3.02 60
    4.7
                                         ─── end of highway.raw, example 1 ───
```

You can read this data by typing

```
    . infile acc_rate spdlimit acc_pts using highway
    (4 observations read)

    . list

           acc_rate   spdlimit    acc_pts
      1.       4.58         55        4.6
      2.       2.86         60        4.4
      3.       1.61          .        2.2
      4.       3.02         60        4.7
```

Note that the spacing of the numbers in the original file is irrelevant.

◁

❑ Technical Note

It is not necessary that missing values be indicated by a single period. The third observation on the speed limit is missing in the previous example. The raw data file indicates this by recording a single period. Let's assume that instead the missing value was indicated by the word **unknown**. Thus, the raw data file appears as

```
                                         ─── top of highway.raw, example 2 ───
    4.58 55 4.6
    2.86  60 4.4
    1.61 unknown 2.2
    3.02 60
    4.7
                                         ─── end of highway.raw, example 2 ───
```

Here is the result of infiling the data:

```
    . infile acc_rate spdlimit acc_pts using highway
    'unknown' cannot be read as a number for spdlimit[3]
    (4 observations read)
```

`infile` warned us that it did not know what to make of the word `unknown`, stored a *missing*, and then continued to read the rest of the data. Thus, aside from the warning message, results are unchanged.

Since not all packages indicate missing data in the same way, this feature can be useful when reading data created by them. Whenever `infile` sees something it does not understand, it warns you, records a *missing*, and continues. If, on the other hand, the missing value were recorded not as `unknown` but as, say 99, Stata would have no difficulty reading the number, but it would also store 99 rather than missing. To convert such coded missing values to true missing values, see [R] **mvencode**.

❑

Reading comma-separated data

In comma-separated-value format, data are separated by commas. You may intermix comma-separated-value and free format. Missing values are indicated either by single periods or by multiple commas which serve as place holders, or both. As with free format, a single observation may span any number of input lines.

▷ Example

We can modify the format of `highway.raw` used in the previous example without affecting `infile`'s ability to read it. The data can be read with the same command and the results would be the same if the file instead contains

————————————————————————— top of highway.raw, example 3 —————————
```
4.58,55 4.6
2.86, 60,4.4
1.61,,2.2
3.02,60
4.7
```
————————————————————————— end of highway.raw, example 3 —————————

◁

Specifying variable types

The variable names you type following the word `infile` are new variables. The syntax for a new variable is

$$[\textit{type}] \ \textit{new\_varname}[\underline{:}\textit{label\_name}]$$

A full discussion of this syntax can be found in [U] **18.4 varlists**. As a quick review, new variables are, by default, of type `float`. This default can be overridden by preceding the variable name with a storage type (`byte`, `int`, `long`, `float`, `double`, or `str#`) or by using the `set type` command. A list of variables placed in parentheses will be given the same type. For example,

`double`(*first_var second_var* ... *last_var*)

causes *first_var second_var* ... *last_var* to all be of type `double`.

There is also a shorthand syntax for variable names with numeric suffixes. The varlist `var1-var4` is equivalent to specifying `var1 var2 var3 var4`.

▷ Example

In the highway example, we could `infile` the data `acc_rate`, `spdlimit`, and `acc_pts` and force the variable `spdlimit` to be of type `int` by typing

```
. infile acc_rate int spdlimit acc_pts using highway, clear
(4 observations read)
```

We could force all variables to be of type `double` by typing

```
. infile double(acc_rate spdlimit acc_pts) using highway, clear
(4 observations read)
```

We could call the three variables `v1`, `v2`, and `v3` and make them all doubles, by typing

```
. infile double(v1-v3) using highway, clear
(4 observations read)
```

◁

Reading string variables

By explicitly specifying the types, we can read string variables as well as numeric variables.

▷ Example

Typing `infile str20 name age sex using myfile` would read

```
──────────────────────────────────────────── top of myfile.raw ────────────
    "Sherri Holliday" 25 1
    Branton 32 1
    "Bill Ross" 27,0
──────────────────────────────────────────── top of myfile.raw ────────────
```

or even

```
──────────────────────────────────────── top of myfile.raw, variation 2 ────────
    ´Sherri Holliday´ 25,1 "Branton" 32
    1,´Bill Ross´, 27,0
──────────────────────────────────────── end of myfile.raw, variation 2 ────────
```

Note that the spacing is irrelevant and either single or double quotes may be used to delimit strings. The quotes do not count when calculating the length of strings. Quotes may be omitted altogether if the string contains no blanks or other special characters (anything other than letters, numbers, or underscores).

Typing

```
. infile str20 name age sex using myfile
(3 observations read)
```

makes `name` a `str20` and `age` and `sex` `float`s. We might have typed

```
. infile str20 name age int sex using myfile
(3 observations read)
```

to make `sex` an `int` or

```
. infile str20 name int(age sex) using myfile
(3 observations read)
```

to make both `age` and `sex` `int`s.

◁

❑ Technical Note

infile can also handle nonnumeric data by using *value labels*. We will briefly review value labels, but you should see [U] **19.6.3 Value labels** for a complete description.

A value label is a mapping from the set of integers to words (character strings of 8 characters or less). For instance, if you had a variable called **sex** in your data that represented the sex of the individual, you might code 0 for male and 1 for female. You could then just remember that every time you see a value of 0 for **sex**, that observation refers to a male, whereas every time you see a value of 1, the observation refers to a female.

Even better, you could inform Stata that 0 represents males and 1 represents females by typing

    . label define sexfmt 0 "Male" 1 "Female"

Then you must tell Stata that this coding scheme is to be associated with the variable **sex**. This is typically done by typing

    . label values sex sexfmt

Thereafter, Stata will print **Male** rather than 0 and **Female** rather than 1 for this variable.

Stata is unique in that it has the ability to turn a value label around. Not only can it go from numeric codes to words like "Male" and "Female", it can go from the words to the numeric code. We tell infile which value label goes with which variable by placing a colon (:) after the variable name and typing the name of the value label. Before we do that, we use the **label define** command to inform Stata of the coding.

Let's assume that we wish to infile a dataset containing the words **Male** and **Female** and that we wish to store numeric codes rather than the strings themselves. This will result in considerable data compression, especially if we store the numeric code as a **byte**. We have a dataset named **persons.raw** that contains name, sex, and age:

——————————————————————————————————————— top of persons.raw ———————

    "Arthur Doyle" Male 22
    "Mary Hope" Female 37
    "Guy Fawkes" Male 48
    "Sherry Crooks" Female 25

——————————————————————————————————————— end of persons.raw ———————

Here is how we read and encode it at the same time:

    . label define sexfmt 0 "Male" 1 "Female"
    . infile str16 name sex:sexfmt age using persons
    (4 observations read)
    . list

                    name   sex   age
        1.   Arthur Doyle   Male   22
        2.   Mary Hope   Female   37
        3.   Guy Fawkes   Male   48
        4.   Sherry Crooks   Female   25

The **str16** in the infile command applies only to the **name** variable; **sex** is a numeric variable, as we can prove by

    . list, nolabel

                    name   sex   age
        1.   Arthur Doyle   0   22
        2.   Mary Hope   1   37
        3.   Guy Fawkes   0   48
        4.   Sherry Crooks   1   25   ❑

❑ Technical Note

When `infile` is directed to use a value label and it finds an entry in the file that does not match any of the codings recorded in the label, it prints a warning message and stores *missing* for the observation. By specifying the `automatic` option, you can instead have `infile` automatically add new entries to the value label.

Say you have a dataset containing three variables. The first, region of the country, is a character string; the remaining two variables, which we will just call `var1` and `var2`, contain numbers. You have stored the data in a file called `geog.raw`:

```
                                                          top of geog.raw
    "NE"      31.23      87.78
    ´NCntrl´  29.52      98.92
    South     29.62     114 69
    West      28.28     218.92
    NE        17.50      44.33
    NCntrl    22.51      55.21
                                                          end of geog.raw
```

The easiest way to read this data would be

```
. infile str6 region var1 var2 using geog
```

making `region` a string variable. You do not want to do this, however, because you are practicing for reading a dataset like this containing 20,000 observations. If `region` were numerically encoded and stored as a `byte`, there would be a 5-byte saving per observation, reducing the size of the data by 100,000 bytes. You also do not want to bother first creating the value label. Using the `automatic` option, `infile` creates the value label as it encounters new regions automatically.

```
. infile byte region:regfmt var1 var2 using geog, automatic
(6 observations read)
. list
           region      var1       var2
   1.          NE      31.23      87.78
   2.      NCntrl      29.52      98.92
   3.       South      29.62     114.69
   4.        West      28.28     218.92
   5.          NE       17.5      44.33
   6.      NCntrl      22.51      55.21
```

`infile` automatically created and defined a new value label called `regfmt`. We can use the `label list` command to view its contents:

```
. label list regfmt
regfmt:
           1 NE
           2 NCntrl
           3 South
           4 West
```

It is not necessary that the value label be undefined prior to the use of `infile` with the `automatic` option. If the value label `regfmt` had been previously defined as

```
. label define regfmt 2 "West"
```

the result of `label list` after the `infile` would have been

```
regfmt:
           2 West
           3 NE
           4 NCntrl
           5 South
```

The `automatic` option is so convenient that you may see no reason for not using it. Here is one. Suppose you had a dataset containing, among other things, an individual's sex. You know that the sex variable is supposed to be coded `male` and `female`. If you read the data using the `automatic` option and if one of the records contains `fmlae`, `infile` will blindly create a third sex rather than print a warning.

❏

Skipping variables

Specifying `_skip` instead of a variable name directs `infile` to ignore the variable in that location. This feature makes it possible to extract manageable subsets from large disk datasets. A number of contiguous variables can be skipped by specifying `_skip(#)` where # is the number of variables to ignore.

▷ Example

In the highway example that started this section, the data file contained three variables: `acc_rate`, `spdlimit`, and `acc_pts`. You can read just the first two variables by typing

        . infile acc_rate spdlimit _skip using highway

You can read the first and last variable by typing

        . infile acc_rate _skip acc_pts using highway, clear

You can read just the first variable by typing

        . infile acc_rate _skip(2) using highway, clear

`_skip` may be specified more than once. If you had a dataset containing four variables, say a, b, c, and d, and you wanted to read just a and c, you could type `infile a _skip c _skip using` *filename*.

◁

Skipping observations

Subsets of observations can be extracted by specifying `if` *exp*, which also makes it possible to extract manageable subsets from large disk datasets. Do not, however, use the *_variable _N* in *exp*. Use the `in` *range* modifier to refer to observation numbers within the disk dataset.

▷ Example

Again referring to the highway example, if you type

        . infile acc_rate spdlimit acc_pts if acc_rate>3
        (2 observations read)

only observations for which `acc_rate` is greater than 3 will be infiled. You can type

        . infile acc_rate spdlimit acc_pts in 2/4, clear
        (3 observations read)

to read only the second, third, and fourth observations.

◁

Reading time-series data

If you are dealing with time-series data, you may receive datasets organized by variables rather than by observations. All the observations on the first variable appear, followed by all the observations on the second variable, and so on. The `byvariable`(#) option specifies that the external data file is organized in this way. You specify the number of observations in the parentheses, since `infile` needs to know that number in order to read the data properly. Alternatively, you can mark the end of one variable's data and the beginning of another's by placing a semicolon ('`;`') in the raw data file. You may then specify a number larger than the number of observations in the dataset and leave it to `infile` to determine the actual number of observations. This method can also be used to read unbalanced data.

▷ Example

You have time-series data on four years recorded in the file `time.raw`. The data contains information on year, amount, and cost and is organized by variable:

```
                                                  top of time.raw
1980 1981 1982 1983
14 17 25 30
120 135 150
180
                                                  end of time.raw
```

You can read this data by typing

```
. infile year amount cost using time, byvariable(4)
(4 observations read)

. list
         year     amount        cost
   1.    1980         14         120
   2.    1981         17         135
   3.    1982         25         150
   4.    1983         30         180
```

If the data instead contained semicolons marking the end of each series and had no information for amount in 1983, the raw data might appear as

```
1980 1981 1982 1983 ;
14 17 25 ;
120 135 150
180
```

You could read this data by typing

```
. infile year amount cost using time, byvariable(100)
(4 observations read)

. list
         year     amount        cost
   1.    1980         14         120
   2.    1981         17         135
   3.    1982         25         150
   4.    1983          .         180
```

◁

Also See

Title

infix (fixed format) — Read ASCII (text) data in fixed format

Syntax

infix using *dfilename* [if *exp*] [in *range*] [, using(*filename₂*) clear]

infix *specifications* using *filename* [if *exp*] [in *range*] [, clear]

where *specifications* is

<u>firstlineoffile</u>

lines

#<u>:</u>

/

[byte | int | float | long | double | str] *varlist* [#<u>:</u>]#[-#]

and *dfilename*, if it exists, contains

── top of dictionary file ─────────

    infix dictionary [using *filename*] {
             * *comments preceded by asterisk may appear freely*
             specifications
    }
    (*your data might appear here*)

── end of dictionary file ─────────

If *dfilename* is specified without an extension, .dct is assumed.

If *filename₂* or *filename* is specified without an extension, .raw is assumed.

Description

infix reads into memory a disk dataset that is *not* in Stata format. infix requires that the data be in fixed-column format.

You have alternatives to infix. infile is one. It can also read data in fixed-format—see [R] **infile (fixed format)**—and it can read data in free format—see [R] **infile (free format)**. Most people think infix is easier to use for reading fixed-format data, but infile has more features. If your data is not fixed-format, another alternative is insheet; see [R] **insheet**. If you are not certain that infix is what you are looking for, see [R] **infile** and [U] **27 Commands to input data**.

In its first syntax, infix reads the data in a two-step process. You first create a disk file describing how the data is recorded. You tell infix to read that file—called a dictionary—and from there infix goes on to read the data. The data can be in the same file as the dictionary or a different file.

In its second syntax, you tell infix how to read the data right on the command line with no intermediate file.

Options

using(*filename₂*) specifies the name of a file containing the data. If using() is not specified, the data is assumed to follow the dictionary in *dfilename* or, if the dictionary specifies the name of some other file, that file is assumed to contain the data. If using(*filename₂*) is specified, *filename₂* is used to obtain the data even if the dictionary itself says otherwise.

clear specifies that it is okay for the new data to replace what is currently in memory. To ensure that you do not lose something important, infix will refuse to read new data if data is already in memory. clear is one way you can tell infix that it is okay. The other is to drop the data yourself by typing drop _all before reading new data.

Specifications

firstlineoffile (abbreviation first) is rarely specified. It states the line of the file where the data begins. first is not specified when the data follows the dictionary; infix can figure that out for itself. first is instead specified when the data appears by itself in a file and the first few lines of that file contain headers or other markers.

first appears only once in the specifications.

lines states the number of lines per observation in the file. Simple datasets typically have '1 lines'. Large datasets often have many lines (sometimes called records) per observation. lines is optional even when there is more than one line per observation because infix can sometimes figure it out for itself. Still, if 1 lines is not right for your data, it is best to specify the directive.

lines appears only once in the specifications.

#: tells infix to jump to line # of the observation. Consider a file with 4 lines, meaning four lines per observation. 2: says to go to the second line of the observation. 4: says to go to the fourth line of the observation. You may jump forward or backward, infix does not care nor is there any inefficiency in going forward to 3:, reading a few variables, jumping back to 1:, reading another variable, and jumping back again to 3:.

It is not your responsibility to ensure that, at the end of your specifications, you are on the last line of the observation. infix knows how to get to the next observation because it knows where you are and it knows lines, the total number of lines per observation.

#: may appear, and typically does, many times in the specifications.

/ is an alternative to #:. / goes forward one line. // goes forward two lines. We do not recommend the use of / because #: is better. If you are currently on line 2 of an observation and want to get to line 6, you could type ////, but your meaning is clearer if you type 6:.

/ may appear many times in the specifications.

[byte | int | float | long | double | str] *varlist* [#:]#[-#] instructs infix to read a variable and, sometimes, more than one.

Begin by realizing that the simplest form of this is *varname* #, such as sex 20. That says that variable *varname* is to be read from column # of the current line; variable sex is to be read from column 20 and here, sex is a one-digit number.

varname #-#, such as age 21-23, says to read *varname* from the column range specified; read age from columns 21 through 23 and here, age is a three-digit number.

You can prefix the variable with a storage type. str name 25-44 means to read the string variable name from columns 25 through 44. If you do not specify str, the variable is assumed to be numeric. You can specify the numeric subtype if you wish.

You can specify more than one variable, with or without a type. `byte q1-q5 51-55` means reads variables q1, q2, q3, q4, and q5 from columns 51 through 55 and store the five variables as `bytes`.

Finally, you can specify the line on which the variable(s) appear. `age 2:21-23` says that age is to be obtained from the second line, columns 21 through 23. Another way you could say this is by putting together the `#:` directive with the input-variable directive: `2: age 21-23`. There is a difference, but not with respect to reading the variable `age`. So let's consider two alternatives:

```
1:  str name 25-44    age 2:21-23    q1-q5 51-55
1:  str name 25-44  2: age 21-23     q1-q5 51-55
```

The difference is that the first directive says variables q1 through q5 are on line 1 whereas the second says they are on line 2.

When the colon is put out front, it says on which line variables are to be found when we do not explicitly say otherwise. When the colon is put inside, it applies only to the variable under consideration.

Remarks

There are two ways to use `infix`. One is to type the specifications that describe how to read the fixed-format dataset on the command line:

```
. infix acc_rate 1-4  spdlimit 6-7  acc_pts 9-11  using highway.raw
```

The other is to type the specifications into a file

─────────────────────────────── top of highway.dct, example 1 ───────────

```
infix dictionary using highway.raw {
        acc_rate 1-4
        spdlimit 6-7
        acc_pts  9-11
}
```

─────────────────────────────── end of highway.dct, example 1 ───────────

and then, inside Stata, type

```
. infix using highway.dct
```

Which you use makes no difference to Stata. The first form is more convenient if there are only a few variables and the second form is less prone to error if you are reading a big, complicated file.

The second form allows two variations, the one we just showed—where the data is in another file—and one where the data is in the same file as the dictionary:

─────────────────────────────── top of highway.dct, example 2 ───────────

```
infix dictionary {
        acc_rate 1-4
        spdlimit 6-7
        acc_pts  9-11
}
4.58 55 .46
2.86 60 4.4
1.61    2.2
3.02 60 4.7
```

─────────────────────────────── end of highway.dct, example 2 ───────────

Note that in the first example, the top line of the file read `infix dictionary using highway.raw` whereas in the second the line reads simply `infix dictionary`. When you do not say where the data are it is implied that they follow the dictionary.

▷ Example

So let's complete the example we started. You have data on the accident rate per million vehicle miles along a stretch of highway, the speed limit on that highway, and the number of access points per mile. You have created the dictionary file `highway.dct` which contains the dictionary and the data:

```
─────────────────────────────────── top of highway.dct, example 2 ───────────
    infix dictionary {
            acc_rate 1-4
            spdlimit 6-7
            acc_pts  9-11
    }
    4.58 55 .46
    2.86 60 4.4
    1.61    2.2
    3.02 60 4.7
─────────────────────────────────── end of highway.dct, example 2 ───────────
```

You created this file outside of Stata using an editor or word processor. Inside Stata, you now read the data. `infix` lists the dictionary so you will know the directives it is following:

```
. infix using highway
infix dictionary {
        acc_rate 1-4
        spdlimit 6-7
        acc_pts  9-11
}
(4 observations read)
. list
        acc_rate    spdlimit    acc_pts
    1.      4.58          55        .46
    2.      2.86          60        4.4
    3.      1.61           .        2.2
    4.      3.02          60        4.7
```

Note that we simply typed `infix using highway` rather than `infix using highway.dct`. When we do not specify the file extension, `infix` assumes we mean `.dct`.

◁

Reading string variables

When you do not say otherwise in your specifications—either on the command line or in the dictionary—`infix` assumes variables are numeric. You specify that a variable is a string by placing `str` in front of its name:

```
. infix  id 1-6  str name 7-36  age 38-39  str sex 41  using employee.raw
```

or

```
──────────────────────────────────────────── top of employee.dct ───────────
    infix dictionary using employee.raw {
            id         1-6
            str name   7-36
            age        38-39
            str sex    40
    }
──────────────────────────────────────────── end of employee.dct ───────────
```

Reading multiple-lines-per-observation data

When data has multiple lines per observations, sometimes said as multiple records per observation, you specify the number of lines per observation using lines and you specify on which line elements appear using #:.

```
. infix  2 lines  1: id 1-6  str name 7-36  2: age 1-2  str sex 4  using emp2.raw
```

or

```
——————————————————————————————————————————————— top of emp2.dct ———————
infix dictionary using emp2.raw {
    2 lines
    1:
        id         1-6
        str name   7-36
    2:
        age        1-2
        str sex      4
}
——————————————————————————————————————————————— end of emp2.dct ———————
```

There are lots of different ways to say the same thing.

▷ Example

Consider the following raw data:

```
——————————————————————————————————————————————— top of mydata.raw ———————
id income educ / sex age / rcode, answers to questions 1-5
1024 25000 HS
    Male   28
     1 1 9 5 0 3
1025 27000 C
    Female 24
     0 2 2 1 1 3
1035 26000 HS
    Male   32
     1 1 0 3 2 1
1036 25000 C
    Female 25
     1 3 1 2 3 2
——————————————————————————————————————————————— end of mydata.raw ———————
```

This data has 3 lines per observation and the first line is just a comment. One possible set of specifications to read this data is

```
——————————————————————————————————————————————— top of mydata1.dct ———————
infix dictionary using mydata {
    2 first
    3 lines
    1:   id         1-4
         income     6-10
         str educ  12-13
    2:   str sex    6-11
         int age   13-14
    3:   rcode      6
         q1-q5      7-16
}
——————————————————————————————————————————————— end of mydata1.dct ———————
```

although the one we prefer is

```
                                                    ——————— top of mydata2.dct ———————
infix dictionary using mydata {
    2 first
    3 lines
        id        1: 1-4
        income    1: 6-10
        str educ  1:12-13
        str sex   2: 6-11
        age       2:13-14
        rcode     3: 6
        q1-q5     3: 7-16
}
                                                    ——————— end of mydata2.dct ———————
```

Either will read this data, so we will use the first and then we will explain why we prefer the second.

```
. infix using mydata1
infix dictionary using mydata {
    2 first
    3 lines
    1:    id        1-4
          income    6-10
          str educ  12-13
    2:    str sex   6-11
          int age   13-14
    3:    rcode     6
          q1-q5     7-16
}
(4 observations read)

. list in 1/2

Observation 1
            id        1024    income    25000    educ      HS
           sex        Male       age       28    rcode       1
            q1           1        q2        9       q3       5
            q4           0        q5        3

Observation 2
            id        1025    income    27000    educ       C
           sex      Female       age       24    rcode       0
            q1           2        q2        2       q3       1
            q4           1        q5        3
```

Now, what is better about the second? What is better is that the location of each variable is completely documented on each line, both in terms of line number and column. Since `infix` does not care about the order in which we read the variables, we could take the dictionary, jumble the lines, and it would still work. For instance,

```
                                                    ——————— top of mydata3.dct ———————
infix dictionary using mydata {
    2 first
    3 lines
        str sex   2: 6-11
        rcode     3: 6
        str educ  1:12-13
        age       2:13-14
        id        1: 1-4
        q1-q5     3: 7-16
        income    1: 6-10
}
                                                    ——————— end of mydata3.dct ———————
```

will also read this data even though, for each observation, we start on line 2, go forward to line 3, jump back to line 1, and at the conclusion, end up on line 1. It is not even inefficient to do this because `infix` does not really jump to record 2, then record 3, then record 1 again, etc. `infix` takes what we say and organizes it efficiently. The order in which we say it makes no difference. Well, it does make one: the order of the variables in the resulting Stata dataset will be the order we specify.

In this case the reordering is senseless but, in real data, reordering variables is often desirable. Moreover, we often construct dictionaries, realize that we omitted a variable, and then go back and modify them. By making each line complete in and of itself, we can add new variables anyplace in the dictionary and not worry that, because of our addition, something occurring later will no longer read correctly.

◁

Reading subsets of observations

If you wanted to read only the males from some raw data file, you might type

```
. infix  id 1-6  str name 7-36  age 38-39  str sex 41  using employee.raw if sex=="M"
```

If your specifications were instead recorded in a dictionary, you could type

```
. infix using employee.raw if sex=="M"
```

In another dataset, if you wanted to read just the first 100 observations, you could type

```
. infix 2 lines  1: id 1-6  str name 7-36  2: age 1-2  str sex 4  using emp2.raw
  in 1/100
```

Or, if the specifications were instead recorded in a dictionary and you wanted observations 101 through 573, you could type

```
. infix using emp2.dct in 101/573
```

Also See

[U] **27 Commands to input data**

[R] **infile**, [R] **infile (fixed format)**, [R] **insheet**, [R] **outfile**, [R] **outsheet**, [R] **save**

Title

input — Enter data from keyboard

Syntax

<u>inp</u>ut [*varlist*] [, <u>a</u>utomatic <u>l</u>abel]

Description

input allows you to type data directly into the dataset in memory. Stata for Windows and Stata for Macintosh users should see [R] **edit** for a better alternative to input.

Options

<u>a</u>utomatic causes Stata to create value labels from the nonnumeric data it encounters. Specifying automatic implies label even if you do not explicitly type the label option.

label allows you to type the labels (strings) instead of the numeric values for variables associated with value labels. New value labels are not automatically created unless automatic is specified.

Remarks

If there is no data in memory when you type input, you must specify a *varlist*. Stata will then prompt you to enter the new observations until you type end.

▷ Example

You have data on the accident rate per million vehicle miles along a stretch of highway along with the speed limit on that highway. You wish to type this data directly into Stata:

```
. input
nothing to input
r(104);
```

Typing input by itself does not provide enough information about your intentions. Stata needs to know the names of the variables you wish to create:

```
. input acc_rate spdlimit
       acc_rate     spdlimit
 1. 4.58 55
 2. 2.86 60
 3. 1.61 .
 4. end

 . _
```

We typed input acc_rate spdlimit and Stata responded by repeating the variable names and then prompting us for the first observation. We then typed 4.58 and 55 and pressed *Return*. Stata prompted us for the second observation. We entered it and pressed *Return*. Stata prompted us for the third observation. We knew that the accident rate is 1.61 per million vehicle miles, but we did not know the corresponding speed limit for the highway. We typed the number we knew, 1.61, followed by a period, the missing value indicator. When we pressed *Return*, Stata prompted us for the fourth observation. We were finished entering our data, so we typed end in lowercase letters.

We can now `list` the data to verify that we have entered it correctly:

```
. list
        acc_rate    spdlimit
  1.        4.58          55
  2.        2.86          60
  3.        1.61           .
```

◁

If you have data in memory and type `input` without a *varlist*, you will be prompted to enter additional information on *all* the variables. This continues until you type `end`.

▷ Example

You now have an additional observation you wish to add to the dataset. Typing `input` by itself tells Stata that you wish to add new observations:

```
. input
        acc_rate    spdlimit
  4. 3.02 60
  5. end
  . _
```

Stata reminded us of the names of our variables and prompted us for the fourth observation. We entered the numbers 3.02 and 60 and pressed *Return*. Stata then prompted us for the fifth observation. We could add as many new observations as we wish. Since we needed to add only one observation, we typed' `end`. Our dataset now has four observations.

◁

You may add new variables to the data in memory by typing `input` followed by the names of the new variables. Stata will begin by prompting you for the first observation, then the second, and so on, until either you type `end` or you enter the last observation.

▷ Example

In addition to the accident rate and speed limit, we now obtain data on the number of access points (on-ramps and off-ramps) per mile along each stretch of highway. We wish to enter this new data:

```
. input acc_pts
        acc_pts
  1. 4.6
  2. 4.4
  3. 2.2
  4. 4.7
  . _
```

When we typed `input acc_pts`, Stata responded by prompting us for the first observation. There are 4.6 access points per mile for the first highway, so we entered `4.6` and pressed *Return*. Stata then prompted us for the second observation, and so on. We entered each of the numbers. When we entered the final observation, Stata automatically stopped prompting us—we did not have to type `end`. Stata knows that there are four observations in memory, and since we are adding a new variable, it stops automatically.

We can, however, type `end` anytime we wish. If we do so, Stata fills the remaining observations on the new variables with *missing*. To illustrate this, we enter one more variable to our data and then `list` the result:

```
. input junk
            junk
  1. 1
  2. 2
  3. end
. list
        acc_rate    spdlimit    acc_pts      junk
  1.        4.58          55        4.6         1
  2.        2.86          60        4.4         2
  3.        1.61           .        2.2         .
  4.        3.02          60        4.7         .
```
◁

You can input string variables using `input`, but you must remember to explicitly indicate that the variables are strings by specifying the type of the variable before the variable's name.

▷ Example

String variables are indicated by the types `str#`, where # represents the storage length, or maximum length, of the variable. For instance, a `str4` variable has maximum length 4, meaning it can contain the strings a, ab, abc, and abcd but not abcde. Strings shorter than the maximum length can be stored in the variable, but strings longer than the maximum length cannot. You can create variables up to `str80` in Stata.

Since a `str80` variable can store strings shorter than 80 characters, you might wonder why you should not make all your string variables `str80`. You do not want to do this because Stata allocates space for strings based on their *maximum* length. It would waste the computer's memory.

Let's assume that we have no data in memory and wish to enter the following data:

```
. input str16 name age str6 sex
              name         age       sex
  1. "Arthur Doyle" 22 male
  2. "Mary Hope" 37 "female"
  3. Guy Fawkes 48 male
´Fawkes´ cannot be read as a number
  3. "Guy Fawkes" 48 male
  4. "Sherry Crooks" 25 female
  5. end

. _
```

We first typed `input str16 name age str6 sex`, meaning that `name` is to be a `str16` variable and `sex` a `str6` variable. Since we did not specify anything about `age`, Stata made it a numeric variable.

Stata then prompted us to enter our data. On the first line, the name is Arthur Doyle, which we typed in double quotes. The double quotes are not really part of the string; they merely delimit the beginning and end of the string. We followed that with Mr. Doyle's age, 22, and his sex, male. We did not bother to type double quotes around the word `male` because it contained no blanks or other special characters. For the second observation, we did type the double quotes around `female`; it changed nothing.

In the third observation we omitted the double quotes around the name, and Stata informed us that Fawkes could not be read as a number and reprompted us for the observation. When we omitted the double quotes, Stata interpreted `Guy` as the name, `Fawkes` as the age, and 48 as the sex. All of this would have been okay with Stata except for one problem: `Fawkes` looks nothing like a number. So Stata complained and gave us another chance. This time, we remembered to put the double quotes around the name.

Stata was satisfied, and we continued. We entered the fourth observation and then typed end. Here is our data:

```
. list
               name        age        sex
     1.   Arthur Doyle      22        male
     2.     Mary Hope       37      female
     3.     Guy Fawkes      48        male
     4.   Sherry Crooks     25      female
```

◁

▷ Example

Just as we indicated which variables were strings by placing a storage type in front of the variable name, we can indicate the storage type of our numeric variables as well. Stata has five numeric storage types: byte, int, long, float, and double. When you do not specify the storage type, Stata assumes the variable is a float. You may want to review the definitions of numbers in [U] **19 Data**.

There are two reasons why you might want to explicitly specify the storage type: to induce additional precision or to conserve memory. The default type float has plenty of precision for most circumstances because Stata performs all calculations in double precision no matter how the data is stored. If you were storing 9-digit Social Security Numbers, however, you would want to coerce a different storage type or else the last digit would be rounded. long would be the best choice; double would work equally well, but it would be wasteful of memory.

Sometimes you do not need to store a variable as float. If the variable contains only integers between $-32{,}768$ and $32{,}766$, it can be stored as an int and it would take only half the space. If a variable contains only integers between -127 and 126, it can be stored as a byte which would take only half again as much space. For instance, in the previous example we entered data for age without explicitly specifying the storage type; hence, it was a float. It would have been better to store it as a byte. To do that, we would have typed

```
. input str16 name byte age str6 sex
               name        age        sex
  1. "Arthur Doyle" 22 male
  2. "Mary Hope" 37 "female"
  3. "Guy Fawkes" 48 male
  4. "Sherry Crooks" 25 female
  5. end

  . _
```

Stata understands a number of shorthands. For instance,

```
. input int(a b) c
```

allows you to input three variables, a, b, and c, and makes both a and b ints and c a float. Remember

```
. input int a b c
```

would make a an int but both b and c floats.

```
. input a long b double(c d) e
```

would make a a float, b a long, c and d doubles, and e a float.

Stata has a shorthand for variable names with numeric suffixes. Typing v1-v4 is equivalent to typing v1 v2 v3 v4. Thus,

```
. input int(v1-v4)
```

inputs four variables and stores all of them as ints.

◁

❑ Technical Note

You may want to stop reading now. The rest of this section deals with using input with value labels. If you are not familiar with value labels, you should first read [U] **19.6.3 Value labels**.

Remember that value labels map numbers into words and vice versa. There are two aspects to the process. First, we must define the association between numbers and words. We might tell Stata that 0 corresponds to male and 1 corresponds to female by typing label define sexlbl 0 "male" 1 "female". The correspondences are named, and in this case we have named the 0↔male 1↔female correspondence sexlbl.

Next, we must associate this value label with a variable. If we had already entered the data and the variable was called sex, we would do this by typing label values sex sexlbl. We would have entered the data by typing 0's and 1's, but at least now when we list the data, we would see the words rather than the underlying numbers.

We can do better than that. After defining the value label, we can associate the value label with the variable at the time we input the data and tell Stata to use the value label to interpret what we type:

```
. label define sexlbl 0 "male" 1 "female"
. input str16 name byte(age sex:sexlbl), label
            name        age       sex
  1. "Arthur Doyle" 22 male
  2. "Mary Hope" 37 "female"
  3. "Guy Fawkes" 48 male
  4. "Sherry Crooks" 25 female
  5. end

.
```

After defining the value label, we typed our input command. Two things are noteworthy: We added the label option at the end of the command, and we typed sex:sexlbl for the name of the sex variable. The byte(...) around age and sex:sexlbl was not really necessary: it merely forced both age and sex to be stored as bytes.

Let's first decipher sex:sexlbl. sex is the name of the variable we want to input. The :sexlbl part tells Stata that the new variable is to be associated with the value label named sexlbl. The label option tells Stata that it is to look up any strings we type for labeled variables in their corresponding value label and substitute the number when it stores the data. Thus, when we entered the first observation of our data, we typed male for Mr. Doyle's sex even though the corresponding variable is numeric. Rather than complaining that ""male" could not be read as a number", Stata accepted what we typed, looked up the number corresponding to male, and stored that number in the data.

The fact that Stata has actually stored a number rather than the words male or female is almost irrelevant. Whenever we list the data or make a table, Stata will use the words male and female just as if those words were actually stored in the data rather than their numeric codings:

```
. list
                  name        age       sex
  1.      Arthur Doyle        22      male
  2.        Mary Hope        37    female
  3.       Guy Fawkes        48      male
  4.    Sherry Crooks        25    female
```

```
. tabulate sex

       sex |      Freq.     Percent        Cum.
-----------+-----------------------------------
      male |          2       50.00       50.00
    female |          2       50.00      100.00
-----------+-----------------------------------
     Total |          4      100.00
```

It is only almost irrelevant since we can make use of the underlying numbers in statistical analyses. For instance, if we were to ask Stata to calculate the mean of **sex** by typing **summarize sex**, Stata would report 0.5. We would interpret that to mean that one-half of our sample is female.

Value labels are permanently associated with variables. Thus, once we associate a value label with a variable, we never have to do so again. If we wanted to add another observation to this data, we could type

```
. input, label
                    name          age        sex
  5. "Mark Esman" 26 male
  6. end

.  _
```

❑

❑ Technical Note

The **automatic** option automates the definition of the value label. In the previous example, we informed Stata that **male** corresponds to 0 and **female** corresponds to 1 by typing **label define sexlbl 0 "male" 1 "female"**. It was not necessary to explicitly specify the mapping. Specifying the **automatic** option tells Stata to interpret what we type as follows:

First, see if it is a number. If so, store that number and be done with it. If it is not a number, check the value label associated with the variable in an attempt to interpret it. If an interpretation exists, store the corresponding numeric code. If one does not exist, add a new numeric code corresponding to what was typed. Store that new number and update the value label so that the new correspondence is never forgotten.

We can use these features to reenter our age and sex data. Before reentering the data, we **drop _all** and **label drop _all** to prove that we have nothing up our sleeve:

```
. drop _all
. label drop _all
. input str16 name byte(age sex:sexlbl), automatic
                    name          age        sex
  1. "Arthur Doyle" 22 male
  2. "Mary Hope" 37 "female"
  3. "Guy Fawkes" 48 male
  4. "Sherry Crooks" 25 female
  5. end

.  _
```

We previously defined the value label **sexlbl** so that **male** corresponded to 0 and **female** corresponded to 1. The label that Stata automatically created is slightly different but just as good:

```
. label list sexlbl
sexlbl:
           1 male
           2 female
```

❑

Also See

Title

insheet — Read ASCII (text) data created by a spreadsheet

Syntax

insheet [*varlist*] using *filename* [, <u>d</u>ouble [<u>no</u>]<u>n</u>ames <u>c</u>omma <u>t</u>ab clear]

If *filename* is specified without an extension, `.raw` is assumed.

Description

insheet reads into memory a disk dataset that is not in Stata format. insheet is intended for reading files created by a spreadsheet or database program. Regardless of the creator, insheet reads text (ASCII) files where there is one observation per line and the values are separated by tabs or commas. In addition, the first line of the file can contain the variable names or not. The best thing about insheet is that if you type

. insheet using *filename*

insheet will read your data; that's all there is to it.

Stata has other commands for reading data. If you are not sure that insheet is what you are looking for, see [R] **infile** and [U] **27 Commands to input data**. If you want to save your data in "spreadsheet-style" format, see [R] **outsheet**.

Options

double forces Stata to store variables as doubles rather than floats; see [U] **19.2.2 Numeric storage types**.

[no]names informs Stata whether variable names are included on the first line of the file. Specifying this option will speed insheet's processing—assuming you are right—but that is all. insheet can determine for itself whether the file includes variable names.

comma tells Stata that the values are comma-separated. Specifying this option will speed insheet's processing—assuming you are right—but that is all. insheet can determine for itself whether the separation character is a comma or a tab.

tab tells Stata the values are tab-separated. Specifying this option will speed insheet's processing—assuming you are right—but that is all. insheet can determine for itself whether the separation character is a tab or a comma.

clear specifies that it is okay for the new data to replace what is currently in memory. To ensure that you do not lose something important, insheet will refuse to read new data if data is already in memory. clear is one way you can tell insheet that it is okay. The other is to drop the data yourself by typing drop _all before reading new data.

Remarks

There is nothing to using `insheet`. You type

. insheet using *filename*

and `insheet` will read your data. That is, it will read your data if

1. It can find the file and

2. The file meets `insheet`'s expectations as to the format in which it is written.

Assuring 1 is easy enough; just realize that if you type `infix using myfile`, Stata interprets this as an instruction to read `myfile.raw`. If your file is called `myfile.txt`, type `infix using myfile.txt`.

As for the file's format, most spreadsheets and some database programs write data in the form `insheet` expects. It is easy enough to look—as we will show you—and it is even easier simply to try and see what happens. If typing

. insheet using *filename*

does not produce the desired result, you will have to try one of Stata's other `infile` commands; see [R] **infile**.

▷ Example

You have a raw data file on automobiles called `auto.raw`. This file was saved by a spreadsheet and can be read by typing

```
. insheet using auto
(5 vars, 10 obs)

. _
```

That done, we can now look at what we just loaded:

```
. describe
Contains data
  obs:             10
  vars:             5
  size:           290 (99.9% of memory free)
-------------------------------------------------------------------------------
    1. make        str13   %13s
    2. price       int     %8.0g
    3. mpg         byte    %8.0g
    4. rep78       byte    %8.0g
    5. foreign     str8    %9s
-------------------------------------------------------------------------------
Sorted by:
     Note:  data has changed since last save
. list
              make      price     mpg     rep78    foreign
   1.    AMC Concord      4099      22        3    Domestic
   2.      AMC Pacer      4749      17        3    Domestic
   3.     AMC Spirit      3799      22        .    Domestic
   4.  Buick Century      4816      20        3    Domestic
   5.  Buick Electra      7827      15        4    Domestic
   6.  Buick LeSabre      5788      18        3    Domestic
   7.     Buick Opel      4453      26        .    Domestic
   8.    Buick Regal      5189      20        3    Domestic
   9.  Buick Riviera     10372      16        3    Domestic
  10.  Buick Skylark      4082      19        3    Domestic
```

Note that this data contains a combination of string and numeric variables. insheet figured all that out by itself.

◁

❑ Technical Note

Now let's back up and look at the auto.raw file. Stata's type command will display files to the screen:

```
. type auto.raw
make     price   mpg    rep78   foreign
AMC Concord   4099   22    3       Domestic
AMC Pacer     4749   17    3       Domestic
AMC Spirit    3799   22            Domestic
Buick Century 4816   20    3       Domestic
Buick Electra 7827   15    4       Domestic
Buick LeSabre 5788   18    3       Domestic
Buick Opel    4453   26            Domestic
Buick Regal   5189   20    3       Domestic
Buick Riviera 10372  16    3       Domestic
Buick Skylark 4082   19    3       Domestic
```

This data has tab characters between values. Tab characters are difficult to see since they are invisible and hence indistinguishable from blanks. type's showtabs option makes the tabs visible:

```
. type auto.raw, showtabs
make<T>price<T>mpg<T>rep78<T>foreign
AMC Concord<T>4099<T>22<T>3<T>Domestic
AMC Pacer<T>4749<T>17<T>3<T>Domestic
AMC Spirit<T>3799<T>22<T><T>Domestic
Buick Century<T>4816<T>20<T>3<T>Domestic
Buick Electra<T>7827<T>15<T>4<T>Domestic
Buick LeSabre<T>5788<T>18<T>3<T>Domestic
Buick Opel<T>4453<T>26<T><T>Domestic
Buick Regal<T>5189<T>20<T>3<T>Domestic
Buick Riviera<T>10372<T>16<T>3<T>Domestic
Buick Skylark<T>4082<T>19<T>3<T>Domestic
```

This is an example of the kind of data insheet is willing to read. The first line contains the variable names—although that is not necessary. What is necessary is that the data values have tab characters between them.

insheet would be just as happy if the data values were separated by commas. Here is another variation on auto.raw that insheet can read:

```
. type auto2.raw
make,price,mpg,rep78,foreign
AMC Concord,4099,22,3,Domestic
AMC Pacer,4749,17,3,Domestic
AMC Spirit,3799,22,,Domestic
Buick Century,4816,20,3,Domestic
Buick Electra,7827,15,4,Domestic
Buick LeSabre,5788,18,3,Domestic
Buick Opel,4453,26,,Domestic
Buick Regal,5189,20,3,Domestic
Buick Riviera,10372,16,3,Domestic
Buick Skylark,4082,19,3,Domestic
```

It is easier for us human beings to see the commas rather than the tabs, but computers do not care one way or the other.

❑

▷ Example

The file does not have to contain variable names. Here is another variation on `auto.raw` without the first line and, this time, with commas rather than tabs separating the values:

```
. type auto3.raw
AMC Concord,4099,22,3,Domestic
AMC Pacer,4749,17,3,Domestic
 (output omitted )
Buick Skylark,4082,19,3,Domestic
```

Here is what happens when we read it:

```
. insheet using auto3
you must start with an empty dataset
r(18);

. _
```

Oops; we still have the data from the last example in memory.

```
. insheet using auto3, clear
(5 vars, 10 obs)

. describe

Contains data
  obs:             10
  vars:             5
  size:           290 (99.9% of memory free)
-------------------------------------------------------------------------------
    1. v1           str13   %13s
    2. v2           int     %8.0g
    3. v3           byte    %8.0g
    4. v4           byte    %8.0g
    5. v5           str8    %9s
-------------------------------------------------------------------------------
Sorted by:
     Note:  data has changed since last save

. list
                   v1        v2        v3        v4          v5
   1.     AMC Concord      4099        22         3    Domestic
   2.       AMC Pacer      4749        17         3    Domestic
 (output omitted )
  10. Buick Skylark       4082        19         3    Domestic
```

The only difference is that rather than the variables being nicely named `make`, `price`, `mpg`, `rep78`, and `foreign`, they are named v1, v2, ..., v5. We could now give our variables nicer names:

```
. rename v1 make

. rename v2 price

. _
```

Another alternative is to specify the variable names when we read the data:

```
. insheet make price mpg rep78 foreign using auto3, clear
(5 vars, 10 obs)

. list
                 make     price      mpg     rep78     foreign
   1.     AMC Concord      4099       22         3    Domestic
   2.       AMC Pacer      4749       17         3    Domestic
 (output omitted )
  10. Buick Skylark       4082       19         3    Domestic
```

If we use this approach, we must not specify too few variables

```
. insheet make price mpg rep78 using auto3, clear
too few variables specified
error in line 1 of file
r(102);
```

or too many.

```
. insheet make price mpg rep78 foreign weight using auto3, clear
too many variables specified
error in line 1 of file
r(103);
```

That is why we recommend

```
. insheet using filename
```

It is not difficult to rename your variables afterwards should that be necessary.

◁

▷ Example

About the only other thing that can go wrong is that the data is not appropriate for reading by insheet. Here is yet another version of the automobile data:

```
. type auto4.raw, showtabs
"AMC Concord"    4099 22  3  Domestic
"AMC Pacer"      4749 17  3  Domestic
"AMC Spirit"     3799 22  .  Domestic
"Buick Century"  4816 20  3  Domestic
"Buick Electra"  7827 15  4  Domestic
"Buick LeSabre"  5788 18  3  Domestic
"Buick Opel"     4453 26  .  Domestic
"Buick Regal"    5189 20  3  Domestic
"Buick Riviera" 10372 16  3  Domestic
"Buick Skylark"  4082 19  3  Domestic
```

Note that we specified type's showtabs option and no tabs are shown. This data is not tab-delimited nor comma-delimited and it is not the kind of data insheet is designed to read. Let's try insheet anyway:

```
. insheet using auto4, clear
(1 var, 10 obs)
. describe

Contains data
  obs:          10
  vars:          1
  size:        410 (99.9% of memory free)
-------------------------------------------------------------------------------
  1. v1          str37  %37s
-------------------------------------------------------------------------------
Sorted by:
     Note: data has changed since last save
. list
                                   v1
  1. AMC Concord    4099 22  3  Domestic
  2. AMC Pacer      4749 17  3  Domestic
 (output omitted)
 10. Buick Skylark  4082 19  3  Domestic
```

When `insheet` tries to read data that has no tabs or commas, it is fooled into thinking the data contains just one variable. If you had this data, you would have to read it with one of Stata's other commands. `infile` (free format) could read it.

◁

Also See

[U] **27 Commands to input data**

[R] **infile**, [R] **infile (free format)**, [R] **outfile**, [R] **outsheet**, [R] **save**

Title

inspect — Display simple summary of data's characteristics

Syntax

[by *varlist*:] <u>insp</u>ect [*varlist*] [if *exp*] [in *range*]

Description

The inspect command provides a quick summary of a numeric variable that differs from that provided by summarize or tabulate. It reports the number of negative, zero, and positive values; the number of integers and nonintegers; the number of unique values; the number of *missing*; and produces a small histogram. Its purpose is not analytical—instead it allows you to quickly gain familiarity with unknown data.

Remarks

Typing inspect by itself produces an inspection for all the variables in the data. If you specify the *varlist*, an inspection of just those variables is presented.

▷ Example

inspect is not a replacement or substitute for summarize and tabulate. It is instead a data management or information tool that lets you quickly gain insight into the values stored in a variable.

For instance, you receive data that purports to be on automobiles, and among the variables in the data is one called mpg. Its variable label is Mileage (mpg), which is surely suggestive. You inspect the variable:

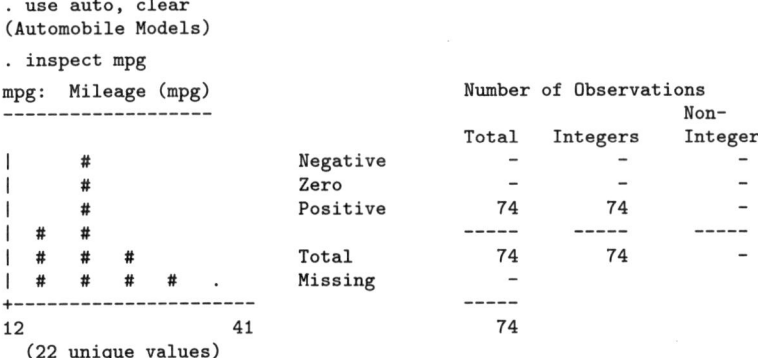

```
. use auto, clear
(Automobile Models)

. inspect mpg
mpg:  Mileage (mpg)                          Number of Observations
-------------------                                         Non-
                                        Total   Integers   Integers
   |     #                 Negative       -         -          -
   |     #                 Zero           -         -          -
   |     #                 Positive      74        74          -
   |  #  #                              -----     -----      -----
   |  #  #  #              Total         74        74          -
   |  #  #  #  #   .       Missing        -
   +---------------------              -----
   12                 41                 74
       (22 unique values)
```

You discover that the variable is never *missing*; all 74 observations in the data have some value for mpg. Moreover, the values are all positive and they are all integers as well. Among those 74 observations are 22 unique (different) values. The variable ranges from 12 to 41, and you are provided with a small histogram that suggests the variable appears to be what it claims.

◁

271

▷ Example

Bob, a co-worker, presents you with some census data. Among the variables in the data is one called `region` which is labeled `Census Region` and is evidently a numeric variable. You `inspect` this variable.

```
. use bobsdata

. inspect region
region:  Census Region                        Number of Observations
----------------------                                          Non-
                                             Total   Integers   Integers
    |         #             Negative           -         -         -
    |         #    #        Zero                -         -         -
    |    #    #    #        Positive           50        50        -
    |  # #    #    #                          -----     -----     -----
    |  # #    #    #        Total              50        50        -
    |  # #    #    #   .    Missing            -
    +----------------------                   -----
    1                  5                       50
         (5 unique values)
            region is labeled but 1 value is NOT documented in the label.
```

In this data something may be wrong. `region` takes on five unique values. The variable has a value label, however, and one of the observed values is not documented in the label. Perhaps there is a typographical error. A call to Bob would be in order.

◁

▷ Example

You call Bob and there was indeed an error. He fixes it and returns the data to you. Here is what `inspect` produces now:

```
. inspect region
region:  Census Region                        Number of Observations
----------------------                                          Non-
                                             Total   Integers   Integers
    |         #             Negative           -         -         -
    |         #             Zero                -         -         -
    |    #    #    #        Positive           50        50        -
    |  # #    #    #                          -----     -----     -----
    |  # #    #    #        Total              50        50        -
    |  # #    #    #        Missing            -
    +----------------------                   -----
    1              4                           50
         (4 unique values)
            region is labeled and all values are documented in the label.
```

◁

▷ Example

You receive data on the climate in 956 U.S. cities. The variable `tempjan` records the Average January temperature in Fahrenheit. The results of `inspect` are

```
. inspect tempjan
tempjan:  Average January temperature      Number of Observations
-------------------------------------                        Non-
                                            Total   Integers  Integers
  |      #                  Negative          -        -        -
  |      #                  Zero              -        -        -
  |      #                  Positive         954       78      876
  |      #   #   #                          -----    -----    -----
  |      #   #   #          Total           954       78      876
  |  .   #   #   #     .    Missing           2
  +----------------------                   -----
  2.2             72.6                       956
  (More than 99 unique values)
```

In two of the 956 observations, `tempjan` is *missing*. Of the 954 cities that have a recorded `tempjan`, all are positive and 78 of them are integer values. `tempjan` varies between 2.2 and 72.6. There are more than 99 unique values of `tempjan` in the data. (Stata gives up counting unique values after 99.)

◁

Saved Results

`inspect` saves in `_result()`:

1. no. of observations	6. no. of positive, integer observations
2. no. of negative observations	7. no. of unique values or . if
3. no. of zero observations	more than 99
4. no. of positive observations	8. no. of undocumented values or .
5. no. of negative, integer observations	if not labeled

Also See

[R] **codebook**, [R] **compare**, [R] **lv**, [R] **summarize**, [R] **table**, [R] **tabsum**, [R] **tabulate**

Title

ipolate — Linearly interpolate (extrapolate) values

Syntax

ipolate *yvar* *xvar*, <u>g</u>enerate(*newvar*) [by(*varnames*) <u>e</u>polate]

Description

ipolate creates *newvar* = *yvar* where *yvar* is not missing and fills in *newvar* with linearly interpolated (and optionally extrapolated) values of *yvar* where *yvar* is missing.

Options

<u>g</u>enerate(*newvar*) is not optional; it specifies the name of the new variable to be created.

by(*varnames*) specifies that interpolation (and extrapolation) is to be performed separately for the groups designated by equal values of *varnames*.

<u>e</u>polate specifies values are to be both interpolated and extrapolated. Interpolation only is the default.

Remarks

▷ Example

You have data points on **y** and **x** although, in some cases the observations on **y** are missing. You believe **y** is a function of **x** justifying filling in the missing values by linear interpolation:

```
. list

          x          y
  1.      0          .
  2.      1          3
  3.     1.5         .
  4.      2          6
  5.      3          .
  6.     3.5         .
  7.      4         18
. ipolate y x, gen(y1)
(1 missing value generated)
. ipolate y x, gen(y2) epolate
. list

          x          y         y1         y2
  1.      0          .          .          0
  2.      1          3          3          3
  3.     1.5         .         4.5        4.5
  4.      2          6          6          6
  5.      3          .         12         12
  6.     3.5         .         15         15
  7.      4         18         18         18
```

◁

274

▷ Example

You have a dataset of circulation of a magazine from 1970 through 1993. Circulation is recorded in a variable called `circ` and the year in `year`. In a few of the years, the circulation is not known as you want to fill it in by linear interpolation:

```
. ipolate circ year, gen(icirc)
```

Now assume you have data on the circulations of 50 magazines; the identity of the magazines is recorded in **magazine** (which might be a string variable—it does not matter):

```
. ipolate circ year, gen(icirc) by(magazine)
```

If **by()** is specified, interpolation is performed separately for each group.

◁

▷ Example

You have data on y and x although some of the y values are missing. You wish to smooth $y(x)$ using lowess (see [R] **ksm**) and then fill in missing values of y using interpolated values:

```
. ksm y x, gen(yls) lowess
. ipolate yls x, gen(iyls)
```

◁

Methods and Formulas

`ipolate` is implemented as an ado-file.

The value y at x is found by finding the closest points (x_0, y_0) and (x_1, y_1), such that $x_0 < x$ and $x_1 > x$, where y_0 and y_1 are observed, and calculating

$$y = \frac{y_1 - y_0}{x_1 - x_0}(x - x_0) + y_0$$

If `epolate` is specified and if (x_0, y_0) and (x_1, y_1) cannot be found on both sides of x, the two closest points on the same side of x are found and the same formula applied.

Also See

[R] **ksm**

Title

joinby — Form all pairwise combinations within groups

Syntax

joinby *varlist* using *filename*

Description

joinby joins, within groups formed by *varlist*, observations of the dataset in memory with *filename*, a Stata-format dataset. By join is meant "form all pairwise combinations". *filename* is required to be sorted by *varlist*. If *filename* is specified without an extension, '.dta' is assumed.

Observations unique to one or the other datasets are ignored. Whether one loads one dataset and joins the other or vice versa makes no difference in terms of the number of resulting observations.

If there are variables in common between the two datasets, however, the combined data will contain the values from the master data for those observations.

Remarks

The following, admittedly artificial, example illustrates joinby.

▷ Example

You have two datasets: child.dta and parent.dta. Both contain a famid variable which identifies the people belonging to the same family.

```
. use child
(Data on Children)

. describe

Contains data from child.dta
  obs:            5                          Data on Children
  vars:           4                          3 Jul 1996 09:17
  size:          50 (99.9% of memory free)
--------------------------------------------------------------------------------
  1. famid      int    %9.0g                 Family Id Number
  2. childid    byte   %9.0g                 Child Id Number
  3. x1         byte   %9.0g
  4. x2         int    %9.0g
--------------------------------------------------------------------------------
Sorted by:  famid

. list
        famid    childid       x1       x2
  1.    1025          3       11      320
  2.    1025          1       12      300
  3.    1025          4       10      275
  4.    1026          2       13      280
  5.    1027          5       15      210
```

```
. use parent, clear
(Data on Parents)

. describe

Contains data from parent.dta
  obs:            6                          Data on Parents
  vars:           4                          3 Jul 1996 09:16
  size:         108 (99.9% of memory free)
-------------------------------------------------------------------------------
   1. famid       int     %9.0g             Family Id Number
   2. parentid    float   %9.0g             Parent Id Number
   3. x1          float   %9.0g
   4. x3          float   %9.0g
-------------------------------------------------------------------------------
Sorted by:

. list

       famid    parentid        x1        x3
  1.    1030          10        39       600
  2.    1025          11        20       643
  3.    1025          12        27       721
  4.    1026          13        30       760
  5.    1026          14        26       668
  6.    1030          15        32       684
```

You want to "join" the information for the parents and their children. The data on parents is in memory; the data on children on disk. child.dta has been sorted by famid, but parent.dta has not been, so first we sort the parents data on famid:

```
. sort famid

. joinby famid using child

. describe

Contains data
  obs:            8                          Data on Parents
  vars:           6
  size:         168 (99.8% of memory free)
-------------------------------------------------------------------------------
   1. famid       int     %9.0g             Family Id Number
   2. parentid    float   %9.0g             Parent Id Number
   3. x1          float   %9.0g
   4. x3          float   %9.0g
   5. childid     byte    %9.0g             Child Id Number
   6. x2          int     %9.0g
-------------------------------------------------------------------------------
Sorted by:  famid

. list

       famid    parentid        x1        x3     childid        x2
  1.    1025          12        27       721           3       320
  2.    1025          11        20       643           4       275
  3.    1025          11        20       643           1       300
  4.    1025          12        27       721           1       300
  5.    1025          12        27       721           4       275
  6.    1025          11        20       643           3       320
  7.    1026          13        30       760           2       280
  8.    1026          14        26       668           2       280
```

Notice that

1. `famid` of 1027, which appears only in `child.dta`, and `famid` of 1030, which appears only in `parent.dta`, are not in the combined dataset. Observations for which the matching variable(s) are not in both datasets are omitted.

2. The `x1` variable is in both datasets. Values for this variable in the joined dataset are the values from `parent.dta`—the dataset in memory when we issued the `joinby` command. If we had `child.dta` in memory and `parent.dta` on disk when we requested `joinby`, the values for `x1` would have been from `child.dta`. Values from the dataset in memory take precedence over the dataset on disk.

◁

Methods and Formulas

`joinby` is implemented as an ado-file.

Also See

[U] **28 Commands for combining data**

[R] **append**, [R] **cross**, [R] **fillin**, [R] **merge**

Title

> **kappa** — Interrater agreement

Syntax

kap *varname*$_1$ *varname*$_2$ $\big[$*weight*$\big]$ $\big[$if *exp*$\big]$ $\big[$in *range*$\big]$ $\big[$, <u>t</u>ab <u>w</u>gt(*wgtid*) $\big]$

kapwgt *wgtid* $\big[$ 1 \ # 1 $\big[$\ # # 1 ...$\big]\big]$

kappa *varlist* $\big[$if *exp*$\big]$ $\big[$in *range*$\big]$

fweights are allowed; see [U] **18.1.6 weight**.

Description

kap calculates the kappa-statistic measure of interrater agreement when there are two unique raters and two or more ratings.

kapwgt defines weights for use by kap in measuring the importance of disagreements.

kappa calculates the kappa-statistic measure of interrater agreement in the case of two or more (nonunique) raters and two outcomes, more than two outcomes when the number of raters is fixed, and more than two outcomes when the number of raters varies.

Options

tab displays a tabulation of the assessments by the two raters.

wgt(*wgtid*) specifies that *wgtid* is to be used to weight disagreements. User-defined weights can be created using kapwgt. wgt(w), however, uses the "prerecorded" weights $1 - |i - j|/(k - 1)$, where i and j index the rows and columns of the ratings by the two raters and k is the maximum number of possible ratings. wgt(w2) uses the prerecorded weights $1 - [(i - j)/(k - 1)]^2$.

Remarks

The kappa-statistic measure of agreement is scaled to be 0 when the amount of agreement is what would be expected to be observed by chance and 1 when there is perfect agreement. For intermediate values, Landis and Koch (1977a, 165) suggest the following interpretations:

below 0.0	Poor
0.00–0.20	Slight
0.21–0.40	Fair
0.41–0.60	Moderate
0.61–0.80	Substantial
0.81–1.00	Almost Perfect

The case of 2 raters

▷ Example

Consider the classification by two radiologists of 85 xeromammograms as normal, benign disease, suspicion of cancer, or cancer (a subset of the data from Boyd et al. 1982 and discussed in the context of kappa in Altman 1991, 403—405).

```
. tabulate rada radb

Radiologist| Radiologist B's assessment
A's        |
assessment |    Normal     benign    suspect     cancer |     Total
-----------+--------------------------------------------+----------
    Normal |        21         12          0          0 |        33
    benign |         4         17          1          0 |        22
   suspect |         3          9         15          2 |        29
    cancer |         0          0          0          1 |         1
-----------+--------------------------------------------+----------
     Total |        28         38         16          3 |        85
```

Our data contains two variables: `rada`, radiologist A's assessment; `radb`, radiologist B's assessment. Each observation is a patient.

We can obtain the kappa measure of interrater agreement by typing

```
. kap rada radb
              Expected
Agreement    Agreement      Kappa          Z        Pr>Z
----------------------------------------------------------
  63.53%       30.82%       0.4728       6.81      0.0000
```

Had each radiologist made his determination randomly (but with probabilities equal to the overall proportions), we would expect the two radiologists to agree on 30.8% of the patients. In fact, they agreed on 63.5% of the patients, or 47.3% of the way between random agreement and perfect agreement. The amount of agreement indicates that we can reject that they are making their determinations randomly.

◁

▷ Example

There is a difference between two radiologists disagreeing whether a xeromammogram indicates cancer or the suspicion of cancer and disagreeing whether it indicates cancer or is normal. The weighted kappa attempts to deal with this. `kap` provides two "prerecorded" weights, `w` and `w2`:

```
. kap rada radb, wgt(w)
Ratings weighted by:
    1.0000    0.6667    0.3333    0.0000
    0.6667    1.0000    0.6667    0.3333
    0.3333    0.6667    1.0000    0.6667
    0.0000    0.3333    0.6667    1.0000

              Expected
Agreement    Agreement      Kappa          Z        Pr>Z
----------------------------------------------------------
  86.67%       69.11%       0.5684       7.22      0.0000
```

The `w` weights are given by $1 - |i - j|/(k - 1)$ where i and j index the rows of columns of the ratings by the two raters and k is the maximum number of possible ratings. The weighting matrix is printed above the table. In our case, the rows and columns of the 4×4 matrix correspond to the ratings normal, benign, suspicious, and cancerous.

A weight of 1 indicates an observation should count as perfect agreement. The matrix has 1's down the diagonals—when both radiologists make the same assessment, they are in agreement. A weight of, say, 0.6667 means they are in two-thirds agreement. In our matrix they get that score if they are "one apart"—one radiologist assesses cancer and the other is merely suspicious, or one is suspicious and the other says benign, and so on. An entry of 0.3333 means they are in one-third agreement or, if you prefer, two-thirds disagreement. That is the score attached when they are "two apart". Finally, they are in complete disagreement when the weight is zero, which happens only when they are three apart—one says cancer and the other says normal.

◁

▷ Example

The other prerecorded weight is w2 where the weights are given by $1 - [(i-j)/(k-1)]^2$:

```
. kap rada radb, wgt(w2)
Ratings weighted by:
   1.0000   0.8889   0.5556   0.0000
   0.8889   1.0000   0.8889   0.5556
   0.5556   0.8889   1.0000   0.8889
   0.0000   0.5556   0.8889   1.0000
                Expected
 Agreement    Agreement      Kappa         Z        Pr>Z
-------------------------------------------------------------
   94.77%       84.09%       0.6714       6.22      0.0000
```

The w2 weight makes the categories even more alike and is probably inappropriate here.

◁

▷ Example

In addition to prerecorded weights, you can define your own weights with the **kapwgt** command. For instance, you might feel that suspicious and cancerous are reasonably similar, benign and normal reasonably similar, but the suspicious/cancerous group is nothing like the benign/normal group:

```
. kapwgt xm 1 \ .8 1 \ 0 0 1 \ 0 0 .8 1
. kapwgt xm
1.0000
0.8000 1.0000
0.0000 0.0000 1.0000
0.0000 0.0000 0.8000 1.0000
```

You name the weights—we named ours **xm**—and after the weight name, you enter the lower triangle of the weighting matrix, using \ to separate rows. In our example we have four outcomes and so continued entering numbers until we had defined the fourth row of the weighting matrix. If you type **kapwgt** followed by a name and nothing else, it shows you the weights recorded under that name. Satisfied that we have entered them correctly, we now use the weights to recalculate kappa:

```
. kap rada radb, wgt(xm)
```

```
Ratings weighted by:
   1.0000    0.8000    0.0000    0.0000
   0.8000    1.0000    0.0000    0.0000
   0.0000    0.0000    1.0000    0.8000
   0.0000    0.0000    0.8000    1.0000
```

Agreement	Expected Agreement	Kappa	Z	Pr>Z
80.47%	52.67%	0.5874	6.79	0.0000

◁

❏ Technical Note

In addition to weights for weighting the differences in categories, you can specify Stata's traditional weights for weighting the data. In the examples above, we have 85 observations in our dataset—one for each patient. If all we knew was the table of outcomes—that there were 21 patients rated normal by both radiologists, etc.—it would be easier to enter the table into Stata and work from it. The easiest way to enter the data is with `tabi`; see [R] **tabulate**.

```
. tabi 21 12 0 0 \ 4 17 1 0 \ 3 9 15 2 \ 0 0 0 1, replace
          | col
      row |         1         2         3         4 |     Total
----------+--------------------------------------------+----------
        1 |        21        12         0         0 |        33
        2 |         4        17         1         0 |        22
        3 |         3         9        15         2 |        29
        4 |         0         0         0         1 |         1
----------+--------------------------------------------+----------
    Total |        28        38        16         3 |        85

          Pearson chi2(9) =  77.8111   Pr = 0.000
```

`tabi` felt obligated to tell us the Pearson χ^2 for this table, but we do not care about it. The important thing is that, with the `replace` option, `tabi` left the table in memory:

```
. list in 1/5
          row       col       pop
   1.       1         1        21
   2.       1         2        12
   3.       1         3         0
   4.       1         4         0
   5.       2         1         4
```

The variable `row` is radiologist A's assessment; `col`, radiologist B's assessment; and `pop` the number so assessed by both. Thus,

```
. kap row col [freq=pop]
```

Agreement	Expected Agreement	Kappa	Z	Pr>Z
63.53%	30.82%	0.4728	6.81	0.0000

If we are going to keep this data, the names `row` and `col` are not indicative of what the data reflects. We could (see [U] **19.6 Dataset, variable, and value labels**)

```
. rename row rada
. rename col radb
. label var rada "Radiologist A's assessment"
. label var radb "Radiologist B's assessment"
```

```
. label define assess 1 normal 2 benign 3 suspect 4 cancer
. label values rada assess
. label values radb assess
. label data "Altman p. 403"
```

kap's tab option, which can be used with or without weighted data, shows the table of assessments:

```
. kap rada radb [freq=pop], tab
Radiologist| Radiologist B's assessment
A's        |
assessment |   normal    benign   suspect    cancer |    Total
-----------+--------------------------------------------+----------
    normal |       21        12         0         0 |       33
    benign |        4        17         1         0 |       22
   suspect |        3         9        15         2 |       29
    cancer |        0         0         0         1 |        1
-----------+--------------------------------------------+----------
     Total |       28        38        16         3 |       85

             Expected
Agreement   Agreement     Kappa         Z       Pr>Z
-------------------------------------------------------
 63.53%       30.82%      0.4728      6.81     0.0000
```

The case of more than two raters

In the case of more than two raters, the mathematics are such that the two raters are not considered unique. For instance, if there are three raters, there is no assumption that the three raters who rate the first subject are the same as the three raters that rate the second. Although we call this the more than two raters case, it can be used with two raters when the identities of the two raters vary.

The nonunique rater case can be usefully broken down into three subcases: (a) there are two possible ratings which we will call positive and negative; (b) there are more than two possible ratings but the number of raters per subject is the same for all subjects; and (c) there are more than two possible ratings and the number of raters per subject varies. kappa handles all of these cases. To emphasize that there is no assumption of constant identity of raters across subjects, the variables specified contain counts of the number of raters rating the subject into a particular category.

▷ Example

(Two ratings.) Fleiss (1981, 227) offers the following hypothetical ratings by different sets of raters on 25 subjects:

Subject	No. of raters	No. of pos. ratings	Subject	No. of raters	No. of pos. ratings
1	2	2	14	4	3
2	2	0	15	2	0
3	3	2	16	2	2
4	4	3	17	3	1
5	3	3	18	2	1
6	4	1	19	4	1
7	3	0	20	5	4
8	5	0	21	3	2
9	2	0	22	4	0
10	4	4	23	3	0
11	5	5	24	3	3
12	3	3	25	2	2
13	4	4			

We have entered this data into Stata and the variables are called `subject`, `raters`, and `pos`. `kappa`, however, requires we specify variables containing the number of positive ratings and negative ratings; that is, `pos` and `raters-pos`:

```
. gen neg = raters-pos
. kappa pos neg
Two-outcomes, multiple raters:
        Kappa       Z        Pr>Z
      -----------------------------
        0.5415     5.28      0.0000
```

We would have obtained the same results if we had typed **kappa neg pos**.

◁

▷ Example

(More than two ratings, constant number of raters.) Each of ten subjects is rated into one of three categories by five raters (Fleiss 1981, 230):

```
. list
        subject     cat1     cat2     cat3
  1.        1         1        4        0
  2.        2         2        0        3
  3.        3         0        0        5
  4.        4         4        0        1
  5.        5         3        0        2
  6.        6         1        4        0
  7.        7         5        0        0
  8.        8         0        4        1
  9.        9         1        0        4
 10.       10         3        0        2
```

We obtain the kappa statistic:

```
. kappa cat1-cat3
        Outcome |   Kappa          Z        Pr>Z
    ------------+--------------------------------
          cat1 |   0.2917       2.92       0.0018
          cat2 |   0.6710       6.71       0.0000
          cat3 |   0.3490       3.49       0.0002
    ------------+--------------------------------
      combined |   0.4179       5.83       0.0000
```

The first part of the output shows the results of calculating kappa for each of the categories separately against an amalgam of the remaining categories. For instance, the `cat1` line is the two-rating kappa where positive is `cat1` and negative is `cat2` or `cat3`. The test statistic, however, is calculated differently (see *Methods and Formulas*). The combined kappa is the appropriately weighted average of the individual kappas. Note that there is considerably less agreement about the rating of subjects into the first category than there is for the third.

◁

▷ Example

(More than two ratings, varying number of raters.) In this unfortunate case, kappa can be calculated, but there is no test statistic for testing against $\kappa > 0$. You do nothing differently—**kappa** calculates the total number of raters for each patient and, if it is not a constant, suppresses the calculation of test statistics:

```
. kappa cat1-cat3
             Outcome |   Kappa         Z        Pr>Z
    -----------------+----------------------------------
                cat1 |   0.3520        .         .
                cat2 |   0.7781        .         .
                cat3 |   0.3380        .         .
    -----------------+----------------------------------
            combined |   0.4674        .         .
```
note: Number of ratings per subject vary; cannot calculate test
       statistics.

◁

Saved Results

kap and kappa save in the S_# macros:

S_1	number of subjects	S_4	kappa
S_2	observed proportion of agreement	S_5	z statistic
S_3	expected proportion of agreement		

kappa defines S_4 and S_5 only.

Methods and Formulas

kap, kapwgt, and kappa are implemented as ado-files.

The kappa statistic was first proposed by Cohen (1960). The generalization for weights reflecting the relative seriousness of each possible disagreement is due to Cohen (1968). The analysis-of-variance approach for $k = 2$ and $m \geq 2$ is due to Landis and Koch (1977b). See Altman (1991, 403–409) for an introductory treatment and Fleiss (1981, 212–236) for a more thorough treatment. All formulas below are as presented in Fleiss (1981). Let m be the number of raters and k be the number of rating outcomes.

kap: m = 2

Define w_{ij} ($i = 1, \ldots, k$, $j = 1, \ldots, k$) as the weights for agreement and disagreement (wgt()) or, if not weighted, define $w_{ii} = 1$ and $w_{ij} = 0$ for $i \neq j$. If wgt(w) is specified, $w_{ij} = 1 - |i - j|/(k-1)$. If wgt(w2) is specified, $w_{ij} = 1 - \left((i - j)/(k - 1) \right)^2$.

The observed proportion of agreement is

$$p_o = \sum_{i=1}^{k} w_{ii} p_{ii}$$

where p_{ij} is the fraction of ratings i by the first rater and j by the second. The expected proportion of agreement is

$$p_e = \sum_{i=1}^{k} \sum_{j=1}^{k} w_{ij} p_{i\cdot} p_{\cdot j}$$

where $p_{i.} = \sum_j p_{ij}$ and $p_{.j} = \sum_i p_{ij}$.

Kappa is given by $\widehat{\kappa} = (p_o - p_e)/(1 - p_e)$.

The standard error of $\widehat{\kappa}$ for testing against 0 is

$$\widehat{s}_0 = \frac{1}{(1 - p_e)\sqrt{n}}\sqrt{\left(\sum_i \sum_j p_{i.} p_{.j}[w_{ij} - (\overline{w}_{i.} + \overline{w}_{.j})]^2\right) - p_e^2}$$

where n is the number of subjects being rated and $\overline{w}_{i.} = \sum_j p_{.j} w_{ij}$ and $\overline{w}_{.j} = \sum_i p_{i.} w_{ij}$. The test statistic $Z = \kappa/s_0$ is assumed to be distributed $N(0,1)$.

kappa: m > 2, k = 2

Each subject i, $i = 1, \ldots, n$, is found by x_i of m_i raters to be positive (the choice as to what is labeled positive being arbitrary).

The overall proportion of positive ratings is $\overline{p} = \sum_i x_i/(n\overline{m})$, where $\overline{m} = \sum_i m_i/n$. The between-subjects mean square is (approximately)

$$B = \frac{1}{n}\sum_i \frac{(x_i - m_i\overline{p})^2}{m_i}$$

and the within-subject mean square is

$$W = \frac{1}{n(\overline{m} - 1)}\sum_i \frac{x_i(m_i - x_i)}{m_i}$$

Kappa is then defined

$$\widehat{\kappa} = \frac{B - W}{B + (\overline{m} - 1)W}$$

The standard error for testing against 0 (Fleiss and Cuzick 1979) is approximately equal to and calculated as

$$\widehat{s}_0 = \frac{1}{(\overline{m} - 1)\sqrt{n\overline{m}_H}}\sqrt{2(\overline{m}_H - 1) + \frac{(\overline{m} - \overline{m}_H)(1 - 4\overline{p}\overline{q})}{\overline{m}\,\overline{p}\overline{q}}}$$

where $\overline{m}_H$ is the harmonic mean of m_i and $\overline{q} = 1 - \overline{p}$.

The test statistic $Z = \widehat{\kappa}/\widehat{s}_0$ is assumed to be distributed $N(0,1)$.

kappa: m > 2, k > 2

Let x_{ij} be the number or ratings on subject i, $i = 1, \ldots, n$, into category j, $j = 1, \ldots, k$. Define $\overline{p}_j$ as the overall proportion of ratings in category j, $\overline{q}_j = 1 - \overline{p}_j$, and let $\widehat{\kappa}_j$ be the kappa statistic given above for $k = 2$ when category j is compared with the amalgam of all other categories. Kappa is (Landis and Koch 1977b)

$$\overline{\kappa} = \frac{\sum_j \overline{p}_j \overline{q}_j \widehat{\kappa}_j}{\sum_j \overline{p}_j \overline{q}_j}$$

In the case where the number of raters per subject $\sum_j x_{ij}$ is a constant m for all i, Fleiss, Nee, and Landis (1979) derived the following formulas for the approximate standard errors. The standard error for testing $\widehat{\kappa}_j$ against 0 is

$$\widehat{s}_j = \sqrt{\frac{2}{nm(m-1)}}$$

and the standard error for testing $\overline{\kappa}$ is

$$\overline{s} = \frac{\sqrt{2}}{\sum_j \overline{p}_j \overline{q}_j \sqrt{nm(m-1)}} \sqrt{\left(\sum_j \overline{p}_j \overline{q}_j\right)^2 - \sum_j \overline{p}_j \overline{q}_j (\overline{q}_j - \overline{p}_j)}$$

References

Altman, D. G. 1991. *Practical Statistics for Medical Research.* London: Chapman & Hall.

Boyd, N. F., C. Wolfson, M. Moskowitz, T. Carlile, M. Petitclerc, H. A. Ferri, E. Fishell, A. Gregoire, M. Kiernan, J. D. Longley, I. S. Simor, and A. B. Miller. 1982. Observer variation in the interpretation of xeromammograms. *Journal of the National Cancer Institute* 68: 357–63.

Cohen, J. 1960. A coefficient of agreement for nominal scales. *Educational and Psychological Measurement* 20: 37–46.

———. 1968. Weighted kappa: Nominal scale agreement with provision for scaled disagreement or partial credit. *Psychological Bulletin* 70: 213–220.

Fleiss, J. L. 1981. *Statistical Methods for Rates and Proportions.* 2d ed. New York: John Wiley & Sons.

Fleiss, J. L. and J. Cuzick. 1979. The reliability of dichotomous judgments: unequal numbers of judges per subject. *Applied Psychological Measurement* 3: 537–542.

Fleiss, J. L., J. C. M. Nee, and J. R. Landis. 1979. Large sample variance of kappa in the case of different sets of raters. *Psychological Bulletin* 86: 974–977.

Landis, J. R. and G. G. Koch. 1977a. The measurement of observer agreement for categorical data. *Biometrics* 33: 159–174.

———. 1977b. A one-way components of variance model for categorical data. *Biometrics* 33: 671–679.

Also See

[R] **tabulate**

Title

> **kdensity** — Univariate kernel density estimation

Syntax

kdensity *varname* [*weight*] [if *exp*] [in *range*]

    [, <u>noden</u>sity <u>nog</u>raph generate(*newvar$_x$ newvar$_{density}$*) n(#) <u>w</u>idth(#)

        { <u>bi</u>weight| <u>cos</u>ine| <u>epan</u>| <u>gauss</u>| <u>parzen</u>| <u>rec</u>tangle| <u>tri</u>angle }

        <u>nor</u>mal <u>stud</u>(#) at(*var$_x$*) symbol(...) <u>c</u>onnect(...) <u>t</u>itle(*string*)

        graph_options]

fweights and aweights are allowed; see [U] **18.1.6 weight**.

Description

kdensity produces kernel density estimates and graphs the result.

Options

nodensity specifies that the graph should not be drawn on a density scale and/or that *newvar$_{density}$* in the **gen** option should not be returned on the density scale. You can convert the scale to the density scale (area under the curve to equal one) using the scale factor that is saved in the global macro S_4. This option is included for backward compatibility.

nograph suppresses drawing the graph. This option is often used in combination with the generate() option.

generate(*newvar$_x$ newvar$_{density}$*) stores the results of the estimation. *newvar$_{density}$* will contain the density estimate. *newvar$_x$* will contain the points at which the density is estimated.

n(#) specifies the number of points at which the density estimate is to be evaluated. The default is min($N, 50$), where N is the number of observations in memory.

width(#) specifies the halfwidth of the kernel, the width of the density window around each point. If w() is not specified, then the "optimal" width is calculated and used. The optimal width is the width that would minimize the mean integrated square error if the data were Gaussian and a Gaussian kernel were used and so is not optimal in any global sense. In fact, for multimodal and highly skewed densities, this width is usually too wide and oversmooths the density (Silverman 1986).

biweight, cosine, epan, gauss, parzen, rectangle, and triangle specify the kernel. By default, epan, specifying the Epanechnikov kernel, is used.

normal requests that a normal density be overlaid on the density estimate for comparison.

stud(#) specifies that a Student's t distribution with # degrees of freedom be overlaid on the density estimate for comparison.

288

at(*var$_x$*) specifies a variable that contains the values at which the density should be estimated. This option allows you to more easily obtain density estimates for different variables or different subsamples of a variable and then overlay the estimated densities for comparison.

symbol(...) is graph, twoway's symbol() option for specifying the plotting symbol. The default is symbol(o); see [R] **graph symbol**.

connect(...) is graph, twoway's connect() option for how points are connected. The default is connect(l), meaning points are connected with straight lines; see [R] **graph connect**.

title(*string*) is graph, twoway's title() option for specifying the title. The default title is "Kernel Density Estimate"; see [R] **graph titles**.

graph_options are any of the other options allowed with graph, twoway; see [R] **graph twoway**.

Remarks

Kernel density estimators approximate the density $f(x)$ from observations on x. Histograms do this too, and, in fact, the histogram itself is a kind of kernel density estimate. The data is divided into nonoverlapping intervals and counts of the number of data points within each interval are made. Histograms are bar graphs that depict these frequency counts—the bar is centered at the midpoint of each interval—and its height reflects the average number of data points in the interval.

In more general kernel density estimates, the range is still divided into intervals and estimates of the density at the center of intervals are produced. One difference is that the intervals are allowed to overlap. One can think of sliding the interval—called a window—along the range of the data and collecting the center-point density estimates. The second difference is that, rather than merely counting the number of observations in a window, a weight between 0 and 1 is assigned—based on the distance from the center of the window—and it is the weighted values that are summed. The function that determines these weights is called the kernel.

Kernel density estimates have the advantages of being smooth and of being independent of the choice of origin (corresponding to the location of the bins in a histogram).

See Salgado-Ugarte, Shimizu, and Taniuchi (1993) and Fox (1990) for discussions of kernel density estimators, stressing their use as exploratory data analysis tools.

▷ Example

Goeden (1978) reports data consisting of 316 length observations of coral trout. We wish to investigate the underlying density of the lengths. To begin on familiar ground, we might draw a histogram. In [R] **graph histogram**, we suggest setting the bins to $\min(\sqrt{n}, 10 \cdot \log_{10}n)$, which for $n = 316$ is roughly 18:

. graph length, xlab ylab bin(18)

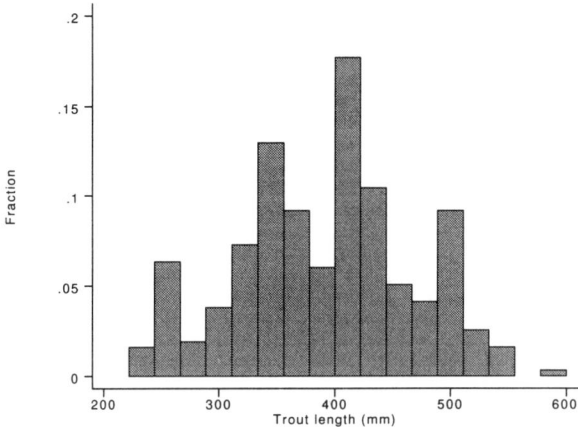

The kernel density estimate, on the other hand, is smooth.

. kdensity length, xlab ylab

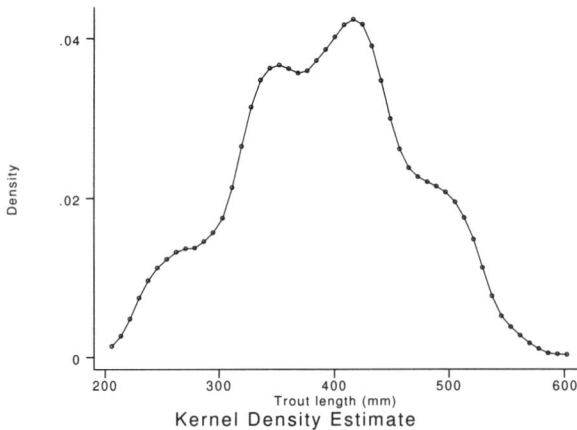

Kernel Density Estimate

Kernel density estimators are, however, sensitive to an assumption just as are histograms. In histograms, we specify a number of bins. For kernel density estimators, we specify a width. In the graph above, we used the default width. kdensity is smarter than graph, histogram in that its default width is not a fixed constant, but even so, the default width is not necessarily best.

kdensity saves the width it used in the global macro S_3, so typing display $S_3 reveals it. Doing this, we discover the width is approximately 20.

Widths are similar to the inverse of the number of bins in a histogram; smaller widths mean more detail. The units of the width are the units of x, the variable being analyzed. The width is specified as a halfwidth, meaning the kernel density estimator with halfwidth 20 corresponds to sliding a window of size 40 across the data.

We can specify halfwidths for ourselves using the w() option. Smaller widths do not smooth the density as much:

. kdensity length, epan xlab ylab w(10)

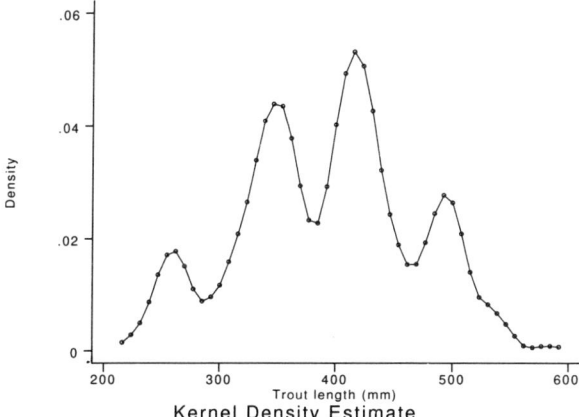

Kernel Density Estimate

. kdensity length, epan xlab ylab w(15)

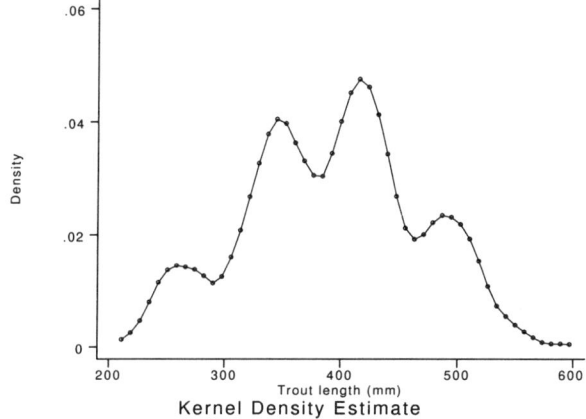

Kernel Density Estimate

◁

▷ Example

Widths held constant, different kernels can produce surprisingly different results. This is really an attribute of the kernel and width combination; for a given width, some kernels are more sensitive than others at identifying peaks in the density estimate.

We can see this using a dataset with lots of peaks. In the automobile data, we characterize the density of weight, the weight of the vehicles. Below, we compare the Epanechnikov and Parzen kernels.

```
. kdensity weight, epan nogr g(x epan)
. kdensity weight, parzen nogr g(x2 parzen)
. label var epan "Epanechnikov Density Estimate"
. label var parzen "Parzen Density Estimate"
. gr epan parzen x, xlab ylab c(ll)
```

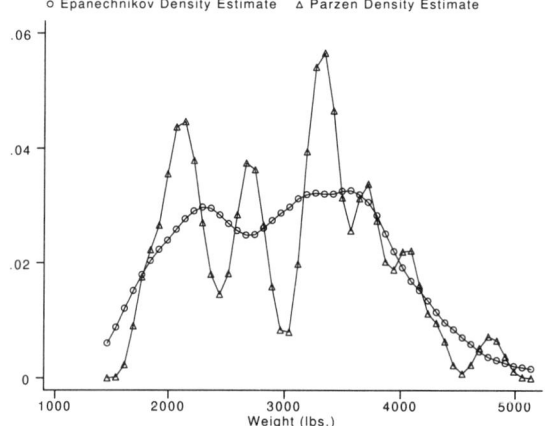

We did not specify a width and so obtained the default width. That width is not a function of the selected kernel, but of data. See the *Methods and Formulas* section for the calculation of the optimal width.

◁

▷ Example

In examining the density estimates, we may wish to overlay a normal density or a Student's t density for comparison. Again using the weights of automobiles, we can get an idea of the distance from normality with the normal option

```
. kdensity weight, epan normal xlab ylab
```

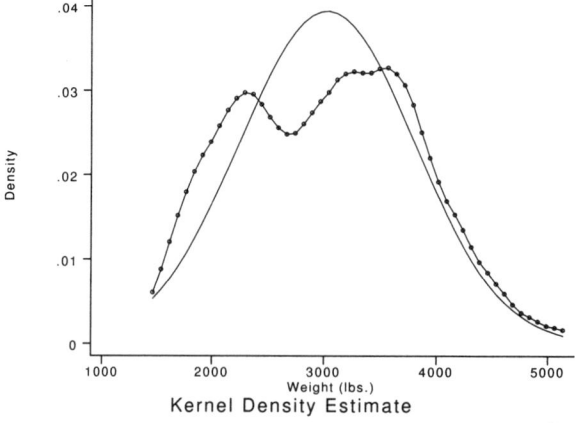

◁

▷ Example

Another common desire in examining density estimates is to compare two or more densities. In this example, we will compare the density estimates of the weights for the foreign and domestic cars.

```
. kdensity weight, nogr gen(x fx)
. kdensity weight if foreign==0, nogr gen(fx0) at(x)
. kdensity weight if foreign==1, nogr gen(fx1) at(x)
. label var fx0 "Domestic cars"
. label var fx1 "Foreign cars"
. gr fx0 fx1 x, c(ll) s(TS) xlab ylab
```

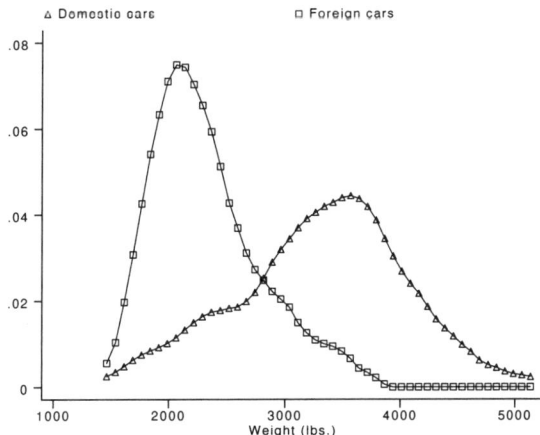

◁

Saved Results

kdensity saves in the S_# macros:

S_1   Name of the kernel used in the estimation exercise
S_2   Number of points at which the estimate was evaluated
S_3   Window width
S_4   Scale factor

Methods and Formulas

kdensity is implemented as an ado-file.

A kernel density estimate is formed by summing the weighted values calculated with the kernel function K as in

$$\widehat{f_K} = \frac{1}{nh} \sum_{i=1}^{n} K\left[\frac{x - X_i}{h}\right]$$

where we may define various kernel functions. **kdensity** includes seven different kernel functions. The Epanechnikov is the default function if no other kernel is specified and has the property that it is the most efficient in minimizing the mean integrated squared error.

Kernel	Formula	
Biweight	$K[z] = \begin{cases} \frac{15}{16}(1-z^2)^2 \\ 0 \end{cases}$	if $|z| < 1$ otherwise
Cosine	$K[z] = \begin{cases} 1 + \cos(2\pi z) \\ 0 \end{cases}$	if $|z| < 1/2$ otherwise
Epanechnikov	$K[z] = \begin{cases} \frac{3}{4}(1 - \frac{1}{5}z^2)/\sqrt{5} \\ 0 \end{cases}$	if $|z| < \sqrt{5}$ otherwise
Gaussian	$K[z] = \frac{1}{\sqrt{2\pi}}e^{-z^2/2}$	
Parzen	$K[z] = \begin{cases} \frac{4}{3} - 8z^2 + 8|z|^3 \\ 8(1 - |z|)^3/3 \end{cases}$	if $|z| \leq 1/2$ otherwise
Rectangular	$K[z] = \begin{cases} 1/2 \\ 0 \end{cases}$	if $|z| < 1$ otherwise
Triangular	$K[z] = \begin{cases} 1 - |z| \\ 0 \end{cases}$	if $|z| < 1$ otherwise

From the definitions given in the table one can see that the choice of h will drive how many values are included in estimating the density at each point. This value is called the *window width* or *bandwidth*. If the window width is not specified, then it is determined as

$$m = \min\left(\sqrt{\text{variance}_x}, \; \frac{\text{interquartile range}_x}{1.349}\right)$$

$$h = \frac{0.9m}{n^{1/5}}$$

where x is the variable for which we wish to estimate the kernel and n is the number of observations.

Most researchers agree that the choice of kernel is not as important as the choice of bandwidth. There is a great deal of literature on choosing bandwidths under various conditions; see for example Parzen (1962) or Tapia and Thompson (1978). See also Newton (1988) for a comparison with sample spectral density estimation in time series applications.

Acknowledgment

We gratefully acknowledge the previous work by Isaías H. Salgado-Ugarte, Makoto Shimizu, and Toru Taniuchi (1993) of the University of Tokyo. Their article provides the reader with a good overview of the subject of univariate kernel density estimation and presents arguments for its use in exploratory data analysis.

References

Fox, J. 1990. Describing univariate distributions. In *Modern Methods of Data Analysis*, ed. J. Fox and J. S. Long, 58–125. Newbury Park, CA: Sage Publications.

Goeden, G. B. 1978. A monograph of the coral trout, *Plectropomus leopardus* (Lacépède). *Res. Bull. Fish. Serv. Queensl.* 1: 42 p.

Newton, H. J. 1988. *TIMESLAB: A Time Series Analysis Laboratory*. Belmont, CA: Wadsworth & Brooks/Cole.

Parzen, E. 1962. On estimation of a probability density function and mode. *Annals of Mathematical Statistics* 32: 1065–1076.

Salgado-Ugarte, I. H., M. Shimizu, and T. Taniuchi. 1993. snp6: Exploring the shape of univariate data using kernel density estimators. *Stata Technical Bulletin* 16: 8–19. Reprinted in *Stata Technical Bulletin Reprints*, vol. 3, pp. 155–173.

——. 1995. snp6.1: ASH, WARPing, and kernel density estimation for univariate data. *Stata Technical Bulletin* 26: 23–31. Reprinted in *Stata Technical Bulletin Reprints*, vol. 5, pp. 161–172.

——. 1995. snp6.2: Practical rules for bandwidth selection in univariate density estimation. *Stata Technical Bulletin* 27: 5–19. Reprinted in *Stata Technical Bulletin Reprints*, vol. 5, pp. 172–190.

Silverman, B. W. 1986. *Density Estimation for Statistics and Data Analysis*. London: Chapman & Hall.

Tapia, R. A., and J. R. Thompson. 1978. *Nonparametric Probability Density Estimation*. Baltimore: Johns Hopkins University Press.

Also See

[R] **graph histogram**, [R] **hist**

Title

ksm — Smoothing including lowess

Syntax

ksm *yvar* *xvar* [if *exp*] [in *range*] [, line weight lowess bwidth(#) logit

adjust gen(*newvar*) nograph *graph_options*]

Description

ksm carries out unweighted and locally weighted smoothing of *yvar* on *xvar*, displays the graph, and optionally saves the smoothed variable. Among ksm's capabilities are lowess (robust locally weighted regression, Cleveland 1979). See Cleveland (1993, 94–101) for a discussion of lowess.

Warning: ksm is computationally intensive and may therefore take a long time to run on a slow computer. Lowess calculations on 1,000 observations, for instance, require estimating 1,000 regressions.

Options

line specifies running-line least-squares smoothing; default is running mean.

weight specifies use of Cleveland's (1979) tricube weighting function; default is unweighted.

lowess is equivalent to specifying line weight and requests Cleveland's lowess running-line smoother.

bwidth(#) specifies the bandwidth. Centered subsets of bwidth · N observations are used for calculating smoothed values for each point in the data except for the end points, where smaller, uncentered subsets are used. The greater the bwidth, the greater the smoothing. Default is 0.8.

logit transforms the smoothed *yvar* into logits. Predicted values less than .0001 or greater than .9999 are set to $1/N$ and $1 - 1/N$, respectively, before taking logits.

adjust adjusts the mean of the smoothed *yvar* to equal the mean of *yvar* by multiplying by an appropriate factor. This is useful when smoothing binary (0/1) data.

gen(*newvar*) creates *newvar* containing the smoothed values of *yvar* in addition to or instead of displaying the graph.

nograph suppresses displaying the graph.

graph_options are any of the options allowed with graph, twoway; see [R] **graph twoway**.

Remarks

The most common use of ksm is to provide lowess—locally weighted scatterplot smoothing. The basic idea is to create a new variable (*newvar*) that, for each *yvar* y_i, contains the corresponding smoothed value. The smoothed values are obtained by running a regression of *yvar* on *xvar* using only the data (x_i, y_i) and a small amount of the data near the point. In lowess, the regression is weighted so that the central point (x_i, y_i) gets the highest weight and points farther away (based on the distance $|x_j - x_i|$) receive less. The estimated regression is then used to predict the smoothed value $\widehat{y}_i$ for y_i only. The procedure is repeated to obtain the remaining smoothed values, which means a separate weighted regression is estimated for every point in the data.

Lowess is a desirable smoother because of its locality—it tends to follow the data. Polynomial smoothing methods, for instance, are global in that what happens on the extreme left of a scatterplot can affect the fitted values on the extreme right.

▷ Example

The amount of smoothing is affected by the `bwidth` and you are warned to experiment with different values. For instance.

. `ksm h1 depth, lowess ylab xlab s(0i)`

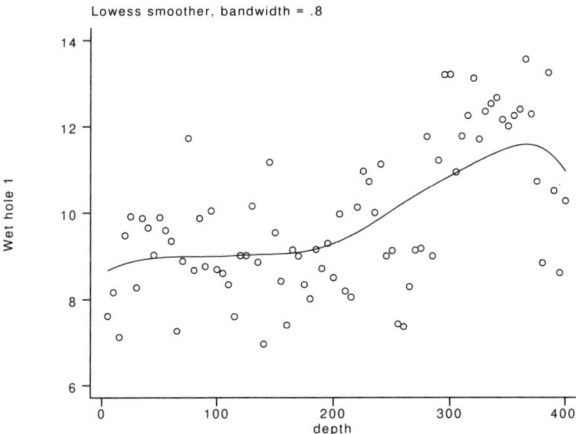

Now compare with

. `ksm h1 depth, lowess ylab xlab s(0i) bwidth(.4)`

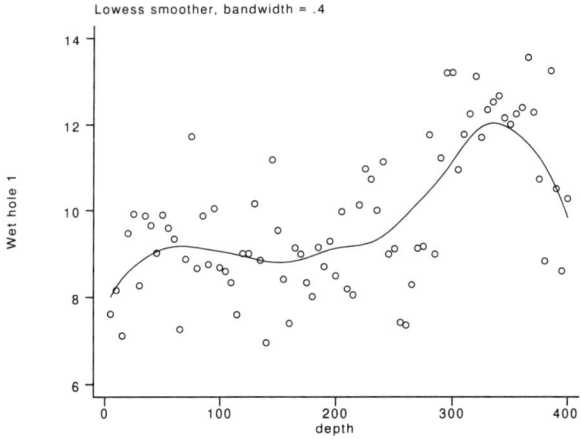

In the first case, the default bandwidth of 0.8 is used, meaning 80% of the data are used in smoothing each point. In the second case, we explicitly specified a bandwidth of 0.4. Smaller bandwidths follow the original data more closely.

◁

▷ Example

Two `ksm` options are especially useful with binary (0/1) data: `adjust` and `logit`. `adjust` adjusts the resulting curve (by multiplication) so that the mean of the smoothed values is equal to the mean of the unsmoothed values. `logit` specifies the smoothed curve is to be in terms of the log of the odds ratio:

. ksm foreign mpg, lowess ylab xlab jitter(5) adjust

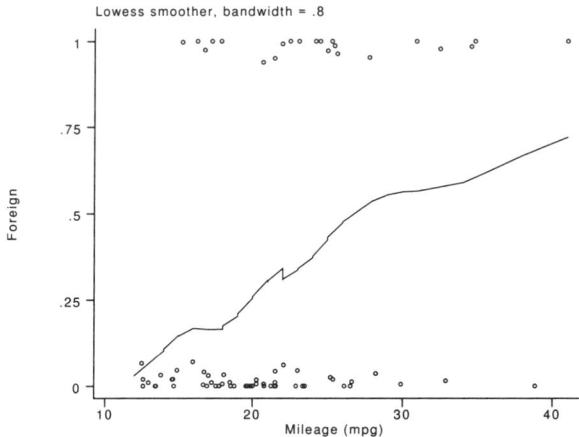

. ksm foreign mpg, lowess ylab xlab logit yline(0)

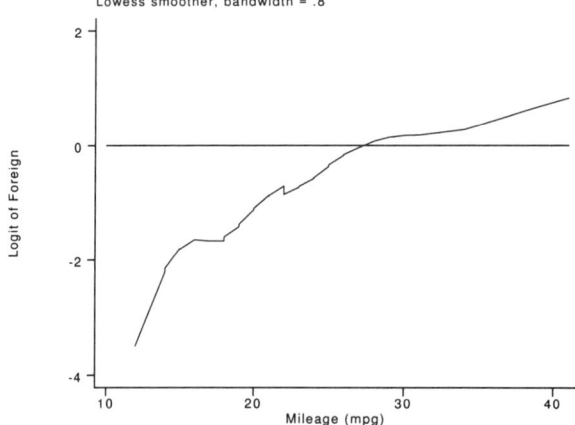

With binary data, if you do not use the `logit` option, it is a good idea to specify `graph`'s `jitter()` option; see [R] **graph twoway**. Since the underlying data (whether the car was manufactured outside the United States in this case) takes on only two values, raw data points are more likely to be on top of each other, thus making it impossible to tell how many points there are. graph's jitter() option adds some noise to the data to shift the points around. This noise affects only the location of points on the graph, not the lowess curve.

When you do specify the logit option, the display of the raw data is suppressed.

◁

❑ Technical Note

ksm can be used for other than lowess smoothing. Lowess can be usefully thought of as a combination of two smoothing concepts: the use of predicted values from regression (rather than means) for imputing a smoothed value and the use of the tricube weighting function (rather than a constant weighting function). ksm allows you to combine these concepts freely. You can use line smoothing without weighting (specify line), or mean smoothing without weighting (specify no options), or mean smoothing with tricube weighting (specify weight). Specifying both weight and line is the same as specifying lowess.

❑

Methods and Formulas

ksm is implemented as an ado-file.

Let y_i and x_i be the two variables and assume the data is ordered so that $x_i \leq x_{i+1}$ for $i = 1, \ldots, N - 1$. For each y_i, a smoothed value y_i^s is calculated.

The subset used in calculation of y_i^s are indices $i_- = \max(1, i - k)$ through $i_+ = \min(i + k, N)$, where $k = N \cdot$ bwidth. The weights for each of the observations between $j = i_-, \ldots, i_+$ are either 1 (default) or the tricube (weight):

$$ w_j = \left(1 - \left(\frac{|x_j - x_i|}{\Delta} \right)^3 \right)^3 $$

where $\Delta = 1.0001 \max(x_+ - x_i, x_i - x_-)$. The smoothed value y_i^s is then the (weighted) mean or the (weighted) regression prediction (line).

Acknowledgments

ksm was written by Patrick Royston of the Royal Postgraduate Medical School, London.

References

Chambers, J. M., W. S. Cleveland, B. Kleiner, and P. A. Tukey. 1983. *Graphical Methods for Data Analysis*. Belmont, CA: Wadsworth International Group.

Cleveland, W. S. 1979. Robust locally weighted regression and smoothing scatterplots. *Journal of the American Statistical Association* 74: 829–836.

——. 1993. *Visualizing Data*. Summit, NJ: Hobart Press.

——. 1994. *The Elements of Graphing Data*. Summit, NJ: Hobart Press.

Goodall, C. 1990. A survey of smoothing techniques. In *Modern Methods of Data Analysis*, ed. J. Fox and J. S. Long, 126–176. Newbury Park, CA: Sage Publications.

Royston, P. 1991. gr6: Lowess smoothing. *Stata Technical Bulletin* 3: 7–9. Reprinted in *Stata Technical Bulletin Reprints*, vol. 1, pp. 41–44.

Salgado-Ugarte, I. H. and M. Shimizu. 1995. snp8: Robust scatterplot smoothing: enhancements to Stata's ksm. *Stata Technical Bulletin* 25: 23–25. Reprinted in *Stata Technical Bulletin Reprints*, vol. 5, pp. 190–194.

Sasieni, P. 1994. snp7: Natural cubic splines. *Stata Technical Bulletin* 22: 19–22. Reprinted in *Stata Technical Bulletin Reprints*, vol. 4, pp. 171–174.

Also See

[R] **graph connect**, [R] **ipolate**, [R] **smooth**

Title

> **ksmirnov** — Kolmogorov–Smirnov equality of distributions test

Syntax

> ksmirnov *varname* = *exp* [if *exp*] [in *range*]
>
> ksmirnov *varname* [if *exp*] [in *range*], by(*groupvar*) [ɛxact]

Description

ksmirnov performs one- and two-sample Kolmogorov–Smirnov tests of the equality of distributions. In the first syntax, *varname* is the variable whose distribution is being tested and *exp* must evaluate to the corresponding (theoretical) cumulative. In the second syntax, *groupvar* must take on two distinct values. The distribution of *varname* for the first value of *groupvar* is compared with that of the second value.

When testing for normality, please see [R] **sktest** and [R] **swilk**.

Options

ɛxact specifies the exact p-value is to be computed. This may take a long time if $n > 50$.

Remarks

▷ Example

You have data on x that resulted from two different experiments, labeled as group==1 and group==2. Your data contains

```
. list
          group       x
  1.         2         2
  2.         1         0
  3.         2         3
  4.         1         4
  5.         1         5
  6.         2         8
  7.         2        10
```

You wish to use the two-sample Kolmogorov–Smirnov test to determine if there are any differences in the distribution of x for these two groups:

```
. ksmirnov x, by(group)
Two-sample Kolmogorov-Smirnov test for equality of distribution functions:
Smaller group        D       P-value  Corrected
----------------------------------------------------
1:                 0.5000     0.424
2:                -0.1667     0.909
Combined K-S:      0.5000     0.785      0.734
```

301

The first line tests the hypothesis that **x** for group 1 contains *smaller* values than group 2. The largest difference between the distribution functions is 0.5. The approximate *p*-value for this is 0.424, which is not significant.

The second line tests the hypothesis that **x** for group 1 contains *larger* values than group 1. The largest difference between the distribution functions in this direction is 0.1667. The approximate *p*-value for this small difference is 0.909.

Finally, the approximate *p*-value for the combined test is 0.785, corrected to 0.734. The *p*-values **ksmirnov** calculates are based on the asymptotic distributions derived by Smirnov (1939). These approximations are not very good for small samples ($n < 50$). They are too conservative—real *p*-values tend to be substantially smaller. We have also included a less conservative approximation for the nondirectional hypothesis based on an empirical continuity correction. That is the 0.734 number reported in the third column.

That number, too, is only an approximation. An exact value can be calculated using the **exact** option:

```
. ksmirnov x, by(group) exact
Two-sample Kolmogorov-Smirnov test for equality of distribution functions:
  Smaller group        D      P-value     Exact
  ----------------------------------------------------
  1:                 0.5000    0.424
  2:                -0.1667    0.909
  Combined K-S:      0.5000    0.785       0.657
```

◁

▷ Example

Let's now test whether **x** in the example above is distributed normally. Kolmogorov–Smirnov is not a particularly powerful test in testing for normality and we do not endorse such use of it; see [R] **sktest** and [R] **swilk** for better tests.

In any case, we will test against a normal distribution with the same mean and standard deviation:

```
. summarize x
Variable |   Obs        Mean    Std. Dev.       Min        Max
---------+-----------------------------------------------------
       x |    7     4.571429    3.457222          0         10
. ksmirnov x = normprob((x-4.571429)/3.457222)
One-Sample Kolmogorov-Smirnov test against theoretical distribution
        normprob((x-4.571429)/3.457222)
  Smaller group        D      P-value   Corrected
  ----------------------------------------------------
  x:                 0.1650    0.683
  Cumulative:       -0.1250    0.803
  Combined K-S:      0.1650    0.991       0.978
```

Since Stata has no way of knowing that you based this calculation on the calculated mean and standard deviation of **x**, the test statistics will be slightly conservative in addition to being approximations. Nevertheless, they clearly indicate that the data cannot be distinguished from normally distributed data.

◁

Saved Results

ksmirnov saves in the S_# macros:

S_1	name of group from line 1	S_6	p-value from line 2
S_2	D from line 1	S_7	(not used)
S_3	p-value from line 1	S_8	Combined D
S_4	name of group from line 2	S_9	Combined p-value
S_5	D from line 2	S_10	Combined corrected or exact p

Methods and Formulas

ksmirnov is implemented as an ado-file.

In general, the Kolmogorov–Smirnov test (Kolmogorov 1933; Smirnov 1939; also see Conover 1980, "Statistics of the Kolmogorov–Smirnov type", 344–385) is not very powerful against differences in the tails of distributions. In return for this, it is fairly powerful for alternative hypotheses that involve lumpiness or clustering in the data.

The directional hypotheses are evaluated with the statistics

$$D^+ = \max_x \Big(F(x) - G(x) \Big)$$

$$D^- = \min_x \Big(F(x) - G(x) \Big)$$

where $F(x)$ and $G(x)$ are the empirical distribution functions for the sample being compared. The combined statistic is

$$D = \max \Big(|D^+|, |D^-| \Big)$$

The p-value for this statistic may be obtained by evaluating the asymptotic limiting distribution. Let m be the sample size for the first sample, and n be the sample size for the second sample. The following was shown by Smirnov (1939):

$$\lim_{m,n\to\infty} P\Big(\sqrt{mn/(m+n)} D_{m,n} \le z \Big) = 1 - 2\sum_{i=1}^{\infty} (-1)^{i-1} \exp\left(-2i^2 z^2 \right)$$

The first 5 terms form the approximation P_a used by Stata. The exact p-value is calculated by a counting algorithm; see Gibbons (1971, 127–131). A corrected p-value was obtained by modifying the asymptotic p-value using a numerical approximation technique

$$Z = \Phi^{-1}(P_a) + 1.04/\min(m,n) + 2.09/\max(m,n) - 1.35/\sqrt{mn/(m+n)}$$
$$P = \Phi(Z)$$

where $\Phi()$ is the cumulative normal distribution.

References

Conover, W. J. 1980. *Practical Nonparametric Statistics*. 2d ed. New York: John Wiley & Sons.

Gibbons, J. D. 1971. *Nonparametric Statistical Inference*. New York: McGraw-Hill.

Kolmogorov, A. N. 1933. Sulla determinazione empirica di una legge di distribuzione. *Giornale dell' Istituto Italiano degli Attuari* 4: 83–91.

Smirnov, N. V. 1939. Estimate of deviation between empirical distribution functions in two independent samples (in Russian). *Bulletin Moscow University* 2(2): 3–16.

Also See

[R] **runtest**, [R] **sktest**, [R] **swilk**

Title

kwallis — Kruskal–Wallis equality of populations rank test

Syntax

kwallis *varname* [if *exp*] [in *range*] , by(*groupvar*)

Description

kwallis tests the hypothesis that several samples are from the same population. In the syntax diagram above, *varname* refers to the variable recording the outcome and *groupvar* refers to the variable denoting the population. Note that the by() "option" is not optional.

Remarks

▷ Example

You have data on the 50 states. The data contains the median age of the population medage and the region of the country region for each state. You wish to test for the equality of the median age distribution across all four regions simultaneously:

```
. kwallis medage, by(region)
Test: Equality of populations (Kruskal-Wallis Test)
   region      _Obs     _RankSum
       NE         9       376.50
  N Cntrl        12       294.00
    South        16       398.00
     West        13       206.50
chi-squared =    17.041 with 3 d.f.
probability =     0.0007
```

From the output we see that we can reject the hypothesis that the populations are the same at any level below 0.07%.

◁

Saved Results

kwallis saves in the S_# macros:

$$S\_1 \quad \chi^2 \qquad S\_2 \quad \text{degrees of freedom}$$

Methods and Formulas

kwallis is implemented as an ado-file.

The Kruskal–Wallis test (Kruskal and Wallis 1952; also see Conover 1980, 229–237 or Altman 1991, 213–215) is a multiple-sample generalization of the two-sample Wilcoxon (also called Mann–Whitney) rank sum test (Wilcoxon 1945; Mann and Whitney 1947). Samples of sizes n_j, $j = 1, \ldots, m$, are combined and ranked in ascending order of magnitude. Tied values are assigned the average ranks. Let n denote the overall sample size and let R_j denote the sum of the ranks for the jth sample. The Kruskal–Wallis one-way analysis-of-variance test H is defined as

$$H = \frac{12}{n(n+1)} \sum_{j=1}^{m} \frac{R_j^2}{n_j} - 3(n+1)$$

The sampling distribution of H is approximately χ^2 with $m - 1$ degrees of freedom.

References

Altman, D. G. 1991. *Practical Statistics for Medical Research*. London: Chapman & Hall.

Conover, W. J. 1980. *Practical Nonparametric Statistics*. 2d ed. New York: John Wiley & Sons.

Kruskal, W. H. and W. A. Wallis. 1952. Use of ranks in one-criterion variance analysis. *Journal of the American Statistical Association* 47: 583–621.

Mann, H. B. and D. R. Whitney. 1947. On a test of whether one of two random variables is stochastically larger than the other. *Annals of Mathematical Statistics* 18: 50–60.

Wilcoxon, F. 1945. Individual comparisons by ranking methods. *Biometrics* 1: 80–83.

Also See

[R] **nptrend**, [R] **oneway**, [R] **runtest**, [R] **signrank**

Title

label — Label manipulation

Syntax

label <u>data</u> $\left["label" \right]$

label <u>def</u>ine *lblname* # "*label*" $\left[\# "label" \ldots \right]$ $\left[, \underline{a}dd \ modify \right]$

label <u>dir</u>

label <u>drop</u> $\left\{ lblname \left[lblname \ldots \right] | \_all \right\}$

label <u>list</u> $\left[lblname \left[lblname \ldots \right] \right]$

label <u>save</u> $\left[lblname \left[lblname \ldots \right] \right]$ using *filename* $\left[, \ replace \right]$

label <u>val</u>ues *varname* $\left[lblname \right]$

label <u>var</u>iable *varname* $\left["label" \right]$

Description

label data attaches a label (up to 31 characters) to the data in memory. Dataset labels are displayed when you use the data and when you **describe** it. If no label is specified, any existing label is removed.

label define defines a list of up to 500 associations of nonnegative integers and text called a value label. The value label is attached to variables by label values.

label dir lists the names of value labels stored in memory.

label drop eliminates value labels.

label list lists the names and contents of value labels stored in memory.

label save saves value labels in a do-file.

label values attaches a value label to a variable. If no value label is specified, any existing value label is detached. The value label, however, is not deleted.

label variable attaches a label (up to 31 characters) to a variable. If no label is specified, any existing variable label is removed.

Options

add allows additional # ↔ *label* correspondences to be added to *lblname*. If **add** is not specified, only new *lblnames* may be created. If **add** is specified, you may create new *lblnames* or add new entries to existing *lblnames*.

306

modify allows modification or deletion of existing # ↔ *label* correspondences as well as allowing additional correspondences to be added. Specifying modify implies add even if you do not type the add option.

replace allows *filename* to be replaced even if it already exists.

Remarks

See [U] **19.6 Dataset, variable, and value labels** for a complete description of labels. This entry deals only with details not covered there.

label dir lists the names of all defined value labels. The label list command displays the contents of a value label.

▷ Example

Although describe shows the names of the value labels, those value labels may not exist. Stata does not consider it an error to label the values of a variable with a nonexistent label. When this occurs, Stata still shows the association on describe but otherwise acts as if the variable's values are unlabeled. This way, you can associate a value label name with a variable before creating the corresponding label. Similarly, you can define labels that you have not yet used.

label dir shows you the labels that you actually have defined:

```
. label dir
yesno
sexlbl
```

We have two value labels stored in memory: one called yesno and the other called sexlbl.

We can display the contents of a value label using the label list command:

```
. label list yesno
yesno:
          1 yes
          2 no
```

The value label yesno labels the values 1 as yes and 2 as no.

If you do not specify the name of the value label on the label list command, a listing of all value labels is produced:

```
. label list
yesno:
          1 yes
          2 no
sexlbl:
          0 Male
          1 Female
```

◁

❏ Technical Note

Since Stata can have more value labels stored in memory than are actually used in the data, you may wonder what happens when you save the data. In that case, Stata stores with the data only those value labels actually associated with variables.

When you use a dataset, Stata eliminates all the value labels stored in memory before loading the data.

❏

You can add new codings to an existing value label using the `add` option with the `label define` command. You can modify existing codings using the `modify` option.

▷ Example

The label `yesno` codes 1 as `yes` and 2 as `no`. Perhaps at some later time you wish to add a third coding: 3 as `maybe`. Typing `label define` without any options results in an error:

```
. label define yesno 3 maybe
label yesno already defined
r(110);
```

If you do not specify the `add` or `modify` options, `label define` can be used only to create *new* value labels. The `add` option lets you add codings to an existing label:

```
. label define yesno 3 maybe, add
. label list yesno
yesno:
             1 yes
             2 no
             3 maybe
```

Perhaps you have accidentally mislabeled a value. For instance, 3 may not mean "maybe" but may instead mean "Don't Know", which you might code as `D.K.`. `add` will not allow you to change an existing labeling:

```
. label define yesno 3 "D.K.", add
invalid attempt to modify label
r(198);
```

Instead, you specify the `modify` option:

```
. label define yesno 3 "D.K.", modify
. label list yesno
yesno:
             1 yes
             2 no
             3 D.K.
```

In this way, Stata attempts to protect you from yourself. If you type `label define` without any options, you can only create a new value label—you cannot accidentally mutilate an existing one. If you specify the `add` option, you can add new labelings to a label, but you cannot accidentally change one of the existing labelings. If you specify the `modify` option, which you may not abbreviate, you can do whatever you want.

You can even use the `modify` option to eliminate existing labelings. To do this, you map the numeric code to a *null string*, that is, `""`:

```
. label define yesno 3 "", modify
. label list yesno
yesno:
             1 yes
             2 no
```

◁

You can eliminate entire value labels using the `label drop` command.

▷ Example

We currently have two value labels stored in memory—sexlbl and yesno. The label dir command reports that:

```
. label dir
yesno
sexlbl
```

The data that we have in memory uses only one of the labels—sexlbl. describe reports that:

```
. describe
Contains data from emp.dta
  obs:            7                         1992 Employee Data
  vars:           4                         28 May 1996 13:04
  size:         224 (99.9% of memory free)
--------------------------------------------------------------------
  1. name        str16   %16s
  2. empno       float   %9.0g              Employee Number
  3. sex         float   %9.0g     sexlbl   Sex
  4. salary      float   %9.0g              Annual Salary
--------------------------------------------------------------------
Sorted by:
```

We can eliminate the yesno label by typing label drop yesno:

```
. label drop yesno
. label dir
sexlbl
```

We could eliminate *all* the value labels in memory by typing

```
. label drop _all
. label dir
. _
```

Remember that the value label sexlbl, which no longer exists, was associated with the variable sex. Even after dropping the value label, sexlbl is still associated with the variable:

```
. describe
Contains data from emp.dta
  obs:            7                         1992 Employee Data
  vars:           4                         28 May 1996 13:04
  size:         224 (99.9% of memory free)
--------------------------------------------------------------------
  1. name        str16   %16s
  2. empno       float   %9.0g              Employee Number
  3. sex         float   %9.0g     sexlbl   Sex
  4. salary      float   %9.0g              Annual Salary
--------------------------------------------------------------------
Sorted by:
```

As stated earlier, Stata does not mind if a nonexistent value label is associated with a variable. When Stata uses such a variable, it simply acts as if it is not labeled:

```
. list in 1/4
                name    empno     sex    salary
    1.    Hank Rogers    57213      0     24000
    2.     Pat Welch     47229      1     27000
    3.   Bob Underhill   57323      0     24000
    4.   Richard Doyle   57401      0     24500
```
◁

The `label save` command creates a *do-file* containing `label define` commands for each label you specify. If you do not specify the *lblnames*, all value labels are stored in the file. If you do not specify the extension for *filename*, `.do` is assumed.

▷ Example

Labels are automatically stored with your dataset when you `save` it. Conversely, the `use` command drops all labels before loading the new dataset. You may occasionally wish to move a value label from one dataset to another. The `label save` command allows you to do this.

For example, assume we currently have the value label `yesno` in memory:

```
. label list yesno
yesno:
            1 yes
            2 no
            3 maybe
```

You have a dataset stored on disk called `survey.dta` to which you wish to add this value label. One alternative is to `use survey` and then retype the `label define yesno` command. Retyping the label would not be too tedious in this case, but if the value label in memory mapped, say, the 50 states of the union, retyping it would be irksome. `label save` provides an alternative:

```
. label save yesno using ynfile
file ynfile.do saved
```

Typing `label save yesno using ynfile` caused Stata to create a do-file called `ynfile.do` containing the definition of the `yesno` label.

If we want to see the contents of the file, we can use the Stata `type` command:

```
. type ynfile.do
#delimit ;
label define yesno
1 "yes"
2 "no"
3 "maybe"
;
```

The resulting file uses the `#delimit` command to set the Stata delimiter to semicolon, and then includes the definition of the label `yesno`.

We can now `use` our new dataset, `survey.dta`:

```
. use survey
(Hsehld survey data)

. label dir

. _
```

Using the new dataset causes Stata to eliminate all value labels stored in memory. The label yesno is now gone. Since we saved it in the file ynfile.do, however, we can get it back by typing either do ynfile or run ynfile. If we type do, we will see the commands in the file execute. If we type run, the file will execute silently:

```
. run ynfile
. label dir
yesno
```

The label is now just as if we had typed it from the keyboard.

◁

❑ Technical Note

You can also use the label save command to make editing of value labels easier. You can save a label in a file, leave Stata and use your word processor or editor to edit the label, and then return to Stata. Using do or run, you can load the edited values.

❑

Also See

[U] **19.6 Dataset, variable, and value labels**

Title

ladder — Ladder of powers

Syntax

ladder *varname* [if *exp*] [in *range*] [, generate(*newvar*) noadjust]

gladder *varname* [if *exp*] [in *range*] [, bin(#) *graph_options*]

Description

ladder searches a subset of the ladder of powers (Tukey 1977) for a transform that converts *varname* into a normally distributed variable. sktest is used to test for normality; see [R] **sktest**. Also see [R] **boxcox**.

gladder displays nine histograms of transforms of *varname* according to the ladder of powers.

Options

generate(*newvar*) saves the transformed values corresponding to the minimum chi-squared value from the table. Its use is not, in general, recommended since generate() is quite literal in its interpretation of minimum, thus ignoring nearly equal but perhaps more interpretable transforms.

noadjust is the noadjust option to sktest; see [R] **sktest**.

bin(#) specifies the number of bins for the histograms. If not specified, an intelligent choice is made for you (see *Methods and Formulas* below).

graph_options are any of the options allowed with graph, histogram; see [R] **graph histogram**.

Remarks

▷ Example

You have data on the mileage rating of 74 automobiles and wish to find a transform that makes the variable normally distributed:

```
. ladder mpg
Transformation        formula           Chi-sq(2)      P(Chi-sq)
-----------------------------------------------------------------
cube                  mpg^3               43.59          0.000
square                mpg^2               27.03          0.000
raw                   mpg                 10.95          0.004
square-root           sqrt(mpg)            4.94          0.084
log                   log(mpg)             0.87          0.647
reciprocal root       1/sqrt(mpg)          0.20          0.905
reciprocal            1/mpg                2.36          0.307
reciprocal square     1/(mpg^2)           11.99          0.002
reciprocal cube       1/(mpg^3)           24.30          0.000
```

Had we typed `ladder mpg, gen(mpgx)`, the variable `mpgx` would have been automatically generated for us containing $1/\sqrt{\text{mpg}}$. This is the perfect example of why you should not, in general, specify the `generate()` option. Note that we also cannot reject that the reciprocal of `mpg` is normally distributed and $1/\text{mpg}$—gallons per mile—has a better interpretation. It is a measure of energy consumption.

◁

▷ Example

`gladder` explores the same transforms as `ladder` but presents results graphically:

. gladder mpg

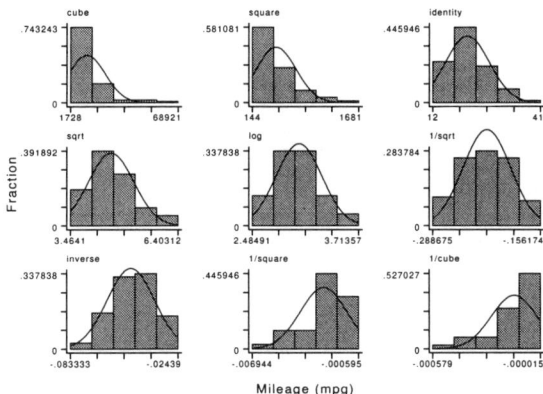

Histograms by Transformation

◁

❏ Technical Note

`gladder` is useful pedagogically, but some caution most be exercised when using it for research work, especially with large numbers of observations. For instance, consider the following data on the average July temperature in Fahrenheit for 954 U.S. cities:

. ladder tempjuly

Transformation	formula	Chi-sq(2)	P(Chi-sq)
cube	tempjuly^3	47.49	0.000
square	tempjuly^2	19.70	0.000
raw	tempjuly	3.83	0.147
square-root	sqrt(tempjuly)	1.83	0.400
log	log(tempjuly)	5.40	0.067
reciprocal root	1/sqrt(tempjuly)	13.72	0.001
reciprocal	1/tempjuly	26.36	0.000
reciprocal square	1/(tempjuly^2)	64.43	0.000
reciprocal cube	1/(tempjuly^3)	.	0.000

The period in the last line indicates that the χ^2 is very large; see [R] **sktest**.

From the table, we see that there is certainly a difference, normality-wise, between the square and square-root transform. If, however, you can see the difference between the transforms in the diagram below, you have better eyes than we do:

. gladder tempjuly

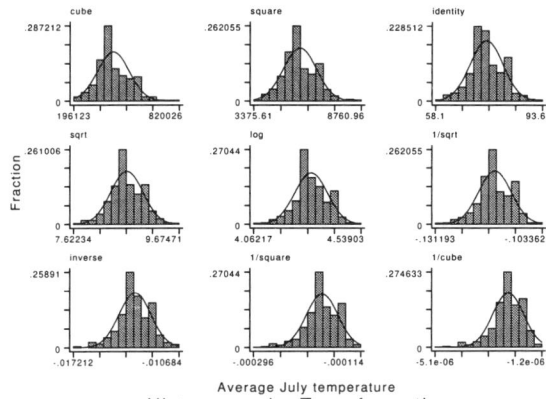

Average July temperature
Histograms by Transformation

A better graph for seeing normality is the quantile-normal graph as produced by qnorm; see [R] **diagplots**. That graph shows that for the square transform, the upper tail, and only the upper tail, diverges from what would be expected. This is detected by sktest as a problem with skewness, as we would learn from using sktest to examine tempjuly squared and square-rooted.

❏

Methods and Formulas

ladder and gladder are implemented as ado-files.

For ladder, results are as reported by sktest; see [R] **sktest**. If generate() is specified, the transform with the minimum χ^2 value is chosen.

gladder sets the number of bins to $\min(\sqrt{n}, 10 \log_{10} n)$, rounded to the closest integer, where n is the number of *unique* values of *varname*. See [R] **graph histogram** for a discussion of the optimal number of bins.

Also see Findley (1990) for a ladder-of-powers variable transformation program that produces one-way graphs with overlaid box plots, in addition to histograms with overlaid normals. Buchner and Findley (1990) discuss ladder-of-powers transformations as one aspect of preliminary data analysis. Also see Hamilton (1992, 18–23).

References

Buchner, D. M. and T. W. Findley. 1990. Research in physical medicine and rehabilitation: viii preliminary data analysis. *American Journal of Physical Medicine and Rehabilitation* 69: 154–169.

Findley, T. W. 1990. sed3: Variable transformation and evaluation. *Stata Technical Bulletin* 2: 15. Reprinted in *Stata Technical Bulletin Reprints*, vol. 1, pp. 85–86.

Hamilton, L. C. 1992. *Regression with Graphics*. Pacific Grove, CA: Brooks/Cole Publishing Company.

Tukey, J. W. 1977. *Exploratory Data Analysis*. Reading, MA: Addison-Wesley Publishing Company.

Also See

[R] **boxcox**, [R] **diagplots**, [R] **lnskew0**, [R] **lv**, [R] **sktest**

Title

---

level — Set default confidence level

Syntax

<u>set</u> <u>level</u> #

Description

set level specifies the default confidence level for confidence intervals for all commands that report confidence intervals. The initial value is 95, meaning 95% confidence intervals. # may be between 10 and 99.

Remarks

To change the width of confidence intervals reported by a particular command, it is not necessary to reset the default confidence level. All commands that report confidence intervals have a level(#) option. When you do not specify the option, the confidence intervals are calculated for the default level set by set level or 95% if you have not reset it.

▷ Example

You use the ci command to obtain the confidence interval for the mean of mpg:

```
. ci mpg
Variable |     Obs        Mean    Std. Err.     [95% Conf. Interval]
---------+-----------------------------------------------------------
     mpg |      74     21.2973    .6725511       19.9569    22.63769
```

To obtain 90% confidence intervals, you could type

```
. ci mpg, level(90)
Variable |     Obs        Mean    Std. Err.     [90% Conf. Interval]
---------+-----------------------------------------------------------
     mpg |      74     21.2973    .6725511      20.17683    22.41776
```

or

```
. set level 90
. ci mpg
Variable |     Obs        Mean    Std. Err.     [90% Conf. Interval]
---------+-----------------------------------------------------------
     mpg |      74     21.2973    .6725511      20.17683    22.41776
```

If you opt for the second alternative, the next time you estimate a model (say with **regress**), 90% confidence intervals will be reported. If you wanted 95% confidence intervals, you could specify level(95) on the estimation command or you could reset the default by typing set level 95.

◁

Also See

[U] **26 Estimation and post-estimation commands**

[R] **ci**, [R] **query**

Title

limits — Quick reference for limits

Description

This entry provides a quick reference for the size limits in Stata. Note that most of these limits are so high that you will never encounter them.

Remarks

Maximum size limits for Small Stata and Intercooled Stata

	Small Stata	Intercooled Stata
Number of observations	about 1,000	2,147,483,647 (1)
Number of variables	99	2,047
Width of a dataset	400	8,192
Value of `matsize`	40	800
Number of characters in a command	1,100	6,144
Number of options for a command	50	50
Number of dyadic operators in an expression	66	66
Number of numeric literals in an expression	50	50
Number of string literals in an expression	256	256
Number of sum functions in an expression	5	5
Number of characters in a macro	1,000	5,400
Number of nested do-files	32	32
Number of lines in a program	1,000	1,000
Number of characters in a program	10,000	10,000
Length of variable name	8	8
Length of ado-command name	8	8
Length of global macro name	8	8
Length of local macro name	7	7
Length of a string variable	80	80
Number of conditions in an `if` statement	30	30

(1) limited by memory.

(*Continued on next page.*)

Maximum size limits for specific commands

	Small Stata	Intercooled Stata
anova		
Number of terms in **anova** model **test** statement	8	8
char		
Maximum length of a single characteristic	1,000	5,400
constraint		
Number of constraints	999	999
encode and **decode**		
Number of unique values for a string variable	500	500
eq define		
Number of equations that may be defined	99	99
estimates hold		
Number of stored estimation results	10	10
graph		
Length of title	69	69
Number of values in **xlab**, **ylab**, **rlab**, and **tlab**	25	25
gap	10	10
set textsize	400	400
graph, bar		
Number of variables	6	6
Number of by-groups	50	50
Number of bars (variables times by-groups)	150	150
graph, box		
Number of variables	6	6
Number of by-groups	50	50
Number of boxes (variables times by-groups)	150	150
graph, histogram		
Number of by-groups	400	400
Number of bins	50	50
Number of points allowed by the **density()** option	300	300
graph, matrix		
Number of variables	30	30
graph, oneway		
Number of variables	20	20
Number of by-groups	52	52
Number of one-way scatterplots (variables times by-groups)	60	60

(Table continued on next page.)

Maximum size limits for specific commands, continued

	Small Stata	Intercooled Stata
graph, pie		
Number of variables	16	16
Number of pie charts in a single image	64	64
graph, star		
Number of variables	16	16
Number of stars in a single image	81	81
graph, twoway		
Number of y-variables	20	20
greigen		
Number of eigenvalues plotted by greigen	13	13
grmeanby		
Number of unique values in *varlist*	_N/2	_N/2
hist		
Number of unique values in *varname*	50	50
impute		
Number of variables in *varlist*	31	31
infile		
record length without data dictionary	none	none
record length with data dictionary (1)	7,998	7,998
infix		
record length without data dictionary	none	none
record length with data dictionary (1)	7,998	7,998
label		
Length of dataset label	31	31
Length of value label	8	8
Length of name of value label	8	8
Length of variable label	31	31
Number of codings within a single value label	500	500
matrix		
Size of a single matrix	40×40	800×800
maximize options		
Number of iterations specified with iterate()	16,000	16,000
merge		
Number of variables that you can specify in a match-merge	10	10
mlogit		
Number of outcomes in model	20	50

(1) For Stata for Unix, the maximum record length is 18,998; for Stata for Macintosh, it is 3,998.

Maximum size limits for specific commands, continued

	Small Stata	Intercooled Stata
notes		
Maximum length of a single note	1,000	5,400
Number of notes attached to _dta	9,999	9,999
Number of notes attached to each variable	9,999	9,999
ologit		
Number of outcomes in model	20	50
oprobit		
Number of outcomes in model	20	50
plot		
Number of columns specified with column() option	133	133
Number of lines specified with lines() option	83	83
set adosize		
Maximum amount of memory that ado-files may consume	500K	500K
tabdisp and table		
Number of by variables	4	4
Number of margins; that is, the sum of the rows, columns, supercolumns, and by groups	3,000	3,000
tabulate		
Number of rows for a one-way table	500	3,000
Number of rows for a two-way table	160	300
Number of columns for a two-way table	20	20
tabulate, summarize		
Number of cells	376	376
xtgee		
Number of time periods	40	800
xtgls		
Number of time periods	40	800
xtpois		
Number of time periods	40	800
xtprobit		
Number of time periods	40	800
xtreg, mle		
Number of time periods	40	800

Also See

[U] **11 Setting the size of memory**

[R] **matsize**, [R] **memory**

Title

---
lincom — Linear combinations of estimators

Syntax

> lincom *exp* [, <u>level</u>(#) or <u>irr</u> <u>rrr</u>]

exp is any linear combination of coefficients that is valid syntax for **test**; see [R] **test**. Note, however, that *exp* must not contain any additive constants nor equal signs.

Description

lincom computes point estimates, standard errors, t or Z statistics, p-values, and confidence intervals for a linear combination of coefficients after any estimation command except **anova**. Results can optionally be displayed as odds ratios, incidence rate ratios, or relative risk ratios.

The **svy** estimation commands for survey data have their own special command **svylc** for estimating linear combinations; see [R] **svylc**.

Options

level(#) specifies the confidence level, in percent, for confidence intervals. The default is **level(95)** or as set by **set level**; see [U] **26.4 Specifying the width of confidence intervals**.

or reports the estimated coefficients transformed to odds ratios, i.e., e^b rather than b. Standard errors and confidence intervals are similarly transformed. **or** is the default after **logistic**.

irr reports the estimated coefficients transformed to incidence rate ratios, i.e., e^b rather than b. Standard errors and confidence intervals are similarly transformed.

rrr reports the estimated coefficients transformed to relative risk ratios, i.e., e^b rather than b. Standard errors and confidence intervals are similarly transformed. See [R] **mlogit**.

Note: **or**, **irr**, and **rrr** all do exactly the same thing computationally. The only difference is how the output is labeled.

Remarks

After fitting a model and obtaining estimates for coefficients $\beta_1, \beta_2, \ldots, \beta_k$, one often wants to view estimates for linear combinations of the β_i, such as $\beta_1 - \beta_2$. **lincom** can display estimates for any linear combination of the form $c_1\beta_1 + c_2\beta_2 + \cdots + c_k\beta_k$.

lincom works after any estimation command for which **test** works, except **anova**. Any expression that is a valid expression for **test** Syntax 1 (see [R] **test**) is a valid expression for **lincom**. There is only one exception to this rule: **lincom** does not allow additive constants; i.e., it cannot display estimates for $c_0 + c_1\beta_1 + \cdots + c_k\beta_k$ when $c_0 \neq 0$.

lincom is useful for viewing odds ratios or incidence rate ratios for one group (i.e., one set of covariates) relative to another group (i.e., another set of covariates). See examples below.

▷ Example

We estimate a linear regression

```
. reg y x1 x2 x3

      Source |       SS       df       MS                  Number of obs =     148
-------------+------------------------------              F(  3,   144) =   96.12
       Model |  3259.3561        3  1086.45203            Prob > F      =  0.0000
    Residual |  1627.56282     144  11.3025196            R-squared     =  0.6670
-------------+------------------------------              Adj R-squared =  0.6600
       Total |  4886.91892     147  33.2443464            Root MSE      =  3.3619

------------------------------------------------------------------------------
           y |      Coef.   Std. Err.       t    P>|t|     [95% Conf. Interval]
-------------+----------------------------------------------------------------
          x1 |   1.457113    1.07461      1.356   0.177    -.6669339    3.581161
          x2 |   2.221682    .8610358     2.580   0.011     .5197797    3.923583
          x3 |   -.006139    .0005543   -11.076   0.000    -.0072345   -.0050435
       _cons |   36.10135    4.382693     8.237   0.000     27.43863    44.76407
------------------------------------------------------------------------------
```

Suppose that we want to see the difference of the coefficients of x2 and x1. We type

```
. lincom x2 - x1

 ( 1) - x1 + x2 = 0.0

------------------------------------------------------------------------------
           y |      Coef.   Std. Err.       t    P>|t|     [95% Conf. Interval]
-------------+----------------------------------------------------------------
         (1) |   .7645682   .9950282      0.768   0.444     -1.20218    2.731316
------------------------------------------------------------------------------
```

The expression can be any linear combination without a constant.

```
. lincom 3*x1 + 500*x3

 ( 1)   3.0 x1 + 500.0 x3 = 0.0

------------------------------------------------------------------------------
           y |      Coef.   Std. Err.       t    P>|t|     [95% Conf. Interval]
-------------+----------------------------------------------------------------
         (1) |   1.301825   4.871691      0.267   0.790    -8.414455     11.0181
------------------------------------------------------------------------------
```

Expressions with additive constants are not allowed.

```
. lincom x1 - 1
constant terms not allowed
invalid syntax
r(101);
```

Nor are nonlinear expressions.

```
. lincom x2/x1
not possible with test
r(131);
```

◁

❑ Technical Note

lincom uses the same shorthands for coefficients as does test (see [R] test). When you type x1, for instance, lincom knows that you mean the coefficient of x1. The formal syntax for referencing this coefficient is actually _b[x1], or alternatively _coef[x1]. So, more formally, in the last example we could have typed

```
. lincom 3*_b[x1] + 500*_b[x3]
```

❑

Odds ratios and incidence rate ratios

After logistic regression, the `or` option can be specified with `lincom` to display odds ratios for any effect. Incidence rate ratios after commands such as `poisson` can be obtained in a similar fashion—you simply specify the `irr` option.

▷ Example

Consider the low birth weight data from Hosmer and Lemeshow (1989, Table 4.1). We estimate a logistic regression of low birth weight (variable `low`) on the following variables:

Variable	Description	Coding
age	age in years	
black	race black	1 if black, 0 otherwise
other	race other	1 if race other, 0 otherwise
smoke	smoking status	1 if smoker, 0 if nonsmoker
ht	history of hypertension	1 if yes, 0 if no
ui	uterine irritability	1 if yes, 0 if no
lwd	maternal weight before pregnancy	1 if weight $<$ 110, 0 otherwise
ptd	history of premature labor	1 if yes, 0 if no
agelwd	age $\times$ lwd	
smokelwd	smoke $\times$ lwd	

We first estimate a model without the interaction terms `agelwd` and `smokelwd` (Hosmer and Lemeshow 1989, Table 4.8) using `logit`.

```
. logit low age lwd black other smoke ptd ht ui

Iteration 0:  Log Likelihood =  -117.336
Iteration 1:  Log Likelihood =-99.431174
Iteration 2:  Log Likelihood =-98.785718
Iteration 3:  Log Likelihood =  -98.778
Iteration 4:  Log Likelihood =-98.777998

Logit Estimates                          Number of obs =      189
                                         chi2(8)       =    37.12
                                         Prob > chi2   =   0.0000
Log Likelihood = -98.777998              Pseudo R2     =   0.1582

------------------------------------------------------------------------------
     low |      Coef.   Std. Err.       z     P>|z|     [95% Conf. Interval]
---------+--------------------------------------------------------------------
     age |  -.0464796   .0373888    -1.243    0.214    -.1197603     .0268011
     lwd |   .8420615   .4055338     2.076    0.038     .0472299     1.636893
   black |   1.073456   .5150752     2.084    0.037     .0639273     2.082985
   other |    .815367   .4452979     1.831    0.067    -.0574008     1.688135
   smoke |   .8071996    .404446     1.996    0.046     .0145001     1.599899
     ptd |   1.281678   .4621157     2.774    0.006     .3759478     2.187408
      ht |   1.435227   .6482699     2.214    0.027     .1646415     2.705813
      ui |   .6576256   .4666192     1.409    0.159    -.2569313     1.572182
   _cons |  -1.216781   .9556797    -1.273    0.203    -3.089878      .656317
------------------------------------------------------------------------------
```

If we want to get the odds ratio for black smokers relative to white nonsmokers (the reference group), we type

```
. lincom black + smoke, or
 ( 1)   black + smoke = 0.0
```

low	Odds Ratio	Std. Err.	z	P>|z|	[95% Conf. Interval]
(1)	6.557805	4.744692	2.599	0.009	1.588176 27.07811

`lincom` computed $\exp(\beta_{\text{black}} + \beta_{\text{smoke}}) = 6.56$. If we want to see the odds ratio for white smokers relative to black nonsmokers, we type

```
. lincom smoke - black, or
 ( 1)  - black + smoke = 0.0
```

low	Odds Ratio	Std. Err.	z	P>|z|	[95% Conf. Interval]
(1)	.7662425	.4430176	-0.461	0.645	.2467334 2.379603

Now let's add the interaction terms to the model (Hosmer and Lemeshow 1989, Table 4.10). This time we will use the `logistic` command rather than `logit`. By default, `logistic` displays odds ratios.

```
. logistic low age black other smoke ht ui lwd ptd agelwd smokelwd
Logit Estimates                                 Number of obs =      189
                                                chi2(10)      =    42.66
                                                Prob > chi2   =   0.0000
Log Likelihood =  -96.00616                     Pseudo R2     =   0.1818
```

low	Odds Ratio	Std. Err.	z	P>|z|	[95% Conf. Interval]
age	.9194513	.041896	-1.843	0.065	.8408967 1.005344
black	2.95383	1.532788	2.087	0.037	1.068277 8.167462
other	2.137589	.9919132	1.637	0.102	.8608713 5.307749
smoke	3.168096	1.452377	2.515	0.012	1.289956 7.780755
ht	3.893141	2.5752	2.055	0.040	1.064768 14.2346
ui	2.071284	.9931385	1.519	0.129	.8092928 5.301191
lwd	.1772934	.3312383	-0.926	0.354	.0045539 6.902359
ptd	3.426633	1.615282	2.613	0.009	1.360252 8.632086
agelwd	1.15883	.09602	1.779	0.075	.9851216 1.36317
smokelwd	.2447849	.2003996	-1.719	0.086	.0491956 1.217988

Hosmer and Lemeshow (1989, Table 4.13) consider the effects of smoking (smoke = 1) and low maternal weight prior to pregnancy (lwd = 1). The effect of smoking among non-low-weight mothers (lwd = 0) is given by the odds ratio 3.17 for `smoke` in the `logistic` output. The effect of smoking among low-weight mothers is given by

```
. lincom smoke + smokelwd
 ( 1)   smoke + smokelwd = 0.0
```

low	Odds Ratio	Std. Err.	z	P>|z|	[95% Conf. Interval]
(1)	.7755022	.5749508	-0.343	0.732	.1813465 3.316322

Note that we did not have to specify the `or` option. After `logistic`, `lincom` assumes `or` by default.

The effect of low-weight (lwd = 1) is more complicated since we fit an age × lwd interaction. We must specify the age of mothers for the effect. The effect among 30-year old nonsmokers is given by

```
. lincom lwd + 30*agelwd

 ( 1)  lwd + 30.0 agelwd = 0.0

------------------------------------------------------------------------------
     low | Odds Ratio   Std. Err.       z     P>|z|     [95% Conf. Interval]
---------+--------------------------------------------------------------------
     (1) |   14.7669    13.56689     2.931    0.003     2.439266    89.39625
------------------------------------------------------------------------------
```

lincom computed $\exp(\beta_{\text{lwd}} + 30\beta_{\text{agelwd}}) = 14.8$. It seems a little odd to have entered it as lwd + 30*agelwd, but remember that lwd and agelwd are just lincom's (and test's) shorthand for _b[lwd] and _b[agelwd]. We could have typed

```
. lincom _b[lwd] + 30*_b[agelwd]

 ( 1)  lwd + 30.0 agelwd = 0.0

------------------------------------------------------------------------------
     low | Odds Ratio   Std. Err.       z     P>|z|     [95% Conf. Interval]
---------+--------------------------------------------------------------------
     (1) |   14.7669    13.56689     2.931    0.003     2.439266    89.39625
------------------------------------------------------------------------------
```

◁

Multiple-equation models

lincom also works with multiple-equation models. The only difference is how you refer to the coefficients. Recall that for multiple-equation models, coefficients are referenced using the syntax

[eqno] varname

where *eqno* is the equation number or equation name and *varname* is the corresponding variable name for the coefficient; see [U] **20.5 Accessing coefficients and standard errors** and [R] **test** for details.

▷ Example

Consider the example from the [R] **mlogit** entry of the manual (Tarlov et al. 1989; Wells et al. 1989).

```
. mlogit insure age male nonwhite site2 site3, nolog
Multinomial regression                          Number of obs =     615
                                                chi2(10)      =   42.99
                                                Prob > chi2   =  0.0000
Log Likelihood = -534.36165                     Pseudo R2     =  0.0387

------------------------------------------------------------------------------
   insure |     Coef.   Std. Err.       z     P>|z|     [95% Conf. Interval]
---------+--------------------------------------------------------------------
Prepaid  |
     age |  -.011745    .0061946   -1.896    0.058    -.0238862    .0003962
    male |   .5616934    .2027465    2.770    0.006     .1643175    .9590693
nonwhite |   .9747768    .2363213    4.125    0.000     .5115955    1.437958
   site2 |   .1130359    .2101903    0.538    0.591    -.2989296    .5250013
   site3 |  -.5879879    .2279351   -2.580    0.010    -1.034733   -.1412433
   _cons |   .2697127    .3284422    0.821    0.412    -.3740222    .9134476
```

```
---------+-----------------------------------------------------------------
Uninsure |
     age |  -.0077961    .0114418    -0.681    0.496    -.0302217    .0146294
    male |   .4518496    .3674867     1.230    0.219     -.268411     1.17211
nonwhite |   .2170589    .4256361     0.510    0.610    -.6171725     1.05129
   site2 |  -1.211563    .4705127    -2.575    0.010    -2.133751   -.2893747
   site3 |  -.2078123    .3662926    -0.567    0.570    -.9257327     .510108
   _cons |  -1.286943    .5923219    -2.173    0.030    -2.447872   -.1260135
---------+-----------------------------------------------------------------
```

(Outcome insure==Indem is the comparison group)

To see the estimate of the sum of the coefficient of male and the coefficient of nonwhite for the Prepaid outcome, we type

```
. lincom [Prepaid]male + [Prepaid]nonwhite

 ( 1)  [Prepaid]male + [Prepaid]nonwhite = 0.0

------------------------------------------------------------------------------
 insure |      Coef.   Std. Err.       z     P>|z|     [95% Conf. Interval]
--------+---------------------------------------------------------------------
    (1) |    1.53647    .3272489     4.695   0.000      .8950741    2.177866
------------------------------------------------------------------------------
```

To view the estimate as a ratio of relative risks (see [R] **mlogit** for the definition and interpretation), we specify the **rrr** option.

```
. lincom [Prepaid]male + [Prepaid]nonwhite, rrr

 ( 1)  [Prepaid]male + [Prepaid]nonwhite = 0.0

------------------------------------------------------------------------------
 insure |        RRR   Std. Err.       z     P>|z|     [95% Conf. Interval]
--------+---------------------------------------------------------------------
    (1) |   4.648154    1.521103     4.695   0.000      2.447517    8.827451
------------------------------------------------------------------------------
```

◁

Saved Results

lincom saves in the S_# macros:

S_1	point estimate
S_2	estimate of standard error
S_3	degrees of freedom for t statistic (empty if Z statistic)

Methods and Formulas

lincom is implemented as an ado-file.

References

Hosmer, D. W., Jr., and S. Lemeshow. 1989. *Applied Logistic Regression.* New York: John Wiley & Sons.

Tarlov, A. R., J. E. Ware, Jr., S. Greenfield, E. C. Nelson, E. Perrin, and M. Zubkoff. 1989. The medical outcomes study. *Journal of the American Medical Association* 262: 925–930.

Wells, K. E., R. D. Hays, M. A. Burnam, W. H. Rogers, S. Greenfield, and J. E. Ware, Jr. 1989. Detection of depressive disorder for patients receiving prepaid or fee-for-service care. *Journal of the American Medical Association* 262: 3298–3302.

Also See

[U] **20.5 Accessing coefficients and standard errors**, [U] **26 Estimation and post-estimation commands**

[R] **svylc**, [R] **svytest**, [R] **test**, [R] **testnl**

Title

> **linktest** — Specification link test for single-equation models

Syntax

> linktest [*weight*] [if *exp*] [in *range*] [, *estimation_options*]

> aweights and fweights are allowed; see [U] **18.1.6 weight**, but also see the warning below.

Description

> linktest performs a link test for model specification after any single-equation estimation command such as logistic, regress, etc.; see [R] **estimation commands**.

> *Warning:* Although aweights and fweights are allowed, they must be the same as specified in the underlying estimation command.

Options

> *estimation_options* must be the same options specified with the underlying estimation command.

Remarks

> The form of the link test implemented here is based on an idea of Tukey (1949) which was further described by Pregibon (1980), elaborating on work in his unpublished thesis (Pregibon 1979). See *Methods and Formulas* below for more details.

▷ Example

> We attempt to explain the mileage ratings of cars in our automobile dataset using the weight, displacement of the engine, and whether the car is manufactured outside the U.S.:

```
. reg mpg weight displ foreign

      Source |       SS       df       MS              Number of obs =      74
-------------+------------------------------           F(  3,    70) =   45.88
       Model | 1619.71935        3  539.906448          Prob > F      =  0.0000
    Residual |  823.740114       70  11.7677159          R-squared     =  0.6629
-------------+------------------------------           Adj R-squared =  0.6484
       Total | 2443.45946        73  33.4720474          Root MSE      =  3.4304

------------------------------------------------------------------------------
         mpg |      Coef.   Std. Err.       t    P>|t|     [95% Conf. Interval]
-------------+----------------------------------------------------------------
      weight |  -.0067745   .0011665     -5.807   0.000    -.0091011   -.0044479
       displ |   .0019286   .0100701      0.192   0.849    -.0181556    .0220129
     foreign |  -1.600631   1.113648     -1.437   0.155    -3.821732    .6204698
       _cons |   41.84795   2.350704     17.802   0.000     37.15962    46.53628
------------------------------------------------------------------------------
```

Based on the R^2, we are reasonably pleased with this model.

If our model really is specified correctly, then were we to regress mpg on the prediction and the prediction squared, the prediction squared should have no explanatory power. This is what linktest does

```
. linktest
      Source |       SS       df       MS              Number of obs =      74
-------------+------------------------------           F(  2,    71) =   76.75
       Model |  1670.71514      2  835.357572           Prob > F      =  0.0000
    Residual |  772.744316     71  10.8837228           R-squared     =  0.6837
-------------+------------------------------           Adj R-squared =  0.6748
       Total |  2443.45946     73  33.4720474           Root MSE      =   3.299

------------------------------------------------------------------------------
         mpg |      Coef.   Std. Err.      t    P>|t|     [95% Conf. Interval]
-------------+----------------------------------------------------------------
        _hat |  -.4127198   .6577736    -0.627   0.532    -1.724283    .8988433
      _hatsq |   .0338198    .015624     2.165   0.034     .0026664    .0649732
       _cons |   14.00705   6.713276     2.086   0.040     .6211545   27.39294
------------------------------------------------------------------------------
```

We find that the prediction squared does have explanatory power, so our specification is not as good as we thought.

Although linktest is formally a test of the specification of the dependent variable, it is often interpreted as a test that, conditional on the specification, the independent variables are specified incorrectly. We will follow that interpretation and now include weight-squared in our model:

```
. gen weight2 = weight*weight

. regress mpg weight weight2 displ foreign
      Source |       SS       df       MS              Number of obs =      74
-------------+------------------------------           F(  4,    69) =   39.37
       Model |  1699.02634      4  424.756584           Prob > F      =  0.0000
    Residual |  744.433124     69  10.7888859           R-squared     =  0.6953
-------------+------------------------------           Adj R-squared =  0.6777
       Total |  2443.45946     73  33.4720474           Root MSE      =  3.2846

------------------------------------------------------------------------------
         mpg |      Coef.   Std. Err.      t    P>|t|     [95% Conf. Interval]
-------------+----------------------------------------------------------------
      weight |  -.0173257   .0040488    -4.279   0.000    -.0254028   -.0092486
     weight2 |   1.87e-06   6.89e-07     2.711   0.008     4.93e-07    3.24e-06
       displ |  -.0101625   .0106236    -0.956   0.342     -.031356    .011031
     foreign |  -2.560016   1.123506    -2.278   0.026    -4.801349   -.3186833
       _cons |   58.23575   6.449882     9.029   0.000     45.36859   71.10291
------------------------------------------------------------------------------
```

And now we perform the link test on our new model:

```
. linktest
      Source |       SS       df       MS              Number of obs =      74
-------------+------------------------------           F(  2,    71) =   81.08
       Model |  1699.39489      2  849.697445           Prob > F      =  0.0000
    Residual |   744.06457     71  10.4797827           R-squared     =  0.6955
-------------+------------------------------           Adj R-squared =  0.6869
       Total |  2443.45946     73  33.4720474           Root MSE      =  3.2372
```

```
---------------------------------------------------------------------
     mpg |     Coef.    Std. Err.       t     P>|t|    [95% Conf. Interval]
---------+-----------------------------------------------------------
    _hat |   1.141987    .7612218    1.500   0.138    -.3758456    2.65982
  _hatsq |  -.0031916    .0170194   -0.188   0.852    -.0371272    .0307441
   _cons |   -1.50305    8.196444   -0.183   0.855    -17.84629   14.84019
---------------------------------------------------------------------
```

We now pass the link test.

◁

▷ Example

Above we followed a standard misinterpretation of the link test—when we discovered a problem, we focused on the explanatory variables of our model. It is at least worth considering varying exactly what the link test tests. The link test told us that our dependent variable was misspecified. For those with an engineering background, mpg is indeed a strange measure. It would make more sense to model energy consumption—gallons per mile—in terms of weight and displacement:

```
. gen gpm = 1/mpg
. regress gpm weight displ foreign

  Source |       SS       df       MS                Number of obs =      74
---------+------------------------------            F(  3,    70) =   76.32
   Model |  .009157962    3   .003052654            Prob > F      =  0.0000
Residual |  .002799666   70   .000039995            R-squared     =  0.7659
---------+------------------------------            Adj R-squared =  0.7558
   Total |  .011957628   73   .000163803            Root MSE      =  .00632

---------------------------------------------------------------------
     gpm |     Coef.    Std. Err.       t     P>|t|    [95% Conf. Interval]
---------+-----------------------------------------------------------
  weight |   .0000144    2.15e-06    6.719   0.000     .0000102    .0000187
   displ |   .0000186    .0000186    1.004   0.319    -.0000184    .0000557
 foreign |   .0066981    .0020531    3.262   0.002     .0026034    .0107928
   _cons |   .0008917    .0043337    0.206   0.838    -.0077515    .009535
---------------------------------------------------------------------
```

This model looks every bit as reasonable as our original model.

```
. linktest

  Source |       SS       df       MS                Number of obs =      74
---------+------------------------------            F(  2,    71) =  117.06
   Model |  .009175219    2   .004587609            Prob > F      =  0.0000
Residual |  .002782409   71   .000039189            R-squared     =  0.7673
---------+------------------------------            Adj R-squared =  0.7608
   Total |  .011957628   73   .000163803            Root MSE      =  .00626

---------------------------------------------------------------------
     gpm |     Coef.    Std. Err.       t     P>|t|    [95% Conf. Interval]
---------+-----------------------------------------------------------
    _hat |   .6608413    .515275     1.282   0.204    -.3665877    1.68827
  _hatsq |   3.275857    4.936655    0.664   0.509    -6.567553   13.11927
   _cons |   .008365     .0130468    0.641   0.523    -.0176496    .0343795
---------------------------------------------------------------------
```

Specifying the model in terms of gallons-per-mile also solved the specification problem and resulted in a more parsimonious specification.

◁

▷ Example

The link test can be used with any single-equation estimation procedure, not solely regression. Let's turn our problem around and attempt to explain whether a car is manufactured outside the U.S. by its mileage rating and weight. To save paper, we will specify logit's nolog option, which suppresses the iteration log:

```
. logit foreign mpg weight, nolog
```

```
Logit Estimates                           Number of obs =      74
                                          chi2(2)       =   35.72
                                          Prob > chi2   = 0.0000
Log Likelihood = -27.175156               Pseudo R2     = 0.3966
```

foreign	Coef.	Std. Err.	t	P>|t|	[95% Conf. Interval]	
mpg	-.1685869	.0919174	-1.834	0.071	-.3518651	.0146913
weight	-.0039067	.0010116	-3.862	0.000	-.0059238	-.0018896
_cons	13.70837	4.518707	3.034	0.003	4.698322	22.71841

When you run linktest after logit, the result is another logit specification:

```
. linktest, nolog
```

```
Logit Estimates                           Number of obs =      74
                                          chi2(2)       =   36.83
                                          Prob > chi2   = 0.0000
Log Likelihood = -26.615714               Pseudo R2     = 0.4090
```

foreign	Coef.	Std. Err.	t	P>|t|	[95% Conf. Interval]	
_hat	.8438531	.2738759	3.081	0.003	.29776	1.389946
_hatsq	-.1559115	.1568642	-0.994	0.324	-.4686897	.1568668
_cons	.2630557	.4299598	0.612	0.543	-.5942597	1.120371

The link test reveals no problems with our specification.

If there had been a problem, we would have been virtually forced to accept the misinterpretation of the link test—we would have reconsidered our specification of the independent variables. When using logit, we have no control over the specification of the dependent variable other than to change likelihood functions.

We admit to seeing a dataset once where the link test rejected the logit specification. We did change the likelihood function, reestimating the model using probit, and satisfied the link test. Probit has thinner tails than logit. In general, however, you will not be so lucky.

◁

❑ Technical Note

You should specify exactly the same options with linktest as you do with the estimation command, although you do not have to follow this advice as literally as we did in the preceding example. logit's nolog option merely suppresses a part of the output, not what is estimated. We specified nolog both times to save paper.

If you are testing a cox model with censored observations, however, you must specify the dead() option on linktest as well. If you are testing a tobit model, you must specify the censoring points just as you do with the tobit command.

If you are not sure which options are important, duplicate exactly what you specified on the estimation command.

The same applies to the `if` and `in` clauses: If you specified either on the estimation command, include the same clauses with `linktest` as well. There may be occasions where you might purposefully ignore this advice. `linktest` uses all the data it can for estimation of the test. It would certainly be acceptable to omit some data in estimation and then calculate the link test on all the data so long as you believe the model is appropriate for all the data.

❏

Saved Results

`linktest` saves in the S_# macros:

S_1   *t* statistic on _hatsq   S_2   degrees of freedom for *t*

`linktest` is *not* an estimation command in the sense that it leaves previous estimation results unchanged. For instance, one runs a regression and then performs the link test. Typing `regress` without arguments after the link test still replays the *original* regression.

In terms of integrating an estimation command with `linktest`, `linktest` assumes the name of the estimation command is stored in S_E_cmd and the name of the dependent variable in S_E_depv. After estimation, it assumes the number of degrees of freedom for the *t* test is given by S_E_mdf if the macro is defined; otherwise, by _result(5) if _result(5) does not contain missing; and finally by _result(1)-_result(3)-1.

Methods and Formulas

`linktest` is implemented as an ado-file. The link test is based on the idea that if a regression or regression-like equation is properly specified, one should not be able to find any additional independent variables that are significant except by chance. One kind of specification error is called a link error. In regression, this means that the dependent variable needs a transformation or "link" function to properly relate to the independent variables. The idea of a link test is to add an independent variable to the equation that is especially likely to be significant if there is a link error.

Let

$$\mathbf{y} = f(\mathbf{X}\beta)$$

be the model and $\widehat{\beta}$ be the parameter estimates. `linktest` calculates

$$\_hat = \mathbf{X}\widehat{\beta}$$

and

$$\_hatsq = \_hat^2$$

The model is then refit with these two variables, and the test is based on the significance of _hatsq. This is the form suggested by Pregibon (1979) based on an idea of Tukey (1949). Pregibon (1980) suggests a slightly different method that has come to be known as "Pregibon's goodness-of-link test". We preferred the older version because it is universally applicable, straightforward, and a good second-order approximation. It is universally applicable in the sense that it can be applied to any single-equation estimation technique whereas Pregibon's more recent tests are estimation-technique specific.

References

Pregibon, D. 1979. *Data Analytic Methods for Generalized Linear Models*. Ph.D. Dissertation. University of Toronto.

——. 1980. Goodness of link tests for generalized linear models. *Applied Statistics* 29: 15-24.

Tukey, J. W. 1949. One degree of freedom for non-additivity. *Biometrics* 5: 232–242.

Also See

[R] **estimation commands**, [R] **lrtest**, [R] **test**, [R] **testnl**

Title

list — List values of variables

Syntax

[by *varlist*:] <u>l</u>ist [*varlist*] [if *exp*] [in *range*] [, [<u>no</u>]display <u>nol</u>abel <u>noobs</u>]

Description

list displays the values of variables. If no *varlist* is specified, the values of all the variables are displayed. Windows users should also see **browse** in [R] **edit**.

Options

[no]display forces the format into display or tabular (nodisplay) format. If you do not specify one of these two options, then Stata chooses one based on its judgment of which would be most readable.

nolabel causes the numeric codes rather than the label values (strings) to be displayed.

noobs suppresses printing of the observation numbers.

Remarks

list, typed by itself, lists all the observations and all the variables in the data. If you specify *varlist*, only those variables are listed. Specifying one or both of **in** *range* and **if** *exp* limits the observations listed.

▷ Example

list has two output formats, known as tabular and display. The tabular format is suitable for listing a few variables, whereas the display format is suitable for listing an unlimited number of variables. Stata chooses automatically between those two formats:

```
. list in 1/2
Observation 1
     make  AMC Concord    price      4099      mpg         22
    rep78      Average    hdroom      2.5      trunk       11
   weight         2930    length      186      turn        40
    displ          121    gratio     3.58      foreign Domestic
Observation 2
     make    AMC Pacer    price      4749      mpg         17
    rep78      Average    hdroom      3.0      trunk       11
   weight         3350    length      173      turn        40
    displ          258    gratio     2.53      foreign Domestic
. list make mpg weight displ rep78 in 1/5
                   make   mpg   weight   displ    rep78
       1.    AMC Concord    22     2930     121  Average
       2.      AMC Pacer    17     3350     258  Average
       3.      AMC Spirit    22     2640     121        .
       4.   Buick Century    20     3250     196  Average
       5.   Buick Electra    15     4080     350     Good
```

The first case is an example of display format; the second is an example of tabular format. The tabular format is more readable and takes less space, but it is effective only if the variables can fit on a single line across the screen. Stata chose to list all twelve variables in display format, but when the *varlist* was restricted to five variables, Stata chose tabular format.

If you are dissatisfied with Stata's choice, you can make the decision yourself. Specify the `display` option to force display format and the `nodisplay` option to force tabular format.

◁

❑ Technical Note

When Stata lists string variables, it *always* lists them right-justified. Our strings in the example above do not have leading blanks; Stata lined up the rightmost characters automatically.

❑

❑ Technical Note

You can `list` the variables in any order that you desire. When you specify the *varlist*, `list` makes the display in the order you specify. You may also include variables more than once in the *varlist*.

❑

▷ Example

In some cases, you may wish to suppress the observation numbers. You do this by specifying the `noobs` option:

```
. list make mpg weight displ rep78 in 1/5, noobs
          make    mpg   weight   displ    rep78
   AMC Concord     22     2930     121   Average
     AMC Pacer     17     3350     258   Average
    AMC Spirit     22     2640     121       .
 Buick Century     20     3250     196   Average
 Buick Electra     15     4080     350      Good
```

◁

❑ Technical Note

You can suppress the use of value labels by specifying the `nolabel` option. For instance, the variable `rep78` in the examples above really contains numeric codes, 1 meaning `Poor`, 2 meaning `Fair`, and so on. When you `list` the variable, however, you see the corresponding value labels rather than the underlying numeric code:

```
. list rep78 in 1/5
          rep78
  1.   Average
  2.   Average
  3.        .
  4.   Average
  5.      Good
```

Specifying the `nolabel` option displays the underlying numeric codes:

```
. list rep78 in 1/5, nolabel
        rep78
  1.       3
  2.       3
  3.       .
  4.       3
  5.       4
```

❏

References

Riley, A. R. 1993. dm15. Interactively list values of variables. *Stata Technical Bulletin* 16: 2–6. Reprinted in *Stata Technical Bulletin Reprints*, vol. 3, pp. 37–41.

Royston, P. and P. Sasieni. 1994. dm16: Compact listing of a single variable. *Stata Technical Bulletin* 17: 7–8. Reprinted in *Stata Technical Bulletin Reprints*, vol. 3, pp. 41–43.

Also See

[R] **display**, [R] **edit**, [R] **tabdisp**

Title

> **lnskew0** — Find zero-skewness log or Box–Cox transform

Syntax

> **lnskew0** *newvar* = *exp* [if *exp*] [in *range*] [, level(#) delta(#) zero(#)]

> **bcskew0** *newvar* = *exp* [if *exp*] [in *range*] [, level(#) delta(#) zero(#)]

Description

lnskew0 creates *newvar* = $\ln(\pm exp - k)$, choosing k and the sign of *exp* so that the skewness of *newvar* is zero.

bcskew0 creates *newvar* = $(exp^\lambda - 1)/\lambda$, the Box–Cox power transformation (Box and Cox 1964), choosing λ so that the skewness of *newvar* is zero. *exp* must be strictly positive. Also see [R] **boxcox** for maximum-likelihood estimation of λ.

Options

level(#) specifies the confidence level for a confidence interval for k (**lnskew0**) or λ (**bcskew0**). Unlike usual, the confidence interval is calculated only if **level()** is specified. As usual, # is specified as an integer; 95 means 95% confidence intervals. The **level()** option is honored only if the number of observations exceeds 7.

delta(#) specifies the increment used for calculating the derivative of the skewness function with respect to k (**lnskew0**) or λ (**bcskew0**). The default values are 0.02 for **lnskew0** and 0.01 for **bcskew0**.

zero(#) specifies a value for skewness to determine convergence that is small enough to be considered zero and is by default 0.001.

Remarks

▷ Example

Using our automobile data (see [U] **13 Stata's on-line tutorials and sample datasets**), we want to generate a new variable equal to $\ln(\text{mpg} - k)$ to be approximately normally distributed. **mpg** records the miles per gallon for each of our cars. One feature of the normal distribution is that it has skewness 0.

```
. lnskew0 new = mpg
       Transform |       k    [95% Conf. Interval]     Skewness
-----------------+-----------------------------------------------
      ln(mpg-k) |  5.383659     (not calculated)       -7.05e-06
```

This created the new variable **lnmpg** = $\ln(\text{mpg} - 5.384)$:

```
. describe lnmpg
 19. lnmpg          float   %9.0g                  ln(mpg-5.3836595)
```

338

Since we did not specify the `level()` option, no confidence interval was calculated. At the outset, we could have typed

```
. lnskew0 lnmpg = mpg, level(95)
        Transform |         k    [95% Conf. Interval]     Skewness
-----------------+-----------------------------------------------
       ln(mpg-k) |  5.383659    -17.12339   9.892416     -7.05e-06
```

The confidence interval is calculated under the assumption that $\ln(\text{mpg} - k)$ really does have a normal distribution. It would be perfectly reasonable to use `lnskew0` even if we did not believe the transformed variable would have a normal distribution—if we literally wanted the zero-skewness transform—although in that case the confidence interval would be an approximation of unknown quality to the true confidence interval. If we now wanted to test the believability of the confidence interval, we could also test our new variable `lnmpg` using `swilk` with the `lnnormal` option.

◁

❏ Technical Note

`lnskew0` (and `bcskew0`) reports the resulting skewness of the variable merely to reassure you of the accuracy of its results. In our above example, `lnskew0` found k such that the resulting skewness was $-7 \cdot 10^{-6}$, a number close enough to zero for all practical purposes. If you wanted to make it even smaller, you could specify the `zero()` option. Typing `lnskew0 new=mpg, zero(1e-8)` changes the estimated k to -5.383552 from -5.383659 and reduces the calculated skewness to $-2 \cdot 10^{-11}$.

When you request a confidence interval, it is possible that `lnskew0` will report the lower confidence interval as '.', which should be taken as indicating the lower confidence limit $k_L = -\infty$. (This cannot happen with `bcskew0`.)

As an example, consider a sample of size n on x and assume the skewness of x is positive, but not significantly so at the desired significance level, say 95%. Then no matter how large and negative you make k_L, there is no value extreme enough to make the skewness of $\ln(x - k_L)$ equal the corresponding percentile (97.5 for a 95% confidence interval) of the distribution of skewness in a normal distribution of the same sample size. You cannot because the distribution of $\ln(x - k_L)$ tends to that of x—apart from location and scale shift—as $x \to \infty$. This "problem" never applies to the upper confidence limit k_U because the skewness of $\ln(x - k_U)$ tends to $-\infty$ as k tends upwards to the minimum value of x.

❏

▷ Example

In the above example, using `lnskew0` with a variable like `mpg` is probably undesirable. `mpg` has a natural zero and we are shifting that zero arbitrarily. On the other hand, use of `lnskew0` with a variable such as temperature measured in Fahrenheit or Celsius would be more appropriate as the zero is indeed arbitrary.

For a variable like `mpg`, it makes more sense to use the Box–Cox power transform (Box and Cox 1964):

$$y^{(\lambda)} = \frac{y^\lambda - 1}{\lambda}$$

λ is free to take on any value, but note that $y^{(1)} = y - 1$, $y^{(0)} = \ln(y)$, and $y^{(-1)} = 1 - 1/y$.

bcskew0 works like lnskew0:

```
. bcskew0 bcmpg = mpg, level(95)
          Transform |        L     [95% Conf. Interval]      Skewness
   -----------------+---------------------------------------------------
        (mpg^L-1)/L | -.3673283    -1.212752   .4339645      .0001898
```

It is worth noting that the 95% confidence interval includes $\lambda = -1$ (λ is labeled L in the output), which has a rather more pleasing interpretation—gallons per mile—rather than $(\mathbf{mpg}^{-.3673} - 1)/(-.3673)$. The confidence interval, however, is calculated under the assumption that the power transformed variable is normally distributed. It makes perfect sense to use bcskew0 even when one does not believe that the transformed variable will be normally distributed, but in that case the confidence interval is an approximation of unknown quality. If one believes that the transformed data is normally distributed, one can alternatively use boxcox to estimate λ; see [R] **boxcox**.

◁

Saved Results

lnskew0 and bcskew0 save in the S_# macros:

S_1 k (lnskew0) or λ (bcskew0)
S_2   lower confidence interval if requested
S_3   upper confidence interval if requested
S_4   resulting skewness of transformed variable

Note, when confidence intervals are calculated, S_2 is set to missing to indicate negative infinity.

Methods and Formulas

lnskew0 and bcskew0 are implemented as ado-files.

Skewness is as calculated by summarize; see [R] **summarize**. Newton's method with numeric, uncentered derivatives is used to estimate k (lnskew0) and λ (bcskew0). In the case of lnskew0, the initial value is chosen so that the minimum of $x - k$ is 1 and thus $\ln(x - k)$ is 0. bcskew0 starts with $\lambda = 1$.

Acknowledgments

lnskew0 and bcskew0 were written by Patrick Royston of the Royal Postgraduate Medical School, London.

References

Box, G. E. P. and D. R. Cox. 1964. An analysis of transformations. *Journal of the Royal Statistical Society*, Series B 26: 211–243.

Also See

[R] **boxcox**, [R] **swilk**

Title

> **log** — Echo copy of session to file or device

Syntax

<u>log</u> using *filename* [, <u>nop</u>roc append replace]

<u>log</u> { on | <u>off</u> | <u>c</u>lose }

<u>set</u> { <u>d</u>isplay | <u>l</u>og } { <u>l</u>inesize | <u>p</u>agesize } #

In addition to the above, Stata for Windows and Stata for Macintosh users may click on the **Log** button.

Description

log using opens *filename* and echoes a copy of your session to the file. If *filename* is specified without an extension, .log is assumed.

log close stops logging the session and closes the file. **log off** temporarily stops logging the session, leaving the file open. **log on** resumes logging to the file.

set log controls the dimensions of output sent to the log. **set display** does the same for the terminal.

Options

noproc causes Stata to record only the characters you type. No output of any kind, including error messages, is sent to the file. This option offers a convenient way to create a do-file of your session.

append directs Stata to append to the end of an existing file. **append** may not be abbreviated.

replace directs Stata to allow overwriting of an existing file. **replace** may not be abbreviated.

Remarks

For an explanation of the **log** command, see [U] **21 Printing and preserving output**.

The character width of the lines written to the log file may differ from that of the video monitor. **set log linesize** allows you to change the maximum width of lines sent to the log. **set log pagesize** currently has no effect.

set display sets the size of the display rather than the log file. The **linesize** parameter indicates the number of characters that can be placed on a line and should be set to 1 less than the full width of the screen. On PCs under DOS, Stata initializes **linesize** to 79. On Unix systems, Stata obtains the value from the /etc/termcap(5) file or /usr/lib/terminfo(4) directory. On certain windowing systems, such as Sunview, the dimension of the window is obtained from the windowing system.

The **pagesize** parameter of **set display** indicates the number of lines that can be displayed before a --more-- condition. It should be specified as 2 less than the physical number of lines on the screen. On PCs under DOS, the default value is 23. On Unix systems, Stata obtains the value from **termcap** or **terminfo** or the windowing system.

341

Setting the `display pagesize` to zero is the same as making it infinite; `--more--` conditions will never occur, effectively turning off more. `set more 1`, however, is preferred; see [R] **more**.

Also See

Getting Started with Stata for Macintosh   Getting Started with Stata for Windows

[U] **14 –more– conditions**, [U] **18.6 File-naming conventions**, [U] **21 Printing and preserving output**

[R] **more**, [R] **query**

Title

> **logistic** — Logistic regression

Syntax

> **logistic** *depvar varlist* [*weight*] [**if** *exp*] [**in** *range*] [**,** <u>l</u>evel(*#*) <u>r</u>obust
>
> <u>cl</u>uster(*varname*) <u>sc</u>ore(*newvarname*) *maximize_options*]

> **lfit** [*depvar*] [*weight*] [**if** *exp*] [**in** *range*] [**,** **group**(*#*) <u>t</u>able <u>out</u>sample
>
> **all** <u>rule</u>s **asif** **beta**(*matname*)]

> **lstat** [*depvar*] [*weight*] [**if** *exp*] [**in** *range*] [**,** <u>c</u>utoff(*#*)
>
> **all** <u>rule</u>s **asif** **beta**(*matname*)]

> **lroc** [*depvar*] [*weight*] [**if** *exp*] [**in** *range*] [**,** <u>no</u>graph *graph_options*
>
> **all** <u>rule</u>s **asif** **beta**(*matname*)]

> **lsens** [*depvar*] [*weight*] [**if** *exp*] [**in** *range*] [**,** <u>no</u>graph *graph_options*
>
> <u>genp</u>rob(*varname*) <u>gense</u>ns(*varname*) <u>gensp</u>ec(*varname*) **replace**
>
> **all** <u>rule</u>s **asif** **beta**(*matname*)]

> **lpredict** *newvar* [**,** { <u>db</u>eta | <u>de</u>viance | <u>dx</u>2 | **ddeviance** | **hat** | <u>num</u>ber | <u>re</u>sid |
>
> <u>rs</u>tandard }]

logistic allows **fweight**s and **pweight**s; **lfit**, **lstat**, **lroc**, and **lsens** allow only **fweight**s; see [U] **18.1.6 weight**.

logistic shares the features of all estimation commands; see [U] **26 Estimation and post-estimation commands**.

To reset problem-size limits, see [R] **matsize**.

logistic may be used with **sw** to perform stepwise estimation; see [R] **sw**.

Description

logistic estimates a logistic regression of *depvar* on *varlist*, where *depvar* is a 0/1 variable (or, more precisely, a 0/non-0 variable). Without arguments, logistic redisplays the last logistic estimates. logistic displays estimates as odds ratios; to view coefficients, type logit after running logistic. To obtain odds ratios for any covariate pattern relative to another, see [R] **lincom**.

lfit displays either the Pearson goodness-of-fit test or the Hosmer–Lemeshow goodness-of-fit test.

lstat displays various summary statistics, including the classification table.

lroc graphs and calculates the area under the ROC curve.

lsens graphs sensitivity and specificity versus probability cutoff and optionally creates new variables containing this data.

lfit, lstat, lroc, and lsens can produce statistics and graphs either for the estimation sample or for any set of observations. However, they always use the estimation sample by default. When weights, if, or in are used with logistic, it is not necessary to repeat them with these commands when you want statistics computed for the estimation sample. Specify if, in, or the all option only when you want statistics computed for a set of observations other than the estimation sample. Specify weights (only fweights are allowed with these commands) only when you want to use a different set of weights.

By default, lfit, lstat, lroc, and lsens use the last model estimated by logistic. Alternatively, the model can be specified by inputting a vector of coefficients with the beta() option and passing the name of the dependent variable *depvar* to the commands.

lpredict creates new variables containing predicted probabilities, residuals, or influence statistics based on the last model estimated by logistic for the estimation sample.

Options

level(#) specifies the confidence level, in percent, for confidence intervals. The default is level(95) or as set by set level; see [U] **26.4 Specifying the width of confidence intervals**.

robust specifies that the Huber/White/sandwich estimator of variance is to be used in place of the traditional calculation; see [U] **26.10 Obtaining robust variance estimates**. robust combined with cluster() allows observations which are not independent within cluster (although they must be independent between clusters).

If you specify pweights, robust is implied; see [U] **26.12 Weighted estimation**.

cluster(*varname*) specifies that the observations are independent across groups (clusters) but not necessarily within groups. *varname* specifies to which group each observation belongs; e.g., cluster(personid) in data with repeated observations on individuals. cluster() affects the estimated standard errors and variance-covariance matrix of the estimators (VCE), but not the estimated coefficients; see [U] **26.10 Obtaining robust variance estimates**. cluster() can be used with pweights to produce estimates for unstratified cluster-sampled data, but see the svylogit command in [R] **svyreg** for a command designed especially for survey data.

cluster() implies robust; specifying robust cluster() is equivalent to typing cluster() by itself.

score(*newvar*) creates *newvar* containing $u_j = \partial \ln L_j / \partial(\mathbf{x}_j \mathbf{b})$ for each observation j in the sample. The score vector is $\sum \partial \ln L_j / \partial \mathbf{b} = \sum u_j \mathbf{x}_j$; i.e., the product of *newvar* with each covariate summed over observations. See [U] **26.11 Obtaining scores**.

maximize_options control the maximization process; see [R] **maximize**. You should never have to specify them.

group(#) specifies the number of quantiles to be used to group the data for the Hosmer–Lemeshow goodness-of-fit test. group(10) is typically specified. If this option is not given, the Pearson goodness-of-fit test is computed using the covariate patterns in the data as groups.

table displays a table of the groups used for the Hosmer–Lemeshow or Pearson goodness-of-fit test with predicted probabilities, observed and expected counts for both outcomes, and totals for each group.

outsample adjusts the degrees of freedom for the Pearson and Hosmer–Lemeshow goodness-of-fit tests for samples outside of the estimation sample. See the section *Samples other than estimation sample* later in this entry.

all requests that the statistic be computed for all observations in the dataset ignoring any if or in restriction specified with logistic. Note: Any observations dropped by logistic because their covariates determined success or failure perfectly are excluded (as are any other observations in the dataset with the same values as the ones dropped); to include these observations, use the rules or asif options.

rules requests that the predicted probabilities be set to 0 or 1 according to the "rules" determined during estimation for those observations dropped by logistic because their covariates determined success or failure perfectly. See [R] **logit** for a description of the rules option for predict.

asif requests that the predicted probabilities be computed using the estimated coefficients ignoring any exclusion criteria or "rules" determined during estimation for those observations dropped by logistic because their covariates determined success or failure perfectly. See [R] **logit** for a description of the asif option for predict.

beta(*matname*) specifies a row vector containing coefficients for a logistic model. The columns of the row vector must be labeled with the corresponding names of the independent variables in the dataset. The dependent variable *depvar* must be specified immediately after the command name. See the section *Models other than last estimated model* later in this entry.

nograph suppresses graphical output.

graph_options are any of the options allowed with graph, twoway; see [R] **graph twoway**.

cutoff(#) specifies the value for determining whether an observation has a predicted positive outcome. An observation is classified as positive if its predicted probability is $\geq$ #. Default is 0.5.

genprob(*varname*), gensens(*varname*), and genspec(*varname*) specify the names of new variables created to contain, respectively, the probability cutoffs and corresponding sensitivity and specificity.

replace requests that if existing variables are specified for genprob(), gensens(), or genspec(), they should be overwritten.

dbeta, ..., rstandard. Without options, lpredict calculates the predicted probability of a positive outcome over the estimation sample. "Due to deletion" in the explanations below means due to deletion of all observations sharing the same covariate pattern. All statistics are, in Hosmer and Lemeshow (1989) jargon, M-asymptotic, that is, adjusted for the number of observations that share the same covariate pattern.

dbeta calculates the Pregibon (1981) $\Delta\widehat{\beta}$ influence statistic, a standardized measure of the difference in the coefficient vector due to deletion of the observation along with all others that share the same covariate pattern.

deviance calculates the deviance residual.

dx2 calculates the Hosmer and Lemeshow (1989) ΔX^2 influence statistic reflecting the decrease in the Pearson χ^2 due to deletion of the observation and all others that share the same covariate pattern.

ddeviance calculates the Hosmer and Lemeshow (1989) ΔD influence statistic, which is the change in the deviance residual due to deletion of the observation and all others that share the same covariate pattern.

hat calculates the Pregibon (1981) leverage or the diagonal elements of the hat matrix adjusted for the number of observations that share the same covariate pattern.

number numbers the covariate patterns—observations with the same covariate pattern have the same **number**. Observations not used in estimation have **number** set to missing. The "first" covariate pattern is numbered 1, the second 2, and so on.

resid calculates the Pearson residual as given by Hosmer and Lemeshow (1989) and adjusted for the number of observations that share the same covariate pattern.

rstandard calculates the standardized Pearson residual as given by Hosmer and Lemeshow (1989) and adjusted for the number of observations that share the same covariate pattern.

Remarks

Remarks are presented under the headings

> *logistic and logit*
> *Robust estimate of variance*
> *lfit*
> *lstat*
> *lroc*
> *lsens*
> *Samples other than estimation sample*
> *Models other than last estimated model*
> *lpredict*

logistic and logit

logistic provides an alternative and preferred way to estimate maximum-likelihood logit models, the other choice being **logit** described in [R] **logit**.

First, let us dispose of some confusing terminology. We use the words logit and logistic to mean the same thing: maximum-likelihood estimation. To some, one or the other of these words connotes transforming the dependent variable and using weighted least squares to estimate the model, but that is not how we use the word here. Thus, the **logit** and **logistic** commands produce the same results.

The **logistic** command is generally preferred to **logit** because

1. **logistic** presents the estimates in terms of odds ratios rather than coefficients;

2. after **logistic**, you can test the fit, display various summary statistics, graph the ROC curve, and examine residuals and influence statistics.

To a few, item 1 may seem a disadvantage, but you can type **logit** without arguments after **logistic** to see the underlying coefficients. In fact, you can do anything after **logistic** that you can do after **logit** and you can do more.

Nevertheless, it is still worth reading [R] **logit** because **logistic** shares the same features as **logit**, including omitting variables due to collinearity or one-way causation.

For a basic introduction to logistic regression, see Pagano and Gauvreau (1993, 427–443); for a thorough discussion, see Hosmer and Lemeshow (1989).

▷ Example

Consider the following dataset from a study of risk factors associated with low birth weight described in Hosmer and Lemeshow (1989, appendix 1).

```
. describe
Contains data from lbw.dta
  obs:            189                        Hosmer & Lemeshow data
  vars:            11                        29 May 1996 13:18
  size:         3,402 (99.6% of memory free)
-----------------------------------------------------------------------------
  1. id          int    %8.0g               identification code
  2. low         byte   %8.0g               birth weight<2500g
  3. age         byte   %8.0g               age of mother
  4. lwt         int    %8.0g               weight at last menstrual period
  5. race        byte   %8.0g    race       race
  6. smoke       byte   %8.0g               smoked during pregnancy
  7. ptl         byte   %8.0g               premature labor history (count)
  8. ht          byte   %8.0g               has history of hypertension
  9. ui          byte   %8.0g               presence, uterine irritability
 10. ftv         byte   %8.0g               # phs. visits, 1st trimester
 11. bwt         int    %8.0g               birth weight (grams)
-----------------------------------------------------------------------------
Sorted by:
```

They want to investigate the causes of low birth weight. In this dataset, race is a categorical variable indicating whether a person is white (race = 1), black (race = 2), or other (race = 3). The authors want indicator (dummy) variables for race included in the regression. (One of the dummies, of course, must be omitted.) Thus, before we can estimate the model, we must create the race dummy variables.

There are a number of ways we could do this, but the easiest is to let another Stata command, xi, do it for us. We type xi: in front of our logistic command and in our *varlist* include not race but i.race to indicate we want the indicator variables for this categorical variable; see [R] xi for the full details.

```
. xi: logistic low age lwt i.race smoke ptl ht ui
i.race              Irace_1-3    (naturally coded; Irace_1 omitted)
Logit Estimates                              Number of obs =      189
                                             chi2(8)       =    33.22
                                             Prob > chi2   = 0.0001
Log Likelihood =   -100.724                  Pseudo R2     = 0.1416

-----------------------------------------------------------------------------
     low | Odds Ratio   Std. Err.      z     P>|z|    [95% Conf. Interval]
---------+-------------------------------------------------------------------
     age |  .9732636    .0354759    -0.743   0.457     .9061578   1.045339
     lwt |  .9849634    .0068217    -2.188   0.029     .9716834   .9984249
  Irace_2 |  3.534767   1.860737     2.399   0.016     1.259736   9.918406
  Irace_3 |  2.368079   1.039949     1.963   0.050     1.001356   5.600207
   smoke |  2.517698   1.00916      2.304   0.021     1.147676   5.523162
     ptl |  1.719161    .5952579    1.565   0.118     .8721455   3.388787
      ht |  6.249602   4.322408     2.650   0.008     1.611152   24.24199
      ui |   2.1351     .9808153    1.651   0.099     .8677528    5.2534
-----------------------------------------------------------------------------
```

The odds ratios are for a one-unit change in the variable. If we wanted the odds ratio for age to be in terms of 4-year intervals, we would

```
. gen age4 = age/4
. xi: logistic low age4 lwt i.race smoke ptl ht ui
```
(*output omitted*)

After `logistic`, we can type `logit` to see the model in terms of coefficients and standard errors:

```
. logit
Logit Estimates                                Number of obs =      189
                                               chi2(8)       =    33.22
                                               Prob > chi2   =   0.0001
Log Likelihood =   -100.724                    Pseudo R2     =   0.1416

------------------------------------------------------------------------
     low |     Coef.   Std. Err.       z     P>|z|    [95% Conf. Interval]
---------+--------------------------------------------------------------
     age |  -.0271003   .0364504    -0.743   0.457    -.0985418    .0443412
     lwt |  -.0151508   .0069259    -2.188   0.029    -.0287253   -.0015763
 Irace_2 |   1.262647   .5264101     2.399   0.016     .2309024    2.294392
 Irace_3 |   .8620792   .4391531     1.963   0.050     .0013548    1.722804
   smoke |   .9233448   .4008266     2.304   0.021     .1377391    1.708951
     ptl |   .5418366    .346249     1.565   0.118     -.136799    1.220472
      ht |   1.832518   .6916292     2.650   0.008     .4769494    3.188086
      ui |   .7585135   .4593768     1.651   0.099    -.1418484    1.658875
   _cons |   .4612239    1.20459     0.383   0.702    -1.899729    2.822176
------------------------------------------------------------------------
```

If we wanted to see the `logistic` output again, we would type `logistic` without arguments.

◁

▷ Example

You can specify the confidence interval for the odds ratios with the `level()` option, and you can do this either at estimation time or when you replay the model. For instance, to see our previous models with narrower, 90% confidence intervals:

```
. logistic, level(90)
Logit Estimates                                Number of obs =      189
                                               chi2(8)       =    33.22
                                               Prob > chi2   =   0.0001
Log Likelihood =   -100.724                    Pseudo R2     =   0.1416

------------------------------------------------------------------------
     low | Odds Ratio  Std. Err.       z     P>|z|    [90% Conf. Interval]
---------+--------------------------------------------------------------
     age |   .9732636   .0354759    -0.743   0.457     .9166258    1.033401
     lwt |   .9849634   .0068217    -2.188   0.029     .9738063    .9962483
 Irace_2 |   3.534767   1.860737     2.399   0.016     1.487028    8.402379
 Irace_3 |   2.368079   1.039949     1.963   0.050     1.149971    4.876471
   smoke |   2.517698    1.00916     2.304   0.021     1.302185    4.867819
     ptl |   1.719161   .5952579     1.565   0.118     .9726876    3.038505
      ht |   6.249602   4.322408     2.650   0.008     2.003487   19.49478
      ui |    2.1351    .9808153     1.651   0.099     1.00291    4.545424
------------------------------------------------------------------------
```

◁

Robust estimate of variance

If you specify `robust`, Stata reports the robust estimate of variance described in [U] **26.10 Obtaining robust variance estimates**. Here is the model previously estimated with the robust estimate of variance:

```
. xi: logistic low age lwt i.race smoke ptl ht ui, robust
i.race              Irace_1-3    (naturally coded; Irace_1 omitted)
Logit Estimates                              Number of obs =      189
                                             chi2(8)       =    29.02
                                             Prob > chi2   =   0.0003
Log Likelihood =   -100.724                  Pseudo R2     =   0.1416

------------------------------------------------------------------------------
         |               Robust
     low | Odds Ratio   Std. Err.      z    P>|z|     [95% Conf. Interval]
---------+--------------------------------------------------------------------
     age |   .9732636   .0329376    -0.801   0.423     .9108015    1.040009
     lwt |   .9849634   .0070209    -2.126   0.034     .9712984    .9988206
 Irace_2 |   3.534767   1.793616     2.488   0.013     1.307504    9.556051
 Irace_3 |   2.368079   1.026563     1.989   0.047     1.012512    5.538501
   smoke |   2.517698   .9736416     2.388   0.017     1.179852    5.372537
     ptl |   1.719161   .7072902     1.317   0.188     .7675715    3.850476
      ht |   6.249602   4.102026     2.792   0.005     1.726445    22.6231
      ui |    2.1351    1.042775     1.553   0.120     .8197749    5.560858
------------------------------------------------------------------------------
```

Additionally, `robust` allows you to specify `cluster()` and is then able, within cluster, to relax the assumption of independence. To illustrate this, we have made some fictional additions to the low-birth-weight data.

Pretend that this data is not a random sample of mothers but instead is a random sample of mothers from a random sample of hospitals. In fact, that may be true—we do not know the history of this data—but we can pretend in any case.

Hospitals specialize and it would not be too incorrect to say that some hospitals specialize in more difficult cases. We are going to show two extremes. In one, all hospitals are alike but we are going to estimate under the possibility that they might differ. In the other, hospitals are strikingly different. In both cases, we assume patients are drawn from 20 hospitals.

In both examples, we will estimate the same model and we will type the same command to estimate it. Below is the same data we have been using but with a new variable `hospid`, which identifies from which of the 20 hospitals each patient was drawn (and which we have made up):

```
. xi: logistic low age lwt i.race smoke ptl ht ui, robust cluster(hospid)
i.race              Irace_1-3    (naturally coded; Irace_1 omitted)
Logit Estimates                              Number of obs =      189
                                             chi2(8)       =    49.67
                                             Prob > chi2   =   0.0000
Log Likelihood =   -100.724                  Pseudo R2     =   0.1416

                        (standard errors adjusted for clustering on hospid)
------------------------------------------------------------------------------
         |               Robust
     low | Odds Ratio   Std. Err.      z    P>|z|     [95% Conf. Interval]
---------+--------------------------------------------------------------------
     age |   .9732636   .0397476    -0.664   0.507     .898396     1.05437
     lwt |   .9849634   .0057101    -2.613   0.009     .9738352    .9962187
 Irace_2 |   3.534767   2.013285     2.217   0.027     1.157563    10.79386
 Irace_3 |   2.368079   .8451325     2.416   0.016     1.176562    4.766257
   smoke |   2.517698   .8284259     2.806   0.005     1.321062    4.79826
     ptl |   1.719161   .6676221     1.395   0.163     .8030814    3.680219
      ht |   6.249602   4.066275     2.816   0.005     1.745911    22.37086
      ui |    2.1351    1.093144     1.482   0.138     .7827337    5.824014
------------------------------------------------------------------------------
```

The standard errors are quite similar to the standard errors we have previously obtained, whether we used the robust or conventional estimators. In this example, we invented the hospital ids randomly.

Now, here are the results of the estimating with the same data but with a different set of hospital ids:

```
. xi: logistic low age lwt i.race smoke ptl ht ui, robust cluster(hospid)
i.race                  Irace_1-3    (naturally coded; Irace_1 omitted)

Logit Estimates                               Number of obs =      189
                                              chi2(8)       =     7.19
                                              Prob > chi2   = 0.5167
Log Likelihood =    -100.724                  Pseudo R2     = 0.1416

                      (standard errors adjusted for clustering on hospid)
----------------------------------------------------------------------------
             |               Robust
         low | Odds Ratio  Std. Err.      z     P>|z|    [95% Conf. Interval]
----------+-----------------------------------------------------------------
         age |  .9732636   .0293064    -0.900   0.368    .9174862   1.032432
         lwt |  .9849634   .0106123    -1.406   0.160    .9643817   1.005984
     Irace_2 |  3.534767   3.120338     1.430   0.153    .6265521   19.9418
     Irace_3 |  2.368079   1.297738     1.573   0.116    .8089594   6.932114
       smoke |  2.517698   1.570287     1.480   0.139    .7414969   8.548654
         ptl |  1.719161   .6799153     1.370   0.171    .7919046   3.732161
          ht |  6.249602   7.165454     1.598   0.110     .660558   59.12808
          ui |    2.1351   1.411977     1.147   0.251    .5841231   7.804266
----------------------------------------------------------------------------
```

Note the strikingly larger standard errors. What happened? In this data, women most likely to have low-birth-weight babies are sent to certain hospitals and the decision on likeliness is based not just on age, smoking history, etc., but on other things that doctors can see but are not recorded in our data. Thus, merely because a woman is at one of the centers identifies her to be more likely to have a low-birth-weight baby.

So much for our fictional example. The rest of this section uses the real low-birth-weight data. To remind you, the last model we left off with was

```
. xi: logistic low age lwt i.race smoke ptl ht ui
i.race                  Irace_1-3    (naturally coded; Irace_1 omitted)

Logit Estimates                               Number of obs =      189
                                              chi2(8)       =    33.22
                                              Prob > chi2   = 0.0001
Log Likelihood =    -100.724                  Pseudo R2     = 0.1416

----------------------------------------------------------------------------
         low | Odds Ratio  Std. Err.      z     P>|z|    [95% Conf. Interval]
----------+-----------------------------------------------------------------
         age |  .9732636   .0354759    -0.743   0.457    .9061578   1.045339
         lwt |  .9849634   .0068217    -2.188   0.029    .9716834   .9984249
     Irace_2 |  3.534767   1.860737     2.399   0.016    1.259736   9.918406
     Irace_3 |  2.368079   1.039949     1.963   0.050    1.001356   5.600207
       smoke |  2.517698    1.00916     2.304   0.021    1.147676   5.523162
         ptl |  1.719161   .5952579     1.565   0.118    .8721455   3.388787
          ht |  6.249602   4.322408     2.650   0.008    1.611152   24.24199
          ui |    2.1351   .9808153     1.651   0.099    .8677528     5.2534
----------------------------------------------------------------------------
```

lfit

lfit computes goodness-of-fit tests, either the Pearson χ^2 test or the Hosmer–Lemeshow test.

By default, lfit, lstat, lroc, and lsens compute statistics for the estimation sample using the last model estimated by logistic. However, samples other than the estimation sample can be specified; see the section *Samples other than estimation sample* later in this entry. Models other than the last model estimated by logistic can also be specified; see the section *Models other than last estimated model.*

▷ Example

lfit, typed without options, presents the Pearson χ^2 goodness-of-fit test for the estimated model. The Pearson χ^2 goodness-of-fit test is a test of the observed against expected number of responses using cells defined by the covariate patterns:

```
. lfit
Logistic model for low, goodness-of-fit test
        number of observations =      189
number of covariate patterns =      182
           Pearson chi2(173) =   179.24
                Prob > chi2 =    0.3567
```

Our model fits reasonably well. We should note, however, that the number of covariate patterns is close to the number of observations, making the applicability of the Pearson χ^2 test questionable, but not necessarily inappropriate. Hosmer and Lemeshow (1989) suggest regrouping the data by ordering on the predicted probabilities and then forming, say, 10 nearly equal-size groups. lfit with the group() option does this:

```
. lfit, group(10)
Logistic model for low, goodness-of-fit test
(Table collapsed on quantiles of estimated probabilities)
        number of observations =      189
               number of groups =       10
     Hosmer-Lemeshow chi2(8) =     9.65
                Prob > chi2 =    0.2904
```

Again, we cannot reject our model. If you specify the table option, lfit displays the groups along with the expected and observed number of positive responses (low-birth-weight babies):

```
. lfit, group(10) table
Logistic model for low, goodness-of-fit test
(Table collapsed on quantiles of estimated probabilities)
```

_Group	_Prob	_Obs_1	_Exp_1	_Obs_0	_Exp_0	_Total
1	0.0827	0	1.2	19	17.8	19
2	0.1276	2	2.0	17	17.0	19
3	0.2015	6	3.2	13	15.8	19
4	0.2432	1	4.3	18	14.7	19
5	0.2792	7	4.9	12	14.1	19
6	0.3138	7	5.6	12	13.4	19
7	0.3872	6	6.5	13	12.5	19
8	0.4828	7	8.2	12	10.8	19
9	0.5941	10	10.3	9	8.7	19
10	0.8391	13	12.8	5	5.2	18

```
            number of observations =      189
                   number of groups =       10
         Hosmer-Lemeshow chi2(8) =     9.65
                    Prob > chi2 =    0.2904
```
◁

❏ Technical Note

lfit with the group() option puts all observations with the same predicted probabilities into the same group. If, as in previous example, we request 10 groups, the groups that lfit makes are $[p_0, p_{10}]$, $(p_{10}, p_{20}]$, $(p_{20}, p_{30}]$, ..., $(p_{90}, p_{100}]$, where p_k is the kth percentile of the predicted probabilities, with p_0 the minimum and p_{100} the maximum.

If there are large numbers of ties at the quantile boundaries—as will frequently happen if all independent variables are categorical and there are only a few of them, the sizes of the groups will be uneven. If the totals in some of the groups are small, the χ^2 statistic for the Hosmer–Lemeshow test may be unreliable. In this case, either fewer groups should be specified or the Pearson goodness-of-fit test may be a better choice.

❏

▷ Example

The table option can be used without the group() option. We would not want to specify this for our current model because there were 182 covariate patterns in the data, caused by the inclusion of the two continuous variables age and lwt in the model. As an aside, we estimate a simpler model and specify table with lfit:

```
. logistic low Irace_2 Irace_3 smoke ui
```

Logit Estimates				Number of obs =	189
				chi2(4) =	18.80
				Prob > chi2 =	0.0009
Log Likelihood = -107.93404				Pseudo R2 =	0.0801

low	Odds Ratio	Std. Err.	z	P>|z|	[95% Conf. Interval]	
Irace_2	3.052746	1.498084	2.274	0.023	1.166749	7.987368
Irace_3	2.922593	1.189226	2.636	0.008	1.31646	6.488269
smoke	2.945742	1.101835	2.888	0.004	1.41517	6.131701
ui	2.419131	1.047358	2.040	0.041	1.03546	5.651783

```
. lfit, tab
```

Logistic model for low, goodness-of-fit test

_Group	_Prob	_Obs_1	_Exp_1	_Obs_0	_Exp_0	_Total
1	0.1230	3	4.9	37	35.1	40
2	0.2533	1	1.0	3	3.0	4
3	0.2907	16	13.7	31	33.3	47
4	0.2923	15	12.6	28	30.4	43
5	0.2997	3	3.9	10	9.1	13
6	0.4978	4	4.0	4	4.0	8
7	0.4998	4	4.5	5	4.5	9
8	0.5087	2	1.5	1	1.5	3
9	0.5469	2	4.4	6	3.6	8
10	0.5577	6	5.6	4	4.4	10
11	0.7449	3	3.0	1	1.0	4

_Group	_Prob	Irace_2	Irace_3	smoke	ui
1	0.1230	0	0	0	0
2	0.2533	0	0	0	1
3	0.2907	0	1	0	0
4	0.2923	0	0	1	0
5	0.2997	1	0	0	0
6	0.4978	0	1	0	1
7	0.4998	0	0	1	1
8	0.5087	1	0	0	1
9	0.5469	0	1	1	0
10	0.5577	1	0	1	0
11	0.7449	0	1	1	1

```
        number of observations =      189
  number of covariate patterns =       11
               Pearson chi2(6) =     5.71
                  Prob > chi2 =   0.4569
```

◁

❑ Technical Note

logistic and lfit keep track of the estimation sample. If you type logistic ... if x==1, then when you type lfit the statistics will be calculated on the x==1 subsample of the data automatically.

You should specify if or in with lfit only when you wish to calculate statistics for a set of observations other than the estimation sample. See the section *Samples other than estimation sample* later in this entry.

If the logistic model was estimated with fweights, lfit properly accounts for the weights in its calculations. (Note: lfit does not allow pweights.) You do not have to specify the weights when you run lfit. Weights should only be specified with lfit when you wish to use a different set of weights.

❑

(Continued on next page.)

lstat

▷ Example

lstat presents the classification statistics and classification table after logistic.

```
. lstat
Logistic model for low
                -------- True --------
Classified |        D              ~D          Total
-----------+--------------------------+-----------
    +      |       21             12 |            33
    -      |       38            118 |           156
-----------+--------------------------+-----------
  Total    |       59            130 |           189

Classified + if predicted Pr(D) >= .5
True D defined as low ~= 0
-------------------------------------------------
Sensitivity                  Pr( +| D)    35.59%
Specificity                  Pr( -|~D)    90.77%
Positive predictive value    Pr( D| +)    63.64%
Negative predictive value    Pr(~D| -)    75.64%
-------------------------------------------------
False + rate for true ~D     Pr( +|~D)     9.23%
False - rate for true D      Pr( -| D)    64.41%
False + rate for classified +  Pr(~D| +)  36.36%
False - rate for classified -  Pr( D| -)  24.36%
-------------------------------------------------
Correctly classified                      73.54%
-------------------------------------------------
```

By default, lstat uses a cutoff of 0.5, although you can vary this with the cutoff() option. The lsens command can be used to review the potential cutoffs; see lsens below.

◁

lroc

lroc graphs the receiver operating characteristic (ROC) curve—a graph of sensitivity versus $1 -$ specificity as the cutoff c is varied—and calculates the area under it. Sensitivity is the fraction of observed positive-outcome cases that are correctly classified; specificity is the fraction of observed negative-outcome cases that are correctly classified. When the purpose of the analysis is classification, one must choose a cutoff.

The curve starts at $(0,0)$, corresponding to $c = 1$, and continues to $(1,1)$, corresponding to $c = 0$. A model with no predictive power would be a $45°$ line. The greater the predictive power, the more bowed the curve, and hence the area beneath the curve is often used as a measure of the predictive power. A model with no predictive power has area 0.5; a perfect model has area 1.

The ROC curve was first discussed in signal detection theory (Peterson, Birdsall, and Fox 1954) and then was quickly introduced into psychology (Tanner and Swets 1954). It has since been applied in other fields, particularly medicine (for instance, Metz 1978). For a classic text on ROC techniques, see Green and Swets (1974).

▷ Example

ROC curves are typically used when the point of the analysis is classification, which it is not in our low-birth-weight model. Nevertheless, the ROC curve is

```
. lroc

Logistic model for low

number of observations =      189
area under ROC curve    =   0.7462
```

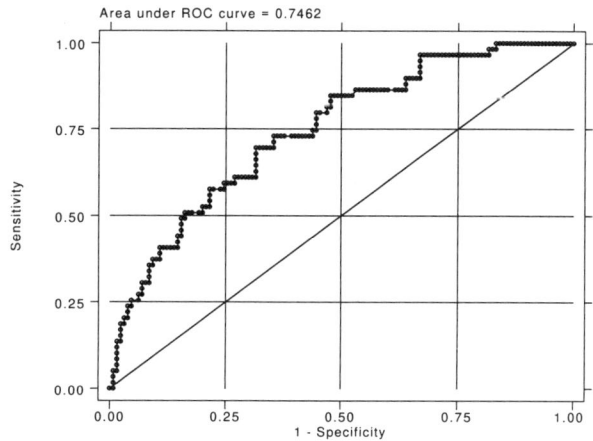

We see that the area under the curve is 0.7462.

◁

lsens

lsens also plots sensitivity and specificity; it plots both sensitivity and specificity versus probability cutoff c. The graph is equivalent to what you would get from lstat if you varied the cutoff probability from 0 to 1.

```
. lsens
```

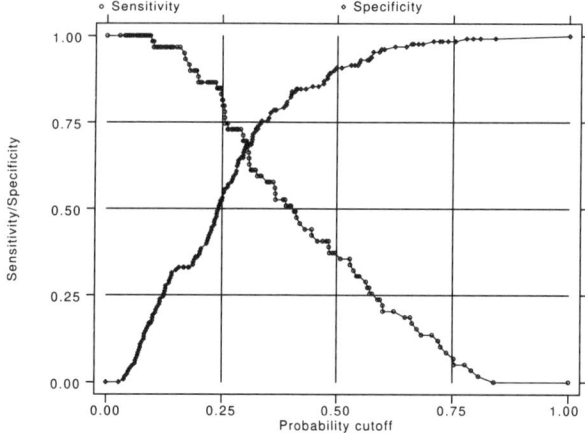

`lsens` will optionally create new variables containing the probability cutoff, sensitivity, and specificity.

```
. lsens, genprob(p) gensens(sens) genspec(spec) nograph
```

Note that the variables created will have $M + 2$ nonmissing values, one for each of the M covariate patterns plus one for $c = 0$ and another for $c = 1$.

Samples other than estimation sample

`lfit`, `lstat`, `lroc`, and `lsens` can be used with samples other than the estimation sample. By default, these commands remember the estimation sample used with the last `logistic` command. To override this, you simply use an `if` or `in` restriction to select another set of observations, or specify the `all` option to force the command to use all the observations in the dataset.

If you use `lfit` with a sample that is completely different from the estimation sample (i.e., no overlap), you should also specify the `outsample` option so that the χ^2 statistic properly adjusts the degrees of freedom upward. For an overlapping sample, the conservative thing to do is to leave the degrees of freedom the same as they are for the estimation sample.

▷ Example

Suppose that we wish to develop a model for predicting low-birth-weight babies. One approach to developing a prediction model would be to divide our data into two groups, a developmental sample and a validation sample. See Lemeshow and Le Gall (1994) and Tilford et al. (1995) for more information on developing prediction models and severity scoring systems.

We will do this with the low-birth-weight data we considered previously. First, we randomly divide the data into two samples.

```
. use lbw, clear
(Hosmer & Lemeshow data)
. set seed 1
. gen r = uniform()
. sort r
. gen group = 1 if _n <= _N/2
(95 missing values generated)
. replace group = 2 if group==.
(95 real changes made)
```

Then we estimate a model using the first sample (group==1), our developmental sample.

```
. xi: logistic low age lwt i.race smoke ptl ht ui if group==1
i.race              Irace_1-3    (naturally coded; Irace_1 omitted)
```

```
Logit Estimates                              Number of obs =       94
                                             chi2(8)       =    29.14
                                             Prob > chi2   =   0.0003
Log Likelihood = -44.293342                  Pseudo R2     =   0.2475
```

low	Odds Ratio	Std. Err.	z	P>|z|	[95% Conf. Interval]	
age	.91542	.0553937	-1.460	0.144	.8130414	1.03069
lwt	.9744276	.0112295	-2.248	0.025	.9526649	.9966874
Irace_2	5.063678	3.78442	2.170	0.030	1.170327	21.90913
Irace_3	2.606209	1.657608	1.506	0.132	.7492483	9.065522
smoke	.909912	.5252898	-0.164	0.870	.2934966	2.820953

```
   ptl |  3.033543   1.507048    2.234  0.025    1.145718   8.03198
    ht | 21.07656   22.64788     2.837  0.005    2.565304  173.1652
    ui |  .988479   .6699458    -0.017  0.986    .2618557  3.731409
-----------------------------------------------------------------------------
```

To test calibration in the developmental sample, the Hosmer–Lemeshow goodness-of-fit test is calculated using lfit.

```
. lfit, group(10)
Logistic model for low, goodness-of-fit test
(Table collapsed on quantiles of estimated probabilities)
             number of observations =        94
                    number of groups =        10
          Hosmer-Lemeshow chi2(8) =         6.67
                       Prob > chi2 =       0.5721
```

Note that we did not specify an if statement with lfit since we wanted to use the estimation sample. Since the test is nonsignificant, we are satisfied with the fit of our model.

Running lroc gives a measure of the discrimination:

```
. lroc, nograph
Logistic model for low

number of observations =        94
area under ROC curve   =    0.8156
```

Now we test the calibration of our model by performing a goodness-of-fit test on the validation sample. We specify the outsample option so that the degrees of freedom are 10 rather than 8.

```
. lfit if group==2, group(10) table outsample
Logistic model for low, goodness-of-fit test
(Table collapsed on quantiles of estimated probabilities)
```

_Group	_Prob	_Obs_1	_Exp_1	_Obs_0	_Exp_0	_Total
1	0.0725	1	0.4	9	9.6	10
2	0.1202	4	0.8	5	8.2	9
3	0.1549	3	1.3	7	8.7	10
4	0.1888	1	1.5	8	7.5	9
5	0.2609	3	2.2	7	7.8	10
6	0.3258	4	2.7	5	6.3	9
7	0.4217	2	3.7	8	6.3	10
8	0.4915	3	4.1	6	4.9	9
9	0.6265	4	5.5	6	4.5	10
10	0.9737	4	7.1	5	1.9	9

```
             number of observations =        95
                    number of groups =        10
         Hosmer-Lemeshow chi2(10) =        28.03
                       Prob > chi2 =       0.0018
```

We must acknowledge that our model does not fit well on the validation sample. The model's discrimination in the validation sample is appreciably lower as well.

```
. lroc if group==2, nograph
Logistic model for low

number of observations =        95
area under ROC curve   =    0.5839
```

◁

Models other than estimated model

By default, lfit, lstat, lroc, and lsens use the last model estimated by logistic. One can specify other models using the beta() option.

▷ Example

Suppose that someone publishes the following logistic model of low birth weight.

$$\Pr(\text{low} = 1) = F(-0.02\,\text{age} - 0.01\,\text{lwt} + 1.3\,\text{black} + 1.1\,\text{smoke} + 0.5\,\text{ptl} + 1.8\,\text{ht} + 0.8\,\text{ui} + 0.5)$$

where F is the cumulative logistic distribution. Note that these coefficients are not odds ratios; they are the equivalent of what logit produces.

We can see whether this model fits our data. First, we enter the coefficients as a row vector and label its columns with the names of the independent variables plus _cons for the constant (see [R] **matrix define** and [R] **matrix rowname**).

```
. matrix b = (-.02 -.01 1.3 1.1 .5 1.8 .8 .5)
. matrix colnames b = age lwt black smoke ptl ht ui _cons
```

We run lfit using the beta() option to specify b. The dependent variable is entered right after the command name, and the outsample option gives the proper degrees of freedom.

```
. lfit low, beta(b) group(10) outsample
Logistic model for low, goodness-of-fit test
(Table collapsed on quantiles of estimated probabilities)
        number of observations =       189
              number of groups =        10
    Hosmer-Lemeshow chi2(10) =      26.99
                  Prob > chi2 =     0.0026
```

Although the fit of the model is poor, lroc shows that it does exhibit some predictive ability.

```
. lroc low, beta(b) nograph
Logistic model for low
number of observations =       189
area under ROC curve   =    0.7274
```

◁

lpredict

lpredict is used after logistic to obtain predicted probabilities, residuals, and influence statistics for the estimation sample. The suggested diagnostic graphs below are from Hosmer and Lemeshow (1989), where they are more elaborately explained. Also see Collett (1991, 120–160) for a thorough discussion of model checking.

lpredict without options

Typing lpredict p and predict p after estimation do almost the same thing—both calculate the predicted probability of a positive outcome. lpredict, however, restricts its calculation to the estimation subsample whereas predict uses all data possible; that is, all data for which the independent variables are not missing. In data without missing values and when you have not specified if *exp* or in *range* on the logistic command, there is no difference. If you did restrict the sample, however, predict will make predictions in cases where lpredict will calculate missing. In making out-of-sample predictions, use predict. When analyzing results of estimation, it is usually better to use lpredict.

We previously ran the model `logistic low age lwt Irace_2 Irace_3 smoke ptl ht ui`. We obtain the predicted probabilities of a positive outcome by typing

```
. lpredict p
. summarize p low
Variable |     Obs        Mean    Std. Dev.        Min         Max
---------+-----------------------------------------------------------
       p |     189    .3121693    .1913915    .0272559    .8391283
     low |     189    .3121693    .4646093           0           1
```

lpredict with the residual option

`lpredict` can calculate more than predicted probabilities. The Pearson residual is defined as the square root of the contribution of the covariate pattern to the Pearson χ^2 goodness-of-fit statistic, signed according to whether the observed number of positive responses within the covariate pattern is less or greater than expected. For instance,

```
. lpredict r, resid
. summarize r, detail

                        Pearson residual
-------------------------------------------------------------
        Percentiles      Smallest
  1%    -1.750923       -2.283885
  5%    -1.129907       -1.750923
 10%     -.9581174      -1.636279      Obs                189
 25%     -.6545911      -1.636279      Sum of Wgt.        189

 50%     -.3806923                     Mean         -.0242299
                          Largest      Std. Dev.     .9970949
 75%      .8162894        2.23879
 90%     1.510355        2.317558      Variance      .9941981
 95%     1.747948        3.002206      Skewness      .8618271
 99%     3.002206        3.126763      Kurtosis      3.038448
```

We notice the prevalence of a few, large positive residuals:

```
. sort r
. list id r low p age race in -5/l
             id          r     low          p      age       race
185.         33   2.224501       1    .1681123       19      white
186.         57    2.23879       1     .166329       15      white
187.         16   2.317558       1    .1569594       27      other
188.         77   3.002206       1    .0998678       26      white
189.         36   3.126763       1    .0927932       24      white
```

lpredict with the number option

Covariate patterns play an important role in logistic regression. Two observations are said to share the same covariate pattern if the independent variables for the two observations are identical. Although one thinks of having individual observations, the statistical information in the sample can be summarized by the covariate patterns, the number of observations with that covariate pattern, and the number of positive outcomes within the pattern. Depending on the model, the number of covariate patterns can approach or be equal to the number of observations or it can be considerably less.

All the residual and diagnostic statistics calculated by Stata are in terms of covariate patterns, not observations. That is, all observations with the same covariate pattern are given the same residual and diagnostic statistics. Hosmer and Lemeshow (1989) argue that such "M-asymptotic" statistics are more useful than "N-asymptotic" statistics.

To understand the difference, think of an observed positive outcome with predicted probability of 0.8. Taking the observation in isolation, the "residual" must be positive—we expected 0.8 positive responses and observed 1. This may indeed be the "correct" residual, but not necessarily. Under the M-asymptotic definition, we ask how many successes we observed across all observations with this covariate pattern. If that number were, say, 6, and there were a total of 10 observations with this covariate pattern, then the residual is negative for the covariate pattern—we expected 8 positive outcomes but observed 6. lpredict makes this kind of calculation and then attaches the same residual to all observations in the covariate pattern.

Thus, there may be occasions when you want to find all observations sharing a covariate pattern. number allows you to do this:

```
. lpredict pattern, number

. summarize pattern

Variable |     Obs        Mean    Std. Dev.       Min        Max
---------+-----------------------------------------------------------
 pattern |     189     89.2328    53.16573          1        182
```

We previously estimated the model logistic low age lwt Irace_2 Irace_3 smoke ptl ht ui over 189 observations. There are 182 covariate patterns in our data.

lpredict with the deviance option

The deviance residual is defined as the square root of the contribution to the likelihood-ratio test statistic of a saturated model versus the fitted model. It has slightly different properties from the Pearson residual (see Hosmer and Lemeshow, 1989):

```
. lpredict d, deviance

. summarize d, detail

                      deviance residual
-----------------------------------------------------------------
          Percentiles      Smallest
 1%       -1.843472       -1.911621
 5%        -1.33477       -1.843472
10%       -1.148316       -1.843472       Obs                 189
25%       -.8445325       -1.674869       Sum of Wgt.         189

50%       -.5202702                       Mean          -.1228811
                           Largest        Std. Dev.      1.049237
75%        .9129041        1.894089
90%        1.541558        1.924457       Variance       1.100898
95%        1.673338        2.146583       Skewness       .6598857
99%        2.146583        2.180542       Kurtosis       2.036938
```

lpredict with the rstandard option

Pearson residuals do not have a standard deviation equal to one, a fine point. rstandard generates Pearson residuals normalized to have *expected* standard deviation equal to one.

```
. lpredict rs, rstandard

. sum r rs

Variable |     Obs        Mean    Std. Dev.       Min        Max
---------+-----------------------------------------------------------
       r |     189    -.0242299    .9970949   -2.283885   3.126763
      rs |     189    -.0279135    1.026406     -2.4478   3.149081
```

```
. correlate r rs
(obs=189)

             |        r       rs
    ---------+------------------
           r|   1.0000
          rs|   0.9998   1.0000
```

Remember that we previously created r containing the (unstandardized) Pearson residuals. In this data, whether you use standardized or unstandardized residuals does not much matter.

lpredict with the hat option

hat calculates the leverage of a covariate pattern—a scaled measure of distance in terms of the independent variables. Large values indicate covariate patterns "far" from the average covariate pattern—patterns that can have a large effect on the estimated model even if the corresponding residual is small. This suggests

```
. lpredict h, hat
. graph h r, border yline(0) ylab xlab
```

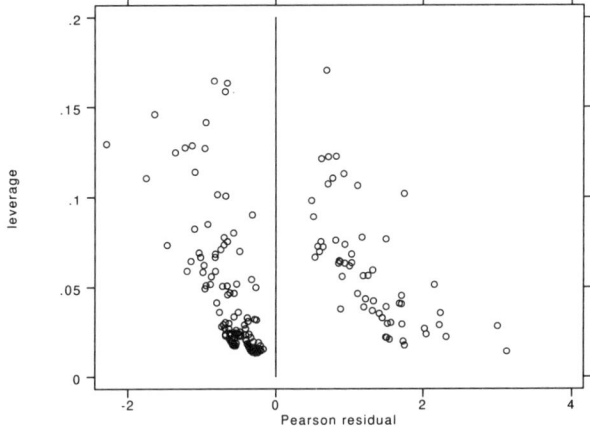

The points to the left of the vertical line are observed negative outcomes; in this case, our data contains almost as many covariate patterns as observations, so most covariate patterns are unique. In such unique patterns, we observe either 0 or 1 successes and expect p, thus forcing the sign of the residual. If we had fewer covariate patterns, which is to say, if we did not have continuous variables in our model, there would be no such interpretation and we would not have drawn the vertical line at 0.

Points on the left and right edges of the graph represent large residuals—covariate patterns that are not fitted well by our model. Points at the top of our graph represent high leverage patterns. When analyzing the influence of observations on the model, we are most interested in patterns with high leverage and small residuals—patterns that might otherwise escape our attention.

lpredict with the dx2 option

There are many ways to measure influence of which hat is one example. dx2 measures the decrease in the Pearson χ^2 goodness-of-fit statistic that would be caused by deleting an observation (and all others sharing the covariate pattern):

```
. lpredict dx2, dx2
. graph dx2 p, border ylab xlab
```

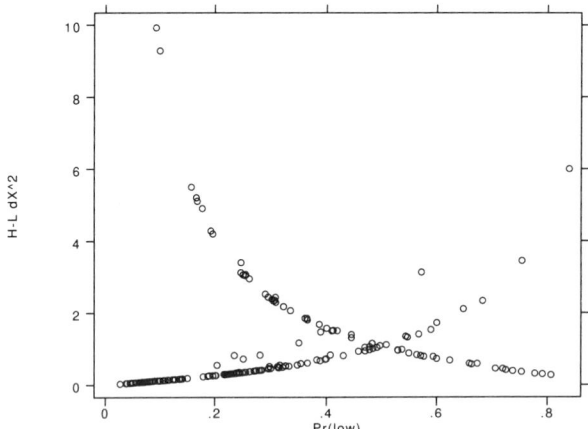

Paraphrasing Hosmer and Lemeshow (1989), the points going from the top left to the bottom right correspond to covariate patterns with the number of positive outcomes equal to the number in the group; the points on the other curve correspond to 0 positive outcomes. In our data, most of the covariate patterns are unique, so the points tend to lie along one or the other curves; the points that are off the curves correspond to the few repeated covariate patterns in our data in which all the outcomes are not the same.

We examine this graph for large values of **dx2**—there are two at the top left.

lpredict with the ddeviance option

Another measure of influence is the change in the deviance residuals due to deletion of a covariate pattern:

```
. lpredict dd, ddeviance
```

As with **dx2**, one typically graphs **ddeviance** against the probability of a positive outcome. We direct you to Hosmer and Lemeshow (1989) for an example and the interpretation of this graph.

lpredict with the dbeta option

One of the more direct measures of influence of interest to model fitters is the Pregibon (1981) **dbeta** measure, a measure of the change in the coefficient vector that would be caused by deleting an observation (and all others sharing the covariate pattern):

```
. lpredict db, dbeta
. graph db p, border ylab xlab
```

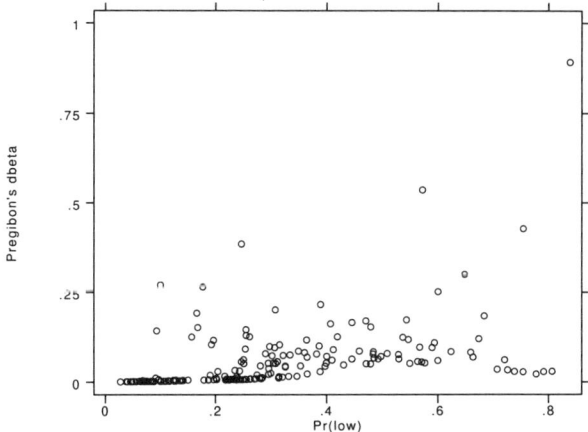

We discover one observation with a large effect on the estimated coefficients. We can easily find this point:

```
. sort db
. list in 1
Observation 189
            id        188      low          0      age          25
           lwt         95     race      white    smoke           1
           ptl          3       ht          0       ui           1
           ftv          0      bwt       3637   Irace_2           0
       Irace_3          0        p  .8391283154  pattern        117
             r -2.283885479      d -1.911621332       rs -2.447800159
             h  .1294439435    dx2  5.991725445       dd  4.197657585
            db  .8909162879
```

Hosmer and Lemeshow (1989) suggest a graph that combines two of the influence measures:

```
. graph dx2 p [w=db], border ylab xlab t1("Symbol size proportional to dBeta")
```

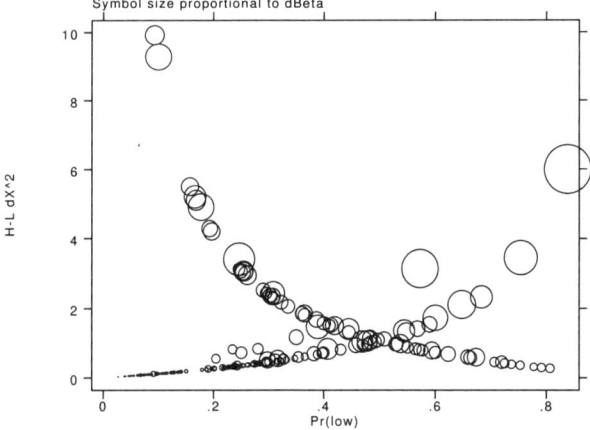

We can easily spot the points most influential by the **dbeta** and **dx2** measures.

Saved Results

See [R] **maximize** for results saved by `logistic`.

In most programming situations, the results saved in `_result()` by `logistic` should be sufficient, but for programmers wishing to couple their program closely to `logistic` (e.g., a post-estimation with `logistic` command such as `lstat`), `logistic` defines the following S_E_ macros:

S_E_cmd	logistic
S_E_depv	dependent variable name
S_E_vl	*varlist* specified including dependent variable
S_E_if	if *exp* specified
S_E_in	in *range* specified
S_E_wgt	weight type
S_E_exp	expression for weight
S_E_nobs	number of observations; same as _result(1)
S_E_ll	log-likelihood value; same as _result(2)
S_E_mdf	model degrees of freedom; same as _result(3)

`lfit` saves in the S_# macros:

S_1	number of observations	S_3	χ^2 statistic
S_2	number of covariate patterns or groups	S_4	χ^2 degrees of freedom

`lstat` saves in the S_# macros (all amounts are in percent):

S_1	percent correctly classified	S_6	positive predictive value
S_2	sensitivity	S_7	negative predictive value
S_3	specificity	S_8	false positive rate given classified positive
S_4	false positive rate given true negative	S_9	false negative rate given classified negative
S_5	false negative rate given true positive		

`lroc` saves in the S_# macros:

S_1	number of observations	S_2	area under the ROC curve

`lsens` saves the number of observations in S_1.

Methods and Formulas

`logistic`, `lfit`, `lstat`, `lroc`, `lsens`, and `lpredict` are implemented as ado-files.

Define $\mathbf{x}_j$ as the (row) vector of independent variables, augmented by 1, and $\mathbf{b}$ as the corresponding estimated parameter (column) vector. The logistic regression model is estimated by `logit`; see [R] **logit** for details of estimation.

The odds ratio corresponding to the ith coefficient is $\psi_i = \exp(b_i)$. The standard error of the odds ratio is $s_i^{\psi} = \psi_i s_i$, where s_i is the standard error of b_i estimated by `logit`.

Define $I_j = \mathbf{x}_j \mathbf{b}$ as the predicted index of the jth observation. The predicted probability of a positive outcome is

$$p_j = \frac{\exp(I_j)}{1 + \exp(I_j)}$$

lfit

Let M be the total number of covariate patterns among the N observations. View the data as collapsed on covariate patterns $j = 1, 2, \ldots, M$ and define m_j as the total number of observations having covariate pattern j and y_j as the total number of positive responses among observations with covariate pattern j. Define p_j as the predicted probability of a positive outcome in covariate pattern j.

The Pearson χ^2 goodness-of-fit statistic is

$$\chi^2 = \sum_{j=1}^{M} \frac{(y_j - m_j p_j)^2}{m_j p_j (1 - p_j)}$$

This χ^2 statistic has approximately $M - k$ degrees of freedom for the estimation sample, where k is the number of independent variables including the constant. For a sample outside of the estimation sample, the statistic has M degrees of freedom.

The Hosmer–Lemeshow goodness-of-fit χ^2 (Hosmer and Lemeshow 1980; Lemeshow and Hosmer 1982; Hosmer, Lemeshow, and Klar 1988) is calculated similarly, except rather than using the M covariate patterns as the group definition, the quantiles of the predicted probabilities are used to form groups. Let $G = \#$ be the number of quantiles requested with group($\#$). The smallest index $1 \leq q(i) \leq M$ such that

$$W_{q(i)} = \sum_{j=1}^{q(i)} m_j \geq \frac{Ni}{G}$$

gives $p_{q(i)}$ as the upper boundary of the ith quantile for $i = 1, 2, \ldots, G$. Let $q(0) = 1$ denote the first index.

The groups are then

$$\left[p_{q(0)}, p_{q(1)} \right], \left(p_{q(1)}, p_{q(2)} \right], \ldots, \left(p_{q(G-1)}, p_{q(G)} \right]$$

If the **table** option is given, the upper boundaries $p_{q(1)}, \ldots, p_{q(G)}$ of the groups appear next to the group number on the output.

The resulting χ^2 statistic has approximately $G - 2$ degrees of freedom for the estimation sample. For a sample outside of the estimation sample, the statistic has G degrees of freedom.

lpredict

Index j will now be used to index observations, not covariate patterns. Redefine m_j for each observation as the total number of observations sharing j's covariate pattern. Redefine y_j as the total number of positive responses among observations sharing j's covariate pattern.

The Pearson residual for the jth observation is defined

$$r_j = \frac{y_j - m_j p_j}{\sqrt{m_j p_j (1 - p_j)}}$$

For $m_j > 1$, the deviance residual d_j is defined

$$d_j = \pm \sqrt{ 2 \left[y_j \ln\left(\frac{y_j}{m_j p_j} \right) + (m_j - y_j) \ln\left(\frac{m_j - y_j}{m_j (1 - p_j)} \right) \right] }$$

where the sign is the same as the sign of $(y_j - m_j p_j)$. In the limiting cases, the deviance residual is given by

$$d_j = \begin{cases} -\sqrt{2m_j |\ln(1 - p_j)|} & \text{if } y_j = 0 \\ \sqrt{2m_j |\ln p_j|} & \text{if } y_j = m_j \end{cases}$$

The *unadjusted* diagonal elements of the hat matrix h_{Uj} are given by $h_{Uj} = (\mathbf{XVX'})_{jj}$, where V is the estimated covariance matrix of parameters. The adjusted diagonal elements h_j created by hat are then $h_j = m_j p_j (1 - p_j) h_{Uj}$.

The standardized Pearson residual r_{Sj} is $r_j / \sqrt{1 - h_j}$.

The Pregibon (1981) $\Delta\widehat{\beta}_j$ influence statistic is

$$\Delta\widehat{\beta}_j = \frac{r_j^2 h_j}{(1 - h_j)^2}$$

The corresponding change in the Pearson χ^2 is r_{Sj}^2. The corresponding change in the deviance residual is $\Delta D_j = d_j / (1 - h_j)$.

lstat and lsens

Again, let j index observations. Define c as the `cutoff()` specified by the user or, if not specified, as 0.5. Let p_j be the predicted probability of a positive outcome and y_j be the actual outcome, which we will treat as 0 or 1, although Stata treats it as 0 and non-0, excluding missing observations.

A prediction is classified as *positive* if $p_j \geq c$ and otherwise is classified as *negative*. The classification is *correct* if it is *positive* and $y_j = 1$ or if it is *negative* and $y_j = 0$.

Sensitivity is the fraction of $y_j = 1$ observations that are correctly classified. *Specificity* is the percent of $y_j = 0$ observations that are correctly classified.

lroc

The ROC curve is a graph of *specificity* against $1 - sensitivity$. This is guaranteed to be a monotone nondecreasing function, since the number of correctly predicted successes increases, and the number of correctly predicted failures decreases, as the classification cutoff c decreases.

The area under the ROC curve is the area on the bottom of this graph, and is determined by integrating the curve. The vertices of the curve are determined by sorting the data according to the predicted index, and the integral is computed using the trapezoidal rule.

References

Collett, D. 1991. *Modelling Binary Data*. London: Chapman & Hall.

Green, D. M. and J. A. Swets. 1974. *Signal Detection Theory and Psychophysics*. rev. ed. Huntington, NY: Krieger.

Hosmer, D. W., Jr., and S. Lemeshow. 1980. Goodness-of-fit tests for the multiple logistic regression model. *Communications in Statistics* A9: 1043–1069.

———. 1989. *Applied Logistic Regression*. New York: John Wiley & Sons.

Hosmer, D. W., Jr., S. Lemeshow, and J. Klar. 1988. Goodness-of-fit testing for the logistic regression model when the estimated probabilities are small. *Biometric Journal* 30: 911–924.

Lemeshow, S. and D. W. Hosmer, Jr. 1982. A review of goodness of fit statistics for use in the development of logistic regression models. *American Journal of Epidemiology* 115: 92–106.

Lemeshow, S. and J.-R. Le Gall. 1994. Modeling the severity of illness of ICU patients: a systems update. *Journal of the American Medical Association* 272: 1049–1055.

Metz, C. E. 1978. Basic principles of ROC analysis. *Seminars in Nuclear Medicine* 8: 283–298.

Pagano, M. and K. Gauvreau. 1993. *Principles of Biostatistics.* Belmont, CA: Duxbury Press.

Peterson, W. W., T. G. Birdsall, and W. C. Fox. 1954. The theory of signal detection. *Trans. IRE Professional Group on Information Theory*, PGIT-4: 171–212.

Pregibon, D. 1981. Logistic regression diagnostics. *Annals of Statistics* 9: 705–724.

Tanner, W. P., Jr., and J. A. Swets. 1954. A decision-making theory of visual detection. *Psychological Review* 61: 401–409.

Tilford, J. M., P. K. Roberson, and D. H. Fiser. 1995. sbe12: Using lfit and lroc to evaluate mortality prediction models. *Stata Technical Bulletin* 28: 14–18. Reprinted in *Stata Technical Bulletin Reprints*, vol. 5, pp. 77–81.

Also See

[U] **20.5 Accessing coefficients and standard errors**, [U] **26 Estimation and post-estimation commands**, [U] **26.10 Obtaining robust variance estimates**, [U] **26.11 Obtaining scores**

[R] **brier**, [R] **clogit**, [R] **cusum**, [R] **glm**, [R] **glogit**, [R] **lincom**, [R] **linktest**, [R] **logit**, [R] **lrtest**, [R] **maximize**, [R] **ologit**, [R] **predict**, [R] **probit**, [R] **sw**, [R] **test**, [R] **testnl**, [R] **vce**, [R] **xi**

Title

> **logit** — Maximum-likelihood logit estimation

Syntax

$\big[$ by *varlist*: $\big]$ <u>logit</u>   *depvar* $\big[$*indepvars*$\big]$ $\big[$*weight*$\big]$ $\big[$**if** *exp*$\big]$ $\big[$**in** *range*$\big]$

$\big[$, <u>level</u>(#) <u>nocoef</u> <u>noconst</u>ant or <u>r</u>obust <u>cl</u>uster(*varname*) <u>sc</u>ore(*newvarname*)

maximize_options $\big]$

`fweights`, `pweights`, and `aweights` are allowed; see [U] **18.1.6 weight**.

`logit` shares the features of all estimation commands; see [U] **26 Estimation and post-estimation commands**.

To reset problem-size limits, see [R] **matsize**.

`logit` may be used with `sw` to perform stepwise estimation; see [R] **sw**.

Description

`logit` estimates a maximum-likelihood logit model.

Also see [R] **logistic**; many prefer to use the `logistic` command. Results are the same no matter which you use, but `logistic` has a number of auxiliary commands that can be run after the estimation.

If estimating on grouped data, see [R] **glogit**.

You may also wish to see [R] **probit**—the `probit` command differs from `logit` only in the distributional assumption about the error term.

Options

`level(#)` specifies the confidence level, in percent, for confidence intervals. The default is `level(95)` or as set by `set level`; see [U] **26.4 Specifying the width of confidence intervals**.

`nocoef` specifies that the coefficient table is not to be displayed. This option is sometimes used by program writers but is of no use interactively.

`noconstant` suppresses the constant term (intercept) in the logit model.

`or` reports the estimated coefficients transformed to odds ratios, i.e., e^b rather than b. Standard errors and confidence intervals are similarly transformed. This option affects how results are displayed, not how they are estimated. `or` may be specified at estimation or when replaying previously estimated results.

`robust` specifies that the Huber/White/sandwich estimator of variance is to be used in place of the traditional calculation; see [U] **26.10 Obtaining robust variance estimates**. `robust` combined with `cluster()` allows observations which are not independent within cluster (although they must be independent between clusters).

If you specify `pweights`, `robust` is implied; see [U] **26.12 Weighted estimation**.

See [R] **logistic** for examples using this option.

cluster(*varname*) specifies that the observations are independent across groups (clusters) but not necessarily within groups. *varname* specifies to which group each observation belongs; e.g., cluster(personid) in data with repeated observations on individuals. cluster() affects the estimated standard errors and variance-covariance matrix of the estimators (VCE), but not the estimated coefficients; see [U] **26.10 Obtaining robust variance estimates**. cluster() can be used with pweights to produce estimates for unstratified cluster-sampled data, but see the svylogit command in [R] **svyreg** for a command designed especially for survey data.

cluster() implies robust; specifying robust cluster() is equivalent to typing cluster() by itself.

See [R] **logistic** for examples using this option.

score(*newvar*) creates *newvar* containing $u_j - \partial \ln L_j / \partial(\mathbf{x}_j \mathbf{b})$ for each observation j in the sample. The score vector is $\sum \partial \ln L_j / \partial \mathbf{b} = \sum u_j \mathbf{x}_j$; i.e., the product of *newvar* with each covariate summed over observations. See [U] **26.11 Obtaining scores**.

maximize_options control the maximization process; see [R] **maximize**. You should never have to specify them.

Remarks

logit performs maximum-likelihood estimation of models with dichotomous dependent (left-hand-side) variables coded as 0/1 (or, more precisely, coded as 0 and not-0).

▷ Example

You have data on the make, weight, and mileage rating of 22 foreign and 52 domestic automobiles. You wish to estimate a logit model explaining whether a car is foreign based on its weight and mileage. Here is an overview of your data:

```
. describe
Contains data from auto.dta
  obs:            74                      1978 Automobile Data
  vars:            4
  size:        2,072 (99.7% of memory free)
-------------------------------------------------------------------
  1. make         str18  %18s                    Make and Model
  2. mpg          int    %8.0g                    Mileage (mpg)
  3. weight       int    %8.0g                    Weight (lbs.)
  4. foreign      int    %8.0g         foreign    Car type
-------------------------------------------------------------------
Sorted by:  foreign
     Note:  data has changed since last save
```

(Example continued on next page.)

```
. inspect foreign
foreign:  Car type                              Number of Observations
------------------                                              Non-
                                            Total   Integers   Integers
  |  #                      Negative          -         -          -
  |  #                      Zero             52        52          -
  |  #                      Positive         22        22          -
  |  #                                      -----     -----      -----
  |  #   #                  Total            74        74          -
  |  #   #                  Missing           -
  +--------------------                     -----
  0                    1                     74
    (2 unique values)
        foreign is labeled and all values are documented in the label.
```

The variable **foreign** takes on two unique values, 0 and 1. The value 0 denotes a domestic car and 1 denotes a foreign car.

The model you wish to estimate is

$$\Pr(\texttt{foreign} = 1) = F(\beta_0 + \beta_1 \texttt{weight} + \beta_2 \texttt{mpg})$$

where $F(z) = e^z/(1 + e^z)$ is the cumulative logistic distribution.

To estimate this model, you type

```
. logit foreign weight mpg
Iteration 0:   Log Likelihood = -45.03321
Iteration 1:   Log Likelihood =-29.898968
Iteration 2:   Log Likelihood =-27.495771
Iteration 3:   Log Likelihood =-27.184006
Iteration 4:   Log Likelihood =-27.175166
Iteration 5:   Log Likelihood =-27.175156

Logit Estimates                                Number of obs =       74
                                               chi2(2)       =    35.72
                                               Prob > chi2   =   0.0000
Log Likelihood = -27.175156                    Pseudo R2     =   0.3966

------------------------------------------------------------------------
 foreign |      Coef.    Std. Err.      z      P>|z|   [95% Conf. Interval]
---------+--------------------------------------------------------------
  weight |   -.0039067    .0010116    -3.862   0.000   -.0058894    -.001924
     mpg |   -.1685869    .0919174    -1.834   0.067   -.3487418     .011568
   _cons |    13.70837    4.518707     3.034   0.002    4.851864    22.56487
------------------------------------------------------------------------
```

You find that heavier cars are less likely to be foreign and that cars yielding better gas mileage are also less likely to be foreign, at least holding the weight of the car constant.

See [R] **maximize** for an explanation of the output.

◁

❏ Technical Note

Stata interprets a value of 0 as a negative outcome (failure) and treats all other values (except missing) as positive outcomes (successes). Thus, if your dependent variable takes on the values 0 and 1, 0 is interpreted as failure and 1 as success. If your dependent variable takes on the values 0, 1, and 2, 0 is still interpreted as failure, but both 1 and 2 are treated as successes.

If you prefer a more formal mathematical statement, when you type logit y x, Stata estimates the model

$$\Pr(y_j \neq 0 \mid \mathbf{x}_j) = \frac{\exp(\mathbf{x}_j\boldsymbol{\beta})}{1 + \exp(\mathbf{x}_j\boldsymbol{\beta})}$$

❑

Model identification

The logit command has one more feature, and it is probably the most useful. logit will automatically check the model for identification and, if it is underidentified, drop whatever variables and observations are necessary for estimation to proceed.

▷ Example

Have you ever estimated a logit model where one or more of your independent variables perfectly predicted one or the other outcome?

For instance, consider the following small amount of data:

Outcome y	Independent Variable x
0	1
0	1
0	0
1	0

Let's imagine we wish to predict the outcome on the basis of the independent variable. Notice that the outcome is always zero whenever the independent variable is one. In our data $\Pr(y = 0 \mid x = 1) = 1$, which in turn means that the logit coefficient on x must be minus infinity with a corresponding infinite standard error. At this point, you may suspect we have a problem.

Unfortunately, not all such problems are so easily detected, especially if you have a lot of independent variables in your model. If you have ever had such difficulties, then you have experienced one of the more unpleasant aspects of computer optimization. The computer has no idea that it is trying to solve for an infinite coefficient as it begins its iterative process. All it knows is that, at each step, making the coefficient a little bigger, or a little smaller, works wonders. It continues on its merry way until either (1) the whole thing comes crashing to the ground when a numerical overflow error occurs or (2) it reaches some predetermined cutoff that stops the process. Meantime, you have been waiting. In addition, the estimates that you finally receive, if you receive any at all, may be nothing more than numerical roundoff.

Stata watches for these sorts of problems, alerts you, fixes them, and properly estimates the model.

Let's return to our automobile data. Among the variables we have in the data is one called repair that takes on three values. A value of 1 indicates that the car has a poor repair record, 2 indicates an average record, and 3 indicates a better-than-average record. Here is a tabulation of our data:

```
. tabulate foreign repair

          | repair
  foreign |         1          2          3 |     Total
----------+---------------------------------+----------
 Domestic |        10         27          9 |        46
  Foreign |         0          3          9 |        12
----------+---------------------------------+----------
    Total |        10         30         18 |        58
```

Notice that all of the cars with poor repair records (`repair==1`) are domestic. If we were to attempt to predict `foreign` on the basis of the repair records, the predicted probability for the `repair==1` category would have to be zero. This in turn means that the logit coefficient must be minus infinity, and that would set most computer programs buzzing.

Let's try Stata on this problem. First, we make up two new variables, `rep_is_1` and `rep_is_2`, that indicate the `repair` category.

```
. generate rep_is_1 = (repair==1)
. generate rep_is_2 = (repair==2)
```

The statement `generate rep_is_1 = (repair==1)` creates a new variable, `rep_is_1`, that takes on the value 1 when `repair` is one and zero otherwise. Similarly, the next `generate` statement creates `rep_is_2` that takes on the value 1 when `repair` is two and zero otherwise. We are now ready to estimate our logit model. See [R] **probit** for the corresponding probit model.

```
. logit for rep_is_1 rep_is_2
Note: rep_is_1~=0 predicts failure perfectly
      rep_is_1 dropped and 10 obs not used
Iteration 0:  Log Likelihood =-26.992087
Iteration 1:  Log Likelihood =-22.483187
Iteration 2:  Log Likelihood =-22.230498
Iteration 3:  Log Likelihood =-22.229139
Iteration 4:  Log Likelihood =-22.229138
Iteration 5:  Log Likelihood =-22.229138
Iteration 6:  Log Likelihood =-22.229138
Iteration 7:  Log Likelihood =-22.229138

Logit Estimates                          Number of obs =      48
                                         chi2(1)       =    9.53
                                         Prob > chi2   =  0.0020
Log Likelihood = -22.229138              Pseudo R2     =  0.1765

------------------------------------------------------------------------
 foreign |    Coef.   Std. Err.       z     P>|z|    [95% Conf. Interval]
---------+--------------------------------------------------------------
rep_is_2 | -2.197225   .7698004    -2.854   0.004    -3.706006   -.6884436
   _cons |  7.47e-16   .4714045     0.000   1.000    -.9239359    .9239359
------------------------------------------------------------------------
```

Remember that all the cars with poor repair records (`rep_is_1`) are domestic, so the model cannot be estimated, or at least it cannot be estimated if we restrict ourselves to finite coefficients. Stata noted that fact. It said, "Note: rep_is_1~=0 predicts failure perfectly". This is Stata's mathematically precise way of saying what we said in English. When `rep_is_1` is not equal to 0, the car is domestic.

Stata then went on to say, "rep_is_1 dropped and 10 obs not used". This is Stata eliminating the problem. First, the variable `rep_is_1` had to be removed from the model because it would have an infinite coefficient. Then, the 10 observations that led to the problem had to be eliminated as well so as not to bias the remaining coefficients in the model. The 10 observations that are not used are the 10 domestic cars that have poor repair records.

Finally, Stata estimated what was left of the model, which is all that can be estimated.

◁

❏ Technical Note

Stata is pretty smart about catching problems of these sorts. It will catch "one-way causation by a dummy variable", as we demonstrated above.

Stata also watches for "two-way causation"; that is, a variable that perfectly determines the outcome, both successes and failures. In this case Stata says, "so-and-so predicts outcome perfectly" and stops. Statistics dictates that no model can be estimated.

Stata also checks your data for collinear variables; it will say "so-and-so dropped due to collinearity". No observations need to be eliminated in this case, and model estimation will proceed without the offending variable.

It will also catch a subtle problem that can arise with continuous data. For instance, if we were estimating the chances of surviving the first year after an operation, and if we included in our model **age**, and if all the persons over 65 died within the year, Stata will say, "age > 65 predicts failure perfectly". It will then inform us about the fixup it takes and estimate what can be estimated of our model.

logit (and **logistic** and **probit**) will also occasionally display messages such as

```
Note: 4 failures and 0 successes completely determined.
```

There are two causes for a message like this. Let us deal with the most unlikely case first. This case occurs when a continuous variable (or a combination of a continuous variable with other continuous or dummy variables) is simply a great predictor of the dependent variable. Consider Stata's `auto.dta` dataset with 6 observations removed.

```
. use auto
(1978 Automobile Data)

. drop if foreign==0 & gratio>3.1
(6 observations deleted)

. logit foreign mpg weight gratio, nolog

Logit Estimates                                Number of obs =       68
                                               chi2(3)       =    72.64
                                               Prob > chi2   =   0.0000
Log Likelihood = -6.4874814                    Pseudo R2     =   0.8484

------------------------------------------------------------------------------
  foreign |      Coef.   Std. Err.       z     P>|z|     [95% Conf. Interval]
----------+-------------------------------------------------------------------
      mpg |  -.4944907   .2655508    -1.862    0.063    -1.014961    .0259792
   weight |  -.0060919    .003101    -1.964    0.049    -.0121698    -.000014
   gratio |   15.70509   8.166234     1.923    0.054    -.3004359    31.71061
    _cons |  -21.39527   25.41486    -0.842    0.400    -71.20747    28.41694
------------------------------------------------------------------------------

Note: 4 failures and 0 successes completely determined.
```

Note that there are no missing standard errors in the output. If you receive the "completely determined" message and have one or more missing standard errors in your output, see the second case discussed below.

What's happening here is simply that **gratio** is a great predictor of **foreign**. Note **gratio**'s large coefficient. **logit** thought that the 4 observations with the smallest predicted probabilities were essentially predicted perfectly.

```
. predict p

. sort p
```

```
. list p in 1/4

            p
  1.   1.34e-10
  2.   6.26e-09
  3.   7.84e-09
  4.   1.49e-08
```

If this happens to you, there is no need to do anything. Computationally, the model is sound. It is the second case discussed below that requires careful examination.

The second case occurs when the independent terms are all dummy variables or continuous ones with repeated values (e.g., age). In this case, one or more of the estimated coefficients will have missing standard errors. For example, consider this dataset consisting of 5 observations.

```
. list

            y        x1        x2
  1.        0         0         0
  2.        0         1         0
  3.        1         1         0
  4.        0         0         1
  5.        1         0         1

. logit y x1 x2, nolog

Logit Estimates                                 Number of obs =        5
                                                chi2(2)       =     1.18
                                                Prob > chi2   =   0.5530
Log Likelihood = -2.7725887                     Pseudo R2     =   0.1761

------------------------------------------------------------------------------
       y |      Coef.   Std. Err.       z     P>|z|     [95% Conf. Interval]
---------+--------------------------------------------------------------------
      x1 |   18.26157          2     9.131    0.000      14.34164     22.1815
      x2 |   18.26157          .         .        .             .           .
   _cons |  -18.26157   1.414214   -12.913    0.000     -21.03338   -15.48976
------------------------------------------------------------------------------

Note: 1 failure and 0 successes completely determined.

. predict p

. list

            y        x1        x2          p
  1.        0         0         0    1.17e-08
  2.        0         1         0          .5
  3.        1         1         0          .5
  4.        0         0         1          .5
  5.        1         0         1          .5
```

Two things are happening here. The first is that **logit** is able to fit the outcome $(y = 0)$ for the covariate pattern $x1 = 0$ and $x2 = 0$ (i.e., the first observation) perfectly. It is this observation that is the "1 failure ... completely determined". The second thing to note is that if this observation is dropped, then $x1$, $x2$, and the constant are collinear.

This is the cause of the message "completely determined" and the missing standard errors. It happens when you have a covariate pattern (or patterns) with only one outcome, and there is collinearity when the observations corresponding to this covariate pattern are dropped.

If this happens to you, confirm the causes. First identify the covariate pattern with only one outcome. (For your data, replace $x1$ and $x2$ with the independent variables of your model.)

```
. egen pattern = group(x1 x2)

. quietly logit y x1 x2

. predict p
```

```
. summarize p
Variable |     Obs       Mean   Std. Dev.      Min       Max
---------+-------------------------------------------------------
       p |       5         .4   .2236068   1.17e-08        .5
```

If successes were completely determined, that means there are predicted probabilities that are almost 1. If failures were completely determined, that means there are predicted probabilities that are almost 0. The latter is the case here. So we locate the corresponding value of pattern:

```
. tab pattern if p < 1e-7
group(x1 x2)|     Freq.     Percent       Cum.
------------+-----------------------------------
          1 |         1      100.00      100.00
------------+-----------------------------------
      Total |         1      100.00
```

Once we omit this covariate pattern from the estimation sample, logit can deal with the collinearity:

```
. logit y x1 x2 if pattern~=1, nolog
Note: x2 dropped due to collinearity.
Logit Estimates                             Number of obs =        4
                                            chi2(1)       =     0.00
                                            Prob > chi2   = 1.0000
Log Likelihood = -2.7725887                 Pseudo R2     = 0.0000

------------------------------------------------------------------------------
       y |      Coef.   Std. Err.       z     P>|z|      [95% Conf. Interval]
---------+--------------------------------------------------------------------
      x1 |          0          2     0.000    1.000     -3.919928    3.919928
   _cons |          0   1.414214     0.000    1.000     -2.771808    2.771808
------------------------------------------------------------------------------
```

We omit the collinear variable. Then we must decide whether to include or to omit the observations with pattern = 1. We could include them:

```
. logit y x1, nolog
Logit Estimates                             Number of obs =        5
                                            chi2(1)       =     0.14
                                            Prob > chi2   = 0.7098
Log Likelihood = -3.2958369                 Pseudo R2     = 0.0206

------------------------------------------------------------------------------
       y |      Coef.   Std. Err.       z     P>|z|      [95% Conf. Interval]
---------+--------------------------------------------------------------------
      x1 |   .6931472   1.870827     0.371    0.711     -2.973605      4.3599
   _cons |  -.6931472   1.224742    -0.566    0.571     -3.093597    1.707302
------------------------------------------------------------------------------
```

Or exclude them:

```
. logit y x1 if pattern~=1, nolog
Logit Estimates                             Number of obs =        4
                                            chi2(1)       =     0.00
                                            Prob > chi2   = 1.0000
Log Likelihood = -2.7725887                 Pseudo R2     = 0.0000

------------------------------------------------------------------------------
       y |      Coef.   Std. Err.       z     P>|z|      [95% Conf. Interval]
---------+--------------------------------------------------------------------
      x1 |          0          2     0.000    1.000     -3.919928    3.919928
   _cons |          0   1.414214     0.000    1.000     -2.771808    2.771808
------------------------------------------------------------------------------
```

If the covariate pattern that predicts outcome perfectly is meaningful, you may want to exclude these observations from the model. In this case, one would report covariate pattern such and such predicted outcome perfectly and that the best model for the rest of the data is ... . But, more likely, the perfect prediction was simply the result of having too many predictors in the model. In this case, one would omit the extraneous variable(s) from further consideration and report the best model for all of the data.

❏

Obtaining predicted values

Once you have estimated a logit model, you can obtain the predicted probabilities using the `predict` command for both the estimation sample and other samples; see [U] **26 Estimation and post-estimation commands** and [R] **predict**. Here we will make only a few additional comments.

`predict` without arguments calculates the predicted probability of a positive outcome; i.e., $\Pr(y_j = 1) = F(\mathbf{x}_j\mathbf{b})$. With the `index` option, it calculates the linear combination $\mathbf{x}_j\mathbf{b}$, where $\mathbf{x}_j$ are the independent variables in the jth observation and $\mathbf{b}$ is the estimated parameter vector. This is known as the index function since the cumulative density indexed at this value is the probability of a positive outcome.

In both cases, Stata remembers any "rules" used to identify the model and calculates missing for excluded observations unless `rules` or `asif` is specified. This is covered in the following example.

With the `stdp` option, `predict` calculates the standard error of the prediction, which is *not* adjusted for replicated covariate patterns in the data.

One can calculate the unadjusted-for-replicated-covariate-patterns diagonal elements of the hat matrix, or leverage, by typing

```
. predict pred
. predict stdp, stdp
. generate hat = stdp^2*pred*(1-pred)
```

When the number of covariate patterns is close to the number of observations, this is acceptable (Hosmer and Lemeshow 1989). One would be better advised to use the `logistic` command to estimate the model and `lpredict` to obtain influence statistics; see [R] **logistic**.

▷ Example

In the previous example, we estimated the logit model `logit foreign rep_is_1 rep_is_2`. To obtain predicted probabilities:

```
. predict p
(10 missing values generated)
. summarize foreign p
```

Variable	Obs	Mean	Std. Dev.	Min	Max
foreign	58	.2068966	.4086186	0	1
p	48	.25	.1956984	.1	.5

Stata remembers any "rules" used to identify the model and sets predictions to missing for any excluded observations. In the previous example, `logit` dropped the variable `rep_is_1` from our model and excluded 10 observations. Thus, when we typed `predict p`, those same 10 observations were again excluded and their predictions set to missing.

predict's rules option will use the rules in the prediction. During estimation, we were told "rep_is_1~=0 predicts failure perfectly", so the rule is that when rep_is_1 is not zero, one should predict 0 probability of success or a positive outcome:

```
. predict p2, rules

. summarize foreign p p2
Variable |    Obs       Mean    Std. Dev.       Min        Max
---------+-------------------------------------------------------
 foreign |     58   .2068966    .4086186          0          1
       p |     48        .25    .1956984         .1         .5
      p2 |     58   .2068966    .2016268          0         .5
```

predict's asif option will ignore the rules and the exclusion criteria, and calculate predictions for all observations possible using the estimated parameters from the model:

```
. predict p3, asif

. summarize for p p2 p3
Variable |    Obs       Mean    Std. Dev.       Min        Max
---------+-------------------------------------------------------
 foreign |     58   .2068966    .4086186          0          1
       p |     48        .25    .1956984         .1         .5
      p2 |     58   .2068966    .2016268          0         .5
      p3 |     58   .2931034    .2016268         .1         .5
```

Which is right? What predict does by default is the most conservative approach. If a large number of observations had been excluded due to a simple rule, one could be reasonably certain that the rules prediction is correct. The asif prediction is only correct if the exclusion is a fluke and you would be willing to exclude the variable from the analysis anyway. In that case, however, you should reestimate the model to include the excluded observations.

◁

Performing hypothesis tests

After estimation with logit, you can perform hypothesis tests using the test command; see [U] 26 Estimation and post-estimation commands.

Saved Results

See [R] maximize for the results stored by logit.

Methods and Formulas

The word logit is due to Berkson (1944) and is by analogy with the word probit. For an introduction to logit and probit, see, for example, Aldrich and Nelson (1984) or Hamilton (1992).

The likelihood function for logit is

$$\ln L = \sum_{j \in S} w_j \ln F(\mathbf{x}_j \mathbf{b}) + \sum_{j \in \sim S} w_j \ln \left[1 - F(\mathbf{x}_j \mathbf{b}) \right]$$

where S is the set of all observations j such that $y_j \neq 0$, $F(z) = e^z/(1 + e^z)$, and w_j denotes the optional weights, which are normalized to sum to N if aweights are specified. $\ln L$ is maximized as described in [R] **maximize**.

If robust standard errors are requested, the calculation described in *Methods and Formulas* of [R] **regress** is carried forward with $\mathbf{u}_j = [1 - F(\mathbf{x}_j \mathbf{b})]\mathbf{x}_j$ for the positive outcomes and $-F(\mathbf{x}_j \mathbf{b})\mathbf{x}_j$ for the negative outcomes. q_c is given by its asymptotic-like formula.

References

Aldrich, J. H. and F. D. Nelson. 1984. *Linear Probability, Logit, and Probit Models.* Newbury Park, CA: Sage Publications.

Berkson, J. 1944. Application of the logistic function to bio-assay. *Journal of the American Statistical Association* 39: 357–365.

Hamilton, L. C. 1992. *Regression with Graphics.* Pacific Grove, CA: Brooks/Cole Publishing Company.

Hosmer, D. W., Jr., and S. Lemeshow. 1989. *Applied Logistic Regression.* New York: John Wiley & Sons.

Judge, G. G., W. E. Griffiths, R. C. Hill, H. Lütkepohl, and Tsoung-Chao Lee. 1985. *The Theory and Practice of Econometrics.* 2d. ed. New York: John Wiley & Sons.

Also See

Title

loneway — Large one-way ANOVA, random effects, and reliability

Syntax

`loneway` *response_var group_var* [*weight*] [`if` *exp*] [`in` *range*]

`aweights` are allowed; see [U] **18.1.6 weight**.

Description

`loneway` estimates one-way analysis-of-variance (ANOVA) models on datasets with a large number of levels of *group_var* and presents different ancillary statistics from `oneway`:

Feature	oneway	loneway
Estimate one-way model	x	x
on fewer than 376 levels	x	x
on more than 376 levels		x
Bartlett's test for equal variance	x	
Multiple-comparison tests	x	
Intragroup correlation and S.E.		x
Est. reliability of group-averaged score		x
Est. S.D. of group effect		x
Est. S.D. within group		x
Conservative t deflator		x

Also see [R] **oneway**.

▷ Example

`loneway`'s output looks like that of `oneway` except that, at the end, additional information is presented. Using our automobile data (see [U] **13 Stata's on-line tutorials and sample datasets**), we have created a (numeric) variable called `manuf` identifying the manufacturer of each car:

```
. loneway mpg manuf
              One Way Analysis of Variance for mpg: Mileage (mpg)
       Source           SS          df       MS           F      Prob > F
    ----------------------------------------------------------------------
    Between manuf     1462.2907     22    66.467761       2.79     0.0013
    Within manuf      1213.8714     51    23.801401
    ----------------------------------------------------------------------
    Total             2676.1622     73    36.659756
                                       R-squared = 0.5464
                    Estimated SD of manuf effect = 3.5858549
                       Estimated SD within manuf = 4.8786679
                          Intra-manuf correlation = 0.3578 (SD = 0.1056)
         Estimated reliability of a manuf-averaged score = 0.5255
                          Conservative t-deflator = 1.5024
```

◁

In addition to the standard one-way ANOVA output, `loneway` produces the R-squared, estimated standard deviation of the group effect and estimated standard deviation within group, the intragroup correlation, the estimated reliability of the group-averaged score, and a conservative t deflator. Each is explained in the context of the previous example.

R-squared

The R-squared is, of course, simply the underlying R^2 for a regression of *response_var* on the levels of *group_var*, or mpg on the various manufacturers in this case.

Standard errors of random-effects models

The standard deviation of the group effect and standard deviation within group are estimated for random-effects models. In our example, the model is

$$\text{mpg} = \alpha_{\text{manuf}} + \gamma_{\text{residual within manuf}}$$

The notion here is that the value of mpg is created in two steps. First, a manufacturer is chosen and a value of α_{manuf} is determined—the typical mpg for that manufacturer. Then, a deviation is chosen for the model within manufacturer. This is how much that particular automobile differs from the typical value.

The standard deviation of the α's is 3.6 and of the γ's is 4.9. Thus, most of the variation between cars is still attributable to the model, though manufacturer is also important. These standard deviations differ from those that would be produced by a (standard) fixed-effects regression in that the regression would require the sum within manufacturer of γ be zero while these estimates merely impose the constraint that the sum is *expected* to be zero.

Intragroup correlation

The intragroup correlation is the theoretical upper bound on the variation in *response_var* that is explainable by *group_var*, of which R-squared is an overestimate because of the serendipity of fitting. Note, this correlation is comparable to an R-squared—you do not have to square it.

In our example, the intra-manuf correlation, the correlation of mpg within manufacturer, is 0.36. One way to calculate this number (although it is not the method actually used) would be to form a dataset where each observation is the mileage rating of two randomly drawn cars from the same manufacturer and then calculate the correlation.

Estimated reliability of the group-averaged score

The estimated reliability of the group-averaged score has an interpretation similar to that of the intragroup correlation; it is the comparable number if we average *response_var* by *group_var*, or mpg by manuf in our example. It is the theoretical upper bound of a regression of manufacturer-averaged mpg on characteristics of manufacturers. Why would we want to collapse our 74-observation data into a 23-observation dataset of manufacturer averages? Because the 74 observations might be a mirage. When General Motors builds cars, do they sometimes put a Pontiac label and sometimes a Chevrolet label on them, so that it appears in our data as if we have two cars when we really have only one, replicated? If that were the case, and if it were the case for many other manufacturers, then we would be forced to admit that we do not have data on 74 cars; we have data on 23 manufacturer-averaged characteristics.

Saved Results

loneway saves in the S_# macros:

S_1	intragroup correlation
S_2	square of conservative t deflator
S_3	average cluster size

Methods and Formulas

loneway is implemented as an ado-file.

See [R] **oneway** for a description of obtaining one-way ANOVA results and a definition of terms. The R^2 is calculated as S_1/S.

The estimated standard deviation of the group effect is $\sqrt{S/(n-1) - s_e}$. This comes from the assumption that an observation is derived by adding a group effect to a within-group effect.

The estimated standard deviation within group is the square root of the mean square due to error, or $\sqrt{s_e}$.

The intragroup correlation is defined as Kish's roh (Kish 1965). Stata's equivalent computing formula is

$$\text{roh} = \frac{(F-1)k/n}{1 + (F-1)k/n}$$

where F is the F statistic from the ANOVA table and k is the number of groups.

The estimated reliability of the group-averaged score is defined by the *Spearman–Brown Prophecy Formula* (Nunnally and Bernstein 1994, 232) with assumed group size n/k:

$$\alpha = \frac{(\text{roh})n/k}{1 + (\text{roh})n/k}$$

Define deff (Kish 1965, 162) as

$$\text{deff} = 1 + (B-1)\text{roh}$$

where B is the average group (cluster) size. The average group size B is the population-weighted average group size, i.e., $(\sum_{i=1}^{k} n_i^2)/(\sum_{i=1}^{k} n_i)$, where n_i is the number of observations in the ith group. The conservative t deflator is the square root of deff.

References

Kish, L. 1965. *Survey Sampling*. New York: John Wiley & Sons.

Nunnally, J. C. and I. H. Bernstein. 1994. *Psychometric Theory*. 3d ed. New York: McGraw-Hill.

Also See

[R] **oneway**

Title

lookup — Look up documentation

Syntax

<u>lo</u>okup *word* [*word* ...] [, <u>a</u>uthor <u>entry</u> <u>ex</u>act <u>h</u>istorical or <u>man</u>ual stb]

Description

lookup searches a keyword database. It is available in all versions of Stata. In addition, Stata for Windows users can also access some of lookup's features by pulling down *Help*.

Capitalization of the words following lookup is irrelevant, as is the inclusion or exclusion of special characters such as commas, dashes, and the like.

Options

author specifies that the search is to be performed on the basis of author's name rather than keywords.

entry specifies that the search is to be performed on the basis of entry ids rather than keywords.

exact prevents matching on abbreviations.

historical adds to the search entries that are of historical interest only. By default, such entries are not listed. Past entries are classified historical if they discuss a feature that later became an official part of Stata. Updates to historical entries will always be found, even if historical is not specified.

or specifies that an entry should be listed if any of the words typed after lookup are associated with the entry. The default is to list the entry only if all the words specified are associated with the entry.

manual limits the search to entries in the Stata Reference Manual; that is, the search is limited to the *User's Guide* and the *Reference* manuals.

stb limits the search to entries in the *Stata Technical Bulletin*.

Remarks

See [U] **12 Stata's on-line help and lookup facilities** for a tutorial introduction to lookup. lookup is one of Stata's most useful commands. To understand the advanced features of lookup, you need to know how it works.

lookup has a database—a file—containing the titles, etc., of every entry in the *User's Guide*, the *Reference* manual, the *Getting Started* manuals, and the inserts in the *Stata Technical Bulletin*. In this file is a list of words associated with each entry, called keywords.

When you type lookup *xyz*, lookup reads this file and compares the list of keywords with *xyz*. If it finds *xyz* in the list or a keyword that allows an abbreviation of *xyz*, it displays the entry.

When you type lookup *xyz abc*, lookup does the same thing, but displays an entry only if it contains both keywords. The order does not matter, so you can lookup linear regression or lookup regression linear or even lookup regression, linear because lookup ignores special characters such as commas.

Obviously, how many entries lookup finds depends on how the lookup database was constructed. We have included a plethora of keywords under the theory that, for a given request, it is better to list too much rather than risk listing nothing at all. Still, you are in the position of guessing the keywords. Do you look up normality test, normality tests, or tests of normality? Answer: normality test would be best, but all would work. In general, use the singular and strike the unnecessary words. We provide guidelines for specifying keywords in [U] **12.5 More on lookup**.

Author searches

lookup ordinarily compares the words following lookup with the keywords for the entry. If you specify the author option, however, it compares the words with the author's name. In the lookup database, we have filled in author names for all STB inserts.

For instance, in [R] **kdensity** in this manual you will discover that Isaías H. Salgado-Ugarte wrote the first version of Stata's kdensity command and published it in the STB. Assume you read his original and find the discussion useful. You might now wonder what else he has written in the STB. To find out, you type

        . lookup Salgado-Ugarte, author
        (*output omitted*)

Names like Salgado-Ugarte are confusing to people in the U.S. lookup does not require you specify the entire name; what you type is compared to each "word" of the name and, if any part matches, the entry is listed. The dash, like the comma, is a special character and you can omit it. Thus, you can obtain the same list by looking up Salgado, Ugarte, or Salgado Ugarte without the dash.

Actually, to find all entries written by Salgado-Ugarte, you need to type

        . lookup Salgado-Ugarte, author historical
        (*output omitted*)

Prior inserts in the STB that provide a feature that later were superseded by a built-in feature of Stata are marked as historical in the lookup database and, by default, not listed. The historical option ensures that all entries are listed.

Entry id searches

If you specify the entry option, lookup compares what you have typed with the entry id. The entry id is not the title—it is the reference listed to the left of the title that tells you where to look. For instance, in

        [R]   regress . . . . Linear regression
                (help regress)

[R] **regress** is the entry id. This is a reference, of course, to this manual. In

        GS   . . . . Getting Started manual

"GS" is the entry id. In

```
STB-28   dm36 . . . . . . . . . . . . . . . . . Comparing two Stata data sets
         (help compdta if installed) . . . . . . . . . . . . . John R. Gleason
         11/95   STB Reprints Vol 5, pages 39--43
         compares the varlist from the dataset in memory with like-named
         variables in the Stata-format dataset on disk; alternative to cf
         command
```

"STB-28 dm36" is the entry id.

lookup with the entry option searches these entry ids.

Thus, one could generate a table of contents for the *User's Guide* by typing

```
. lookup [U], entry
```
(*output omitted*)

You could generate a table of contents for the 16th issue of the STB by typing

```
. lookup STB-16, entry historical
```
(*output omitted*)

The historical option in this case is possibly important. STB-16 was published in November 1993 and perhaps some of its inserts have already been marked historical.

You could obtain a complete list of all inserts associated with sg26 by typing

```
. lookup sg26, entry historical
```
(*output omitted*)

Again, we include the historical option in case any of the relevant inserts have been marked historical.

Return codes

In addition to indexing the entries in the *User's Guide*, the *Reference* manual, and the *Getting Started* manuals, lookup also can be used to lookup return codes.

To see information on return code 131, type

```
. lookup rc 131
rc       . . . . . . . . . . . . . . . . . . . . . . . . . . Return code 131
         not possible with test;
         You requested a test of a hypothesis that is nonlinear in the
         variables.  test tests only linear hypotheses.  Use testnl.
```

If you wanted to get a list of all Stata return codes, type

```
.lookup rc, entry
```
(*output omitted*)

Also See

[U] **12 Stata's on-line help and lookup facilities**

[R] **help**

Title

lrtest — Likelihood-ratio test after model estimation

Syntax

lrtest [, <u>s</u>aving(*name*) <u>u</u>sing(*name*) <u>m</u>odel(*name*) <u>df</u>(#)]

Note: *name* may be a name or number but may not exceed 4 characters.

Description

lrtest saves information about and performs likelihood-ratio tests between pairs of maximum-likelihood models such as those estimated by cox, logit, logistic, poisson, etc. lrtest may be used with any estimation command that reports a log-likelihood value or, equivalently, displays output like that described in [R] **maximize**.

lrtest, typed without arguments, performs a likelihood-ratio test of the most recently estimated model against the model previously saved by lrtest, saving(0). It is your responsibility to ensure that the most recently estimated model is nested within the previously saved model.

lrtest provides an important alternative to test for maximum-likelihood models.

Options

saving(*name*) specifies that the summary statistics associated with the most recently estimated model are to be saved as *name*. If no other options are specified, the statistics are saved and no test is performed. The larger model is typically saved by typing lrtest, saving(0).

using(*name*) specifies the name of the larger model against which a model is to be tested. If this option is not specified, using(0) is assumed.

model(*name*) specifies the name of the nested model (a constrained model) to be tested. If not specified, the most recently estimated model is used.

df(#) is seldom specified; it overrides the automatic degree-of-freedom calculation.

Remarks

The standard use of lrtest is

1. Estimate the larger model using one of Stata's estimation commands and then type lrtest, saving(0).

2. Estimate an alternative, nested model (a constrained model) and then type lrtest.

▷ Example

You have data on infants born with low birth weights along with characteristics of the mother (Hosmer and Lemeshow 1989 and more fully described in [R] **logistic**). You estimate the following model:

```
. logistic low age lwt race2 race3 smoke ptl ht ui
Logit Estimates                              Number of obs =     189
                                             chi2(8)       =   33.22
                                             Prob > chi2   = 0.0001
Log Likelihood =   -100.724                  Pseudo R2     = 0.1416

---------------------------------------------------------------------
    low | Odds Ratio  Std. Err.      z     P>|z|    [95% Conf. Interval]
--------+------------------------------------------------------------
    age |  .9732636   .0354759    -0.743   0.457    .9061578   1.045339
    lwt |  .9849634   .0068217    -2.188   0.029    .9716834   .9984249
  race2 |  3.534767   1.860737     2.399   0.016    1.259736   9.918406
  race3 |  2.368079   1.039949     1.963   0.050    1.001356   5.600207
  smoke |  2.517698   1.00916      2.304   0.021    1.147676   5.523162
    ptl |  1.719161   .5952579     1.565   0.118    .8721455   3.388787
     ht |  6.249602   4.322408     2.650   0.008    1.611152   24.24199
     ui |   2.1351    .9808153     1.651   0.099    .8677528   5.2534
---------------------------------------------------------------------
```

You now wish to test the constraint that the coefficients on age, lwt, ptl, and ht are all zero (or equivalently in this case, that the odds ratios are all 1). One solution is

```
. test age lwt ptl ht
 ( 1)   age = 0.0
 ( 2)   lwt = 0.0
 ( 3)   ptl = 0.0
 ( 4)   ht = 0.0

          chi2(  4) =    12.38
          Prob > chi2 =   0.0147
```

This test is based on the inverse of the information matrix and is therefore based on a quadratic approximation to the likelihood function; see [R] **test**. A more precise test would be to reestimate the model, applying the proposed constraints, and then calculate the likelihood-ratio test. lrtest assists you in doing this.

You first save the statistics associated with the current model:

```
. lrtest, saving(0)
```

The "name" 0 was not chosen arbitrarily, although we could have chosen any name. Why we chose 0 will become clear shortly. Having saved the information on the current model, we now estimate the constrained model, which in this case is the model omitting age, lwt, ptl, and ht:

```
. logistic low race2 race3 smoke ui
Logit Estimates                              Number of obs =     189
                                             chi2(4)       =   18.80
                                             Prob > chi2   = 0.0009
Log Likelihood = -107.93404                  Pseudo R2     = 0.0801

---------------------------------------------------------------------
    low | Odds Ratio  Std. Err.      z     P>|z|    [95% Conf. Interval]
--------+------------------------------------------------------------
  race2 |  3.052746   1.498084     2.274   0.023    1.166749   7.987368
  race3 |  2.922593   1.189226     2.636   0.008    1.31646    6.488269
  smoke |  2.945742   1.101835     2.888   0.004    1.41517    6.131701
     ui |  2.419131   1.047358     2.040   0.041    1.03546    5.651783
---------------------------------------------------------------------
```

That done, typing lrtest will compare this model with the model we previously saved:

```
. lrtest
Logistic: likelihood-ratio test              chi2(4)     =      14.42
                                             Prob > chi2 =     0.0061
```

The more precise syntax for the test is `lrtest, using(0)`, meaning that the current model is to be compared with the model saved as 0. The name 0, as we previously said, is special—when you do not specify the name of the `using()` model, `using(0)` is assumed. Thus, saving the original model as 0 saved us some typing when we performed the test.

Comparing results, `test` reported that `age`, `lwt`, `ptl`, and `ht` were jointly significant at the 1.5% level; `lrtest` reports they are significant at the 0.6% level. `lrtest`'s results should be viewed as more accurate.

◁

▷ Example

Typing `lrtest, saving(0)` and later `lrtest` by itself is the way `lrtest` is most commonly used, although here is how we might use the other options:

```
. logit chd age age2 sex        estimate full model
. lrtest, saving(0)             save results
. logit chd age sex             estimate simpler model
. lrtest                        obtain test
. lrtest, saving(1)             save logit results as 1
. logit chd sex                 estimate simplest model
. lrtest                        compare with full model
. lrtest, using(1)              compare with model 1
. lrtest, model(1)              repeat against full model test
```

◁

▷ Example

Returning to the low birth weight data in the first example, you now wish to test that the coefficient on `race2` is equal to that on `race3`. The base model is still stored in 0, so you need only estimate the constrained model and perform the test. Letting z be the index of the logit, the base model is

$$z = \beta_0 + \beta_1\text{age} + \beta_2\text{lwt} + \beta_3\text{race2} + \beta_4\text{race3} + \dots$$

If $\beta_3 = \beta_4$, this can be written

$$z = \beta_0 + \beta_1\text{age} + \beta_2\text{lwt} + \beta_3(\text{race2} + \text{race3}) + \dots$$

To estimate the constrained model, we create a variable equal to the sum of `race2` and `race3` and estimate the model including that variable in their place:

```
. gen race23 = race2 + race3
. logistic low age lwt race23 smoke ptl ht ui
```

Logit Estimates   Number of obs =   189
                                             chi2(7)   =   32.67
                                             Prob > chi2   =   0.0000
Log Likelihood = -100.9997   Pseudo R2   =   0.1392

```
------------------------------------------------------------------------
    low | Odds Ratio   Std. Err.      z     P>|z|    [95% Conf. Interval]
--------+---------------------------------------------------------------
    age | .9716799     .0352638    -0.792   0.429    .9049649    1.043313
    lwt | .9864971     .0064627    -2.075   0.038    .9739114    .9992453
 race23 | 2.728186     1.080206     2.535   0.011    1.255586    5.927907
  smoke | 2.664498     1.052379     2.481   0.013    1.228633    5.778414
    ptl | 1.709129     .5924775     1.546   0.122    .8663666    3.371691
     ht | 6.116391     4.215585     2.628   0.009    1.58425    23.61385
     ui | 2.09936      .9699702     1.605   0.108    .8487997    5.192407
------------------------------------------------------------------------
```

Comparing this model with our original model, we obtain

```
. lrtest
Logistic:  likelihood-ratio test                    chi2(1)    =      0.55
                                                     Prob > chi2 =    0.4577
```

By comparison, typing test race2=race3 after estimating our base model results in a significance level of .4572.

◁

Saved Results

lrtest saves in the S_# macros:

S_3	degrees of freedom	S_6	χ^2
		S_7	significance level

In terms of making an estimation command lrtest compatible, lrtest assumes that, after estimation, the following S_E_ macros are defined

S_E_cmd	name of estimation command
S_E_ll	log-likelihood value
S_E_mdf	model degrees of freedom
S_E_nobs	number of observations

Methods and Formulas

lrtest is implemented as an ado-file.

Let L_0 and L_1 be the log-likelihood values associated with the full and constrained models, respectively. Then $\chi^2 = -2(L_1 - L_0)$ with $d_0 - d_1$ degrees of freedom, where d_0 and d_1 are the model degrees of freedom associated with the full and constrained models (Judge et al. 1985, 216–217).

References

Hosmer, D. W., Jr., and S. Lemeshow. 1989. *Applied Logistic Regression.* New York: John Wiley & Sons.

Judge, G. G., W. E. Griffiths, R. C. Hill, H. Lütkepohl, and Tsoung-Chao Lee. 1985. *The Theory and Practice of Econometrics.* 2d ed. New York: John Wiley & Sons.

Also See

[R] **estimation commands**, [R] **linktest**, [R] **test**, [R] **testnl**

Title

ltable — Life tables for survival data

Syntax

ltable *timevar* [*deadvar*] [*weight*] [if *exp*] [in *range*] [, by(*groupvar*) level(#)

survival failure hazard intervals(*interval*) test tvid(*varname*) noadjust

notab graph *graph_options* noconf]

where *interval* is { w | # | #,#,... }

fweights are allowed; see [U] **18.1.6 weight**.

Description

ltable displays and graphs life tables for individual-level or aggregate data and optionally presents the likelihood-ratio and log-rank tests for equivalence of groups. ltable also allows examining the empirical hazard function through aggregation. Also see [R] **st sts** for alternative commands.

timevar specifies the time of failure or censoring. If *deadvar* is not specified, all values of *timevar* are interpreted as failure times; otherwise, *timevar* is interpreted as a failure time where *deadvar* $\neq 0$ and as a censoring time otherwise. Observations with *timevar* or *deadvar* equal to missing are ignored.

Note carefully that *deadvar* does *not* specify the *number* of failures. An observation with *deadvar* equal to 1 or 50 has the same interpretation—the observation records one failure. Specify frequency weights for aggregated data (e.g., ltable time [freq=number]).

Options

by(*groupvar*) creates separate tables (or graphs within the same image) for each value of *groupvar*. *groupvar* may be string or numeric.

level(#) specifies the confidence level, in percent, for confidence intervals. The default is level(95) or as set by set level; see [R] **level**.

survival, failure, and hazard indicate the table to be displayed. If not specified, the default is the survival table. Specifying failure would display the cumulative failure table. Specifying survival failure would display both the survival and the cumulative failure table. If graph is specified, multiple tables may not be requested.

intervals(*interval*) specifies the time intervals into which the data are to be aggregated for tabular presentation. A single numeric argument is interpreted as the width of the interval. For instance, interval(2) aggregates data into the time intervals $0 \leq t < 2$, $2 \leq t < 4$, and so on. Not specifying interval() is equivalent to specifying interval(1). Since in most data failure times are recorded as integers, this amounts to no aggregation except that implied by the recording of the time variable and so produces Kaplan–Meier product-limit estimates of the survival curve (with an actuarial adjustment; see the noadjust option below). Also see [R] **st sts list**. Although it is possible to examine survival and failure without aggregation, some form of aggregation is almost always required for examining the hazard.

When more than one argument is specified, time intervals are aggregated as specified. For instance, `interval(0,2,8,16)` aggregates data into the intervals $0 \leq t < 2$, $2 \leq t < 8$, $8 \leq t < 16$, and (if necessary) the open-ended interval $t \geq 16$.

`interval(w)` is equivalent to `interval(0,7,15,30,60,90,180,360,540,720)`, corresponding to one week, (roughly) two weeks, one month, two months, three months, six months, 1 year, 1.5 years, and 2 years when failure times are recorded in days. The `w` is meant to suggest widening intervals.

`test` presents two χ^2 measures of the differences between groups when `by()` is specified. `test` does nothing if `by()` is not specified.

`tvid(`*varname*`)` is for use with longitudinal data with time-varying parameters as processed by `cox`; see [R] **cox**. Each subject appears in the data more than once and equal values of *varname* identify observations referring to the same subject. When `tvid()` is specified, only the last observation on each subject is used in making the table. The order of the data does not matter, "last" here means the last observation chronologically.

`noadjust` suppresses the actuarial adjustment for deaths and censored observations. The default is to consider the adjusted number at risk at the start of the interval as the total at the start minus (the number dead or censored)/2. If `noadjust` is specified, the number at risk is simply the total at the start, corresponding to the standard Kaplan and Meier assumption. `noadjust` should be specified when using `ltable` to list results corresponding to those produced by `sts list`; see [R] **st sts list**.

`notab` suppresses displaying the table. This option is often used with `graph`.

`graph` requests that the table be presented graphically as well as in tabular form; when `notab` is also specified, only the graph is presented. When specifying `graph`, only one table can be calculated and graphed at a time; see `survival`, `failure`, and `hazard` above.

graph_options are any of the options allowed with `graph`, `twoway`; see [R] **graph twoway**. When `noconf` is specified, `twoway`'s `connect()` and `symbol()` may be specified with one argument; the default is `connect(1) symbol(0)`.

When `noconf` is not specified, the `connect()` and `symbol()` options may be specified with one or three arguments. The default is `connect(1||)` and `symbol(0ii)`, drawing the confidence band as vertical lines at each point. When you specify one argument, you modify the first argument of the default. When you specify three, you completely control the graph. Thus, `connect(111)` would draw the confidence band as a separate curve around the survival, failure, or hazard.

`noconf` suppresses graphing the confidence intervals around survival, failure, or hazard.

Remarks

Life tables date back to the seventeenth century; Edmund Halley (1693) is often credited with their development. `ltable` is for use with "cohort" data and, although one often thinks of such tables as following a population from the "birth" of the first member to the "death" of the last, more generally, such tables can be thought of as a reasonable way to list any kind of survival data. For an introductory discussion of life tables, see Pagano and Gauvreau (1993, 446–451); for an intermediate discussion, see, for example, Armitage and Berry (1987, 421–435) or Selvin (1996, 311–355); and for a more complete discussion, see Chiang (1984).

▷ Example

In Pike (1966), two groups of rats were exposed to a carcinogen and the number of days to death from vaginal cancer recorded (reprinted in Kalbfleisch and Prentice 1980, 2):

Group 1	143	164	188	188	190	192	206	209	213	216
	220	227	230	234	246	265	304	216*	244*	
Group 2	142	156	163	198	205	232	232	233	233	233
	233	239	240	261	280	280	296	296	323	204*
	344*									

The '*' on a few of the entries indicate that the observation was censored—as of the recorded day, the rat had still not died due to vaginal cancer but was withdrawn from the experiment for other reasons.

Having entered this data into Stata, the first few observations are

```
. list in 1/5
        group       t     died
 1.         1      143        1
 2.         1      164        1
 3.         1      188        1
 4.         1      188        1
 5.         1      190        1
```

That is, the first observation records a rat from group 1 that died on the 143rd day. The variable died records whether that rat died or was withdrawn (censored):

```
. list if died==0
         group       t     died
18.          1      216        0
19.          1      244        0
39.          2      204        0
40.          2      344        0
```

Four rats, two from each group, did not die but were withdrawn.

The survival table for group 1 is

```
. ltable t died if group==1
```

Interval		Beg. Total	Deaths	Lost	Survival	Std. Error	[95% Conf. Int.]	
143	144	19	1	0	0.9474	0.0512	0.6812	0.9924
164	165	18	1	0	0.8947	0.0704	0.6408	0.9726
188	189	17	2	0	0.7895	0.0935	0.5319	0.9153
190	191	15	1	0	0.7368	0.1010	0.4789	0.8810
192	193	14	1	0	0.6842	0.1066	0.4279	0.8439
206	207	13	1	0	0.6316	0.1107	0.3790	0.8044
209	210	12	1	0	0.5789	0.1133	0.3321	0.7626
213	214	11	1	0	0.5263	0.1145	0.2872	0.7188
216	217	10	1	1	0.4709	0.1151	0.2410	0.6712
220	221	8	1	0	0.4120	0.1148	0.1937	0.6194
227	228	7	1	0	0.3532	0.1125	0.1502	0.5648
230	231	6	1	0	0.2943	0.1080	0.1105	0.5070
234	235	5	1	0	0.2354	0.1012	0.0750	0.4459
244	245	4	0	1	0.2354	0.1012	0.0750	0.4459
246	247	3	1	0	0.1570	0.0930	0.0312	0.3721
265	266	2	1	0	0.0785	0.0724	0.0056	0.2864
304	305	1	1	0	0.0000	.	.	.

The reported survival rates are the survival rates at the end of the interval. Thus, 94.7% of rats survived 144 days or more.

◁

□ Technical Note

If you compare the table just printed with the corresponding table in Kalbfleisch and Prentice (1980, 14), you will notice that the survival estimates differ beginning with the interval 216–217, the first interval containing a censored observation. ltable treats censored observations as if they were withdrawn half way through the interval. The table printed in Kalbfleisch and Prentice treated censored observations as if they were withdrawn at the end of the interval even through Kalbfleisch and Prentice (1980, 15) mention how results could be adjusted for censoring.

In this case, the same results as printed in Kalbfleisch and Prentice could be obtained by incrementing the time of withdrawal by 1 for the four censored observations. We say "in this case" because there were no deaths on the incremented dates. For instance, one of the rats was withdrawn on the 216th day, a day on which there was also a real death. There were no deaths on day 217, however, so moving the withdrawal forward one day is equivalent to assuming the withdrawal occurred at the end of the day 216–217 interval. If the adjustments are made and ltable used to calculate survival in both groups, results are as printed in Kalbfleisch and Prentice except that, for group 2 in the interval 240–241, they report the survival as .345 when they mean .354.

In any case, the one-half adjustment for withdrawals is generally accepted but it is important to remember that it is only a crude adjustment and one that becomes cruder the wider the intervals.

□

▷ Example

When you do not specify the intervals, ltable uses unit intervals. The only aggregation performed on the data was aggregation due to deaths or withdrawals occurring on the same "day". If we wanted to see the table aggregated into 30-day intervals, we would type

```
. ltable t died if group==1, interval(30)
```

Interval		Beg. Total	Deaths	Lost	Survival	Std. Error	[95% Conf. Int.]	
120	150	19	1	0	0.9474	0.0512	0.6812	0.9924
150	180	18	1	0	0.8947	0.0704	0.6408	0.9726
180	210	17	6	0	0.5789	0.1133	0.3321	0.7626
210	240	11	6	1	0.2481	0.1009	0.0847	0.4552
240	270	4	2	1	0.1063	0.0786	0.0139	0.3090
300	330	1	1	0	0.0000	.	.	.

The interval printed 120 150 means the interval including 120, and up to but not including 150. The reported survival rate is the survival rate just after the close of the interval.

When you specify more than one number as the argument to **interval()**, you specify not the widths but the cutoff points themselves.

```
. ltable t died if group==1, interval(120,180,210,240,330)
```

	Interval	Beg. Total	Deaths	Lost	Survival	Std. Error	[95% Conf. Int.]	
120	180	19	2	0	0.8947	0.0704	0.6408	0.9726
180	210	17	6	0	0.5789	0.1133	0.3321	0.7626
210	240	11	6	1	0.2481	0.1009	0.0847	0.4552
240	330	4	3	1	0.0354	0.0486	0.0006	0.2245

If any of the underlying failure or censoring times are larger than the last cutoff specified, they are treated as being in the open-ended interval:

```
. ltable t died if group==1, interval(120,180,210,240)
```

	Interval	Beg. Total	Deaths	Lost	Survival	Std. Error	[95% Conf. Int.]	
120	180	19	2	0	0.8947	0.0704	0.6408	0.9726
180	210	17	6	0	0.5789	0.1133	0.3321	0.7626
210	240	11	6	1	0.2481	0.1009	0.0847	0.4552
240	.	4	3	1	0.0354	0.0486	0.0006	0.2245

Whether the last interval is treated as open-ended or not makes no difference for survival and failure tables, but does affect hazard tables. If the interval is open-ended, the hazard is not calculated for it.

◁

▷ Example

The by(*varname*) option specifies that separate tables are to be presented for each value of *varname*. Remember that our rat data contains two groups:

```
. ltable t died, by(group) interval(30)
```

	Interval	Beg. Total	Deaths	Lost	Survival	Std. Error	[95% Conf. Int.]	
group 1								
120	150	19	1	0	0.9474	0.0512	0.6812	0.9924
150	180	18	1	0	0.8947	0.0704	0.6408	0.9726
180	210	17	6	0	0.5789	0.1133	0.3321	0.7626
210	240	11	6	1	0.2481	0.1009	0.0847	0.4552
240	270	4	2	1	0.1063	0.0786	0.0139	0.3090
300	330	1	1	0	0.0000	.	.	.
group 2								
120	150	21	1	0	0.9524	0.0465	0.7072	0.9932
150	180	20	2	0	0.8571	0.0764	0.6197	0.9516
180	210	18	2	1	0.7592	0.0939	0.5146	0.8920
210	240	15	7	0	0.4049	0.1099	0.1963	0.6053
240	270	8	2	0	0.3037	0.1031	0.1245	0.5057
270	300	6	4	0	0.1012	0.0678	0.0172	0.2749
300	330	2	1	0	0.0506	0.0493	0.0035	0.2073
330	360	1	0	1	0.0506	0.0493	0.0035	0.2073

◁

▷ Example

A failure table is simply a different way of looking at a survival table; failure is $1 -$ survival:

```
. ltable t died if group==1, interval(30) failure
```

Interval		Beg. Total	Deaths	Lost	Cum. Failure	Std. Error	[95% Conf. Int.]	
120	150	19	1	0	0.0526	0.0512	0.0076	0.3188
150	180	18	1	0	0.1053	0.0704	0.0274	0.3592
180	210	17	6	0	0.4210	0.1133	0.2374	0.6679
210	240	11	6	1	0.7519	0.1009	0.5448	0.9153
240	270	4	2	1	0.8937	0.0786	0.6910	0.9861
300	330	1	1	0	1.0000	.	.	.

◁

▷ Example

Selvin (1996, 332) presents follow-up data from Cutler and Ederer (1958) on six cohorts of kidney cancer patients. The goal is to estimate the 5-year survival probability.

Year	Interval	Alive	Deaths	Lost	With-drawn	Year	Interval	Alive	Deaths	Lost	With-drawn
1946	0–1	9	4	1		1948	0–1	21	11	0	
	1–2	4	0	0			1–2	10	1	2	
	2–3	4	0	0			2–3	7	0	0	
	3–4	4	0	0			3–4	7	0	0	7
	4–5	4	0	0		1949	0–1	34	12	0	
	5–6	4	0	0	4		1–2	22	3	3	
1947	0–1	18	7	0			2–3	16	1	0	15
	1–2	11	0	0		1950	0–1	19	5	1	
	2–3	11	1	0			1–2	13	1	1	11
	3–4	10	2	2		1951	0–1	25	8	2	15
	4–5	6	0	0	6						

The following is the Stata dataset corresponding to the table:

```
. list
```

	year	t	died	pop
1.	1946	.5	1	4
2.	1946	.5	0	1
3.	1946	5.5	0	4
4.	1947	.5	1	7
5.	1947	2.5	1	1

etc.

As summary data may often come in the form shown above, it is worth understanding exactly how the data was translated for use with ltable. t records the time of death or censoring (lost to follow-up or withdrawal). died contains 1 if the observation records a death and 0 if it instead records lost or withdrawn patients. pop records the number of patients in the category. The first line of the table stated that, in the 1946 cohort, there were 9 patients at the start of the interval 0–1, and during the interval, 4 died, and 1 was lost to follow-up. Thus, we entered in observation 1 that at $t = .5$, 4 patients died and, in observation 2, that at $t = .5$, 1 patient was censored. We ignored the information on the total population because ltable will figure that out for itself.

The second line of the table indicated that in the interval 1–2, 4 patients were still alive at the beginning of the interval and, during the interval, 0 died or were lost to follow-up. Since no patients died or were censored, we entered nothing into our data. Similarly, we entered nothing for lines 3, 4, and 5 of the table. The last line for 1946 stated that, in the interval 5–6, 4 patients were alive at the beginning of the interval and that those 4 patients were withdrawn. In observation 3, we entered that there were 4 censorings at $t = 5.5$.

The fact that we chose to record the times of deaths or censoring as midpoints of intervals does not matter; we could just as well have recorded the times as 0.8 and 5.8. By default, ltable will form intervals 0–1, 1–2, and so on, and place observations into the intervals to which they belong. We suggest using 0.5 and 5.5 because those numbers correspond to the underlying assumptions made by ltable in making its calculations. Using midpoints reminds you of the assumptions.

To obtain the survival rates, we type

```
. ltable t died [freq=pop]
```

Interval		Beg. Total	Deaths	Lost	Survival	Std. Error	[95% Conf. Int.]	
0	1	126	47	19	0.5966	0.0454	0.5017	0.6792
1	2	60	5	17	0.5386	0.0478	0.4405	0.6269
2	3	38	2	15	0.5033	0.0508	0.4002	0.5977
3	4	21	2	9	0.4423	0.0602	0.3225	0.5554
4	5	10	0	6	0.4423	0.0602	0.3225	0.5554
5	6	4	0	4	0.4423	0.0602	0.3225	0.5554

We estimate the 5-year survival rate as .4423 and the 95% confidence interval as .3225 to .5554.

Selvin (1996, 336), in presenting these results, lists the survival in the interval 0–1 as 1, in 1–2 as .597, in 2–3 as .539, and so on. That is, relative to us, he shifted the rates down one row and inserted a 1 in the first row. In his table, the survival rate is the survival rate at the *start* of the interval. In our table, the survival rate is the survival rate at the *end* of the interval (or, equivalently, at the start of the next interval). This is, of course, simply a difference in the way the numbers are presented and not in the numbers themselves.

◁

▷ Example

The discrete hazard function is the rate of failure—the number of failures occurring within a time interval divided by the width of the interval (assuming there are no censored observations). While the survival and failure tables are meaningful at the "individual" level—with intervals so narrow that each contains only a single failure—that is not true for the discrete hazard. If all intervals contained one death and if all intervals were of equal width, the hazard function would be $1/\Delta t$ and so appear to be a constant!

The empirically determined discrete hazard function can only be revealed by aggregation. Gross and Clark (1975, 37) print data on malignant melanoma at the M. D. Anderson Tumor Clinic between 1944 and 1960. The interval is the time from initial diagnosis:

Interval (years)	number lost to follow-up	Number with-drawn alive	Number dying
0–1	19	77	312
1–2	3	71	96
2–3	4	58	45
3–4	3	27	29
4–5	5	35	7
5–6	1	36	9
6–7	0	17	3
7–8	2	10	1
8–9	0	8	3
9+	0	0	32

For our statistical purposes, there is no difference between the number lost to follow-up (patients who disappeared) and the number withdrawn alive (patients dropped by the researchers)—both are censored. We have entered the data into Stata; here is a small amount of it:

```
. list in 1/6

          t        d      pop
1.       .5        1      312
2.       .5        0       19
3.       .5        0       77
4.      1.5        1       96
5.      1.5        0        3
6.      1.5        0       71
```

We entered each group's time of death or censoring as the midpoint of the intervals and entered the numbers of the table, recording d as 1 for deaths and 0 for censoring. The hazard table is

```
. ltable t d [freq=pop], hazard interval(0,1,2,3,4,5,6,7,8,9)
```

Interval		Beg. Total	Cum. Failure	Std. Error	Hazard	Std. Error	[95% Conf. Int.]	
0	1	913	0.3607	0.0163	0.4400	0.0243	0.3924	0.4877
1	2	505	0.4918	0.0176	0.2286	0.0232	0.1831	0.2740
2	3	335	0.5670	0.0182	0.1598	0.0238	0.1133	0.2064
3	4	228	0.6260	0.0188	0.1461	0.0270	0.0931	0.1991
4	5	169	0.6436	0.0190	0.0481	0.0182	0.0125	0.0837
5	6	122	0.6746	0.0200	0.0909	0.0303	0.0316	0.1502
6	7	76	0.6890	0.0208	0.0454	0.0262	0.0000	0.0969
7	8	56	0.6952	0.0212	0.0202	0.0202	0.0000	0.0598
8	9	43	0.7187	0.0235	0.0800	0.0462	0.0000	0.1704
9	.	32	1.0000	.	.	.	.	.

We specified the `interval()` option as we did and not as `interval(1)` (or omitting the option altogether) to force the last interval to be open-ended. Had we not, and if we had recorded t as 9.5 for observations in that interval (as we did), `ltable` would have calculated a hazard rate for the "interval". In this case, the result of that calculation would have been 2, but no matter what the result, it would have been meaningless since we do not know the width of the interval.

You are not limited to merely examining a column of numbers. With the `graph` option, you can see the result graphically:

```
. ltable t d [freq=pop], hazard i(0,1,2,3,4,5,6,7,8,9) graph notab
> xlab(0,2,4,6,8,10) border
```

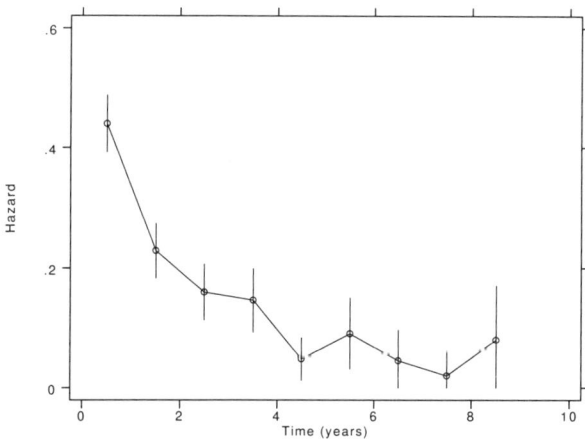

The vertical lines in the graph represent the 95% confidence intervals for the hazard; specifying noconf would have suppressed them. Among the options we did specify, but it is not required, notab suppressed printing the table, saving us some paper. xlab() and border were passed through to the graph command (see [R] **graph twoway**) and were similarly unnecessary, but made the graph look better.

◁

▷ Example

You can graph the survival function the same way you graph the hazard function: just omit the hazard option.

◁

Methods and Formulas

ltable is implemented as an ado-file.

Let τ_i be the individual failure or censoring times. The data is aggregated into intervals given by t_j, $j = 1, \ldots, J$ and $t_{J+1} = \infty$ with each interval containing counts for $t_j \leq \tau < t_{j+1}$. Let d_j and m_j be the number of failures and censored observations during the interval and N_j the number alive at the start of the interval. Define $n_j = N_j - m_j/2$ as the adjusted number at risk at the start of the interval. If the noadjust option is specified $n_j = N_j$.

The product-limit estimate of the survivor function is

$$S_j = \prod_{k=1}^{j} \frac{n_k - d_k}{n_k}$$

(Kalbfleisch and Prentice 1980, 12, 15). Greenwood's formula for the asymptotic standard error of S_j is

$$s_j = S_j \sqrt{\sum_{k=1}^{j} \frac{d_k}{n_k(n_k - d_k)}}$$

(Greenwood 1926; Kalbfleisch and Prentice 1980, 14, 15). s_j is reported as the standard deviation of survival but is not used in generating the confidence intervals since it can produce intervals outside 0 and 1. The "natural" units for the survival function are $\log(-\log S_j)$ and the asymptotic standard error of that quantity is

$$\widehat{s}_j = \sqrt{\frac{\sum d_k/\big(n_k(n_k - d_k)\big)}{\big[\sum \log\big((n_k - d_k)/n_k\big)\big]^2}}$$

(Kalbfleisch and Prentice 1980, 15). The corresponding confidence intervals are $S_j^{\exp(\pm z_{1-\alpha/2}\widehat{s}_j)}$.

The cumulative failure time is defined as $G_j = 1 - S_j$ and thus the variance is the same as for S_j and the confidence intervals are $1 - S_j^{\exp(\pm z_{1-\alpha/2}\widehat{s}_j)}$.

For purposes of graphing, both S_j and G_j are graphed against t_{j+1}.

Define the within-interval failure rate as $f_j = d_j/n_j$. The maximum-likelihood estimate of the (within-interval) hazard is then

$$\lambda_j = \frac{f_j}{(1 - f_j/2)(t_{j+1} - t_j)}$$

The standard error of λ_j is

$$s_{\lambda_j} = \lambda_j \sqrt{\frac{1 - [(t_{j+1} - t_j)\lambda_j/2]^2}{d_j}}$$

from which a confidence interval is calculated. For graphing purposes, λ_j is graphed against $(t_j + t_{j+1})/2$.

If the **noadjust** option is specified, the estimate of the hazard is

$$\lambda_j = \frac{f_j}{t_{j+1} - t_j}$$

and its standard error is

$$s_{\lambda_j} = \frac{\lambda_j}{\sqrt{d_j}}$$

The confidence interval is

$$\left[\frac{\lambda_j}{2d_j}\chi^2_{2d_j,\alpha/2}, \ \frac{\lambda_j}{2d_j}\chi^2_{2d_j,1-\alpha/2} \right]$$

where $\chi^2_{2d_j,q}$ is the qth quantile of the χ^2 distribution with $2d_j$ degrees of freedom (Cox and Oakes 1984, 53–54, 38–40).

For the likelihood-ratio test for homogeneity, let d_g be the total number of deaths in the gth group. Define $T_g = \sum_{i \in g} \tau_i$, where i indexes the individual failure or censoring times. The χ^2 value with $G - 1$ degrees of freedom (where G is the total number of groups) is

$$\chi^2 = 2\left[\left(\sum d_g\right) \log\left(\frac{\sum T_g}{\sum d_g}\right) - \sum d_g \log\left(\frac{T_g}{d_g}\right) \right]$$

(Lawless 1982, 113).

The log-rank test for homogeneity is the test presented by **sts test**; see [R] **st sts**.

Acknowledgments

ltable is based on the lftbl command by Henry Krakauer and John Stewart (1991). We also thank Michel Henry-Amar, Centre Regional Francois Baclesse, Cedex, France for his comments.

References

Armitage, P. and G. Berry. 1987. *Statistical Methods in Medical Research.* 2d ed. Oxford: Blackwell Scientific Publications.

Chiang, C. L. 1984. *The Life Table and Its Applications.* Malabar, FL: Krieger.

Cox, D. R. and D. Oakes. 1984. *Analysis of Survival Data.* London: Chapman and Hall.

Cutler, S. J. and E. Ederer. 1958. Maximum utilization of the life table method in analyzing survival. *Journal of Chronic Diseases* 8: 699–712.

Greenwood, M. 1926. The natural duration of cancer. *Reports on Public Health and Medical Subjects* 33: 1–26. London: His Majesty's Stationery Office.

Gross, A. J. and V. A. Clark. 1975. *Survival Distributions: Reliability Applications in the Biomedical Sciences.* New York: John Wiley & Sons.

Halley, E. 1693. An estimate of the degrees of mortality of mankind, drawn from curious tables of the births and funerals at the city of Breslau, with an attempt to ascertain the price of annuities on lives. *Philosophical Transactions* 17: 596–610. London: The Royal Society.

Kahn, H. A. and C. T. Sempos. 1989. *Statistical Methods in Epidemiology.* New York: Oxford University Press.

Kalbfleisch, J. D. and R. L. Prentice. 1980. *The Statistical Analysis of Failure Time Data.* New York: John Wiley & Sons.

Krakauer, H. and J. Stewart. 1991. ssa1: Actuarial or life-table analysis of time-to-event data. *Stata Technical Bulletin* 1: 23–25. Reprinted in *Stata Technical Bulletin Reprints*, vol. 1, pp. 200–202.

Lawless, J. F. 1982. *Statistical Models and Methods for Lifetime Data.* New York: John Wiley & Sons.

Pagano, M. and K. Gauvreau. 1993. *Principles of Biostatistics.* Belmont, CA: Duxbury Press.

Pike, M. C. 1966. A method of analysis of a certain class of experiments in carcinogenesis. *Biometrics* 22: 142–161.

Selvin, S. 1996. *Statistical Analysis of Epidemiologic Data.* 2d ed. New York: Oxford University Press.

Also See

[R] **cox**, [R] **st**, [R] **weibull**

Title

lv — Letter-value displays

Syntax

lv [*varlist*] [if *exp*] [in *range*] [, generate tail(#)]

Description

lv shows a letter-value display (Tukey 1977, 44–49; Hoaglin 1983) for each variable in *varlist*. If no variables are specified, letter-value displays are shown for each numeric variable in the data.

Options

generate adds four new variables to the data: _mid, containing the midsummaries; _spread, containing the spreads; _psigma, containing the pseudosigmas; and _z2, containing the squared values from a $N(0, 1)$ corresponding to the particular letter value. If the variables _mid, _spread, _psigma, and _z2 already exist, their contents are replaced. At most, only the first 11 observations of each variable are used; the remaining observations contain missing. If *varlist* specifies more than one variable, the newly created variables contain results for the last variable specified.

tail(#) indicates the inverse of the tail density through which letter values are to be displayed. 2 corresponds to the median (meaning half in each tail), 4 to the fourths (roughly the 25th and 75th percentiles), 8 to the eighths, and so on. # may be specified as 4, 8, 16, 32, 64, 128, 256, 512, or 1,024 and defaults to a value of # that has corresponding depth just greater than 1. The default is taken as 1,024 if the calculation results in a number larger than 1,024. Given the intelligent default, this option is rarely specified.

Remarks

Letter-value displays are a collection of observations drawn systematically from the data, focusing especially on the tails rather than the middle of the distribution. The displays are called letter-value displays because letters have been (almost arbitrarily) assigned to tail densities:

Letter	Tail Area	Letter	Tail Area
M	1/2	B	1/64
F	1/4	A	1/128
E	1/8	Z	1/256
D	1/16	Y	1/512
C	1/32	X	1/1024

▷ Example

You have data on the mileage ratings of 74 automobiles. To obtain a letter-value display:

```
. lv mpg
```

```
#      74                    Mileage (mpg)
               ------------------------------------
M    37.5 |                   20             |    spread   pseudosigma
F      19 |         18       21.5       25 |        7       5.216359
E      10 |         15       21.5       28 |       13       5.771728
D     5.5 |         14      22.25     30.5 |     16.5       5.576303
C       3 |         14       24.5       35 |       21       5.831039
B       2 |         12       23.5       35 |       23       5.732448
A     1.5 |         12        25        38 |       26       6.040635
        1 |         12       26.5       41 |       29       6.16562

          |                                 |    # below       # above
inner fence |        7.5               35.5 |        0              1
outer fence |         -3                 46 |        0              0
```

The decimal points can be made to line up and thus the output made more readable by specifying a display format for the variable; see [U] **19.5 Formats: controlling how data is displayed**.

```
. format mpg %9.2f

. lv mpg

#      74                    Mileage (mpg)
               ------------------------------------
M    37.5 |                 20.00           |    spread   pseudosigma
F      19 |       18.00     21.50     25.00 |      7.00       5.22
E      10 |       15.00     21.50     28.00 |     13.00       5.77
D     5.5 |       14.00     22.25     30.50 |     16.50       5.58
C       3 |       14.00     24.50     35.00 |     21.00       5.83
B       2 |       12.00     23.50     35.00 |     23.00       5.73
A     1.5 |       12.00     25.00     38.00 |     26.00       6.04
        1 |       12.00     26.50     41.00 |     29.00       6.16

          |                                 |    # below       # above
inner fence |      7.50               35.50 |        0              1
outer fence |     -3.00               46.00 |        0              0
```

At the top, the number of observations is indicated as 74. The first line shows the statistics associated with M, the letter value that puts half the density in each tail, or the median. The median has *depth* 37.5 (that is, in the ordered data, M is 37.5 observations in from the extremes) and has value 20. The next line shows the statistics associated with F or the fourths. The fourths have depth 19 (that is, in the ordered data, the lower fourth is observation 19 and the upper fourth is observation $74 - 19 + 1$), and the values of the lower and upper fourths are 18 and 25. The number in the middle is the point halfway between the fourths—called a midsummary. If the distribution were perfectly symmetric, the midsummary would equal the median. The spread is the difference between the lower and upper summaries ($25 - 18 = 7$). For fourths, half the data lies within a 7-mpg band. The pseudosigma is a calculation of the standard deviation using only the lower and upper summaries and assuming that the variable is normally distributed. If the data really were normally distributed, all the pseudosigmas would be roughly equal.

After the letter values, the line labeled with depth 1 reports the minimum and maximum values. In this case, the halfway point between the extremes is 26.5, which is greater than the median, indicating that 41 is more extreme than 12, at least relative to the median. Also note that, with each letter value, the midsummaries are increasing—our data is skewed. The pseudosigmas are also increasing, indicating that the data is spreading out relative to a normal distribution although, given the evident skewness, this elongation may be an artifact of the skewness.

At the end is an attempt to identify outliers, although the points so identified are merely outside some predetermined cutoff. Points outside the inner fence are called *outside values* or *mild outliers*. Points outside the outer fence are called *severe outliers*. The inner fence is defined as $(3/2)$IQR and the outer fence as 3IQR above and below the F summaries, where the IQR is the spread of the fourths.

◁

❑ Technical Note

The form of the letter-value display has varied slightly with different authors. lv displays appear as described by Hoaglin (1983) but as modified by Emerson and Stoto (1983), where they included the midpoint of each of the spreads. This format was later adopted by Hoaglin (1985). If the distribution is symmetric, the midpoints will all be roughly equal. On the other hand, if the midpoints vary systematically, the distribution is skewed.

The pseudosigmas are obtained from the lower and upper summaries for each letter value. For each letter value, they are the standard deviation a normal distribution would have if its spread for the given letter value were to equal the observed spread. If the pseudosigmas are all roughly equal, the data is said to have *neutral elongation*. If the pseudosigmas increase systematically, the data is said to be more elongated than a normal; i.e., have thicker tails. If the pseudosigmas decrease systematically, the data is said to be less elongated than a normal; i.e., have thinner tails.

Interpretation of the number of mild and severe outliers is more problematic. The following discussion is drawn from Hamilton (1991):

Obviously, the presence of any such outliers does not rule out that the data has been drawn from a normal; in large datasets, there will most certainly be observations outside $(3/2)$IQR and 3IQR. Severe outliers, however, comprise about two per million (.0002%) of a normal population. In samples, they lie far enough out to have substantial effects on means, standard deviations, and other classical statistics. The .0002%, however, should be interpreted carefully; outliers appear more often in small samples than one might expect from population proportions due to sampling variation in estimated quartiles. Monte Carlo simulation by Hoaglin, Iglewicz, and Tukey (1986) obtained these results on the percentages and numbers of outliers in random samples from a normal population:

n	percentage		number	
	any outliers	severe	any outliers	severe
10	2.83	.362	.283	.0362
20	1.66	.074	.332	.0148
50	1.15	.011	.575	.0055
100	.95	.002	.95	.002
200	.79	.001	1.58	.002
300	.75	.001	2.25	.003
∞	.70	.0002	∞	∞

Thus, the presence of any severe outliers in samples of less than 300 is sufficient to reject normality. Hoaglin, Iglewicz, and Tukey (1981) suggested the approximation $.00698 + .4/n$ for the fraction of mild outliers in a sample of size n or, equivalently, $.00698n + .4$ for the number of outliers.

❑

▷ Example

The **generate** option adds the variables _mid, _spread, _psigma, and _z2 to your data, making possible many of the diagnostic graphs suggested by Hoaglin (1985).

```
. lv mpg, generate
(output omitted )
. list _mid _spread _psigma _z2 in 1/12
            _mid    _spread   _psigma         _z2
    1.        20          .         .           0
    2.      21.5          7   5.216359    .4501955
    3.      21.5         13   5.771728     1.26828
    4.     22.25       16.5   5.576303    2.188846
    5.      24.5         21   5.831039     3.24255
    6.      23.5         23   5.732448    4.024532
    7.        25         26   6.040635    4.631499
    8.         .          .         .           .
    9.         .          .         .           .
   10.         .          .         .           .
   11.      26.5         29   6.126127     5.60227
   12.         .          .         .           .
```

Observations 12 through the end are missing for these new variables. The definition of the observations is always the same. The first observation contains the M summary, the second the F, the third the E, and so on. Observation 11 always contains the summary for depth 1. Observations 8 through 10—corresponding to letter values Z, Y, and X—contain missing because these statistics were not calculated. We have only 74 observations and their depth would be 1.

Hoaglin (1985) suggests graphing the midsummary against z^2. If the distribution is not skewed, the points in the resulting graph will be along a horizontal line:

```
. graph _mid _z2, border ylabel xlabel
```

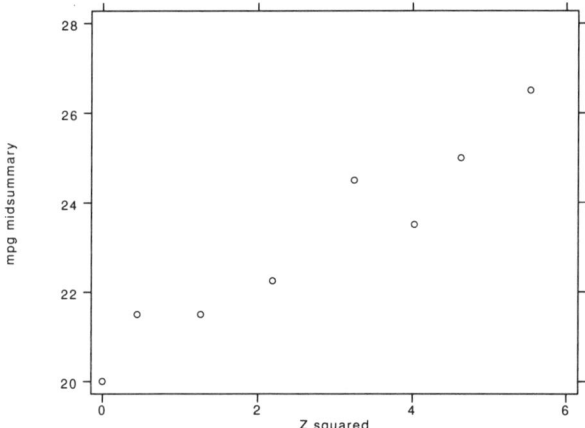

The graph clearly indicates the skewness of the distribution. One might also graph _psigma against _z2 to examine elongation.

◁

Saved Results

lv saves in the S_# macros:

S_1	number of observations	S_12	upper 32nd
S_2	median	S_13	lower 64th
S_3	lower fourth	S_14	upper 64th
S_4	upper fourth	S_15	lower 128th
S_5	minimum	S_16	upper 128th
S_6	maximum	S_17	lower 256th
S_7	lower eighth	S_18	upper 256th
S_8	upper eighth	S_19	lower 512th
S_9	lower sixteenth	S_20	upper 512th
S_10	upper sixteenth	S_21	lower 1024th
S_11	lower 32nd	S_22	upper 1024th

S_1 through S_6 are always defined. Remaining values are defined only if there is sufficient data.

Methods and Formulas

lv is implemented as an ado-file.

Let N be the number of (nonmissing) observations on x, and let $x_{(i)}$ refer to the ordered data when i is an integer. Define $x_{(i+.5)} = (x_{(i)} + x_{(i+1)})/2$; the median is defined as $x_{((N+1)/2)}$.

Define $x_{[d]}$ as the pair of numbers $x_{(d)}$ and $x_{(N+1-d)}$ where d is called the *depth*. Thus, $x_{[1]}$ refers to the minimum and maximum of the data. Define $m = (N+1)/2$ as the depth of the median, $f = (\lfloor m \rfloor + 1)/2$ as the depth of the fourths, $e = (\lfloor f \rfloor + 1)/2$ as the depth of the eighths, and so on. Depths are reported on the far left of the letter-value display. The corresponding fourths of the data are $x_{[f]}$, the eighths $x_{[e]}$, and so on. These values are reported inside the display. The middle value is defined as the corresponding midpoint of $x_{[\cdot]}$. The spreads are defined as the difference in $x_{[\cdot]}$.

The corresponding point z_i on a standard normal distribution is obtained as (Hoaglin 1985, 456–457)

$$z_i = \begin{cases} F^{-1}\big[(d_i - 1/3)/(N + 1/3)\big] & \text{if } d_i > 1 \\ F^{-1}\big[0.695/(N + 0.390)\big] & \text{otherwise} \end{cases}$$

where d_i is the depth of the letter value. The corresponding pseudosigma is obtained as the ratio of the spread to $-2z_i$ (Hoaglin 1985, 431).

Define $(F_l, F_u) = x_{[f]}$. The inner fence has cutoffs $F_l - \frac{3}{2}(F_u - F_l)$ and $F_u + \frac{3}{2}(F_u - F_l)$. The outer fence has cutoffs $F_l - 3(F_u - F_l)$ and $F_u + 3(F_u - F_l)$.

The inner fence values reported by lv are almost exactly equal to those used by **graph, box** to identify outside points. The only difference is that **graph** uses a slightly different definition of fourths; namely, the 25th and 75th percentiles as defined by **summarize**.

References

Emerson, J. D. and M. A. Stoto. 1983. Transforming data. In *Understanding Robust and Exploratory Data Analysis*, ed. D. C. Hoaglin, F. Mosteller, and J. W. Tukey, 97–128. New York: John Wiley & Sons.

Fox, J. 1990. Describing univariate distributions. In *Modern Methods of Data Analysis*, ed. J. Fox and J. S. Long, 58–125. Newbury Park, CA: Sage Publications.

Hamilton, L. C. 1991. sed4: Resistant normality check and outlier identification. *Stata Technical Bulletin* 3: 15–18. Reprinted in *Stata Technical Bulletin Reprints*, vol. 1, pp. 86–90.

Hoaglin, D. C. 1983. Letter values: a set of selected order statistics. In *Understanding Robust and Exploratory Data Analysis*, ed. D. C. Hoaglin, F. Mosteller, and J. W. Tukey, 33–57. New York: John Wiley & Sons.

——. 1985. Using quantiles to study shape. In *Exploring Data Tables, Trends, and Shapes*, ed. D. C. Hoaglin, F. Mosteller, and J. W. Tukey, 417–460. New York: John Wiley & Sons.

Hoaglin, D. C., B. Iglewicz, and J. W. Tukey. 1981. Small-sample performance of a resistant rule for outlier detection. *1980 Proceedings of the Statistical Computing Section*, 144–152. Washington, D.C.: American Statistical Association.

——. 1986. Performance of some resistant rules for outlier labeling. *Journal of the American Statistical Association* 81: 991–999.

Tukey, J. W. 1977. *Exploratory Data Analysis*. Reading, MA: Addison-Wesley Publishing Company.

Also See

[R] **diagplots**, [R] **graph box**, [R] **stem**, [R] **summarize**

Title

macro — Macro definition and manipulation

Syntax

<u>gl</u>obal *mname* [=*exp* | :*extended_fcn* | " [*string*] "]

<u>loca</u>l *lclname* [=*exp* | :*extended_fcn* | " [*string*] "]

tempvar *lclname* [*lclname* [...]]

tempname *lclname* [*lclname* [...]]

tempfile *lclname* [*lclname* [...]]

<u>ma</u>cro <u>dir</u>

<u>ma</u>cro <u>drop</u> { *mname* [*mname* [...]] | *mname*∗ | _all }

<u>ma</u>cro <u>l</u>ist [*mname* [*mname* [...]] | _all]

<u>ma</u>cro <u>sh</u>ift [#]

where *extended_fcn* is any of

{ <u>type</u> | <u>f</u>ormat | <u>val</u>ue <u>l</u>abel | <u>var</u>iable <u>l</u>abel } *varname*

char { *varname*[[*charname*]] | _dta[[*charname*]] }

<u>di</u>splay ...   (see [R] **display**)

<u>e</u>nvironment *name*

<u>l</u>abel *valuelabelname* #

log [on]

<u>row</u>names(*matrixname*) | <u>col</u>names(*matrixname*)

<u>row</u>eq(*matrixname*) | <u>col</u>eq(*matrixname*)

set { adosize | beep | display linesize | display pagesize | graphics | level |

    log linesize | log pagesize | matsize | more | rmsg | textsize | trace |

    type | virtual }

<u>sort</u>edby

<u>tempvar</u> | <u>tempfile</u>

word count *string*

word # of *string*

Description

global assigns strings to specified global macro names (*mnames*).

local assigns strings to local macro names (*lclnames*).

tempvar assigns names to the specified local macro names that may be used as temporary variable names in the dataset. When the program or do-file concludes, any variables in the dataset with these assigned names are dropped.

tempname assigns names to the specified local macro names that may be used as temporary scalar or matrix names. When the program or do-file concludes, any scalars or matrices in the dataset with these assigned names are dropped.

tempfile assigns names to the specified local macro names that may be used as names for temporary files. When the program or do-file concludes, any datasets created with these assigned names are erased.

Remarks

Remarks are presented under the headings

> Formal definition of a macro
> Global and local macro names
> Macro assignment
> Macro extended functions for extracting data attributes
> Macro extended functions related to matrices
> Macro extended functions for formatting results
> Macro extended functions for working with value labels
> Macro extended functions for parsing
> Macro extended functions for accessing Stata system parameters
> Macro extended functions for accessing operating-system parameters
> The tempvar, tempname, and tempfile commands
> Temporary variables
> Temporary scalars and matrices
> Temporary files
> Manipulation of macros
> Macros as arguments: macro shift

Macros are a tool used in programming Stata and this entry assumes you have read [U] **24 Programming Stata** and especially [U] **24.3 Macros**. This entry concerns advanced issues not previously covered. Also, for your convenience, a table of the predefined system macros can be found in [R] **macro system**.

Formal definition of a macro

A *macro* has a *macro name* and *macro contents*. Everywhere a punctuated macro name appears in a command—punctuation is defined below—the macro contents are substituted for the macro name.

Macros come in two types, called global and local macros. Macro names are up to 8 characters long for global macros and 7 characters long for local macros. The contents of global macros are defined with the global command and local macros with the local command. Global macros are just that. Local macros exist solely within the program or do-file in which they are defined. If that program or do-file calls another program or do-file, the local macros previously defined temporarily cease to exist and their existence is reestablished when the calling program regains control. When a program or do-file ends, its local macros are permanently deleted.

To substitute the macro contents of a global macro name, the macro name is typed (punctuated) with a dollar sign ($) in front. To substitute the macro contents of a local macro name, the macro name is typed (punctuated) with surrounding left and right single quotes (` ´). In either case, braces ({ }) can be used to clarify meaning and form nested constructions. When the contents of an undefined macro are substituted, the macro name (and punctuation) are removed and nothing is substituted in its place.

For example:

The input ...	Means the same as ...
| ```
global a "myvar"
gen $a = oldvar
gen a = oldvar
``` | ```
gen myvar = oldvar
gen a = oldvar
``` |
| ```
local a "myvar"
gen `a´ = oldvar
gen a = oldvar
``` | ```
gen myvar = oldvar
gen a = oldvar
``` |
| ```
global a "newvar"
global i = 2
gen $a$i = oldvar
``` | ```
gen newvar2 = oldvar
``` |
| ```
local a "newvar"
local i = 2
gen `a´`i´ = oldvar
``` | ```
gen newvar2 = oldvar
``` |
| ```
global b1 "newvar"
global i=1
gen ${b$i} = oldvar
``` | ```
gen newvar = oldvar
``` |
| ```
local b1 "newvar"
local i=1
gen `b`i´´ = oldvar
``` | ```
gen newvar = oldvar
``` |
| ```
global b1 "newvar"
global a "b"
global i = 1
gen ${$a$i} = oldvar
``` | ```
gen newvar = oldvar
``` |
| ```
local b1 "newvar"
local a "b"
local i = 1
gen ``a´`i´´ = oldvar
``` | ```
gen newvar = oldvar
``` |

Global and local macro names

What we next say is an exceedingly fine point: Global macro names that begin with an underscore are really local macros; this is why local macro names can have only 7 characters. The command `local` is formally defined as equivalent to `global _`. Thus, the following are equivalent:

```
local x                      global _x
local i=1                    global _i=1
local name "Bill"            global _name "Bill"
local fmt : format myvar     global _fmt : format myvar
local 3 `2´                  global _3 $_2
```

`tempvar` is formally defined as equivalent to `local` *name* : `tempvar` for each name specified after `tempvar`. Thus,

```
tempvar a b c
```

is equivalent to

```
local a : tempvar
local b : tempvar
local c : tempvar
```

which in turn is equivalent to

```
global _a : tempvar
global _b : tempvar
global _c : tempvar
```

`tempfile` is defined similarly.

Macro assignment

When you type

```
. local name "something"
```

that *something* becomes the contents of the macro. When you type

```
. local name = something
```

that *something* is evaluated as an expression and the result becomes the contents of the macro. Note the presence and lack of the equals sign. That is, if you type

```
. local problem "2+2"
. local result = 2+2
```

then `problem` contains 2+2 whereas `result` contains 4.

Finally, when you type

```
. local name : something
```

that *something* is interpreted as an extended macro function. (Note the colon rather than nothing or the equals sign.) Of course, all of this applies to `global` as well as `local`.

Macro extended functions for extracting data attributes

The macro extended functions `type`, `format`, `value label`, `variable label`, and `sortedby` obtain attributes from the dataset in memory. Below we demonstrate these macros interactively so you can see what it is they return. These functions, and macros in general, become useful when used in programs.

```
. describe
Contains data from employee.dta
  obs:           1
  vars:          3                          31 May 1996 12:27
  size:         30 (99.9% of memory free)
-------------------------------------------------------------------------
   1. name       str18   %18s                 Employee name
   2. sex        float   %9.0g      sexlbl
   3. age        float   %9.0g
-------------------------------------------------------------------------
Sorted by:
. global tofname : type name
. display "$tofname"
```

```
str18
. local fmt : format age
. display "`fmt'"
%9.0g
. local vl : value label sex
. display "`vl'"
sexlbl
. local lbl : variable label name
. display "`lbl'"
Employee name
. sort name age
. local sl : sortedby
. display "`sl'"
name age
```

The macro extended function `char` transfers information from characteristics (see [U] **19.8 Characteristics**) to macros:

```
. local tvar : char _dta[tis]
. display "`tvar'"
curyear
. local x : char mpg[note]
. display "mpg[note] is |`x'|"
mpg[note] is ||
```

Notice that when a characteristic is undefined, requesting its contents is not an error.

Macro extended functions related to matrices

The functions `rownames()`, `colnames()`, `roweq()`, and `coleq()` obtain the specified information about the specified matrix; see [R] **matrix define**.

Macro extended functions for formatting results

The `display` command allows you to display formatted output; see [R] **display (for programmers)**. The `display` extended function is the `display` command except that the output is rerouted, appearing not on the screen, but being placed into the contents of a macro. Using `display`, you can format things appearing in macros.

```
. local x = sqrt(2)
. display "`x'"                      /* as string to see entire contents */
1.414213562373095
. display %9.4f sqrt(2)              /* since you can do this */
   1.4142
. local y : display %9.4f sqrt(2)    /* you can do this, too */
. display "`y'"
   1.4142
. local z : display "sqrt(2) = " _col(14) %9.4f sqrt(2)
. display "`z'"
sqrt(2) =      1.4142
```

You can use all the features of `display` that make sense, which is to say, you may not set the colors with in *color* because macros do not have colors, may not use `_continue` to suppress going to a new line on the real display (it is not being displayed), may not use `_newline` (for the same reason), may not use `_quote` (macros may not contain double quote characters, a poor feature), and may not use `_request` to obtain input from the console (because input and output have nothing to do with macro definition). With those exceptions, everything else works. See [R] **display (for programmers)**.

Macro extended functions for working with value labels

The macro extended function `value label` returns the name of a value label associated with a variable. In the example below, variable q2 is associated with the value label named yesno. Variable age has no associated value label:

```
. local vname1 : value label q2
. local vname2 : value label age
. display "vname1 contains `vname1´ and vname2 contains `vname2´
vname1 contains yesno and vname2 contains
```

Notice that in the case of `age`, macro `vname2` contains `""`; variable `age` has no associated value label.

The macro extended function `label` returns the labeling associated with a numeric value. Assume value label yesno associates 0 with no and 1 with yes:

```
. local x : label yesno 0
. display "`x´"
no
. local y : label yesno 3
. display "`y´"
3
```

Since the label yesno does not map 3, the 3 itself was returned in the last case.

Macro extended functions for parsing

`word count` counts the number of "words" (defined as sequence of characters separated by blanks) in a string. `word # of` extracts the #th word. In both cases, the string must not be enclosed in double quotes:

```
. local phrase "this is a test"
. local n : word count `phrase´
. display "n = " `n´
n = 4
. local second : word 2 of `phrase´
. display "The second word is `second´"
The second word is is
```

Macro extended functions for accessing Stata system parameters

The set macro extended function obtains current settings (the ones set by set and shown by query). For instance, we could obtain the current value of matsize:

```
. local x : set matsize
. display "`x'"
40
```

The log on and log functions return the current logging status.

```
. local x : log on
. display "`x'"
off
. log using myfile
. local x : log on
. display "`x'"
on
. local fn : log
. display "`fn'"
C:\data\myfile.log
```

Macro extended functions for accessing operating-system parameters

The Windows, DOS, and Unix operating systems have the concept of environment variables. The macro extended function environment imports their contents into Stata's macros. Here is an example from Windows:

```
. local x: environment TEMP
. display "`x'"
C:\TEMP
```

And here is one from Unix:

```
. local x: environment HOME
. display "`x'"
/home/wwg
```

The tempvar, tempname, and tempfile commands

The tempvar, tempname, and tempfile commands generate names that may be used for temporary variables, temporary scalars and matrices, and temporary files. A temporary something is a something that exists while the program or do-file is running but, once it concludes, ceases to exist automatically.

Temporary variables

You are writing a program and, in the middle of it, you need to calculate a new variable equal to $var1^2 + var2^2$ for use in the calculation. You might be tempted to write

```
( code omitted )
gen sumsq = var1^2 + var2^2
( code continues )
( code uses sumsq in subsequent calculations )
drop sumsq
```

This would be a poor idea. First, users of your program might already have a variable called `sumsq` and if they did, your program will break at the `generate` statement with the error "sumsq already defined". Second, your program in the subsequent code might call some other program, and perhaps that program (poorly) attempts to also create a variable `sumsq`. Third, even if nothing goes wrong, if users press *Break* after your code had executed the `generate` but before the `drop`, you would leave behind the `sumsq` variable, confusing them.

The way around these problems is to use temporary variables. Your code should read:

```
( code omitted )
tempvar sumsq
gen `sumsq´ = var1^2 + var2^2
( code continues )
( code uses `sumsq´  in subsequent calculations )
( you do not bother to drop `sumsq´ )
```

The `tempvar sumsq` command created a local macro called `sumsq` and stored in it a name that is different from any name currently in the data. Subsequently, you then use `sumsq´ with single quotes around it rather than `sumsq` in your calculation, so that rather than calling your temporary variable `sumsq`, you are calling it whatever Stata wants you to call it. With that small change, your program works just as before.

Another advantage to temporary variables is that you do not have to drop them—Stata will do that for you when your program terminates and Stata will do that regardless of the reason for your program terminating. So, if users press *Break* after the `generate`, your program is stopped, the temporary variables dropped, and things really are just as if the user had never run your program in the first place.

❏ Technical Note

So what do these temporary variable names assigned by Stata look like? It should not matter to you; however they look, they are guaranteed to be unique (`tempvar` will not hand out the same name to more than one program concurrently executing). Nevertheless, to satisfy your curiosity:

```
. tempvar var1 var2
. display "`var1´ `var2´"
__000057 __000058
```

Although we reveal the style of the names created by `tempvar`, you should not depend on this style. All that is important is

1. The names are unique; they differ from one call to the next.

2. You should assume that they are so long that you cannot prefix or suffix them with additional characters and make use of them.

3. Stata keeps track of any names created by `tempvar` and, when the program or do-file ends, searches the data for those names. Any variables found with those names are automatically dropped. This happens regardless of whether your program ends with an error.

❏

Temporary scalars and matrices

`tempname` is the equivalent of `tempvar` for obtaining names for scalars and matrices. This use is explained, with examples, in [R] **scalar**.

❑ Technical Note

The temporary names created by `tempname` look just like those created by `tempvar`. The same cautions and features apply to `tempname` as `tempvar`:

1. The names are unique; they differ from one call to the next.

2. You should assume that they are so long that you cannot prefix or suffix them with additional characters and make use of them.

3. Stata keeps track of any names created by `tempname` and, when the program or do-file ends, searches for scalars or matrices with those names. Any scalars or matrices so found are automatically dropped; see [R] **scalar**. This happens regardless of whether your program ends with an error.

❑

Temporary files

`tempfile` is the equivalent of `tempvar` for obtaining names for disk files. Before getting into that, let us discuss how you should not use `tempfile`. Sometimes, in the midst of your program, you will find it necessary to destroy the user's data to obtain your desired result. You do not want to change the data, but it cannot be helped, and therefore you would like to arrange things so that the user's original data is restored at the conclusion of your program.

In such a case, you might be tempted to save the user's data in a (temporary) file, do your damage, and then restore the data. You can do this, but it is complicated because you then have to worry about the user pressing *Break* after you have stored the data, done the damage, but have not yet restored it. Working with `capture` (see [R] **capture**), you can program all of this, but you do not have to. Stata's `preserve` command (see [R] **preserve**) will handle saving the user's data and, however your program concludes, restoring it.

Still, there may be times when you need temporary files. As our example:

```
( code omitted )
preserve                        /* preserve user's data */
keep var1 var2 xvar
save master, replace
drop var2
save part1, replace
use master, clear
drop var1
rename var2 var1
append using part1
erase master.dta
erase part1.dta
( code continues )
```

This is poor code even though it does use `preserve` so that, no matter how this code concludes, the user's original data will be brought back. It is poor because datasets called `master.dta` and `part1.dta` might already exist and, if they do, this program will replace the user's (assumedly valuable) data. It is also poor because, if the user presses *Break* before both (temporary) datasets are erased, they will be left behind consuming (assumedly valuable) disk space.

Here is how the code should read:

```
( code omitted )
preserve                          /* preserve user's data */
keep var1 var2 xvar
tempfile master part1             /* declare temporary files */
save `master'
drop var2
save `part1'
use `master', clear
drop var1
rename var2 var1
append using `part1'
( code continues, temporary files are not erased )
```

In this draft, Stata was asked to provide the names of temporary files in local macros named `master` and `part1`. We then put single quotes around `master` and `part1` wherever we referred to them so that, rather than using the names `master` and `part1`, we used the names Stata handed us. At the end of our program, we no longer bother to erase the temporary files. Since Stata gave us the temporary filenames, it knows they are temporary and will erase them for us and it will do this whether our program completes, has an error, or the user presses *Break*.

❑ Technical Note

So what do the temporary filenames look like? Again, it should not matter to you, but for the curious:

```
. tempfile file1 file2
. display "`file1' `file2'"
/tmp/St17854.00003 /tmp/St17854.00004
```

We were using the Unix version of Stata; had we been using the DOS or Windows version, the last line might read:

```
. display "`file1' `file2'"
C:\WIN\TEMP\__000003.tmp C:\WIN\TEMP\__000004.tmp
```

Under DOS and Windows, Stata uses the environment variable `TEMP` to determine where temporary files are to be located. This variable is typically set in your `autoexec.bat` file. Ours is set to `C:\WIN\TEMP`. If the variable is not defined, Stata locates temporary files in your current directory.

Under Unix, Stata uses the environment variable `TMPDIR` to determine where temporary files are to be located. If the variable is not defined, Stata locates temporary files in `/tmp`.

Although we reveal the style of the names created by `tempfile`, just as with `tempvar`, you should not depend on it. `tempfile` produces names the operating system finds pleasing and all that is important is

1. The names are unique; they differ from one call to the next.

2. You should assume that they are so long that you cannot prefix or suffix them with additional characters and make use of them.

3. Stata keeps track of any names created by `tempfile` and, when your program or do-file ends, looks for files with those names. Any files found are automatically erased. This happens regardless of whether your program ends with an error.

Actually, item 3 is true only for version 3.1 and above. If you set the version to a lower number (see [R] **version**), then item 3 should read: "You, as the programmer, are responsible for removing any temporary files—they are not automatically deleted". We turn off this feature in case some old, user-written programs depended on files being left around.   ❑

Manipulation of macros

macro dir and macro list list the names and contents of all defined macros; both do the same thing:

```
. macro list
_file2:    /tmp/St17854.00004
_file1:    /tmp/St17854.00003
_var2:     __000058
_var1:     __000057
_lbl:      Employee name
_vl:       sexlbl
_fmt:      %9.0g
tofname:   str18
S_FN:      employee.dta
tofmake:   str18
F1:        help
F2:        #review;
F3:        describe;
F7:        save
F8:        use
S_ADO:     /usr/local/stata/ado;/usr/local/ado;~/ado;.
S_FLAVOR:  Intercooled
S_OS:      Unix
S_MACH:    PC
S_level    95
```

macro drop eliminates macros from memory, although it is rarely used since typically most macros are local and automatically disappear when the program ends. Macros can also be eliminated by defining their contents to be nothing using global or local, but macro drop is more convenient.

Typing macro drop *base** drops all global macros whose names begin with *base*.

Typing macro drop _all eliminates all macros except system macros—macros that begin with an "S_".

▷ Example

```
. macro drop _file* _var* _lbl _vl _fmt tofname
. macro list
S_FN:      employee.dta
tofmake:   str18
F1:        help
F2:        #review;
F3:        describe;
F7:        save
F8:        use
S_ADO:     /usr/local/stata/ado;/usr/local/ado;~/ado;.
S_FLAVOR:  Intercooled
S_OS:      Unix
S_MACH:    PC
S_level    95

.macro drop tofmake
.macro list
S_FN:      employee.dta
F1:        help
F2:        #review;
F3:        describe;
F7:        save
F8:        use
```

```
S_ADO:      /usr/local/stata/ado;/usr/local/ado;~/ado;.
S_FLAVOR:   Intercooled
S_OS:       Unix
S_MACH:     PC
S_level     95

. macro drop _all

. macro list
S_FN:       employee.dta
S_ADO:      /usr/local/stata/ado;/usr/local/ado;~/ado;.
S_FLAVOR:   Intercooled
S_OS:       Unix
S_MACH:     PC
S_level     95
```

◁

❏ Technical Note

Stata usually requires you to explicitly drop something before redefining it. For instance, before redefining a value label with the **label define** command or redefining a program with the **program define** command, you must type **label drop** or **program drop**. This way you are protected from accidentally replacing something that might require considerable effort to reproduce.

Macros, however, may be redefined freely. It is *not* necessary to **drop** a macro before redefining it. Macros typically consist of short strings that could be easily reproduced if necessary. The inconvenience of the protection is not justified by the small benefit.

❏

Macros as arguments: macro shift

To understand **macro shift**, you must first understand how arguments are passed to programs. This was explained in [U] **24.3 Macros**, but here is a more formal definition.

The arguments to a do-file or program are parsed on blanks and assigned to the local macros `` `1´ ``, `` `2´ ``, and so on. There is no limit to the number of arguments. Before the do-file or program is invoked, all local macros are saved (pushed) and the new definitions established. At the termination of the do-file or program, currently defined local macros are discarded and the originally defined local macros are restored (popped). Thus, even if programs call other programs, local macros provide guaranteed local storage.

The construct `` `*´ `` can be used as an abbreviation for `` `1´ `` `` `2´ `` *etc.*, all arguments strung together with a single blank in between. For instance **myprog this that what** receives three arguments, `` `1´ `` (this), `` `2´ `` (that), and `` `3´ `` (what). `` `*´ `` is this that what.

When arguments are originally parsed, tokens are bound by double quotes and then double quotes are stripped. For example, **myprog this "that what" else** receives three arguments, `` `1´ `` (this), `` `2´ `` (that what), and `` `3´ `` (else). `` `*´ `` is this that what else.

Arguments may be reparsed by programs or do-files using the **parse** command; see [R] **parse**.

macro shift discards `` `1´ ``, shifts `` `2´ `` to `` `1´ ``, `` `3´ `` to `` `2´ ``, and so on. For instance, if `` `1´ `` is this, `` `2´ `` that, and `` `3´ `` what, after **macro shift**, `` `1´ `` is that, `` `2´ `` is what, and `` `3´ `` is null.

macro shift is often used in program constructs of the sort:

```
while "`1´"~="" {
        do something based on `1´
        macro shift
}
```

or equivalently

```
local i = 1
while "``i´´"~="" {
        do something based on ``i´´
        local i=`i´+1
}
```

This second form is slightly faster than the first.

macro shift # performs multiple macro shifts or, if # is 0, none at all. That is, macro shift 2 is equivalent to two macro shift commands. macro shift 0 does nothing at all.

Also See

[U] **19.8 Characteristics**, [U] **24 Programming Stata**

[R] **char**, [R] **macro system**, [R] **parse**, [R] **scalar**

Title

---

macro estimation — Quick reference for estimation macros

Description

This entry provides a quick reference for estimation macros. See [U] **24.3.9 Built-in global system macros** for details on the system macros.

Remarks

See [U] **24.3 Macros** for an introduction to macros.
See [U] **24.11 Saving estimation results** for an description of the macros listed below.
See [R] **macro** for advanced issues not covered in [U] **24.3 Macros**.
See [R] **macro system** for a list of system macros.

Macros that begin with the characters S_E_ are called *estimation macros*. Although they may be defined to anything that you wish, to ensure that your commands work with Stata's post-estimation commands, such as lrtest, linktest, etc., we recommend that you use these definitions:

Estimation macro	Definition
S_E_cmd	name of estimation command
S_E_depv	name of dependent variable
S_E_exp	weight expression if weight specified
S_E_if	if *exp* if specified
S_E_in	in *range* if specified
S_E_ll	log-likelihood value
S_E_mdf	model degrees of freedom
S_E_neq	number of equations (if multiple-equation model)
S_E_nobs	number of observations
S_E_tdf	residual degrees of freedom
S_E_vce	text to appear above standard errors in estimation output; typically, "Robust" or ""
S_E_cvn	cluster variable name
S_E_cn	number of clusters
S_E_wgt	weight type if weight specified

Understand that not all estimation commands define all of the above and many estimation commands define S_E_ macros not listed above. The standard is merely that if an estimation command defines one of the names listed above, its contents correspond to the definition listed. All estimation commands are required to define S_E_cmd.

Also See

[U] **24.3 Macros**, [U] **24.11 Saving estimation results**

[R] **macro**, [R] **macro system**

Title

macro system — Quick reference for system macros

Description

This entry provides a quick reference for system macros. See [U] **24.3.9 Built-in global system macros** for details on the system macros.

Remarks

See [U] **24.3 Macros** for an introduction to macros.
See [R] **macro** for advanced issues not covered in [U] **24.3 Macros**.
See [R] **macro estimation** for a list of estimation macros.

Macros that begin with the characters S_ are called *system macros* and some are predefined for you:

System macro	Definition
S_ADO	path over which Stata looks for its ado-files
S_DATE	11-character string expressing date
S_FLAVOR	"Small" or "Intercooled"
S_FN	filename last specified with a `use` or `save`
S_FNDATE	date and time the file in S_FN was last saved
S_level	significance level for confidence intervals
S_MACH	type of computer
S_MODE	(Unix only) indicates if in batch mode
S_NOFKEY	indicates whether Stata can change *F*-key definitions
S_OS	name of operating system
S_OSDTL	level of operating system, if significant
S_TIME	8-character string expressing current time

Also See

[U] **24.3 Macros**

[R] **macro**, [R] **macro estimation**

Title

mark — Mark observations for inclusion

Syntax

> mark *newmarkvar* [*weight*] [if *exp*] [in *range*]
>
> markout *markvar* [*varlist*] [, <u>s</u>trok]

aweights, fweights, pweights and iweights are allowed; see [U] **18.1.6 weight**.

Description

mark and markout are for use in Stata programs.

mark creates *newmarkvar*, a **byte** variable, containing 0's and 1's. Observations meeting the if, in, and having nonzero weight will have *newmarkvar* set to 1; the remaining observations will be set to 0. Weights, if specified, are checked for sensibleness (not negative unless iweights, integers if fweights) and the appropriate error message issued if not.

markout resets 1's in a marking variable created by mark to contain 0 wherever any of the variables in *varlist* contain missing values. String variables are treated as if they contain missing values unless option strok is specified.

Options

strok specifies that string variables are allowable in *varlist*. If strok is not specified and string variables appear in *varlist*, all observations will be marked out; the result is as if the string variable contained nothing but missing values which, viewed numerically, they do. markout without strok is used to process *varlist*s where each variable is expected to be numeric.

strok specifies that string variables in *varlist*, if any, are to be treated in the same way as numeric variables; that is, whether they contain missing is based on their contents. Under this interpretation, a string variable contains missing where it contains "" (null string) and is otherwise said to contain a nonmissing value. Only observations for which any of the variables, numeric or string, actually contain missing are marked out.

Remarks

By far the most common programming error—made by us and others—is to use different samples at different parts of a Stata program. We strongly recommend that programmers identify the sample at the outset of the program. mark and markout make this easy. Consider a Stata program that begins

```
program define myprog
        version 5.0
        local varlist "required existing"
        local if "optional"
        local in "optional"
        parse "`*'"
        ( program continues )
```

421

Pretend this Stata program continues to make a statistical calculation based on the observations specified in the varlist that do not contain missing values (such as a linear regression). The program must identify the observations that it is to use. Moreover, since the user can specify if or in, these restrictions, too, must be taken into account. mark and markout make this easy:

```
( myprog, continued from above )
tempvar touse
mark `touse' `if' `in'
markout `touse' `varlist'
( program continues )
```

The mark command creates a (temporary) variable `touse` (temporary because of the preceding tempvar; see [R] **macro**) based on the if and in. If there is no if or in, `touse` will contain 1 for every observation in the data. If if wgt>1000 was specified by the user, only observations for which wgt is greater than 1,000 have touse set to 1; the remaining have touse set to zero.

The markout command updates the `touse` marker created by mark. For observations for which touse is 1—observations that might potentially be used—the variables in the user-specified varlist are checked for missing values. If such an observation has any of the variables in the varlist equal to missing, the observation's touse value is reset to 0.

Thus, observations to be used all have `touse` set to 1; including if `touse` at the end of statistical or data-management commands will restrict the command to operate on the appropriate sample.

▷ Example

Let's write a program to do the same thing as summarize except that our program will engage in casewise deletion—if an observation has a missing value in any of the variables, it is to be excluded from all the calculations.

```
program define cwsumm
        version 5.0
        local varlist "optional"
        local if "optional"
        local in "optional"
        local weight "aweight fweight"
        local options "Detail noFormat"
        parse "`*'"
        tempvar touse
        mark `touse' `if' `in' [`weight'`exp']
        markout `touse' `varlist'
        summarize `varlist' [`weight'`exp'] if `touse', `detail' `format'
end
```

◁

▷ Example

We want to write a command, fsumm, for use after fit that reports the means of all the variables used in the estimation.

[R] **fit** reports that fit saves the original varlist (dependent and independent variables) in S_E_vl, saves the original if and in (if any) in S_E_if and S_E_in, and the weight type and expression for the weight (if any) in S_E_wgt and S_E_exp. Finally, fit saves its own name in S_E_cmd. Thus

```
program define fsumm
        version 5.0
        if "$S_E_cmd"~="fit" { error 301 }
        if "`*´"~="" { error 198 }
        tempvar touse
        mark `touse´ $S_E_if $S_E_in [$S_E_wgt $S_E_exp]
        markout `touse´ $S_E_vl
        summarize $S_E_vl [$S_E_wgt $S_E_exp] if `touse´
end
```

As an alternative, if we did write cwsumm in the first example, we could write

```
program define fsumm
        version 5.0
        if "$S_E_cmd"~="fit" { error 301 }
        if "`*´"~="" { error 198 }
        cwsumm $S_E_vl [$S_E_wgt $S_E_exp] $S_E_if $S_E_in
end
```

◁

Also See

Title

> **matrix** — Introduction to matrix commands

Description

This entry provides an overview of the **matrix** command for defining and manipulating matrices.

Remarks

Matrices can be used interactively in Stata and one might do so, for instance, in a teaching situation. The real power of matrices, however, is unleashed when they are used in Stata programs and ado-files to implement other statistical procedures. We do this ourselves and you can, too.

First, let's define the word matrix since Stata's definition includes a few details that go beyond the mathematics. To Stata, a matrix is a named entity containing an $r \times c$ ($r > 0$, $c > 0$) rectangular array of double-precision numbers, none of which can be missing, which is bordered by a row and column of names.

```
. matrix list A
A[3,2]
     c1  c2
r1    1   2
r2    3   4
r3    5   6
```

In this case, we have a 3×2 matrix named **A** containing elements 1, 2, 3, 4, 5, and 6. Row 1, column 2 (written $A_{1,2}$ in math and **A[1,2]** in Stata) contains 2. The two columns are named **c1** and **c2** and the three rows **r1**, **r2**, and **r3**. These are the default names Stata comes up with when it cannot do better; generally, Stata can do better. The names do not play a role in the mathematics, but they are of great help when it comes to labeling the output.

The names are operated on just as the numbers. For instance:

```
. matrix B=A´*A
. matrix list B
symmetric B[2,2]
     c1  c2
c1   35
c2   44  56
```

We defined $\mathbf{B} = \mathbf{A}'\mathbf{A}$. Note that the row and column names of $\mathbf{B}$ are the same. Multiplication is defined for any $a \times b$ and $b \times c$ matrices, the result being $a \times c$. Thus, the row and column names of the result are the row names of the first matrix and the column names of the second matrix. We formed $\mathbf{A}'\mathbf{A}$, using the transpose of $\mathbf{A}$ for the first matrix—which also interchanged the names—and so obtained the names shown.

▷ Example

In what sense are the names above "correct"? Let's do something more meaningful using another yet-to-be-introduced command. Let $\mathbf{X}$ be the matrix of prices and mileage ratings in the automobile data. The rows are observations on particular cars and the columns are the two variables **price** and **mpg**. Let us form $\mathbf{X}'\mathbf{X}$:

```
. use auto, clear
(1978 Automobile Data)
. matrix accum XX = price mpg, nocons
(obs=74)
. matrix list XX
symmetric XX[2,2]
              price        mpg
price     3.448e+09
  mpg       9132716      36008
```

The names are correct in the sense that the (1,1) element is the sum of squares of `price` and, for instance, the (1,2) element the sum of the interaction of `price` and `mpg` across the observations.

Researchers have long realized that matrix notation simplifies the description of complex calculations. What they may not have realized is that, corresponding to each mathematical definition of a matrix operator, there is a definition of the operator's effect on the names that can be used to carry the names forward through long and complex matrix calculations.

◁

More on names

The names that border the matrices actually have two parts, called equation names and subnames. These two parts are separated by a colon; the examples we have seen so far have only subnames. Matrix rows and columns always have names, and those names always consist of at least a subname. For instance, a row might be named `myrow`, in which case the subname is `myrow` and the equation name is blank, or, it might be named `myeq:myrow`, in which case the equation name is `myeq` and the subname is `myrow`.

Why the term equation name? Because groups of rows and columns of a matrix (think partitioned matrix) often correspond to an underlying equation. In multinomial logistic regression, for instance, there is an equation for each outcome (actually, each outcome except one) and each of those equations contains parameters for each of the variables. It would be natural, in that case, to set the equation names corresponding to the outcome and the subnames corresponding to the variables. `out2:mpg` would refer to something to do with `mpg` in the outcome `out2`, while `out3:mpg` would be related, but refer to the third outcome.

▷ Example

Stata's matrix commands are smart about carrying around these names; if they are set right at the outset of the problem, they will be right at the end. So, let's just show you that you can override the default naming conventions and set the names however you want; here we will use the unintroduced function $J(r,c,z)$ to create an $r \times c$ matrix containing elements z:

```
. matrix A=J(2,3,0)
. matrix list A
A[2,3]
     c1   c2   c3
r1    0    0    0
r2    0    0    0
. matrix rownames A = rows:price mpg
. matrix colnames A = price mpg weight
. matrix list A
A[2,3]
```

```
                  price    mpg  weight
   rows:price         0      0       0
         mpg          0      0       0
. matrix colnames A = eq1:
. matrix list A
A[2,3]
                   eq1:   eq1:    eq1:
                  price    mpg  weight
   rows:price         0      0       0
         mpg          0      0       0
```

See [R] **matrix rowname** for more information.

◁

▷ Example

What is done with the names? Since in statistical contexts matrices are often used to obtain estimates, Stata's output routines exploit the information to label the output. Watch:

```
. matrix accum YXX = price weight mpg
(obs=74)
. local nobs = _result(1)
. local nvar = rowsof(YXX)
. local nvarm1 = `nvar' - 1
. matrix XX = YXX[2...,2...]
. matrix Xy = YXX[1,2...]
. matrix XXi = syminv(XX)
. matrix b = Xy * XXi
. matrix pv = b * Xy'
. local df = `nobs' - `nvarm1'
. scalar rv = (YXX[1,1] - pv[1,1])/`df'
. matrix V = XXi * rv
. matrix post b V, dof(`df') obs(`nobs') depname(price)
. matrix mlout
------------------------------------------------------------------------------
     price |      Coef.   Std. Err.        t    P>|t|     [95% Conf. Interval]
-----------+------------------------------------------------------------------
    weight |   1.746559   .6413538      2.723   0.008      .4677361    3.025382
       mpg |  -49.51222   86.15604     -0.575   0.567     -221.3025     122.278
     _cons |   1946.069    3597.05      0.541   0.590     -5226.244    9118.382
------------------------------------------------------------------------------
```

Of course, nobody would ever interactively type all of those commands and there would be no reason to even write the program—using `fit` or `regress` is easier. Notice, however, the next to last command—the `post`. Given a coefficient vector and a covariance matrix, it posts the results to Stata's internal areas as an estimation result. All post-estimation commands now work: `correlate` can be used to review the covariance matrix of the estimators; `_b[]` and `_se[]` can be used to fetch coefficients and their standard errors; `predict` can be used to calculate linear predictions and the standard error of the prediction; and `test` can be used to test linear hypotheses about the coefficients. The `matrix mlout` command—which one would typically bury in an ado-file—displays the coefficient table. Note that, based on the names bordering the matrices—all of which were automatically determined by Stata at the outset and then carried through the calculation—`mlout` was able to produce appropriately labeled output. See [R] **matrix post**.

◁

Accessing Stata's built-in, internal matrices

Many of Stata's built-in routines (such as **regress** or **factor**) leave behind matrices they have built during their calculations. These can be useful to advanced programmers who wish to build upon these results. Accessing such matrices is described in [R] **matrix get**.

▷ Example

When we issued the **matrix post** command in the previous example, our two matrices **b** and **V** were taken over by Stata—they no longer exist:

```
. matrix list b
b not found
r(111);
```

The **get()** function, however, allows programs access to all of Stata's internal matrices, even ones we have posted ourselves:

```
. matrix b = get(_b)
. matrix list b
b[1,3]
        weight         mpg       _cons
y1    1.7465592   -49.512221   1946.0687
. matrix V = get(VCE)
. matrix list V
symmetric V[3,3]
             weight         mpg       _cons
weight    .41133468
   mpg    44.601659    7422.863
 _cons   -2191.9032   -292759.82   12938766
```

get() can be used to obtain copies of results posted by ado-files or Stata's internal commands.

◁

Vectors and scalars

Stata does not have vectors—they are considered special cases of matrices and are handled by the **matrix** command.

Stata does have scalars, although they are not strictly necessary because they, too, could be handled as special cases. See [R] **scalar** for a description of scalars.

Naming conventions in programs

If you are writing Stata programs or ado-files using matrices, you may have some matrices you wish to leave behind for other programs to build upon, but you will certainly have other matrices which are nothing more than leftovers in making the calculation. Such matrices are called *temporary*. You should use Stata's **tempname** facility (see [R] **macro**) to name such matrices. These matrices will be automatically discarded when your program ends. For example, a piece of your program might read

```
tempname YXX XX
matrix accum `YXX' = price weight mpg
matrix `XX' = `YXX'[2...,2...]
```

Note the single quotes around the names after they are obtained from `tempname`; see [U] **24.3 Macros**.

❑ Technical Note

Let us consider a well-written version of the regression program we performed interactively two examples ago. A well-written estimation command would allow the `level()` option for specifying the width of confidence intervals and it would replay results when the command is typed without arguments. Here is the well-written version:

```
program define myreg
        version 5.0
        local options "Level(integer $S_level)"
        parse "`*'", parse(" ,")
        if "`1'"!="" & "`1'"!="," {
                tempname YXX XX Xy XXi b pv rv  V
                local varlist "req ex min(2)"
                local if "opt"
                local in "opt"
                parse "`*'"
                parse "`varlist'", parse(" ")
                quietly matrix accum `YXX' = `varlist' `if' `in'
                local nobs = _result(1)
                local nvar = rowsof(`YXX')
                local nvarm1 = `nvar'-1
                matrix `XX' = `YXX'[2...,2...]
                matrix `Xy' = `YXX'[1,2...]
                matrix `XXi'= syminv(`XX')
                matrix `b' = `Xy'*`XXi'
                matrix `pv' = `b'*`Xy'
                local df = `nobs' - `nvarm1'
                scalar `rv' = (`YXX'[1,1] - `pv'[1,1])/`df'
                matrix `V'=`XXi'*`rv'
                matrix post `b' `V', dof(`df') obs(`nobs') depname(`1')
                global S_E_depv "`1'"
                global S_E_cmd "myreg"
        }
        else    parse "`*'"
        if "$S_E_cmd"!="myreg" { error 301 }
        if `level'<10 | `level'>99 {
                local level=95
        }
        matrix mlout, level(`level')
end
```

The syntax of our new command is

myreg *depvar indepvars* [if *exp*] [in *range*] [, level(*#*)]

and `myreg`, typed without arguments, redisplays the output of the last `myreg` command. After estimation with `myreg`, the user may use `correlate` to display the covariance matrix of the estimators, `predict` to obtain predicted values or standard errors of the prediction, and `test` to test linear hypotheses about the estimated coefficients. The command is indistinguishable from any other Stata estimation command.

Despite the excellence of our work, we do have some criticisms:

1. `myreg` does not display the ANOVA table, R^2, etc.; it should and could be made to, although we would have to insert our own `display` statements before the `matrix mlout` instruction.

2. The program makes copious use of matrices with different names, resulting in considerable amounts of memory use while the estimation is being made; the code could be made more economical, if less readable, by reusing already existing matrices—at the very least, **XX** could be substituted for **XXi** everywhere it appears.

3. **myreg** makes the least-squares calculation using the absolute cross-product matrix, an invitation to numerical problems if the data are not consistently scaled. Stata's own **fit** and **regress** commands are more careful and we could be, too: **matrix accum** does have an option for forming the cross-product matrix in deviation form, but its use would complicate this program. This does not overly concern us, although we should make a note of it when we document **myreg**. Nowadays, users expect to be protected in linear regression, but have no such expectations for more complicated estimation schemes because avoiding the problem can be difficult to nearly impossible.

There is one nice feature of our program that did not occur to us when we wrote it. We use **syminv()** to form the inverse of the cross-product matrix and **syminv()** can handle singular matrices. If there is a collinearity problem, **myreg** behaves just like **regress** and **fit**: it drops the offending variables and notes they are dropped when it displays the output (at the **matrix mlout** step).

❏

❏ Technical Note

Our linear regression program is quite a bit longer than one might have written in a "real", exclusively matrix programming, programming language. After all, the coefficients can be obtained from $(\mathbf{X'X})^{-1}\mathbf{X'y}$ and in a dedicated language, one would type nearly that, and obtaining the standard errors would require only a couple of more matrix calculations. In fact, we did type nearly that to make the calculation; the extra lines in our program have mostly to do with syntax issues and linking to the rest of Stata. In writing your own programs, you might be tempted not to bother linking to the rest of Stata. Fight the temptation.

Linking to the rest of Stata pays off: in this case, we do not merely display the numerical results, we display them in a readable form, complete with variable names. We made a command that is indistinguishable from Stata's other estimation commands. If the user wants to test **_b[denver]=_b[la]**, the user types literally that; he or she is not called upon to remember the matrix equation and to count variables (such as constrain the third minus the fifteenth variable to sum to zero).

❏

Creating, dimensioning, and replacing matrices

In general, matrices do not have to be preallocated or dimensioned prior to creation, but the exception is when you want to create an $r \times c$ matrix and then fill in each element one-by-one; see the description of the J() function in [R] **matrix define**. Matrices are typically created by **matrix define** or **matrix accum**; see [R] **matrix accum**.

Stata takes a high-handed approach to redefining matrices. You know that, when dealing with data, you must distinguish between creating a new variable or replacing the contents of an existing variable—Stata has two commands: **generate** and **replace**. For matrices, there is no such distinction. If you define a new matrix, it is created. If you give the same command and the matrix already exists, the currently existing matrix is destroyed and then the new one defined. This treatment is the same as that given macros and scalars.

Name space

The term "name space" refers to how names are interpreted. For instance, the variables in your data occupy one name space—other things, such as variable labels, macros, and scalars—can have the same name and there is no confusion.

Macros are something else that have their own name space; macros can have the same names as other things and Stata can still tell by context when you are referring to a macro because of the punctuation. When you type `gen newvar=myname`, myname must refer to a variable. When you type `gen newvar=`myname´`—note the single quotes around myname—myname must refer to a local macro. When you type `gen newvar=$myname`, myname must refer to a global macro.

Scalars and matrices share the same name space, which is to say, scalars and matrices may have the same names as variables in the data, etc., but they cannot have the same names as each other. Thus, when you define a matrix called, say, myres, if a scalar by that name already exists, it is destroyed and the matrix replaces it. Correspondingly, if you define a scalar called myres, if a matrix by that name exists, it is destroyed and the scalar replaces it.

Overview of matrix commands

Basics

[R] **matrix define**	Matrix definition, operators, and functions
[R] **matrix get**	Accessing system matrices
[R] **matrix utility**	Listing and dropping matrices

Programming

[R] **matrix accum**	Forming cross-product matrices
[R] **ml**	Maximum-likelihood estimation
[R] **matrix post**	Posting and redisplaying estimation results
[R] **matrix rowname**	Naming rows and columns
[R] **matrix score**	Scoring data from coefficient vectors

Specialized

[R] **matrix constraint**	Constrained estimation
[R] **matrix mkmat**	Convert variables to matrix and vice versa
[R] **matrix substitute**	Creating partitioned matrices
[R] **matrix svd**	Singular value decomposition
[R] **matrix symeigen**	Eigenvalues and vectors of symmetric matrices

Actually, many users will want to jump immediately to reading about maximum-likelihood estimation in [R] **ml**. They should do so; matrices are used only at the very end of the entry and then only in a special case that most users will never encounter. If your interest is in matrices, however, read [R] **matrix define** first. After that, feel free to skip around.

Also See

[U] **24 Programming Stata**

[R] **matrix define**

Title

matrix accum — Form cross-product matrices

Syntax

<u>mat</u>rix <u>ac</u>cum **A** = *varlist* $\big[weight\big]$ $\big[$if *exp*$\big]$ $\big[$in *range*$\big]$ $\big[$, <u>d</u>eviations

<u>m</u>eans(**m**) <u>noc</u>onstant $\big]$

<u>mat</u>rix <u>gls</u>accum **A** = *varlist* $\big[weight\big]$ $\big[$if *exp*$\big]$ $\big[$in *range*$\big]$, <u>gr</u>oup(*groupvar*)

<u>gl</u>smat($\big\{$**W** | *stringvarname*$\big\}$) <u>row</u>(*rowvar*) $\big[$<u>noc</u>onstant$\big]$

<u>mat</u>rix <u>vec</u>accum **a** = *varlist* $\big[weight\big]$ $\big[$if *exp*$\big]$ $\big[$in *range*$\big]$ $\big[$, <u>noc</u>onstant $\big]$

aweights, fweights, and pweights are allowed; see [U] **18.1.6 weight**.

To reset problem-size limits, see [R] **matsize**.

Description

matrix accum accumulates cross-product matrices from the data to form $\mathbf{A} = \mathbf{X}'\mathbf{X}$.

matrix glsaccum accumulates cross-product matrices from the data using a specified inner weight matrix to form $\mathbf{A} = \mathbf{X}'\mathbf{B}\mathbf{X}$ where $\mathbf{B}$ is a block diagonal matrix.

matrix vecaccum accumulates the first variable against remaining variables in *varlist* to form a row vector of accumulated inner products to form $\mathbf{a} = \mathbf{x}_1'\mathbf{X}$ where $\mathbf{X} = (\mathbf{x}_2, \mathbf{x}_3, \ldots)$.

Options

noconstant suppresses the addition of a "constant" to the $\mathbf{X}$ matrix. If noconstant is not specified, it is as if a column of 1's is added to $\mathbf{X}$ before the accumulation begins. For instance, in the case of accum without noconstant, $\mathbf{X}'\mathbf{X}$ is really $(\mathbf{X}, \mathbf{1})'(\mathbf{X}, \mathbf{1})$, resulting in

$$\begin{pmatrix} \mathbf{X}'\mathbf{X} & \mathbf{X}'\mathbf{1} \\ \mathbf{1}'\mathbf{X} & \mathbf{1}'\mathbf{1} \end{pmatrix}$$

Thus, the last row and column contain the sums of the columns of $\mathbf{X}$ and the element in the last row and column contains the number of observations. If p variables are specified in the *varlist*, the resulting matrix is $(p+1) \times (p+1)$. Specifying noconstant suppresses the addition of this row and column (or just column in the case of vecaccum).

deviations, allowed only with matrix accum, causes the accumulation to be performed in terms of deviations from the mean. If noconstant is not specified, the accumulation of $\mathbf{X}$ is done in terms of deviations, but the added row and column of sums is *not* in deviation format (in which case they would be zeros). With noconstant specified, the resulting matrix divided through by $N-1$, where N is the number of observations, is a covariance matrix.

431

means(*m*), allowed only with accum, creates **m**: $1 \times (p+1)$ or $1 \times p$ (depending whether noconstant is also specified) containing the means of **X**.

group(*groupvar*), allowed only with glsaccum and which is then not optional, specifies the name of a variable that identifies the groups of observations to be individually weighted by glsmat(). The data must be sorted by *groupvar*.

glsmat($\left\{ \mathbf{W} \mid stringvarname \right\}$) is also allowed only with glsaccum and is not optional; it specifies the name of the matrix or the name of a string variable in the data that contains the name of the matrix which is to be used to weight the observations in the group(). *stringvarname* must be str8 or less.

row(*rowvar*) (glsaccum and not optional) specifies the name of a numeric variable containing the row numbers that specify the row and column of the glsmat() matrix to use in the inner-product calculation.

Remarks

accum

matrix accum is a straightforward command and, in [R] **matrix**, we used the command to accumulate a single matrix from which we then extracted $\mathbf{X}'\mathbf{X}$ and $\mathbf{X}'\mathbf{y}$ to make the least-squares calculation $\mathbf{b} = (\mathbf{X}'\mathbf{X})^{-1}\mathbf{X}'\mathbf{y}$. Say we wish to run a regression of the variable price on mpg and weight. We can begin by accumulating the full cross-product matrix for all three variables:

```
. matrix accum A = price weight mpg
(obs=74)

. matrix list A

symmetric A[4,4]
              price      weight         mpg       _cons
price     3.448e+09
weight    1.468e+09   7.188e+08
   mpg      9132716     4493720       36008
 _cons       456229      223440        1576          74
```

In our accumulation, accum automatically added a constant; we specified three variables and got back a 4×4 matrix. The constant term is always added last. In terms of our regression model, the matrix we just accumulated has $\mathbf{y} = $ price and $\mathbf{X} = (\text{weight}, \text{mpg}, \_\text{cons})$, and can be written:

$$\mathbf{A} = \left(\mathbf{y}, \mathbf{X}\right)'\left(\mathbf{y}, \mathbf{X}\right) = \begin{pmatrix} \mathbf{y}'\mathbf{y} & \mathbf{y}'\mathbf{X} \\ \mathbf{X}'\mathbf{y} & \mathbf{X}'\mathbf{X} \end{pmatrix}$$

Thus, we can extract $\mathbf{X}'\mathbf{X}$ from the submatrix of **A** beginning at the second row and column and we can extract $\mathbf{X}'\mathbf{y}$ from the first column of **A**, omitting the first row:

```
. matrix XX = A[2...,2...]
. matrix list XX

symmetric XX[3,3]
              weight         mpg       _cons
weight    7.188e+08
   mpg      4493720       36008
 _cons       223440        1576          74

. matrix Xy = A[2...,1]
```

```
. matrix list Xy
Xy[3,1]
              price
weight  1.468e+09
   mpg    9132716
 _cons     456229
```

We can now calculate $\mathbf{b} = (\mathbf{X}'\mathbf{X})^{-1}\mathbf{X}'\mathbf{y}$:

```
. matrix XXi = syminv(XX)
. matrix b = XXi * Xy
. matrix list b
b[3,1]
              price
weight   1.7465592
   mpg  -49.512221
 _cons   1946.0687
```

❏ Technical Note

     matrix accum, with the **deviations** and **noconstant** options, can also be used to obtain covariance matrices. The covariance between variables x_i and x_j is defined as

$$C_{ij} = \frac{\sum_{k=1}^{n}(x_{ik} - \overline{x}_i)(x_{jk} - \overline{x}_j)}{n-1}$$

Without the **deviations** option **matrix accum** calculates a matrix with elements

$$R_{ij} = \sum_{k=1}^{n} x_{ik}x_{jk}$$

and, with the **deviations** option:

$$A_{ij} = \sum_{k=1}^{n}(x_{ik} - \overline{x}_i)(x_{jk} - \overline{x}_j)$$

Thus, the covariance matrix $\mathbf{C} = \mathbf{A}/(n-1)$.

```
. matrix accum Cov = price weight mpg, deviations noconstant
(obs=74)
. scalar adj = 1/(_result(1)-1)
. matrix Cov = adj*Cov
. matrix list Cov
symmetric Cov[3,3]
              price      weight         mpg
price       8699526
weight    1234674.8   604029.84
   mpg  -7996.2829  -3629.4261   33.472047
```

In addition to calculating the cross-product matrix, **matrix accum** records the number of observations in **_result(1)**, a feature we use in calculating the normalizing factor. With the **corr()** matrix function defined in [R] **matrix define**, we can convert the covariance matrix into a correlation matrix:

```
. matrix P = corr(Cov)
. matrix list P
symmetric P[3,3]
              price      weight         mpg
price             1
weight   .53861146           1
   mpg  -.46859669  -.80717486           1
```

◁

glsaccum

matrix glsaccum is a generalization of matrix accum useful in producing GLS-style weighted accumulations. Whereas matrix accum produces matrices of the form $\mathbf{X}'\mathbf{X}$, glsaccum produces matrices of the form $\mathbf{X}'\mathbf{B}\mathbf{X}$, where

$$B = \begin{pmatrix} \mathbf{W}_1 & 0 & \cdots & 0 \\ 0 & \mathbf{W}_2 & \cdots & 0 \\ \vdots & \vdots & \ddots & \vdots \\ 0 & 0 & \cdots & \mathbf{W}_K \end{pmatrix}$$

The matrices $\mathbf{W}_k$, $k = 1 \ldots K$, are called the weighting matrices for observation group k. In the above, each of the $\mathbf{W}_k$ matrices is square but there is no assumption that they have the same number of rows and columns as each other. Note that by writing

$$\mathbf{X} = \begin{pmatrix} \mathbf{X}_1 \\ \mathbf{X}_2 \\ \vdots \\ \mathbf{X}_K \end{pmatrix}$$

the accumulation made by glsaccum can be written as

$$\mathbf{X}'\mathbf{B}\mathbf{X} = \mathbf{X}_1'\mathbf{W}_1\mathbf{X}_1 + \mathbf{X}_2'\mathbf{W}_2\mathbf{X}_2 + \ldots + \mathbf{X}_K'\mathbf{W}_K\mathbf{X}_K$$

glsaccum requires you to specify three options: group(*groupvar*), glsmat(*matname*) or glsmat(*matvar*), and row(*rowvar*). Observations sharing the same value of *groupvar* are said to be in the same observation group—this specifies the group k in which they are to be accumulated. How $\mathbf{W}_k$ is assembled is the subject of the other two options.

Think of there being a super weighting matrix for the group which we will call $\mathbf{V}_k$. $\mathbf{V}_k$ is specified by glsmat()—the same super matrix can be used for all observations by specifying a *matname* as the argument to glsmat or, if a variable name is specified, different super matrices can be specified—the contents of the variable will be used to obtain the particular name of the super matrix. (More correctly, the contents of the variable for the first observation in the group will be used: super matrices can vary across groups, but must be the same within group.)

Weighting matrix $\mathbf{W}_k$ is made from the super matrix $\mathbf{V}_k$ by selecting the rows and columns specified in row(*rowvar*). In the simple case, $\mathbf{W}_k = \mathbf{V}_k$. This happens when there are m observations in the group and the first observation in the group has *rowvar* = 1, the second *rowvar* = 2, and so on. To fix ideas, let $m = 3$ and write

$$\mathbf{V}_1 = \begin{pmatrix} v_{11} & v_{12} & v_{13} \\ v_{21} & v_{22} & v_{23} \\ v_{31} & v_{32} & v_{33} \end{pmatrix}$$

$\mathbf{V}$ need not be symmetric. Let's pretend the first four observations in our data contain

obs. no.	*groupvar*	*rowvar*
1	1	1
2	1	2
3	1	3
4	2	...

In this data, the first three observations are in the first group because they share an equal *groupvar*. It is not important that *groupvar* happens to equal 1; it is important that the values are equal. The *rowvars* are, in order, 1, 2, and 3, so $\mathbf{W}_1$ is formed by selecting the first row and column of $\mathbf{V}_1$, then the second row and column of $\mathbf{V}_1$, and finally the third row and column of $\mathbf{V}_1$; to wit,

$$\mathbf{W}_1 = \begin{pmatrix} v_{11} & v_{12} & v_{13} \\ v_{21} & v_{22} & v_{23} \\ v_{31} & v_{32} & v_{33} \end{pmatrix}$$

or $\mathbf{W}_1 = \mathbf{V}_1$. Now, consider the same data, but reordered:

obs. no.	*groupvar*	*rowvar*
1	1	2
2	1	1
3	1	3
4	2	...

$\mathbf{W}_1$ is now formed by selecting the second row and column, then the first row and column, and finally the third row and column of $\mathbf{V}_1$. These steps can be performed sequentially, reordering first the rows and then the columns; the result is

$$\mathbf{W}_1 = \begin{pmatrix} v_{22} & v_{21} & v_{23} \\ v_{12} & v_{11} & v_{13} \\ v_{32} & v_{31} & v_{33} \end{pmatrix}$$

This reorganization of the $\mathbf{W}_1$ matrix exactly undoes the reorganization of the $\mathbf{X}_1$ matrix, so $\mathbf{X}_1'\mathbf{W}_1\mathbf{X}_1$ remains unchanged. Given how $\mathbf{W}_k$ is assembled from $\mathbf{V}_k$, the order of the row numbers in the data does not matter.

glsaccum is willing to carry this concept even further. Consider the data:

obs. no.	*groupvar*	*rowvar*
1	1	1
2	1	3
3	1	3
4	2	...

Note that now, *rowvar* equals 1 followed by 3 twice, so the first row and column of $\mathbf{V}_1$ are selected, followed by the third row and column twice; the second column is never selected. The resulting weighting matrix is

$$\mathbf{W}_1 = \begin{pmatrix} v_{11} & v_{13} & v_{13} \\ v_{31} & v_{33} & v_{33} \\ v_{31} & v_{33} & v_{33} \end{pmatrix}$$

Such odd weighting would not occur in, say, time series analysis where the matrix might be weighting lags and leads. It could very well occur in an analysis of individuals in families, where 1 might indicate head of household, 2 a spouse, and 3 a child. In fact, such a case could be handled with a 3×3 super weighting matrix V even if the family became quite large: the appropriate weighting matrix $\mathbf{W}_k$ would be assembled, on a group-by-group (family-by-family) basis, from the underlying super matrix.

vecaccum

The first variable in the *varlist* is treated differently from the others by vecaccum. Think of the first variable as specifying a vector $\mathbf{y}$ and the remaining variables as specifying matrix $\mathbf{X}$. vecaccum makes the accumulation $\mathbf{y}'\mathbf{X}$ to return a row vector with elements

$$a_i = \sum_{k=1}^{n} y_k x_{ki}$$

Like accum, vecaccum adds a constant _cons to $\mathbf{X}$ unless noconstant is specified.

vecaccum serves two purposes. First, terms like $\mathbf{y}'\mathbf{X}$ often occur in calculating derivatives of likelihood functions; vecaccum provides a fast way of calculating them. Second, it is useful in time series accumulations of the form:

$$\mathbf{C} = \sum_{t=1}^{T} \sum_{\delta=-k}^{k} \mathbf{x}'_{t-\delta} \mathbf{x}_t W_\delta r_{t-\delta} r_t$$

In this calculation, $\mathbf{X}$ is an observation matrix with elements x_{tj} with t indexing time (observations) and j variables, $t = 1, \ldots, T$ and $j = 1, \ldots, p$. $\mathbf{x}_t$ $(1 \times p)$ refers to the tth row of this matrix. Thus, $\mathbf{C}$ is a $p \times p$ matrix.

The Newey–West covariance matrix uses the definition $W_\delta = 1 - |\delta|/(k+1)$ for $\delta \leq k$. To make the calculation, the user (programmer) cycles through each of the j variables, forming

$$z_{tj} = \sum_{\delta=-k}^{k} x_{(t-\delta)j} W_\delta r_{t-\delta} r_t$$

Writing $\mathbf{z}_j = (z_{1j}, z_{2j}, \ldots, z_{Tj})'$, $\mathbf{C}$ is then

$$\mathbf{C} = \sum_{j=1}^{p} \mathbf{z}'_j \mathbf{X}$$

In this derivation, the user must decide in advance the maximum lag length k such that observations that are far apart in time must have increasingly small covariances in order to establish the convergence results.

The Newey–West estimator is in the class of generalized methods of moments (GMM) estimators. The choice of a maximum lag length k is a reflection of the length in time beyond which the autocorrelation becomes negligible for the purposes of estimating the variance matrix. The code fragment given below is merely for illustration of the matrix commands as Stata includes estimation with the Newey–West covariance matrix in the newey command. See [R] **newey** or Greene (1993, page 377) for details on this estimator.

Note that it is calculations like $\mathbf{z}'_j \mathbf{X}$ that are made by vecaccum. Also note that $\mathbf{z}_j$ can be treated as a temporary variable in the data.

```
      assume `1´,`2´, etc. contain the x's including constant
      assume `r´ contains the r variable
      assume `k´ contains the k range
      tempname C factor t c tp
      tempvar z

      local p : word count `*´
      matrix `C´ = J(`p´,`p´,0)
      gen double `z´ = 0
      local d = 0
      while `d´ <= `k´ {
              if `d´ > 0 { scalar `factor´ = 1 } /* Add each submatrix twice */
              else scalar `factor´ = 0.5           /* except for the lag=0 case */

              local w = (1 - `d´/(`k´+1))
              capture mat drop `t´
              local j = 1
              while `j´ <= `p´ {
                      replace `z´ = ``j´´[_n-`d´]*`w´*`r´[_n-`d´]*`r´
                      mat vecaccum `c´ = `z´ `*´, nocons
                      mat `t´ = `t´ \ `c´
                      local j = `j´+1
              }
              mat `tp´ = `t´´
              mat `c´ = `t´ + `tp´
              mat `c´ = `c´ * `factor´
              mat `C´ = `C´ + `c´
              local d = `d´+1
      }
      local `p´ = "_cons"                       /* Rename last var to _cons */
      mat rownames `C´ = `*´
      mat colnames `C´ = `*´
      assume inverse and scaling for standard error reports
```

Treatment of user-specified weights

accum, glsaccum, and vecaccum all allow weights. Here is how they are treated:

All three commands can be thought of as returning something of the form $\mathbf{X}_1'\mathbf{B}\mathbf{X}_2$. In the case of accum, $\mathbf{X}_1 = \mathbf{X}_2$ and $\mathbf{B} = \mathbf{I}$; in the case of glsaccum, $\mathbf{X}_1 = \mathbf{X}_2$; in the case of vecaccum, $\mathbf{B} = \mathbf{I}$, $\mathbf{X}_1$ is a column vector, and $\mathbf{X}_2$ is a matrix.

In point of fact, the commands really calculate $\mathbf{X}_1'\mathbf{W}^{1/2}\mathbf{B}\mathbf{W}^{1/2}\mathbf{X}_2$, where $\mathbf{W}$ is a diagonal matrix. If no weights are specified, $\mathbf{W} = \mathbf{I}$. Now assume weights are specified and let $\mathbf{v}$: $1 \times n$ be the specified weights. If fweight frequency weights or pweight sampling weights are specified, then $\mathbf{W} = \mathrm{diag}(\mathbf{v})$. If aweight analytic weights are specified, then $\mathbf{W} = \mathrm{diag}[\mathbf{v}/(\mathbf{1}'\mathbf{v})(\mathbf{1}'\mathbf{1})]$, which is to say, the weights are normalized to sum to the number of observations.

Saved Results

matrix accum, glsaccum, and vecaccum save the number of observations in _result(1). glsaccum and vecaccum also store the sum of the weight in _result(2), but accum does not.

Also See

[R] **matrix**, [R] **ml**

Title

---
matrix constraint — Constrained estimation

Syntax

<u>mat</u>rix makeCns [*clist*]

<u>mat</u>rix dispCns

matcproc **T a C**

where *clist* is a list of constraint numbers, separated by commas or dashes. 1,2,3 would refer to constraints 1, 2, and 3, as would 1-3. 1-3,9 would refer to constraints 1, 2, 3, and 9.

T, **a**, and **C** are names of new or existing matrices.

To reset problem-size limits, see [R] **matsize**.

Description

matrix makeCns makes a constraint matrix; the matrix can be obtained by the get (Cns) function. matrix dispCns displays the system-stored constraint matrix in readable form. matcproc returns matrices helpful for performing constrained estimation including the constraint matrix.

Remarks

Users of estimation commands that allow constrained estimation define constraints using the constraint command; they specify which constraints they want to use by specifying the constraints (*clist*) option to the estimation command. This entry concerns programming such sophisticated estimators. Before reading it, you should be familiar with constraints from a user's perspective; see [R] **constraint**. You should also be familiar with programming estimation commands that do not include constraints; see [R] **matrix post** and [R] **ml**.

Overview

You have an estimation command and wish to allow a set of linear constraints to be specified for the parameters by the user and then to produce estimates subject to those constraints. Stata will do most of the work for you. First, it will collect the constraints—all you have to do is add an option to your estimation command to allow the user to specify which constraints to use. Second, it will process those constraints, converting them from algebraic form (such as group1=group2) to a constraint matrix. Third, it will convert the constraint matrix into two, almost magical matrices that will, in the case of maximum-likelihood estimation, allow you to write your routine almost as if there were no constraints.

There will be a "reduced-form" parameter vector b_c which your likelihood-calculation routine will receive. That vector, multiplied by one of the almost magical matrices and then added to the other, can be converted into a regular parameter vector with the constraints applied, so, other than the few extra matrix calculations, you can calculate the likelihood function as if there were no constraints. You can do the same thing with respect to the first and second derivatives (if you are calculating them) except that, after getting them, you will need to perform another matrix multiplication or two to convert them into the reduced form.

Once the optimum is found, you will have reduced-form parameter vector $\mathbf{b}_c$ along with variance-covariance matrix $\mathbf{V}_c$. Both can be easily converted into full-form-but-constrained $\mathbf{b}$ and $\mathbf{V}$.

Finally, you will `post` the results along with the constraint matrix Stata made up for you in the first place. You can, with a few lines of program code, arrange it so that, every time results are replayed, the constraints under which they were produced are redisplayed and in standard algebraic format.

Mathematics

Let $\mathbf{Rb'} = \mathbf{r}$ be the constraint, for $\mathbf{R}$ a $c \times p$ constraint matrix imposing c constraints on p parameters, $\mathbf{b}$ a $1 \times p$ parameter vector, and $\mathbf{r}$ a $c \times 1$ vector of constraint values.

We wish to construct a $p \times k$ matrix $\mathbf{T}$ that takes $\mathbf{b}$ into a reduced-rank form, where $k = p - c$. There are obviously lots of $\mathbf{T}$ matrices that will do this; we choose one with properties that

$$\mathbf{b}_c = \mathbf{b}_0\mathbf{T}$$
$$\mathbf{b} = \mathbf{b}_c\mathbf{T}' + \mathbf{a}$$

where $\mathbf{b}_c$ is a reduced-form projection of any solution $\mathbf{b}_0$, i.e., $\mathbf{b}_c$ is a vector of lesser dimension ($1 \times k$ rather than $1 \times p$) that can be treated as if it were unconstrained. The second equation says that $\mathbf{b}_c$ can be mapped back into a higher dimensioned, properly constrained $\mathbf{b}$; $1 \times p$ vector $\mathbf{a}$ is a constant that depends only on $\mathbf{R}$ and $\mathbf{r}$.

With such a $\mathbf{T}$ matrix and $\mathbf{a}$ vector, one can engage in unconstrained optimization of $\mathbf{b}_c$. If ultimately the estimate $\mathbf{b}_c$ with variance-covariance matrix $\mathbf{V}_c$ is produced, it can be mapped back into $\mathbf{b} = \mathbf{b}_c\mathbf{T}' + \mathbf{a}$ and $\mathbf{V} = \mathbf{T}\mathbf{V}_c\mathbf{T}'$. The resulting $\mathbf{b}$ and $\mathbf{V}$ can then be posted.

❏ Technical Note

So how did we get so lucky? This happy solution arises if

$$\mathbf{T} = \text{first } k \text{ eigenvectors of } \mathbf{I} - \mathbf{R}'(\mathbf{RR}')^{-1}\mathbf{R} \qquad (p \times k)$$
$$\mathbf{L} = \text{last } c \text{ eigenvectors of } \mathbf{I} - \mathbf{R}'(\mathbf{RR}')^{-1}\mathbf{R} \qquad (p \times c)$$
$$\mathbf{a} = \mathbf{r}'(\mathbf{L}'\mathbf{R}')^{-1}\mathbf{L}'$$

because

$$(\mathbf{b}_c, \mathbf{r}') = \mathbf{b}(\mathbf{T}, \mathbf{R}')$$

If $\mathbf{R}$ consists of a set of consistent constraints, then it is guaranteed to have rank c. Thus, $\mathbf{RR}'$ is a $c \times c$ invertible matrix.

We will now show that $\mathbf{RT} = \mathbf{0}$ and $\mathbf{R}(\mathbf{LL}') = \mathbf{R}$.

Since $\mathbf{R}$: $c \times p$ is assumed to be of rank c, the first k eigenvalues of $\mathbf{P} = \mathbf{I} - \mathbf{R}'(\mathbf{RR}')^{-1}\mathbf{R}$ are positive and the last c are zero. Break $\mathbf{R}$ into a basis spanned by these components. If $\mathbf{R}$ had any components in the first k, they could not be annihilated by $\mathbf{P}$, contradicting

$$\mathbf{RP} = \mathbf{R} - \mathbf{RR}'(\mathbf{RR}')^{-1}\mathbf{R} = \mathbf{0}$$

Therefore, $\mathbf{T}$ and $\mathbf{R}$ are orthogonal to each other. Since $(\mathbf{T}, \mathbf{L})$ is an orthonormal basis, $(\mathbf{T}, \mathbf{L})'$ is its inverse, so $(\mathbf{T}, \mathbf{L})(\mathbf{T}, \mathbf{L})' = \mathbf{I}$. Thus,

$$\mathbf{TT}' + \mathbf{LL}' = \mathbf{I}$$
$$(\mathbf{TT}' + \mathbf{LL}')\mathbf{R}' = \mathbf{R}'$$
$$(\mathbf{LL}')\mathbf{R}' = \mathbf{R}'$$

So, we conclude $\mathbf{r} = \mathbf{bR}(\mathbf{LL}')$. $\mathbf{RL}$ is an invertible $c \times c$ matrix, so

$$\left(\mathbf{b}_c, \mathbf{r}'(\mathbf{L}'\mathbf{R})^{-1}\right) = \mathbf{b}(\mathbf{T}, \mathbf{L})$$

Remember, $(\mathbf{T}, \mathbf{L})$ is a set of eigenvectors, meaning $(\mathbf{T}, \mathbf{L})^{-1} = (\mathbf{T}, \mathbf{L})'$, so $\mathbf{b} = \mathbf{b}_c\mathbf{T}' + \mathbf{r}'(\mathbf{L}'\mathbf{R}')^{-1}\mathbf{L}'$.

□

If a solution is being found by likelihood methods, the reduced form parameter vector will be passed to the maximizer and from there to the program that has to compute a likelihood value from it. In order to find the likelihood value, the inner routines can compute $\mathbf{b} = \mathbf{b}_c\mathbf{T}' + \mathbf{a}$. The routine may then go on to produce a set of $1 \times p$ first derivatives $\mathbf{d}$ and $p \times p$ second derivatives $\mathbf{H}$ even though the problem is of lessor dimension. These matrices can be reduced to the k-dimensional space via

$$\mathbf{d}_c = \mathbf{dT}$$
$$\mathbf{H}_c = \mathbf{T}'\mathbf{HT}$$

□ Technical Note

Alternatively, if a solution were to be found by direct matrix methods, then the programmer must derive a new solution based on $\mathbf{b} = \mathbf{b}_c\mathbf{T}' + \mathbf{a}$. For example, the least-squares normal equations come from differentiating $(\mathbf{y} - \mathbf{Xb})^2$. Setting the derivative with respect to $\mathbf{b}$ to zero results in

$$\mathbf{T}'\mathbf{X}'\left(\mathbf{y} - \mathbf{X}(\mathbf{Tb}_c' + \mathbf{a}')\right) = 0$$

yielding

$$\mathbf{b}_c' = (\mathbf{T}'\mathbf{X}'\mathbf{XT})^{-1}[\mathbf{T}'\mathbf{X}'\mathbf{y} - \mathbf{T}'\mathbf{X}'\mathbf{Xa}']$$
$$\mathbf{b}' = \mathbf{T}\left[(\mathbf{T}'\mathbf{X}'\mathbf{XT})^{-1}[\mathbf{T}'\mathbf{X}'\mathbf{y} - \mathbf{T}'\mathbf{X}'\mathbf{Xa}']\right] + \mathbf{a}'$$

Using the matrices $\mathbf{T}$ and $\mathbf{a}$, the solution is not merely to constrain the $\mathbf{b}'$ obtained from an unconstrained solution $(\mathbf{X}'\mathbf{X})^{-1}\mathbf{X}'\mathbf{y}$ even though you might know that, in this case, with further substitutions this could be reduced to

$$\mathbf{b}' = (\mathbf{X}'\mathbf{X})^{-1}\mathbf{X}'\mathbf{y} + (\mathbf{X}'\mathbf{X})^{-1}\mathbf{R}'[\mathbf{R}(\mathbf{X}'\mathbf{X})^{-1}\mathbf{R}']^{-1}(\mathbf{r} - \mathbf{R}(\mathbf{X}'\mathbf{X})^{-1}\mathbf{X}'\mathbf{y})$$

□

Linkage of the mathematics to Stata

Users define constraints using the `constraint` command; see [R] **constraint**. The constraints are numbered and Stata stores them in algebraic format—the same format in which the user typed them. Stata does this because, until the estimation problem is defined, it cannot know how to interpret the constraint. Think of the constraint `_b[group1]=_b[group2]`, meaning two coefficients are to be constrained to equality, along with the constraint `_b[group3]=2`. The constraint matrices $\mathbf{R}$ and $\mathbf{r}$ are defined so that $\mathbf{Rb}' = \mathbf{r}$ imposes the constraint. The matrices *might* be

$$\begin{pmatrix} 0 & 0 & 1 & -1 & 0 & 0 \\ 0 & 0 & 0 & 0 & 1 & 0 \end{pmatrix} \begin{pmatrix} b_1 \\ b_2 \\ b_3 \\ b_4 \\ b_5 \\ b_6 \end{pmatrix} = \begin{pmatrix} 0 \\ 2 \end{pmatrix}$$

if it just so happened that the third and fourth coefficients corresponded to group1 and group2, and the fifth corresponded to group3. Then again, it might look differently if the coefficients were organized differently.

Therefore, Stata must wait until estimation begins to define the R and r matrices. Stata learns about the organization of a problem from the names bordering the coefficient vector and variance-covariance matrix. Therefore, Stata requires you to post a dummy estimation result that has the correct names. Based on that, it can now determine the organization of the constraint matrix and make it for you. Once a (dummy) estimation result has been posted, makeCns can make the constraint matrices and, once they are built, you can obtain copies of them using matrix *mname*=get(Cns). Stata stores the constraint matrices R and r as a single, $c \times (p + 1)$ matrix $C = (R, r)$. Putting them together makes it easier to pass them to subroutines.

The second step in the process is to convert the constrained problem to a reduced-form problem. We outlined the mathematics above; the matcproc command will produce the T and a matrices. If you are performing maximum likelihood, your likelihood, gradient, and Hessian calculation subroutines can still work in the full metric by using the same T and a matrices to translate the reduced-format parameter vector back to the original metric. If you do this, and if you are calculating gradients or Hessians, you must remember to compress them to reduced form using the T and a matrices.

When you have a reduced-form solution, you translate this back to a constrained solution using T and a. You then post the constrained solutions, along with the original Cns matrix, and use matrix mlout to display the results.

Thus, the outline of a program to perform constrained estimation is

```
program define myest
        version 5.0
        parse "`*´", parse(" ,")
        local options "Level(integer $S_level)"
        if ~("`1´"==","  | "`*´"=="") {
                tempname b V C T a bc Vc
                local options "`options´ Constraints(string) whatever"
                parse the user's estimation request;
                local p=number of parameters
                define the model ( set the row and column names) in `b´
                if "`constra´"!="" {
                        matrix `V´=`b´ ´ `b´
                        matrix post `b´ `V´            /* a dummy solution */
                        matrix makeCns `constra´
                        matrix dispCns                 /* display constraints */
                        local shown "yes"
                        matcproc `T´ `a´ `C´
                        obtain solution in `bc´ and `Vc´
                        matrix `b´ = `bc´*`T´
                        matrix `b´ = `b´ + `a´
                        matrix `V´ = `T´*`Vc´
                        matrix `V´ = `V´*`T´´            /* note prime */
                        matrix post `b´ `V´ `C´, options
                        global S_E_cns "yes"
                }
```

```
                        else {
                                obtain standard solution in `b´ and `V´
                                matrix post `b´ `V´, options
                        }
                        store whatever else you want in S_E_ macros;
                        global S_E_cmd "myest"
                }
                else {
                        if "$S_E_cmd"!="myest" { error 301 }
                        parse "`*´"
                }
                if `level´<10 | `level´>99 {
                        local level = 95
                }
                if "$S_E_cns"=="yes" & "`shown´"~="yes" {
                        matrix dispCns
                }
                output any header above the coefficient table;
                matrix mlout, level(`level´)
        end
```

There is one point that might escape your attention: Immediately after obtaining the constraint, we display the constraints even before we undertake the estimation. This way, if the user has made a mistake, he or she may press *Break* rather than waiting until the estimation is complete to discover the error.

Our code also redisplays the constraints every time the problem output is repeated (by typing *myest* without arguments). So that the constraints are now shown twice at the time of estimation, we set the local macro shown to contain yes. If the output is ever repeated, the local macro shown will never be defined (and so will not contain yes) and we will redisplay the constraints along with the results of our estimation.

Also See

[R] **cnsreg**, [R] **constraint**, [R] **matrix**, [R] **ml**, [R] **matrix post**

Title

matrix define — Matrix definition, operators, and functions

Syntax

matrix [define] *matname* = *matrix_expression*

To reset problem-size limits, see [R] **matsize**.

Description

matrix define performs matrix computations. The word define may be omitted.

Remarks

matrix define calculates matrix results from other matrices. For instance,

. matrix define C = A + B

creates C containing the sum of A and B. The word define may be omitted,

. matrix C = A + B

and the command may be further abbreviated:

. mat C=A+B

In the current version, expressions with more than one operator are not allowed. You may not type

. matrix D=A+B*C

You must type instead

. matrix D=B*C
. matrix D=A+D

The same matrix may, however, appear on both the left and the right of the equal sign in all contexts and Stata will not become confused.

Inputting matrices by hand

Before turning to operations on matrices, let's examine how matrices are created. In general, at least in programming situations, you obtain matrices by accessing one of Stata's internal matrices (see [R] **matrix get**) or accumulating it from the data (see [R] **matrix accum**). Nevertheless, the easiest way to create a matrix is simply to enter it at the keyboard—this may not be the normal way one creates matrices, but it is useful for performing small, experimental calculations.

▷ Example

matrix **A**=(*elements*), where **A** is a name of your choosing, allows you to enter a matrix. You define the values rowwise; commas are used to separate elements within a row and backslashes are used to separate the rows. For instance, to create the matrix

$$\mathbf{A} = \begin{pmatrix} 1 & 2 \\ 3 & 4 \end{pmatrix}$$

you type

```
. matrix A = (1,2 \ 3,4)
```

The spacing does not matter. To define the matrix

$$\mathbf{B} = \begin{pmatrix} 1 & 2 & 3 \\ 4 & 5 & 6 \end{pmatrix}$$

you type

```
. matrix B = (1,2,3 \ 4,5,6)
```

To define the matrix

$$\mathbf{C} = \begin{pmatrix} 1 & 2 \\ 3 & 4 \\ 5 & 6 \end{pmatrix}$$

you type

```
. matrix C = (1,2 \ 3,4 \ 5,6)
```

If you need more than one line and are working interactively, you merely keep typing; Stata will wrap the line around the screen. If you are working in a do- or ado-file, see [U] **22.1.3 Long lines in do-files**.

◁

▷ Example

So how do you create vectors? You enter the elements, separating them either by commas or by backslashes. matrix **A**=(1,2,3) creates **A** containing the row vector $(1,2,3)$. matrix **B**=(1\2\3) creates **B** containing the column vector $(1,2,3)'$. matrix **C**=(2) creates 1×1 matrix **C** containing 2.

◁

Matrix operators

In what follows, uppercase letters **A**, **B**, . . . , stand for matrix names. The matrix operators are

+ and − meaning addition and subtraction. matrix **C**=**A**+**B**, **A**: $r \times c$ and **B**: $r \times c$, creates **C**: $r \times c$ containing the elementwise addition $\mathbf{A} + \mathbf{B}$. matrix **C**=**A**-**B** creates **C** containing the elementwise subtraction $\mathbf{A} - \mathbf{B}$. In both cases, an error is issued if the matrices are not conformable. Row and column names are obtained from **A**.

* meaning multiplication. `matrix` $C=A*B$, A: $a \times b$ and B: $b \times c$, returns C: $a \times c$ containing the matrix product AB; an error is issued if A and B are not conformable. The row names of C are obtained from the row names of A, the column names of C from the column names of B.

Transpose notation may be used. That is,

```
. matrix X = A´ * B
. matrix Y = C * D´
. matrix Z = E´ * F´
```

are all legal assuming the matrices (after transposition) are conformable.

`matrix` $C=A*s$ or `matrix` $C=s*A$, A: $a \times b$ and s a Stata scalar (see [R] **scalar**) or a literal number, returns C: $a \times b$ containing the elements of A each multiplied by s. The row and column names of C are obtained from A. For example, `matrix VC=MYMAT*2.5` multiplies each element of `MYMAT` by 2.5 and stores the result in `VC`.

\# meaning Kronecker product. `matrix` $C=A\#B$, A: $a \times b$ and B: $c \times d$, returns C: $ac \times bd$ containing the Kronecker product $A \otimes B$, all elementwise products of A and B. The upper-left submatrix of C is the product $A_{1,1}B$; the submatrix to the right is $A_{1,2}B$; and so on. Row and column names are obtained by using the subnames of A as resulting equation names and the subnames of B for the subnames of C in each submatrix.

Nothing meaning copy. `matrix` $B=A$ copies A into B. The row and column names of B are obtained from A.

´ meaning transpose. `matrix` $B=A´$, A: $r \times c$, creates B: $c \times r$ containing the transpose of A. The row names of B are obtained from the column names of A and the column names of B from the row names of A.

, meaning join columns by row. `matrix` $C=A,B$, A: $a \times b$ and B: $a \times c$, returns C: $a \times (b+c)$ containing A in columns 1 through b and B in columns $b+1$ through $b+c$ (the columns of B are appended to the columns of A). An error is issued if the matrices are not conformable. The row names of C are obtained from A. The column names are obtained from A and B.

The matrix A need not exist but must be specified. E.g., `matrix BIG=BIG,NEW` is valid even before `BIG` exists, allowing one to begin columnwise construction of `BIG` in a loop. In this case, the row names of `BIG` are obtained from `NEW`. In addition to the example below, see [R] **matrix substitute** for an example of this operator.

\ meaning join rows by column. `matrix` $C=A\backslash B$, A: $a \times b$ and B: $c \times b$, returns C: $(a+c) \times b$ containing A in rows 1 through a and B in rows $a+1$ through $a+c$ (the rows of B are appended to the rows of A). An error is issued if the matrices are not conformable. The column names of C are obtained from A. The row names are obtained from A and B.

The matrix A need not exist but must be specified. E.g., `matrix BIG=BIG\NEW` is valid even before `BIG` exists, allowing one to begin rowwise construction of `BIG` in a loop. In this case, the column names of `BIG` are obtained from `NEW`. In addition to the example below, see [R] **matrix substitute** for an example of this operator.

▷ Example

The following examples are artificial but informative:

```
. matrix A = (1,2\3,4)
. matrix B = (5,7\9,2)

. * addition and subtraction:
. matrix C = A+B
```

```
. matrix list C

C[2,2]
     c1  c2
r1    6   9
r2   12   6

. * The same matrix can appear on both the left and the right side of the
. * equal sign no matter what the operator:
. matrix B = A-B
. matrix list B

B[2,2]
     c1  c2
r1   -4  -5
r2   -6   2

. * multiplication:
. matrix C = A*B
. matrix list C

C[2,2]
      c1   c2
r1   -16   -1
r2   -36   -7

. matrix D = A´*A
. matrix list D

symmetric D[2,2]
     c1  c2
c1   10
c2   14  20

. matrix D=2*D
. matrix list D

symmetric D[2,2]
     c1  c2
c1   20
c2   28  40

. * Kronecker product
. matrix rownames A = aa bb          /* see [R] matrix rowname */
. matrix colnames A = alpha beta     /* see [R] matrix rowname */
. matrix list A

A[2,2]
     alpha   beta
aa       1      2
bb       3      4

. matrix D=A#D
. matrix list D

D[4,4]
        alpha:  alpha:  beta:  beta:
           c1      c2     c1     c2
aa:c1      20      28     40     56
aa:c2      28      40     56     80
bb:c1      60      84     80    112
bb:c2      84     120    112    160

. * copy and transpose:
. matrix E=A
. matrix list E

E[2,2]
     alpha   beta
aa       1      2
bb       3      4
```

```
. matrix F=E´
. matrix list F
F[2,2]
          aa   bb
alpha      1    3
 beta      2    4

. * join columns by row:
. matrix G = A,B
. matrix list G
G[2,4]
      alpha    beta      c1      c2
aa        1       2      -4      -5
bb        3       4      -6       2

. * join rows by column:
. matrix H=A\B
. matrix list H
H[4,2]
      alpha    beta
aa        1       2
bb        3       4
r1       -4      -5
r2       -6       2
```

◁

❏ Technical Note

Programmers: Watch out for confusion when combining ´ meaning transpose with local macros, where ´ is one of the characters that encloses macro names: `` `mname´ ``. Stata will not become confused, but you might. Compare

```
. matrix `new1´ = `old´
. matrix `new2´ = `old´´
```

Note that matrix `` `new2´ `` contains matrix `` `old´ ``, transposed. Stata will become confused if you type

```
. matrix `C´ = `A´\`B´
```

because the backslash in front of the `` `B´ `` makes the macro processor take the left quote literally. No substitution is ever made for `` `B´ ``. Even worse, the macro processor assumes the backslash was meant for it and so removes the character! Pretend `` `A´ `` contained a, `` `B´ `` contained b, and `` `C´ `` contained c. After substitution, the line would read

```
. matrix c = a`B´
```

which is not at all what was intended. To make your meaning clear, put a space after the backslash:

```
. matrix `C´ = `A´\ `B´
```

which would then be expanded to read

```
. matrix c = a\ b
```

❏

Matrix functions

In addition to the operators, the following matrix functions are provided:

matrix **A**=I(#) defines **A** as the $\# \times \#$ identity matrix. # must be a literal number. matrix **A**=I(3) defines **A** as the 3×3 identity matrix. matrix **A**=I(`nvar´) would also define **A** as a 3×3 identity matrix if the local macro **nvar** contained 3.

matrix **A**=J(r,c,z) defines **A** as an $r \times c$ matrix containing elements z. r, c, and z must be literal numbers. matrix **A**=J(2,3,0) returns a 2×3 matrix containing 0 for each element. matrix **A**=J(`r´,`c´,`z´) would also return a 2×3 matrix containing zeros if the local macros **r**, **c**, and **z** contained 2, 3, and 0.

matrix **L**=cholesky(**A**) performs Cholesky decomposition for square, symmetric matrix **A**; an error is issued if **A** is not square or not symmetric. **L** is a lower-triangular (square root) matrix such that $\mathbf{LL'} = \mathbf{A}$. Row and column names of **L** are obtained from **A**.

matrix **B**=syminv(**A**), for **A** square, symmetric, and positive definite, returns $\mathbf{B} = \mathbf{A}^{-1}$. If **A** is not positive definite, rows will be inverted until the diagonal terms are zero or negative; the rows and columns corresponding to these terms will be set to 0, producing a g2 inverse. Row names of **B** are obtained from the column names of **A** and column names of **B** are obtained from the row names of **A**.

matrix **B**=inv(**A**), for **A** square but not required to be symmetric or positive definite, returns $\mathbf{B} = \mathbf{A}^{-1}$. A singular matrix will result in an error. Row names of **B** are obtained from the column names of **A** and column names of **B** are obtained from the row names of **A**. syminv() should be used in preference to inv(), which is less accurate, whenever possible. (Also see [R] **matrix svd** for singular value decomposition.)

matrix **B**=sweep(**A**,#) applies the sweep operator to the #th row and column of square matrix **A**. Note that # must be a literal number, not a scalar expression. The names of **B** are obtained from **A** except that the #th row and column names are interchanged. In a loop, one would typically use macros to specify the second argument:

```
local i=`i´+1
matrix S2 = sweep(S1,`i´)
```

For **A**: $n \times n$, $\mathbf{B} = \text{sweep}(\mathbf{A}, k)$ produces **B**: $n \times n$ defined as

$$B_{kk} = \frac{1}{A_{kk}}$$

$$B_{ik} = -\frac{A_{ik}}{A_{kk}}, \qquad i \neq k \qquad (kth\ column)$$

$$B_{kj} = \frac{A_{ij}}{A_{kk}}, \qquad j \neq k \qquad (jth\ row)$$

$$B_{ij} = A_{ij} - \frac{A_{ik}A_{kj}}{A_{kk}}, \qquad i \neq k, j \neq k$$

matrix **B**=corr(**A**), for **A** a covariance matrix, stores the corresponding correlation matrix in **B**. Row and column names are obtained from **A**.

matrix **B**=diag(**A**), for **A**: $1 \times c$ or **A**: $c \times 1$ (**A** a vector), creates **B**: $c \times c$ with diagonal elements **A** and off-diagonal elements 0. Row and column names are obtained from the column names of **A** if **A** is $1 \times c$ or the row names of **A** if **A** is $c \times 1$.

matrix **B**=vecdiag(**A**), for **A**: $c \times c$, creates **B**: $1 \times c$ containing the diagonal elements of **A**. vecdiag() is the opposite of diag(). The row name is set to **r1**. The column names are obtained from the column names of **A**.

`matrix` **B=get**(*systemname*) returns in **B** a copy of the Stata internal matrix *systemname*; see
[R] **matrix get** for examples of this important function.

▷ Example

The examples are, once again, artificial but informative.

```
. * Identity matrix
. matrix myid = I(3)
. matrix list myid

symmetric myid[3,3]
      c1  c2  c3
r1   1
r2   0   1
r3   0   0   1

. * matrix containing constant
. matrix new=J(2,3,0)
. matrix list new

new[2,3]
      c1  c2  c3
r1   0   0   0
r2   0   0   0

. * symmetric inverse
. matrix A=(1,2\2,5)
. matrix Ainv = syminv(A)
. matrix list Ainv

symmetric Ainv[2,2]
      r1  r2
c1   5
c2  -2   1

. * inverse, general
. matrix A=(1,5,9\2,1,7\3,5,1)
. matrix Ainv = inv(A)
. matrix list Ainv

Ainv[3,3]
            r1          r2          r3
c1  -.27419355   .32258065   .20967742
c2   .15322581  -.20967742   .08870968
c3   .05645161   .08064516  -.07258065

. * sweep
. matrix B=sweep(A,1)
. matrix list B

B[3,3]
      r1   c2    c3
c1   1    5     9
r2  -2   -9   -11
r3  -3  -10   -26

. matrix B=sweep(B,1)
. matrix list B

B[3,3]
      c1  c2  c3
r1   1   5   9
r2   2   1   7
r3   3   5   1

. * corr
. matrix C=(36.6598,-3596.483596.48,604030)
```

```
. matrix R=corr(C)
. matrix list R

symmetric R[2,2]
            c1          c2
r1           1
r2  -.7642815            1

. * make diagonal matrix
. matrix d = (1,2,3)
. matrix D = diag(d)
. matrix list D

symmetric D[3,3]
     c1  c2  c3
c1    1
c2    0   2
c3    0   0   3

. * extract diagonal
. matrix e = vecdiag(D)
. matrix list e

e[1,3]
     c1   c2   c3
r1    1    2    3
```

                                                                              ◁

Subscripting and element-by-element definition

matrix $B=A[r_1,r_2]$, for range expressions r_1 and r_2 (defined below), extracts a submatrix from A and stores it in B. Row and column names of B are obtained from the extracted rows and columns of A. In what follows, assume A is $a \times b$.

A range expression can be a literal number. matrix $B=A[1,2]$ would return a 1×1 matrix containing $A_{1,2}$.

A range expression can be a period, meaning all the rows or columns. matrix $B=A[1,.]$ would return a $1 \times b$ matrix (row vector) consisting of the first row of A. matrix $B=A[.,.]$ is the same as matrix $B=A$.

A range expression can be a number followed by two periods followed by another number, meaning the rows or columns from the first number to the second. matrix $B=A[2..4,.]$ would return a $3 \times b$ matrix containing the second through fourth rows and all the columns of A.

A range expression can be a number followed by three periods, meaning all the remaining rows or columns from that number. matrix $B=A[3,4...]$ would return a $1 \times b-3$ matrix (row vector) containing the fourth through last elements of the third row of A.

A range expression can be a quoted string, in which case it refers to the row or column with the specified name. matrix $B=A["price","mpg"]$ returns a 1×1 matrix containing the element whose row name is price and column name mpg, which would be the same as matrix $B=A[2,3]$ if the second row were named price and the third column mpg. matrix $B=A["price",.]$ would return the $1 \times b$ vector corresponding to the row named price. In either case, if there is no matrix row or column with the specified name, an error is issued and the return code set to 111. If the row and/or column names include both an equation name and a subname, the fully qualified name must be specified, as in matrix $B=A["eq1:price",.]$.

A range expression can be a quoted string containing only an equation name, in which case it refers to all rows or columns with the specified equation name. matrix $B=A["eq1:","eq1:"]$ would return the submatrix of rows and columns that have equation names eq1.

A range expression containing a quoted string referring to an element (not to an entire equation) can be combined with the .. and ... syntaxes above: matrix B=A["price"...,"price"...] would define B as the submatrix of A beginning with the rows and columns corresponding to price. matrix B=A["price".."mpg","price".."mpg"] would define B as the submatrix of A starting at rows and columns corresponding to price and continuing through the rows and columns corresponding to mpg.

A range expression can be mixed. matrix B=A[1.."price",2] defines B as the column vector extracted from the second column of A containing the first element through the element corresponding to price.

In all cases, if a number is specified in the range, it must be a literal number; it cannot be a Stata scalar. Macros can be used to achieve this.

matrix A[*i*,*j*]=*exp* changes the *i*, *j* element of A to contain the result of the evaluated expression, as defined in [U] **20 Functions and expressions** and as further defined below in *Matrix functions returning scalars*. *i* and *j* must be literal numbers. The matrix A must already exist; the matrix function J() can be used to achieve this; see above.

▷ Example

Continuing with our artificial but informative examples:

```
. matrix A=(1,2,3,4\5,6,7,8\9,10,11,12\13,14,15,16)
. matrix rownames A = mercury venus earth mars
. matrix colnames A = poor average good exc
. matrix list A

A[4,4]
            poor   average    good     exc
mercury        1         2       3       4
  venus        5         6       7       8
  earth        9        10      11      12
   mars       13        14      15      16

. matrix b = A[1,2]
. matrix list b

symmetric b[1,1]
          average
mercury         2

. matrix b = A["earth","exc"]
. matrix list b

symmetric b[1,1]
           exc
earth       12

. matrix b = A[1..3,2...]
. matrix list b

b[3,3]
          average     good     exc
mercury         2        3       4
  venus         6        7       8
  earth        10       11      12

. matrix b = A["venus"..., "average".."good"]
. matrix list b
```

```
b[3,2]
            average        good
venus           6            7
earth          10           11
 mars          14           15

. matrix b = A[2,.]
. matrix list b
b[1,4]
           poor  average      good      exc
venus        5        6         7        8

. matrix rownames A = eq1:alpha eq1:beta eq2:alpha eq2:beta
. matrix colnames A = eq1:one eq1:two eq2:one eq2:two
. matrix list A
A[4,4]
            eq1:   eq1:   eq2:   eq2:
            one    two    one    two
eq1:alpha    1      2      3      4
 eq1:beta    5      6      7      8
eq2:alpha    9     10     11     12
 eq2:beta   13     14     15     16

. matrix b = A["eq1:","eq2:"]
. matrix list b
b[2,2]
            eq2:   eq2:
            one    two
eq1:alpha    3      4
 eq1:beta    7      8

. * define a matrix element
. matrix A= J(2,2,0)
. matrix A[1,2] = 4
. matrix list A
A[2,2]
      c1   c2
r1     0    4
r2     0    0
```

◁

❑ Technical Note

matrix **A**[i,j]=*exp* can be used to implement matrix formulas that perhaps Stata does not have built in. Let's pretend Stata could not multiply matrices. We could still multiply matrices, and after some work, we could do so conveniently. Given two matrices **A**: $a \times b$ and **B**: $b \times c$, the (i, j) element of $\mathbf{C} = \mathbf{AB}$, **C**: $a \times c$, is defined as

$$C_{ij} = \sum_{k=1}^{b} A_{ik} B_{kj}$$

Here is a Stata program to make that calculation:

```
program define matmult /* arguments A B C, creates C=A*B */
        version 5.0
        local A "`1'"                       /* unload arguments into better names */
        local B "`2'"
        local C "`3'"
```

```
                if colsof(`A´)~=rowsof(`B´) {       /* check conformability       */
                        display in red "matrices not conformable"
                        exit 198
                }
                local a = rowsof(`A´)           /* obtain dimensioning information  */
                local b = colsof(`A´)           /*    see Matrix functions returning */
                local c = colsof(`B´)           /*    scalars below                  */
                matrix `C´ = J(`a´,`c´,0)       /* create result containing 0´s      */
                local i=1
                while `i´<=`a´ {
                        local j=1
                        while `j´<=`c´ {
                                local k=1
                                while `k´<=`b´ {
                                        matrix `C´[`i´,`j´] = `C´[`i´,`j´] + /*
                                                */ `A´[`i´,`k´]*`B´[`k´,`j´]
                                        local k=`k´+1
                                }
                                local j=`j´+1
                        }
                        local i=`i´+1
                }
        end
```

Now, if in some other program, we needed to multiply matrix XXI by Xy to form result beta, we could type `matmult XXI Xy beta` and never use Stata's built-in method for multiplying matrices (`matrix beta=XXI*Xy`). If we typed the program `matmult` into a file named `matmult.ado`, we would not even have to bother to load `matmult` before using it—it would be loaded automatically; see [U] **23 Ado-files**.

❑

Matrix functions returning scalars

In addition to the above functions used with `matrix define`, functions that can be described as matrix functions returning matrices, there are matrix functions that return mathematical scalars. Trace and determinant are two examples.

The matrix functions returning scalars defined below can be used in any context that allows an expression—what is abbreviated *exp* in the syntax diagrams throughout this manual. For instance, `trace()` returns the (scalar) trace of a matrix. Say you have a matrix called MYX. You could type

```
. generate tr = trace(MYX)
```

although this would be a silly thing to do. It would be silly because it would force Stata to evaluate the trace of the matrix many times, once for each observation in the data, and it would then store that same result over and over again in the new data variable `tr`. But you could do it because, if you examine the syntax diagram for `generate` (see [R] **generate**), `generate` allows an *exp*.

If you just wanted to see the trace of MYX, you could type

```
. display trace(MYX)
```

because the syntax diagram for `display` also allows an *exp*; see [R] **display**. More usefully, you could do either of the following:

```
. local tr = trace(MYX)
. scalar tr = trace(MYX)
```

This is more useful because it will evaluate the trace only once and then store the result. In the first case, the result will be stored in a local macro (see [R] **macro**); in the second, it will be stored in a Stata scalar (see [R] **scalar**).

▷ Example

Storing the number as a scalar is better for two reasons: it is more accurate (scalars are stored in double precision) and it is faster (macros are stored as printable characters and this conversion is a time-consuming operation). Not too much should be made of the accuracy issue; macros are stored with at least 13 digits, but it can make a difference in some cases.

In any case, let us demonstrate that both methods work with the simple trace function:

```
. matrix A=(1,6\8,4)
. local tr = trace(A)
. display `tr´
5
. scalar sctr = trace(A)
. scalar list sctr
      sctr =           5
```
◁

❑ Technical Note

The use of a matrix function returning scalar with `generate` does not have to be silly because, instead of specifying a matrix name, you may specify a string variable in the data. If you do, in each observation the contents of the string variable will be taken as a matrix name and the function applied to that matrix for that observation. If there is no such matrix, missing will be returned. Thus, if your data contained

```
. list
          matname
  1.         X1
  2.         X2
  3.          Z
```

You could type

```
. generate tr = trace(matname)
(1 missing value generated)
. list
          matname        tr
  1.         X1          5
  2.         X2          .
  3.          Z         16
```

Evidently, we have no matrix called X2 stored. All the matrix functions returning scalars allow you to specify either a matrix name directly or a string variable that indirectly specifies the matrix name. When you indirectly specify the matrix and the matrix does not exist—as happened above—the function evaluates to missing. When you directly specify the matrix and it does not exist, you get an error:

```
. display trace(X2)
X2 not found
r(111);
```

This is true not only for `trace()`, but for every function described below.
❑

The list of functions below should be viewed as a continuation of [U] **20.3 Functions**. As before, **A**, **B**, ..., stand for matrix names but that definition is now extended, per the technical note above, and **A**, **B**, ..., may also stand for a string literal or a string variable in the data.

rowsof($\mathbf{A}$) and colsof($\mathbf{A}$) return the number of rows or columns of **A**.

rownumb($\mathbf{A}$,*string*) and colnumb($\mathbf{A}$,*string*) return the row or column number associated with the name specified by *string*. For instance, rownumb(MYMAT,"price") returns the row number (say, 3) in MYMAT that has name price (subname price and equation name blank). colnumb(MYMAT,"out2:price") returns the column number associated with name out2:price (subname price and equation name out2). If row or column name is not found, missing is returned.

rownumb() and colnumb() can also return the first row or column number associated with an equation name. For example, colnumb(MYMAT,"out2:") returns the first column number in MYMAT that has equation name out2. Missing is returned if the equation name out2 is not found.

trace($\mathbf{A}$) returns the sum of the diagonal elements of square matrix **A**. If **A** is not square, missing is returned.

det($\mathbf{A}$) returns the determinant of square matrix **A**. The determinant is the volume of the $p - 1$ dimensional manifold described by the matrix in p-dimensional space. If **A** is not square, missing is returned.

el($\mathbf{A}$,i,j) and $\mathbf{A}[i,j]$ return the i,j element of **A**. In most cases, either construct may be used; el(MYMAT,2,3) and MYMAT[2,3] are equivalent although MYMAT[2,3] is more readable. In the case of the second construct, however, **A** must be a matrix name—it cannot be a string literal or string variable. The first construct allows **A** to be a matrix name, string literal, or string variable. For instance, assume mymat (as opposed to MYMAT) is a string variable in the data containing matrix names. mymat[2,3] refers to the $(2,3)$ element of the matrix named mymat, a matrix which probably does not exist and so produces an error. el(mymat,2,3) refers to the data variable mymat; the contents of that variable will be taken to obtain the matrix name and el() will then return the $(2,3)$ element of that matrix. If that matrix does not exist, Stata will not issue an error; because you referred to it indirectly, the el() function will return missing.

In either construct, i and j may be any expression (an *exp*) evaluating to a real. MYMAT[2,3+1] returns the $(2,4)$ element. In programs that loop, you might refer to MYMAT[`i´,`j´+1].

Name conflicts in expressions (name spaces)

Please see [R] **matrix** for a description of name spaces. A matrix might have the same name as a variable in the data and, if it does, Stata might appear confused when evaluating an expression (an *exp*). When the names conflict, Stata uses the rule that it always takes the data-variable interpretation. You can override this.

First, when working interactively, you can avoid the problem by simply naming your matrices differently from your variables.

Second, when writing programs, you can avoid name conflicts by obtaining names for matrices from tempname; see [R] **macro**.

Third, whether working interactively or writing programs, when using names that might conflict, you can use the matrix() pseudo-function to force Stata to take the matrix name interpretation.

matrix(*name*) says that *name* is to be interpreted as a matrix name. For instance, consider the statement local new=trace(xx). This might work and it might not. If xx is a matrix and there is no variable named xx in your data, it will work. If there is also a numeric variable named xx in your data, it will not. Typing the statement will produce a type-mismatch error—Stata assumes when you type xx you are referring to the data variable xx because there is a data variable xx. Typing local new=trace(matrix(xx)) will produce the desired result in that case. When writing programs using matrix names not obtained from tempname, you are strongly advised to state explicitly that all matrix names are matrix names by using the matrix() function.

The only exception to this recommendation has to do with the construct $\mathbf{A}[i,j]$. The two subscripts key Stata that $\mathbf{A}$ must be a matrix name and not an attempt to subscript a variable and so matrix() is not needed. This exception applies only to $\mathbf{A}[i,j]$; it does not apply to el($\mathbf{A},i,j$) which would be more safely written el(matrix($\mathbf{A}$),i,j).

❏ Technical Note

The matrix() and scalar() pseudo-functions (see [R] **scalar**) are really the same function, but you do not need to understand this fine point to program Stata successfully. Understanding might, however, lead to producing more readable code. The formal definition is this:

scalar(*exp*) (and therefore matrix(*exp*)) evaluates *exp*, but restricts Stata to interpreting all names in *exp* as scalar or matrix names. Remember that scalars and matrices share the same name space.

Ergo, since scalar() and matrix() are the same function, you can type trace(matrix(xx)) or trace(scalar(xx)), both do the same thing even though the second looks wrong. Since scalar() and matrix() allow an *exp*, you could also type scalar(trace(xx)) and achieve the same result. scalar() evaluates the *exp* inside the parentheses: it merely restricts how names are interpreted, so now trace(xx) clearly means the trace of the matrix named xx.

How can you make your code more readable? Pretend you wanted to calculate the trace plus the determinant of matrix xx and store it in the Stata scalar named tpd (no, there is no reason you would ever want to make such a silly calculation). You are writing a program and so want to protect yourself from xx also existing in the data. One solution would be

```
scalar tpd = trace(matrix(xx)) + det(matrix(xx))
```

Knowing the full interpretation rule, however, you realize you can shorten this to

```
scalar tpd = matrix(trace(xx) + det(xx))
```

and then, to make it more readable, you substitute scalar() for matrix():

```
scalar tdp = scalar(trace(xx) + det(xx))
```

❏

Macro extended functions

The following macro extended functions (see [R] **macro**) are also defined:

rownames($\mathbf{A}$) and colnames($\mathbf{A}$) return the list of all the row or column subnames of $\mathbf{A}$, each separated by a single blank. Note that the equation names, even if present, are not included.

roweq($\mathbf{A}$) and coleq($\mathbf{A}$) return the list of all row equation names or column equation names of $\mathbf{A}$, each separated by a single blank, and with each name appearing however many times it appears in the matrix.

▷ Example

These functions are provided as macro functions and standard expression functions because Stata's expression evaluator is limited to working with strings of no more than 80 characters in length, something not true of Stata's macro parser. A matrix with many rows or columns can produce an exceedingly long list of names.

In sophisticated programming situations, you sometimes want to process the matrices by row and column names rather than by row and column number. For instance, assume you are programming and have two matrices, xx and yy. You know they contain the same column names but they might be in a different order. You want to reorganize yy to be in the same order as xx. The following code fragment will create `newyy´ (a matrix name obtained from tempname) containing yy in the same order as xx:

```
tempname newyy newcol
local names : colnames(xx)
local name : word 1 of `names´
local i=1
while "`name´"~="" {
        local j = colnumb(yy,"`name´")
        if `j´==. {
                display in red "column for `name´ not found"
                exit 111
        }
        matrix `newcol´ = yy[.,`j´]
        matrix `newyy´ = `newyy´,`newcol´
        local i=`i´+1
        local name : word `i´ of `names´
}
```

◁

Also See

[R] **matrix**, [R] **matrix get**

Title

> **matrix get** — Access system matrices

Syntax

> <u>matrix</u> [<u>define</u>] *matname* = get(*internal_Stata_matrix_name*)

where *internal_Stata_matrix_name* is

_b	coefficients after any estimation command
VCE	covariance matrix of estimators after any estimation command
Rr	constraint matrix after `test`
Cns	constraint matrix after any estimation command
Ld	factor loadings after `factor`
Ev	eigenvalues after `factor`
Psi	uniquenesses after `factor`
Co	correlation matrix after `factor`
SD	standard deviations after `factor`
Mean	means after `factor`

To reset problem-size limits, see [R] **matsize**.

Description

The get() matrix function obtains a copy of an internal Stata system matrix.

Remarks

get() obtains copies of matrices containing coefficients and the covariance matrix of the estimators after estimation commands (such as `regress`, `probit`, etc.) and obtains copies of matrices left behind by other Stata commands. The other side of get() is `matrix post`, which allows ado-file estimation commands to post results to Stata's internal areas; see [R] **matrix post**.

▷ Example

After any model estimation command the coefficients are available in _b and the variance-covariance matrix of the estimators in VCE.

```
. regress price weight mpg

  Source |       SS       df       MS                Number of obs =      74
---------+------------------------------             F(  2,    71) =   14.74
   Model |  186321280       2  93160639.9            Prob > F      =  0.0000
Residual |  448744116      71  6320339.67            R-squared     =  0.2934
---------+------------------------------             Adj R-squared =  0.2735
   Total |  635065396      73  8699525.97            Root MSE      =  2514.0
```

price	Coef.	Std. Err.	t	P>|t|	[95% Conf. Interval]
weight	1.746559	.6413538	2.723	0.008	.4677361	3.025382
mpg	-49.51222	86.15604	-0.575	0.567	-221.3025	122.278
_cons	1946.069	3597.05	0.541	0.590	-5226.244	9118.382

```
. matrix b = get(_b)
. matrix V = get(VCE)
. matrix list b
b[1,3]
        weight        mpg       _cons
y1   1.7465592  -49.512221  1946.0687
. matrix list V
symmetric V[3,3]
           weight         mpg       _cons
weight   .41133468
   mpg   44.601659    7422.863
 _cons  -2191.9032  -292759.82    12938766
```

Note that the columns of b and both dimensions of V are properly labeled.

◁

▷ Example

After test, the restriction matrix is available in Rr. Having just estimated a regression of price on weight and mpg, we will run a test and then get the restriction matrix:

```
. test weight=1, notest
 ( 1)   weight = 1.0
. test mpg=40, accum
 ( 1)   weight = 1.0
 ( 2)   mpg = 40.0
      F(  2,    71) =    6.29
           Prob > F =   0.0030
. matrix rxtr=get(Rr)
. matrix list rxtr
rxtr[2,4]
    c1  c2  c3  c4
r1   1   0   0   1
r2   0   1   0  40
```

◁

Also See

[U] **20.5 Accessing coefficients and standard errors**

[R] **matrix**

Title

matrix mkmat — Convert variables to matrix and vice versa

Syntax

mkmat *varlist* $\big[$if *exp*$\big]$ $\big[$in *range*$\big]$ $\big[$, <u>matrix</u>(*matname*) $\big]$

svmat $\big[$*type*$\big]$ **A** $\big[$, <u>n</u>ames($\{$col $|$ eqcol $|$ matcol $|$ *string*$\}$) $\big]$

matname **A** *namelist* $\big[$, <u>r</u>ows(*range*) <u>c</u>olumns(*range*) <u>e</u>xplicit $\big]$

where **A** is the name of an existing matrix, *type* is a storage type for the new variables, and *namelist* is either (1) a *varlist*, i.e., names of existing variables possibly abbreviated; (2) _cons and the names of existing variables possibly abbreviated; or (3) arbitrary names when the explicit option is specified.

To reset problem-size limits, see [R] **matsize**.

Description

mkmat stores the variables listed in *varlist* in column vectors of the same name; that is, $N \times 1$ matrices where $N = \_N$, the number of observations in the dataset. Or, optionally, they can be stored as a $N \times k$ matrix, where k is the number of variables in *varlist*.

svmat takes a matrix and stores its columns as new variables. It is the reverse of the mkmat command which creates a matrix from existing variables.

matname renames the rows and columns of a matrix. matname differs from the matrix rownames and matrix colnames commands in that matname expands varlist abbreviations and also allows a restricted range for the rows or columns. See [R] **matrix rownames**.

Options

matrix() requests that the vectors be combined in a matrix, instead of creating the column vectors.

names($\{$col $|$ eqcol $|$ matcol $|$ *string*$\}$) specifies how the new variables are to be named.
    names(col) uses the column names of the matrix to name the variables.
    names(eqcol) uses the equation names prefixed to the column names.
    names(matcol) uses the matrix name prefixed to the column names.
    names(*string*) names the variables *string*1, *string*2, ..., *string n*, where *string* is a user-specified *string* and *n* is the number of columns of the matrix.
    If names() is not specified, the variables are named **A**1, **A**2, ..., **A***n*, where **A** is the name of the matrix. If necessary, names will be truncated to 8 characters; if these names are not unique, an error message will be returned.

rows(*range*) and columns(*range*) specify the rows and columns of the matrix to rename. The number of rows or columns specified must be equal to the number of names in *namelist*. If both rows() and columns() are given, then the specified rows are named *namelist* and the specified columns are also named *namelist*. The range must be given in one of the following forms:

rows(.)	renames all the rows;
rows(2..8)	renames rows 2 through 8;
rows(3)	renames only row 3;
rows(4...)	renames row 4 to the last row.

If neither rows() nor columns() is given, then rows(.) columns(.) is the default. That is, the matrix must be square, and both the rows and the columns are named *namelist*.

explicit suppresses the expansion of varlist abbreviations and omits the verification that the names are those of existing variables. That is, the names in *namelist* are used explicitly and can be any valid row or column names.

Remarks

mkmat

Although cross-products of variables can be loaded into a matrix using the matrix accum command, programmers, in some instances, may find it more convenient to work with the variables in their datasets as vectors instead of as cross products. mkmat allows the user a simple way to load specific variables into matrices in Stata's memory.

▷ Example

mkmat uses the variable name to name the single column in the vector. This feature guarantees that the variable name will be carried along in any additional matrix calculations. This feature is also useful when vectors are combined in a general matrix.

```
. describe
Contains data from test.dta
  obs:            10
  vars:            3                          31 May 1996 15:04
  size:          160 (99.9% of memory free)
-------------------------------------------------------------------------------
    1. x            float   %9.0g
    2. y            float   %9.0g
    3. z            float   %9.0g
-------------------------------------------------------------------------------
Sorted by:
. list
              x           y           z
  1.          1          10           2
  2.          2           9           4
  3.          3           8           3
  4.          4           7           5
  5.          5           6           7
  6.          6           5           6
  7.          7           4           8
  8.          8           3          10
  9.          9           2           1
 10.         10           1           9
. mkmat x y z, matrix(xyzmat)
```

```
. matrix dir
          xyzmat[10,3]
               z[10,1]
               y[10,1]
               x[10,1]

. matrix list xyzmat

xyzmat[10,3]
         x    y    z
    r1   1   10    2
    r2   2    9    4
    r3   3    8    3
    r4   4    7    5
    r5   5    6    7
    r6   6    5    6
    r7   7    4    8
    r8   8    3   10
    r9   9    2    1
   r10  10    1    9
```

If one of the variables has missing values, you will receive an error message and no matrices will be created.

```
. matrix drop _all

. replace y = . in 5
(1 real change made, 1 to missing)

. mkmat x y z
matrix y would have missing values
r(504);

. matrix dir

.
```

This problem can be taken care of by restricting the matrix to nonmissing values.

◁

❑ Technical Note

mkmat provides a useful addition to Stata's matrix commands, but it will work only with small dataset sizes.

Stata limits matrices to being no more than matsize × matsize which, by default, means 40 × 40, and, even with Intercooled Stata, this can be increased to a maximum of 800 × 800. Such limits appear to contradict Stata's claims of being able to process large datasets. By limiting Stata's matrix capabilities to matsize × matsize, has not Stata's matrix language itself been limited to datasets no larger than matsize? It would certainly appear so; in the simple matrix calculation for regression coefficients $(\mathbf{X}'\mathbf{X})^{-1}\mathbf{X}'\mathbf{y}$, $\mathbf{X}$ is an $n \times k$ matrix (n being the number of observations and k the number of variables) and, given the matsize constraint, n must certainly be less than 800.

Our answer is as follows: Yes, $\mathbf{X}$ is limited in the way stated but note that $\mathbf{X}'\mathbf{X}$ is a mere $k \times k$ matrix and, similarly, $\mathbf{X}'\mathbf{y}$ only $k \times 1$. Both these matrices are well within Stata's matrix-handling capabilities and Stata's **matrix accum** command (see [R] **matrix accum**) can directly create both of them.

Moreover, even if Stata could hold the $n \times k$ matrix $\mathbf{X}$, it would still be more efficient to use **matrix accum** to form $\mathbf{X}'\mathbf{X}$. $\mathbf{X}'\mathbf{X}$, interpreted literally, says to load a copy of the data, transpose it, load a second copy of the data, and then form the matrix product. Thus, two copies of the data occupy memory in addition to the original copy Stata already had available (and from which **matrix accum** could directly form the result with no additional memory use). For small n, the inefficiency is not important but, for large n, the inefficiency can be such as to actually make the calculation infeasible. For instance, with $n = 12{,}000$ and $k = 6$, the additional memory use is 1,125K bytes.

More generally, matrices in statistical applications tend to have dimension $k \times k$, $n \times k$, and $n \times n$, with k small and n large. Terms dealing with the data are of the generic form $\mathbf{X}'_{k_1 \times n} \mathbf{W}_{n \times n} \mathbf{Z}_{n \times k_2}$. ($\mathbf{X}'\mathbf{X}$ fits the generic form with $\mathbf{X} = \mathbf{X}$, $\mathbf{W} = \mathbf{I}$, and $\mathbf{Z} = \mathbf{X}$.) Matrix programming languages are not capable of dealing with the deceivingly simple calculation $\mathbf{X}'\mathbf{W}\mathbf{Z}$ because of the staggering size of the $\mathbf{W}$ matrix. For $n = 12{,}000$, storing $\mathbf{W}$ requires a little more than a gigabyte of memory. In statistical formulas, however, $\mathbf{W}$ is given by formula and, in fact, never needs to be stored in its entirety. Exploitation of this fact is all that is needed to resurrect the use of a matrix programming language in statistical applications. Matrix programming languages may be inefficient because of copious memory use, but in statistical applications, the inefficiency is minor for matrices of size $k \times k$ or smaller. Our design of the various `matrix accum` commands allow calculating terms of the form $\mathbf{X}'\mathbf{W}\mathbf{Z}$ and this one feature, we have found, is all that is necessary to allow efficient and robust use of matrix languages.

Programs for creating data matrices such as that offered by `mkmat` are useful for pedagogical purposes and, in addition, for a specific application where Stata's matsize constraint is not binding; it seems so natural. On the other hand, it is important that general tools not be implemented by forming data matrices because such tools will be drastically limited in terms of the dataset size. Coding the problem in terms of the various `matrix accum` commands (see [R] **matrix accum**) is admittedly more tedious but, by abolishing data matrices from your programs, you will produce tools suitable for use on large datasets.

❏

svmat

▷ Example

Let us get the vector of coefficients from a regression and use `svmat` to save the vector as a new variable, save the dataset, load the dataset back into memory, use `mkmat` to create a vector from the variable, and finally, use `matname` to rename the columns of the row vector.

```
. quietly regress mpg weight gratio foreign
. matrix b = get(_b)
. matrix list b
b[1,4]
         weight      gratio     foreign       _cons
y1  -.00613903   1.4571134  -2.2216815   36.101353
. matrix c = b´
. svmat double c, name(bvector)
. list bvector1 in 1/5
        bvector1
  1.  -.00613903
  2.   1.4571134
  3.  -2.2216815
  4.   36.101353
  5.           .
. save example
file example.dta saved
. use example
. mkmat bvector1 if bvector1~=.
```

```
. matrix list bvector1
bvector1[4,1]
        bvector1
r1   -.00613903
r2    1.4571134
r3   -2.2216815
r4    36.101353
. matrix d = bvector1´
. matname d wei gr for _cons, c(.)
. matrix list d
d[1,4]
                weight      gratio     foreign       _cons
bvector1   -.00613903    1.4571134   -2.2216815    36.101353
```

◁

Methods and Formulas

mkmat, svmat, and matname are implemented as ado-files.

Acknowledgment

mkmat was written by Ken Heinecke of the Federal Reserve Bank of Kansas City.

References

Gould, W. W. 1994. ip6.1: Data and matrices. *Stata Technical Bulletin* 20: 10. Reprinted in *Stata Technical Bulletin Reprints*, vol. 4, pp. 70–71.

Heinecke, K. 1994. ip6: Storing variables in vectors and matrices. *Stata Technical Bulletin* 20: 8–9. Reprinted in *Stata Technical Bulletin Reprints*, vol. 4, pp. 68–70.

Sribney, W. M. 1995. ip6.2: Storing matrices as variables. *Stata Technical Bulletin* 24: 9–10. Reprinted in *Stata Technical Bulletin Reprints*, vol. 4, pp. 71–73.

Also See

[R] **matrix**, [R] **matrix accum**

Title

> **matrix post** — Post and redisplay estimation results

Syntax

<u>matrix</u> <u>post</u> **b** **V** $\left[\mathbf{C}\right]$ $\left[,\ \underline{\text{dep}}\text{name}(name)\ \underline{\text{obs}}(\#)\ \underline{\text{dof}}(\#)\ \right]$

<u>matrix</u> <u>mlout</u> $\left[,\ \underline{\text{ef}}\text{orm}(string)\ \underline{\text{first}}\ \underline{\text{level}}(\#)\ \right]$

where **b** is a $1 \times p$ coefficient vector (matrix), **V** is a $p \times p$ covariance matrix, and **C** is a $c \times (p+1)$ constraint matrix.

To reset problem-size limits, see [R] **matsize**.

Description

    matrix post saves estimation results in Stata's system areas, making all the post-estimation features described in [U] **26 Estimation and post-estimation commands** available. The specified matrices cease to exist after **post**; they are literally moved into Stata's system areas. They can be reobtained with the **matrix get()** function; see [R] **matrix get**.

    matrix mlout displays or redisplays the coefficient table corresponding to results that have been previously posted.

    For a discussion of posting results with constraint matrices (**C** in the syntax diagram above), see [R] **matrix constraint**, but only after reading this entry.

Options

    depname(*name*) specified with **matrix post** supplies a name which should be that of the dependent variable but can be anything; that name is saved and added to the appropriate place on the output whenever **matrix mlout** is executed.

    obs(*#*) specified with **matrix post** supplies the number of observations on which the estimation was performed; that number is saved and stored in _result(1) whenever **matrix mlout** is executed.

    dof(*#*) specified with **matrix post** supplies the number of (denominator) degrees of freedom that is to be used with t and F statistics. This number is used in calculating significance levels and confidence intervals by **matrix mlout** and by subsequent **test** commands performed on the posted results. If the option is not specified, normal (Z) and χ^2 statistics are used.

    eform(*string*) specified with **matrix mlout** indicates that the exponentiated form of the coefficients is to be output and reporting of the constant is to be suppressed; *string* is used to label the exponentiated coefficients; see [R] **maximize**.

    first requests that Stata display only the first equation and make it appear as if only one equation were estimated.

    level(*#*) specified with **matrix mlout** supplies the significance level for the confidence intervals of the coefficients; see [U] **26 Estimation and post-estimation commands**.

Remarks

Remarks are presented under the headings

Single-equation models
Multiple-equation models
Single-equation models masquerading as multiple-equation models
Minor details: the depname() option
Minor details: the 'dof() option

An important feature of Stata is that, after any estimation command, you can obtain the coefficients and standard errors using _b[] and _se[] (see [U] **20.5 Accessing coefficients and standard errors**), you can list the variance-covariance matrix of the estimators using vce (see [R] **vce**), you can obtain the linear prediction and its standard error using predict (see [R] **predict**), and you can test linear hypotheses about the coefficients using test (see [R] **test**). All of these features are summarized in [U] **26 Estimation and post-estimation commands**.

If you undertake to write your own estimation command, your command can share all of these features as well. This is accomplished by posting the results you calculate to Stata. The basic outline of an estimation command is

```
program define myest
        version 5.0
        parse "`*'", parse(" ,")
        local options "Level(integer $S_level)"
        if ~("`1'"=="," | "`*'"=="") {
                tempname b V
                local options "`options' whatever"
                parse the user's estimation request;
                perform the estimation to produce coefficient vector in
                `b' and variance-covariance matrix in `V' ;
                assume that you have stored the number of observations and
                the name of the dependent variable in macros nobs and depn ;
                matrix post `b' `V', obs(`nobs') depname(`depn')
                global S_E_depv "`depn'"
                store whatever else you want in S_E_ macros;
                global S_E_cmd "myest"
        }
        else {
                if "$S_E_cmd"!="myest" { error 301 }
                parse "`*'"
        }
        if `level'<10 | `level'>99 {
                local level = 95
        }
        output any header above the coefficient table;
        matrix mlout, level(`level')
end
```

We will not discuss here how the estimates are formed, but see [R] **matrix** for an example of programming linear regression and see [R] **ml** for examples of programming maximum-likelihood estimators. However the estimates are formed, our interest is in the posting of those results to Stata.

Single-equation models

Before posting, the coefficient vector is stored as a $1 \times p$ matrix and the corresponding variance-covariance matrix as a $p \times p$ matrix. The names bordering the coefficient matrix and the covariance matrix play an important role. First, they must be the same. Second, it is these names that tell Stata how the results link to Stata's other features.

User estimation results come in two flavors: single-equation models and multiple-equation models. The lack or presence of equation names in the names bordering the matrix tells Stata which it is. For instance, consider

```
. matrix list b
b[1,3]
        weight         mpg       _cons
y1    1.7465592  -49.512221  1946.0687
. matrix list V
symmetric V[3,3]
            weight         mpg       _cons
weight    .41133468
   mpg    44.601659    7422.863
 _cons   -2191.9032  -292759.82   12938766
```

If these were your estimation results, they would correspond to a single-equation model because the names bordering the matrices have no equation names. Here we post these results:

```
. matrix post b V
. matrix mlout
------------------------------------------------------------------------------
          |      Coef.   Std. Err.        z     P>|z|     [95% Conf. Interval]
----------+-------------------------------------------------------------------
   weight |   1.746559   .6413538      2.723    0.006     .4895288    3.003589
      mpg |  -49.51222   86.15604     -0.575    0.566     -218.375    119.3505
    _cons |   1946.069    3597.05      0.541    0.588    -5104.019    8996.156
------------------------------------------------------------------------------
```

Once the results have been posted, anytime Stata executes the `matrix mlout` command, Stata will redisplay the coefficient table. Moreover, all of Stata's other post-estimation features work; for instance:

```
. correlate, _coef
          |   weight        mpg      _cons
----------+---------------------------------
   weight|   1.0000
      mpg|   0.8072     1.0000
    _cons|  -0.9501    -0.9447     1.0000
. test weight
 ( 1)  weight = 0.0
          chi2(  1) =      7.42
        Prob > chi2 =    0.0065
. test weight=mpg/50
 ( 1)  weight - .02 mpg = 0.0
          chi2(  1) =      4.69
        Prob > chi2 =    0.0303
```

If the user were to type `predict pred`, `predict` would create a new variable based on

$$1.746559 \, \text{weight} - 49.51222 \, \text{mpg} + 1946.069$$

except that it would carry out the calculation using the full, double-precision values of the coefficients. All of these determinations were made by Stata based on the names bordering the posted matrices.

Multiple-equation models

Now consider the following two matrices prior to posting:

```
. matrix list b
b[1,6]
            price:      price:      price:      displ:      displ:      displ:
            weight         mpg       _cons      weight     foreign       _cons
y1    1.7465592  -49.512221   1946.0687   .09675485  -25.612697  -87.235477
. matrix list V
symmetric V[6,6]
                      price:      price:      price:      displ:      displ:
                      weight         mpg       _cons      weight     foreign
price:weight      .41133468
   price:mpg      44.601659    7422.863
 price:_cons     -2191.9032  -292759.82    12938766
displ:weight              0           0           0   .00005715
displ:foreign             0           0           0   .05722175   163.01385
  displ:_cons             0           0           0  -.18958245  -221.24233
                      displ:
                       _cons
  displ:_cons     660.29805
```

Ignore the statistically independent structure of the covariance matrix—it plays no role here. What is important is that the names of the matrices include equation names. Here we post these matrices to Stata and then use the posted results:

```
. matrix post b V
. matrix mlout
------------------------------------------------------------------------------
            |      Coef.   Std. Err.      z    P>|z|     [95% Conf. Interval]
------------+-----------------------------------------------------------------
price       |
     weight |   1.746559   .6413538     2.723   0.006     .4895288    3.003589
        mpg |  -49.51222   86.15604    -0.575   0.566     -218.375    119.3505
      _cons |   1946.069    3597.05     0.541   0.588    -5104.019    8996.156
------------+-----------------------------------------------------------------
displ       |
     weight |   .0967549   .0075599    12.798   0.000     .0819376    .1115721
    foreign |   -25.6127   12.76769    -2.006   0.045     -50.6369   -.5884886
      _cons |  -87.23548   25.69627    -3.395   0.001    -137.5992   -36.87172
------------------------------------------------------------------------------
. test [price]weight
 ( 1)  [price]weight = 0.0
          chi2(  1) =    7.42
        Prob > chi2 =    0.0065
. test weight
 ( 1)  [price]weight = 0.0
 ( 2)  [displ]weight = 0.0
          chi2(  2) =  171.21
        Prob > chi2 =    0.0000
```

Stata determined that this was a multiple-equation model because of the presence of the equation names. All of Stata's equation name features (such as those available with the **test** command) are then made available. The user could type **predict pred** to obtain linear predictions of the [price] equation (because **predict** defaults to the first equation), or the user could type **predict pred, equation(displ)** to obtain predictions of the [displ] equation:

$$.0967549\,\mathtt{weight} - 25.6127\,\mathtt{mpg} - 87.23548$$

Single-equation models masquerading as multiple-equation models

Sometimes, it may be convenient to program a single-equation model as if it were a multiple-equation model. This occurs when there are ancillary parameters. Think of linear regression: in addition to the parameter estimates, there is s, an estimate of σ, the standard error of the residual. This can be calculated on the side in that one can calculate $\mathbf{b} = (\mathbf{X'X})^{-1}\mathbf{X'y}$ independently of s and then calculate s given $\mathbf{b}$. Pretend that were not the case—think of a straightforward maximum-likelihood calculation where s is just one more parameter (in most models, ancillary parameters and the coefficients must be solved for jointly). The right thing to do would be to give s its own equation:

```
. mat list b

b[1,4]
        price:      price:       price:      _anc:
        weight         mpg        _cons      sigma
y1   1.7465592  -49.512221    1946.0687       2514

.matrix list V
 (output omitted )

. matrix post b V

. matrix mlout
```

```
-------------------------------------------------------------------------
          |      Coef.   Std. Err.      z    P>|z|     [95% Conf. Interval]
----------+--------------------------------------------------------------
price     |
   weight |   1.746559    .6413538    2.723   0.006     .4895288   3.003589
      mpg |  -49.51222    86.15604   -0.575   0.566    -218.375    119.3505
    _cons |   1946.069     3597.05    0.541   0.588    -5104.019   8996.156
----------+--------------------------------------------------------------
_anc      |
    sigma |       2514         900    2.793   0.005     750.0324   4277.968
-------------------------------------------------------------------------
```

Now consider the alternative, which would be simply to add s to the estimated parameters without equation names:

```
. matrix list b

b[1,4]
        weight          mpg        _cons       sigma
y1   1.7465592  -49.512221    1946.0687        2514

. matrix list V
 (output omitted )

. matrix post b V

. matrix mlout
```

```
-------------------------------------------------------------------------
          |      Coef.   Std. Err.      z    P>|z|     [95% Conf. Interval]
----------+--------------------------------------------------------------
   weight |   1.746559    .6413538    2.723   0.006     .4895288   3.003589
      mpg |  -49.51222    86.15604   -0.575   0.566    -218.375    119.3505
    _cons |   1946.069     3597.05    0.541   0.588    -5104.019   8996.156
    sigma |       2514         900    2.793   0.005     750.0324   4277.968
-------------------------------------------------------------------------
```

This second solution is inferior because, were the user to type `predict pred`, `predict` would attempt to form the linear combination:

$$1.746559\,\mathtt{weight} - 49.51222\,\mathtt{mpg} + 1946.069 + 2514\,\mathtt{sigma}$$

There are only two possibilities and neither is good; either sigma does not exist in the data—which is to be hoped—and predict produces the error message "sigma not found", or something called sigma does exist and predict goes forth to form this meaningless combination.

On the other hand, if the parameter estimates are separated from the ancillary parameter (which could be parameters) by the equation names—the user can type predict pred, equation(price) to obtain a meaningful result. Moreover, the user can omit the equation(price) part because predict (and Stata's other post-estimation commands) default to the first equation.

We recommend that ancillary parameters be collected together, given their own equation, and that the equation be called _anc.

Minor details: the depname() option

Single-equation models may have a single dependent variable; in those that do, you should specify the identify of this single dependent variable in the depname() option with matrix post. The result is simply to add a little more labeling to the output:

```
. matrix post b V, depname(price)
. matrix mlout
```

price	Coef.	Std. Err.	z	P>|z|	[95% Conf. Interval]	
mpg	-49.51222	86.15604	-0.575	0.566	-218.375	119.3505
weight	1.746559	.6413538	2.723	0.006	.4895288	3.003589
_cons	1946.069	3597.05	0.541	0.588	-5104.019	8996.156

Note the addition of the word price at the top of the table.

Minor details: the dof() option

At the time of posting, if you do not specify the dof(#) option, normal (Z) statistics will be used to calculate significance levels and confidence intervals on subsequent matrix mlout output. If you do specify dof(#), t statistics with # degrees of freedom will be used. Similarly, if dof() is not specified, any subsequent test commands will present a χ^2 statistic; if dof(#) is specified, subsequent test commands will use the F statistic with # denominator degrees of freedom.

In all the examples so far, we have not specified dof(). Here is the result of specifying it:

```
. matrix post b V, dof(71)
. matrix mlout
```

	Coef.	Std. Err.	t	P>|t|	[95% Conf. Interval]	
mpg	-49.51222	86.15604	-0.575	0.567	-221.3025	122.278
weight	1.746559	.6413538	2.723	0.008	.4677361	3.025382
_cons	1946.069	3597.05	0.541	0.590	-5226.244	9118.382

Saved Results

matrix post saves no results. matrix mlout saves the number of observations in _result(1), the dimension of the parameter vector in _result(3), and the number of degrees of freedom, if specified, in _result(5).

Also See

[R] **matrix**, [R] **matrix constraint**, [R] **ml**

Title

> **matrix rowname** — Name rows and columns

Syntax

matrix <u>rown</u>ames **A** = *name(s)*

matrix <u>coln</u>ames **A** = *name(s)*

matrix <u>rowe</u>q **A** = *name(s)*

matrix <u>cole</u>q **A** = *name(s)*

Description

matrix rownames and colnames reset the row and column names of an already existing matrix. Here, name refers to a subname, an equation name followed by a colon, or an equation name, a colon, and a subname.

matrix roweq and coleq also reset the row and column names of an already existing matrix but, if a simple name is specified (a name without a colon), it is interpreted as an equation name.

In either case, the part of the name not specified is left unchanged.

Remarks

See [R] **matrix** for a description of the row and column names bordering a matrix.

▷ Example

In general, the names bordering matrices are set correctly by Stata due to the tracking of the matrix algebra and you will not need to reset them. Nevertheless, imagine you have formed $X'X$ in the matrix named XX and that it corresponds to the underlying variables price, weight, and mpg:

```
. matrix list XX
symmetric XX[3,3]
          c1          c2          c3
r1   3.448e+09
r2   1.468e+09   7.188e+08
r3     9132716     4493720       36008
```

You did not form this matrix with matrix accum because, had you done so, the rows and columns would already be correctly named. However you formed it, you now want to reset the names:

```
. matrix rownames XX = price weight mpg
. matrix colnames XX = price weight mpg
. matrix list XX
symmetric XX[3,3]
              price      weight         mpg
 price   3.448e+09
weight   1.468e+09   7.188e+08
   mpg     9132716     4493720       36008
```

◁

❏ Technical Note

> `matrix rownames` and `colnames` behave in some situations in ways that may surprise you. Among the surprises are

1. If your list of names includes no colons—does not mention the equation names—whatever equation names are in place are left in place; they are not changed.

2. If your list of names has every name ending in a colon—so that it mentions only the equation names and not the subnames—whatever subnames are in place are left in place; they are not changed.

3. If your list of names has fewer names than are required to label all the rows or columns, the last name in the list is replicated. (If you specify too many names, you will get the conformability error message and no names are changed.)

These surprises have their uses but, if you make a mistake, the result really may surprise you. For instance, rule 3, by itself, is just odd. Combined with rule 2, however, rule 3 allows you to set all the equation names in a matrix easily. If you type '`matrix rownames XX = myeq:`', all the equation names in the row are reset while the subnames are left unchanged:

```
. matrix rownames XX = myeq:
. matrix list XX

symmetric XX[3,3]
                    price      weight         mpg
 myeq:price     3.448e+09
myeq:weight     1.468e+09   7.188e+08
  myeq:mpg       9132716     4493720       36008
```

Setting equation names is often done before forming a partitioned matrix so that, when the components are assembled, each has the correct equation name.

> Thus, to review, to get the result above, we could have typed

```
. matrix rownames XX = myeq:price myeq:weight myeq:mpg
```

or

```
. matrix rownames XX = price weight mpg
. matrix rownames XX = myeq:
```

or even:

```
. matrix rownames XX = myeq:
. matrix rownames XX = price weight mpg
```

All would have resulted in the same outcome. The real surprise comes, however, when you make a mistake:

```
. matrix rownames XX = myeq:
. matrix rownames XX = price weight
. matrix list XX

symmetric XX[3,3]
                    price      weight         mpg
 myeq:price     3.448e+09
myeq:weight     1.468e+09   7.188e+08
myeq:weight      9132716     4493720       36008
```

Our mistake above is that we listed only two names for the subnames of the rows of **XX** and `matrix rownames` then labeled both of the last rows with the subname `weight`.

❏

❏ Technical Note

The equation name _: by itself is special; it means the null equation name. For instance, as of the last technical note, we were left with the result:

```
. matrix list XX

symmetric XX[3,3]
                    price       weight          mpg
  myeq:price  3.448e+09
  myeq:weight 1.468e+09   7.188e+08
  myeq:weight   9132716      4493720          36008
```

Let's fix it:

```
. matrix rownames XX = price weight mpg
. matrix rownames XX = _:
. matrix list XX

symmetric XX[3,3]
              price       weight          mpg
  price   3.448e+09
  weight  1.468e+09   7.188e+08
     mpg    9132716      4493720          36008
```

❏

❏ Technical Note

matrix roweq and coleq are really the same commands as matrix rownames and colnames. They differ in only one respect: If a specified name does not contain a colon, roweq and coleq interpret that name as if it did end in a colon.

matrix rownames, colnames, roweq, and coleq are often used in conjunction with the rownames(), colnames(), roweq(), and coleq() macro extended functions introduced in [R] **matrix define**. It is important to remember that the rownames() and colnames() extended functions return only the subname:

```
. matrix list XX

symmetric XX[3,3]
                   myeq:       myeq:       myeq:
                   price       weight        mpg
  myeq:price  3.448e+09
  myeq:weight 1.468e+09   7.188e+08
     myeq:mpg   9132716      4493720       36008
. local rsubs : rownames(XX)
. display "The row subnames of XX are -- `rsubs' --"
The row subnames of XX are -- price weight mpg --
```

Similarly, the roweq() extended macro function returns only the equation names and without the trailing colon:

```
. local reqs : roweq(XX)
. display "the row equations of XX are -- `reqs' --"
the row equations of XX are -- myeq myeq myeq --
```

Thus, now consider the problem that you have two matrices named A and B which have the same number of rows. A is correctly labeled and includes equation names. You want to copy the names of A to B. You might be tempted to type

```
. local names : rownames(A)
. matrix rownames B = `names'
```

This is not adequate. You will have copied the subnames but not the equation names. To copy both parts of the names, you must type

```
. local subs : rownames(A)
. local eqs : roweq(A)
. matrix rownames B = `subs´
. matrix roweq B = `eqs´
```

This method can be used even when there might not be equation names. The equation name _ is special not only in that setting an equation to that name removes the equation name but, when there is no equation name, the roweq() and coleq() macro extended functions return that name.

❑

Also See

[R] **matrix**, [R] **matrix define**

Title

> **matrix score** — Score data from coefficient vectors

Syntax

matrix <u>score</u> [*type*] *newvar* = **b** [if *exp*] [in *range*]

where **b** is a $1 \times p$ matrix.

To reset problem-size limits, see [R] **matsize**.

Description

matrix score creates $newvar_j = \mathbf{x}_j \mathbf{b}'$ (**b** a row vector) where $\mathbf{x}_j$ is the row vector of values of the variables specified by the column names of **b**. The name _cons is treated as a variable equal to 1.

Remarks

Scoring refers to forming linear combinations of variables in the data with respect to a coefficient vector. For instance, consider the vector coefs:

```
. matrix list coefs

coefs[1,3]
          weight        mpg       _cons
y1     1.7465592  -49.512221   1946.0687
```

Scoring the data with this vector would create a new variable equal to the linear combination:

$$1.7465592\,\texttt{weight} - 49.512221\,\texttt{mpg} + 1946.0687$$

The vector is interpreted as coefficients; the corresponding names of the variables are obtained from the column names (row names if coefs were a column vector). To form this linear combination, we type

```
. matrix score lc = coefs

. summarize lc

Variable |     Obs        Mean    Std. Dev.        Min         Max
---------+-----------------------------------------------------------
      lc |      74    6165.257    1597.606     3406.46    9805.269
```

❑ Technical Note

Even if the coefficient vector has equation names, **matrix score** ignores them. For instance, given

```
. matrix list coefs

coefs[1,5]
           price:       price:      price:      displ:      displ:
          weight          mpg       _cons      weight       _cons
y1     1.7465592  -49.512221   1946.0687   .10574552  -121.99702
```

`matrix score lc = coefs` would produce the (meaningless) linear combination

$$lc = 1.7465592\,\text{weight} - 49.512221\,\text{mpg} + 1946.0687 +$$
$$.10574552\,\text{weight} - 121.99702$$

```
. matrix score lc = coefs
. summarize lc
Variable |      Obs        Mean   Std. Dev.       Min        Max
---------+-------------------------------------------------------
     lc |       74    6362.554   1679.352    3474.805   10195.08
```

As a programmer, it is your responsibility to extract the equations. It is not difficult:

```
. matrix coefs1 = coefs[1,"price:"]
. matrix coefs2 = coefs[1,"displ:"]
. matrix score lc1 = coefs1
. matrix score lc2 = coefs2
. summarize lc1 lc2
Variable |      Obs        Mean   Std. Dev.       Min        Max
---------+-------------------------------------------------------
    lc1 |       74    6165.257   1597.606     3406.46   9805.269
    lc2 |       74    197.2973   82.18474     64.1151   389.8113
```

❑

Also See

[R] **matrix**

> **matrix substitute** — Create partitioned matrices

Syntax

<u>matrix</u> <u>subs</u>titute **A** [*i*,*j*] = **B**

where **A** and **B** are existing matrices and *i* and *j* are literal numbers.

To reset problem-size limits, see [R] **matsize**.

Description

`matrix substitute` copies matrix **B** into the i, j and above elements of A.

Remarks

`matrix substitute` **A** [*i*,*j*]=**B** changes the values of $A_{i,j}$, $A_{i,j+1}$, ..., $A_{i+1,j}$, etc., to contain **B**; that is, $A_{i,j} = B_{1,1}$, $A_{i,j+1} = B_{1,2}$, ..., $A_{i+1,j} = B_{2,1}$, etc. If **B** is $m \times n$, **A** must be at least $(m + i - 1) \times (n + j - 1)$ or an error is returned. If **A** is larger than that, the elements outside the range necessary to hold **B** are unchanged.

▷ Example

In addition to `matrix substitute`, the matrix operators , and \ (see [R] **matrix define**) are useful for constructing a partitioned matrix. For instance:

```
. matrix list A
A[3,2]
     c1  c2
r1    1   2
r2    3   4
r3    5   6
. matrix list B
B[3,2]
     c1  c2
r1    7   8
r2    9  10
r3   11  12
. matrix list C
C[2,2]
     c1  c2
r1   13  14
r2   15  16
. matrix list D
D[2,2]
     c1  c2
r1   17  18
r2   19  20
```

478

```
. matrix AB = A,B
. matrix list AB

AB[3,4]
     c1  c2  c1  c2
r1    1   2   7   8
r2    3   4   9  10
r3    5   6  11  12
. matrix CD = C,D
. matrix ABCD = AB\CD
. matrix list ABCD

ABCD[5,4]
     c1  c2  c1  c2
r1    1   2   7   8
r2    3   4   9  10
r3    5   6  11  12
r1   13  14  17  18
r2   15  16  19  20
```

matrix substitute is used when you already have an existing matrix and want to substitute in the elements from another matrix:

```
. matrix substitute ABCD[2,2]=A
. matrix list ABCD

ABCD[5,4]
     c1  c2  c1  c2
r1    1   2   7   8
r2    3   1   2  10
r3    5   3   4  12
r1   13   5   6  18
r2   15  16  19  20
```

◁

Also See

[R] **matrix**, [R] **matrix define**

Title

matrix svd — Singular value decomposition

Syntax

<u>matrix</u> <u>svd</u> **U w V = A**

where **U**, **w**, and **V** are matrix names (the matrices may exist or not) and **A** is the name of an existing $m \times n, m \geq n$ matrix.

To reset problem-size limits, see [R] **matsize**.

Description

The svd matrix command produces the singular value decomposition (SVD) of **A**.

Remarks

The singular value decomposition of $m \times n$ matrix **A**, $m \geq n$, is defined as

$$\mathbf{A} = \mathbf{U} \operatorname{diag}(\mathbf{w}) \mathbf{V}'$$

U: $m \times n$, **w**: $1 \times n$ (diag(**w**): $n \times n$), and **V**: $n \times n$, where **U** is column orthogonal (**U'U = I** if $m = n$), all the elements of **w** are positive or zero, and **V'V = I**.

Singular value decomposition can be used to obtain a g2-inverse of **A** (**A***: $n \times m$, such that **AA*A = A**) via **A* = V**[diag$(1/w_j)$]**U'** where $1/w_j$ refers to individually taking the reciprocal of the elements of **w** and substituting 0 if $w_j = 0$ or is small. If **A** is square and of full rank, **A* = A^{-1}**.

▷ Example

Singular value decomposition is used to obtain accurate inverses of nearly singular matrices and to obtain g2 inverses of matrices which are singular, to construct orthonormal bases, and to develop approximation matrices. Our example will merely prove that matrix svd works:

```
. matrix A = (1,2,9\2,7,5\2,4,18)
. matrix svd U w V = A
. matrix list U

U[3,3]
            c1          c2          c3
r1   -.42313293    .89442719   -.1447706
r2    -.3237169   -6.016e-17   .94615399
r3   -.84626585   -.4472136   -.2895412

. matrix list w

w[1,3]
            c1          c2          c3
r1   21.832726   2.612e-16   5.5975071
```

```
. matrix list V

V[3,3]
             c1          c2          c3
c1   -.12655765   -.96974658     .2087456
c2   -.29759672    .23786237    .92458514
c3   -.94626601    .05489132   -.31869671

. matrix W = diag(w)
. matrix UWV = U*W
. matrix UWV = newA*V´
. matrix list UWV

UWV[3,3]
             c1          c2          c3
r1   -.18734043    8.4993943   -3.7047537
r2   -5.9976134    5.6927689   -3.1017703
r3   -.37468086   16.998789    -7.4095074

. matrix Winv = W
. matrix Winv[1,1]=1/W[1,1]
. matrix Winv[2,2]=0
. matrix Winv[3,3]=1/W[3,3]
. matrix Ainv = V*Winv
. matrix Ainv = Ainv*U´
. matrix list Ainv

Ainv[3,3]
             r1          r2          r3
c1    -.0029461    .03716103   -.0058922
c2    -.0181453    .16069635   -.03629059
c3    .02658185    -.0398393    .05316371

. matrix AAinv = A*Ainv
. matrix list AAinv

symmetric AAinv[3,3]
             r1          r2          r3
r1          .2
r2   -8.327e-17           1
r3          .4    5.551e-16          .8

. matrix AAinvA = AAinv*A
. matrix list AAinvA

AAinvA[3,3]
      c1  c2  c3
r1    1   2   9
r2    2   7   5
r3    2   4  18
```

◁

Also See

[R] **matrix**, [R] **matrix define**

Title

matrix symeigen — Eigenvalues and vectors of symmetric matrices

Syntax

matrix symeigen X v = A

To reset problem-size limits, see [R] **matsize**.

Description

Given an $n \times n$ symmetric matrix **A**, matrix symeigen returns the eigenvectors in the columns of **X**: $n \times n$ and the corresponding eigenvalues in **v**: $1 \times n$. The eigenvalues are sorted; v[1,1] contains the largest eigenvalue (and X[.,1] its corresponding eigenvector) and v[1,n] contains the smallest eigenvalue (and X[.,n] its corresponding eigenvector).

Remarks

Typing matrix symeigen **X** v = **A** for **A** $n \times n$ returns

$$\mathbf{v} = \big(\lambda_1, \lambda_2, \ldots, \lambda_n\big)$$
$$\mathbf{X} = \big(\mathbf{x}_1, \mathbf{x}_2, \ldots, \mathbf{x}_n\big)$$

where $\lambda_1 \geq \lambda_2 \geq \ldots \geq \lambda_n$. Each $\mathbf{x}_i$ and λ_i is a solution to

$$\mathbf{A}\mathbf{x}_i = \lambda_i \mathbf{x}_i$$

or, more compactly,

$$\mathbf{A}\mathbf{X} = \mathbf{X}\,\mathrm{diag}(\mathbf{v})$$

▷ Example

Eigenvalues and vectors have many uses. We will merely demonstrate that symeigen returns matrices meeting the definition:

```
. matrix list A
symmetric A[3,3]
             weight        mpg        _cons
weight    .41133468
   mpg    44.601659    7422.863
 _cons   -2191.9032   -292759.82    12938766
. matrix symeigen X lambda = A
. matrix list lambda
lambda[1,3]
            e1          e2          e3
r1    12945391    798.33648    .00879302
```

```
. matrix list X

X[3,3]
                 e1           e2           e3
weight    -.00016935    -.0062574    .99998041
   mpg    -.02262217    .99972454    .00625197
 _cons     .99974407    .02262067    .00031086

. matrix AX = A*X
. matrix Lambda = diag(lambda)
. matrix XLambda = X*Lambda
. matrix list AX

AX[3,3]
                 e1           e2           e3
weight    2192.3513    -4.9955145    .00879285
   mpg   -292852.83    798.11657     .00005497
 _cons    12942078     18.058904    2.733e-06

. matrix list XLambda

XLambda[3,3]
                 e1           e2           e3
weight   -2192.3513    -4.9955145    .00879285
   mpg   -292852.83    798.11657     .00005497
 _cons    12942078     18.058904    2.733e-06
```

◁

Methods and Formulas

Stata's internal eigenvalue and eigenvector extraction routines are translations of the public domain EISPACK routines, Smith et al. (1976), which are in turn based on Wilkinson and Reinsch (1971). EISPACK was developed under contract for the Office of Scientific and Technical Information, U.S. Department of Energy, by Argonne National Laboratory and supported by funds provided by the Nuclear Regulatory Commission. Stata's use of these routines is by permission of the National Energy Software Center of the Argonne National Laboratory. A brief but excellent introduction to the techniques employed by these routines can be found in Press et al. (1992, 456–495).

References

Press, W. H., S. A. Teukolsky, W. T. Vetterling, and B. P. Flannery. 1992. *Numerical Recipes in C: The Art of Scientific Computing.* 2d ed. Cambridge University Press.

Smith, B. T., et al. 1976. *Matrix Eigen System Routines—EISPACK Guide.* 2d ed, vol. 6 of Lecture Notes in Computer Science. New York: Springer-Verlag.

Wilkinson, J. H. and C. Reinsch. 1971. *Linear Algebra,* vol. 2 of *Handbook for Automatic Computation.* New York: Springer-Verlag.

Also See

[R] **matrix**

Title

Syntax

matrix <u>dir</u>

matrix <u>l</u>ist *mname* $\left[\right.$, <u>nob</u>lank <u>noh</u>alf <u>noh</u>eader <u>non</u>ames <u>f</u>ormat(*%fmt*) <u>t</u>itle(*string*) $\left. \right]$

matrix drop $\left\{ \right.$ _all | *mname(s)* $\left. \right\}$

Description

matrix dir lists the names of currently existing matrices. matrix list lists the contents of a matrix. matrix drop eliminates a matrix.

Options

noblank suppresses printing a blank line before printing the matrix. This is useful in programs.

nohalf specifies that, even if the matrix is symmetric, the full matrix is to be printed. The default is to print only the lower triangle in such cases.

noheader suppresses the display of the matrix name and dimension before the matrix itself. This is useful in programs.

nonames suppresses the display of the bordering names around the matrix.

format(*%fmt*) specifies the format to be used to display the individual elements of the matrix. The default is format(%10.0g).

title(*string*) adds the specified title *string* to the header displayed before the matrix itself. If noheader is specified, title() does nothing because displaying the header is suppressed.

Remarks

▷ Example

Little needs to be said by way of introduction. In the example below, however, note that matrix list normally displays only the lower half of symmetric matrices; nohalf prevents this.

```
. matrix dir
          a[2,2]
          b[3,3]
```

```
. matrix list b
symmetric b[3,3]
      c1   c2   c3
r1    2
r2    5    8
r3    4    6    3
. matrix list b, nohalf
symmetric b[3,3]
      c1   c2   c3
r1    2    5    4
r2    5    8    6
r3    4    6    3
. matrix drop b
. matrix dir
              a[2,2]
. matrix drop _all
. matrix dir

.  _
```

◁

❏ Technical Note

When writing programs and using matrix names obtained through `tempname` (see [R] **macro**), it is not necessary to explicitly drop matrices; the matrices are removed automatically at the conclusion of the program.

```
. program define example
  1.          tempname a
  2.          matrix `a´ = (1,2\3,4)              /* this is temporary   */
  3.          matrix b = (5,6\7,8)                /* and this permanent  */
  4.          display "The temporary matrix a contains:"
  5.          matrix list `a´, noheader
  6. end
. example
The temporary matrix a contains
      c1   c2
r1    1    2
r2    3    4
. matrix dir
              b[2,2]
```

Nevertheless, dropping matrices with temporary names in programs when they are no longer needed is recommended unless the program is about to exit (when they will be dropped anyway). Matrices consume memory; dropping them frees memory.

❏

Also See

[R] **matrix**

Title

> **matsize** — Set the maximum number of variables in a model

Syntax

<u>set</u> <u>mat</u>size #

where $10 \leq \# \leq 800$

Description

set matsize sets the maximum number of variables that can be included in any of Stata's model-estimation commands. The command may not be used with Small Stata; **matsize** is permanently frozen at 40. For Intercooled Stata, the initial value is 40, but it may be changed upward or downward. The upper limit is 800.

Remarks

set matsize affects the internal size of matrices that Stata uses. The default of 40, for instance, means that linear regression models are limited to 38 independent variables—38 because the constant uses one position and the dependent variable another, making a total of 40.

Under Stata for Windows 3.1, Stata for DOS, and Stata for Macintosh, there must be no data in memory when you change **matsize** and increasing **matsize** decreases the amount of memory available for data. Under Stata for Windows 95 and Stata for Unix, you may change **matsize** with data in memory, but increasing **matsize** increases the amount of memory consumed by Stata, increasing the probability of page faults and thus of making Stata run more slowly.

▷ Example

You wish to estimate a model of **y** on the variables **x1** through **x100**. Without thinking, you type

```
. regress y x1-x100
matsize too small
r(908);
```

You realize that you need to increase **matsize**; you are using Intercooled Stata and type

```
. set matsize 150
no; data in memory would be lost
r(4);
```

You are using Stata for Windows 3.1, Stata for DOS, or Stata for Macintosh. You must

```
. save mydata
file mydata.dta saved
. drop _all
. set matsize 150
. use mydata
. regress y x1-x100
  (output omitted )
```

Under Stata for Windows 95 or Stata for Unix, you do not have to go to that trouble:

```
. regress y x1-x100
matsize too small
r(908);
```

```
. set matsize 150
```

```
. regress y x1-x100
  (output omitted )
```

◁

Also See

[U] **11 Setting the size of memory**

Title

maximize — Details of iterative maximization

Syntax

mle_cmd ... [, <u>tol</u>erance(#) <u>ltol</u>erance(#) <u>iter</u>ate(#) <u>trace</u> [no]<u>log</u>]

Description

This entry discusses the details of Stata's iterative maximization process used by Stata's maximum-likelihood estimators.

Options

<u>tol</u>erance(#) specifies a threshold such that, when the relative change in the coefficient vector from one iteration to the next is less than tolerance(), estimates are declared to have converged.

tolerance(1e-4) is the default for estimators programmed internally in Stata.

This option is not available for estimators programmed with ml.

<u>ltol</u>erance(#) specifies a threshold such that, when the relative change in the log-likelihood function from one iteration to the next is less than ltolerance(), estimates are declared to have converged.

ltolerance(0) is the default for estimators programmed internally in Stata.

ltolerance(1e-7) is the default for estimators programmed with ml.

<u>iter</u>ate(#) specifies a threshold such that, when the number of iterations exceeds iterate(), estimates are partially declared to have converged. Iterations stop and results are presented, but a note appears on the output that giving the reason as being due to the iteration count.

iterate(16000) is the default for estimators programmed internally in Stata and for estimators programmed with ml.

<u>trace</u> requests that coefficients be listed at each iteration so that one can study their convergence.

<u>log</u> and nolog specify whether an iteration log is to be displayed during the iteration process. For most commands, the default is that the log be listed and option nolog suppresses it. A few commands work in the reverse.

Remarks

Stata's maximum-likelihood estimators use one of two maximization routines:

1. A built-in Newton–Raphson maximizer with step halving (to avoid downhill steps) and emergency steepest-ascent logic.

2. An equivalent Newton–Raphson maximizer (with step halving and emergency steepest-ascent logic) called ml and programmed in Stata's programming language.

Estimators programmed internally in Stata use the first, and estimators implemented in Stata's programming language use the second. The two optimizers are intended to be equivalent and are nearly so. The primary difference between them is that the internal optimizer provides an `tolerance()` option allowing convergence to be declared based on changes in the coefficient vector (which is its default) whereas the external optimizer provides a `ltolerance()` option instead and declares convergence based on changes in the log-likelihood function. Actually, the internal optimizer also has a `ltolerance()` option but it is, by default, set off.

In any case, you as a user should never have to specify either `tolerance()` or `ltolerance()`, nor should you have to specify `iterate()`. In all cases, we have set these to what we consider conservative values (conservative in terms of not too optimistically declaring convergence).

Most maximum-likelihood commands produce an iteration log:

```
. mlcmd ...
Iteration 0:   Log Likelihood = -45.03321
Iteration 1:   Log Likelihood =-29.942722
Iteration 2:   Log Likelihood =-27.493729
Iteration 3:   Log Likelihood =-27.165689
Iteration 4:   Log Likelihood =-27.156091
Iteration 5:   Log Likelihood =-27.156079
  (output omitted)
. _
```

If a command does not present this log, you can specify the `log` option to see it. In any case, iteration 0 refers to the value of the log likelihood function at the starting values and the subsequent values are then reported. Sometimes you will see something like,

```
. mlcmd ...
Iteration 0:   Log Likelihood = -45.03321
(unproductive step attempted)
Iteration 1:   Log Likelihood =-29.942722
(unproductive step attempted)
Iteration 2:   Log Likelihood =-27.493729
Iteration 3:   Log Likelihood =-27.165689
Iteration 4:   Log Likelihood =-27.156091
Iteration 5:   Log Likelihood =-27.156079
  (output omitted)
. _
```

This should not concern you. It just means that the Newton–Raphson procedure suggested a direction that did not result in an increase of the log-likelihood function and the optimizer substituted a steepest-ascent step in its place. This can happen because the likelihood function is not globally concave or, rarely, because of numerical issues in evaluating the likelihood function at the current parameter estimates.

The unproductive-step message should only concern you if it appears at the last iteration and, were that to happen, you would not miss it because some or all of the standard errors will be reported as missing.

Output explained

In addition to the iteration log, all maximum-likelihood commands present a similarly formatted coefficient table. For instance:

```
. logit foreign weight mpg
Iteration 0:  Log Likelihood = -45.03321
Iteration 1:  Log Likelihood =-29.898968
Iteration 2:  Log Likelihood =-27.495771
Iteration 3:  Log Likelihood =-27.184006
Iteration 4:  Log Likelihood =-27.175166
Iteration 5:  Log Likelihood =-27.175156

Logit Estimates                              Number of obs =      74
                                             chi2(2)       =   35.72
                                             Prob > chi2   =  0.0000
Log Likelihood = -27.175156                  Pseudo R2     =  0.3966

------------------------------------------------------------------------
 foreign |    Coef.    Std. Err.      z      P>|z|   [95% Conf. Interval]
---------+--------------------------------------------------------------
  weight | -.0039067    .0010116   -3.862   0.000   -.0058894    -.001924
     mpg | -.1685869    .0919174   -1.834   0.067   -.3487418     .011568
   _cons |  13.70837    4.518707    3.034   0.002    4.851864    22.56487
------------------------------------------------------------------------
```

After the iteration log is presented the header. Shown is the estimation type, the number of observations, the χ^2 value and its significance, the obtained value of the log-likelihood function, and the pseudo R^2.

Define L_0 as the value of the log-likelihood function with just the constant and L_1 the value with all the included variables (i.e., the log-likelihood value shown on the output).

The χ^2 value is defined as $2(L_1 - L_0)$ which, in our example, is 35.72. The degrees of freedom for the χ^2 is the number of estimated parameters less the number of estimated parameters in a "constant-only" model, which is typically 1. (In the case of mlogit, the constant-only model has $g - 1$ parameters, where g is the number of outcomes.) The reported significance level of "0.0000" is Stata's way of saying that the coefficients are significant at better than the 0.00005 level.

The pseudo R^2 is defined as $1 - L_1/L_0$. This is simply the log-likelihood value on a scale where 0 corresponds to the "constant-only" model and 1 corresponds to perfect prediction, i.e., a log-likelihood value of 0.

Below the header information is the coefficient table. In addition to coefficients and standard errors (obtained from the diagonal elements of the information matrix), the table reports t or (asymptotic) Z statistics and their corresponding significance levels and confidence intervals. The confidence interval is calculated as $b \pm t_{1-\alpha/2}s$ or $b \pm z_{1-\alpha/2}s$, where b is the estimated coefficient and s the reported standard error.

Some maximum-likelihood routines have the ability to report the table in an exponentiated form. A partial list includes logit with the or option (for reporting odds ratios) and cox with the hr option (for reporting hazard ratios). Even regress with the eform option has the ability to report the exponentiated form and, although this option is of no direct use, it can be useful in ado-files such as glm.

The transformation to exponentiated form is performed as follows. Let b be the coefficient, s the standard error, t the z or t value, p the significance level, and b_0 and b_1 the confidence interval for some variable that would be reported if the table were reported in standard form. In exponentiated form, the "coefficient" is e^b, the standard error $e^b s$, the z or t value t, the significance level p, and the confidence interval e^{b_0} and e^{b_1}. The reported t, therefore, is a test that e^b is equal to 1.

Saved Results

All internal maximum-likelihood estimators that refer to this entry in their *Saved Results* section save in _result():

1.	number of observations	5.	(not used)
2.	log-likelihood value	6.	χ^2
3.	χ^2 degrees of freedom	7.	pseudo *R*-squared
4.	(not used)		

Commands implemented in terms of ml save in the global $S_E_ macros

S_E_nobs	number of observations		
S_E_ll	log-likelihood value	S_E_chi2	χ^2
S_E_mdf	χ^2 degrees of freedom	S_E_pr2	pseudo *R*-squared

Regardless of whether internal or external, also saved in the global $S_E_ macros are

S_E_cmd	name of estimation command
S_E_depv	name of dependent variable
S_E_vce	nothing or robust
S_E_cvn	nothing or name of clustering variable
S_E_cn	nothing or number of clusters

S_E_vce, S_E_cvn, and S_E_cn concern the robust and cluster() options if the estimator provides it and if the user specifies it; see [U] **26.10 Obtaining robust variance estimates**.

References

Judge, G. G., W. E. Griffiths, R. C. Hill, H. Lütkepohl, and Tsoung-Chao Lee. 1985. *The Theory and Practice of Econometrics*. 2d ed. New York: John Wiley & Sons.

Also See

[U] **26 Estimation and post-estimation commands**

[R] **lrtest**, [R] **ml**

Title

means — Arithmetic, geometric, and harmonic means

Syntax

means [*varlist*] [if *exp*] [in *range*]

Description

means reports the arithmetic, geometric, and harmonic means of each variable in *varlist* or for all the variables in the data if *varlist* is not specified. If you simply want arithmetic means; see [R] **summarize**.

Remarks

▷ Example

You have a dataset containing 8 observations on a variable named x. The eight values are 5, 4, −2, −3, 0, 0, *missing*, and 47.

```
. means x
        |    Arithmetic       Geometric        Harmonic
        |    Mean    Obs      Mean    Obs      Mean    Obs
--------+-------------------------------------------------
      x |  7.285714    7    9.795861   3    6.365688   3
```

The number of observations displayed under the arithmetic mean is the number of nonmissing observations. The number of observations displayed under the geometric and harmonic means is the number of nonmissing, positive observations.

◁

Saved Results

means saves in the S_# macros:

S_1	number of obs. for arithmetic mean	S_3	arithmetic mean
S_2	number of obs. for geometric and harmonic mean	S_4	geometric mean
		S_5	harmonic mean

Methods and Formulas

means is implemented as an ado-file.

See, for example, Armitage and Berry (1987) or Snedecor and Cochran (1989). For a history of the concept of the mean, see Plackett (1958).

When restricted to the same set of values (i.e., to positive values), the arithmetic mean ($\overline{x}$) is greater than or equal to the geometric mean (G.M.) which in turn is greater than or equal to the harmonic mean (H.M.). Exact equality holds only if all values within a sample are equal to a positive constant. The formula for the arithmetic mean $\overline{x}$ is

$$\frac{1}{n}\sum_{j} x_j$$

The formula for the geometric mean is

$$\exp\left(\frac{1}{n}\sum_{j}\ln(x_j)\right)$$

The formula for the harmonic mean is

$$\frac{n}{\sum_{j}\dfrac{1}{x_j}}$$

References

Armitage, P. and G. Berry. 1987. *Statistical Methods in Medical Research.* 2d ed. Oxford: Blackwell Scientific Publications.

Plackett, R. L. 1958. The principle of the arithmetic mean. *Biometrika* 45: 130–135.

Snedecor, G. W. and W. G. Cochran. 1989. *Statistical Methods.* 8th ed. Ames, IA: Iowa State University Press.

Also See

[R] **summarize**

Title

> **memory** — Memory size considerations

Syntax

`set memory #[k|m]`

`memory`

`set virtual { on | off }`

where # is specified in terms of kilobytes or megabytes.

Description

`set memory`, `memory`, and `set virtual` are relevant only if you are using Intercooled Stata.

`set memory` allows you to increase or decrease the amount of memory allocated to Stata while Stata is running. Increases are obtained from the operating system; decreases are returned to the operating system. `set memory` can be specified only if you are using Stata for Windows 95 or Stata for Unix.

Windows 3.1 and Macintosh users must instead set the amount of memory at the time they invoke Stata; see [U] **6.6 Specifying the amount of memory allocated** (Windows 3.1) or [U] **7.5 Specifying the amount of memory allocated** (Macintosh).

`memory` displays a report on Stata's memory usage. `memory` is available on all Intercooled Statas regardless of platform.

`set virtual` controls whether Stata should perform extra work to arrange its memory to keep objects close together. By default, `virtual` is set `off`. `set virtual` is available on all Intercooled Statas regardless of platform.

Remarks

Remarks are presented under the headings

Resetting the amount of memory
Obtaining the memory report and how Stata uses memory
Using virtual memory

If you use Stata for Windows 3.1 or Stata for Macintosh, skip the first heading.

Resetting the amount of memory

If you use Stata for Windows 95 or any flavor of Stata for Unix, you can change the amount of memory Stata has allocated while Stata is running:

```
. set memory 4m
no; data in memory would be lost
r(4);
```

You can change the amount of memory, but only when there is no data in memory:

```
. drop _all
. set memory 4m
(4096k)
```

You can increase it

```
. set memory 32m
(32768k)
```

or decrease it:

```
. set memory 1m
(1024k)
```

If you ask for more than your operating system can provide, you will be told so:

```
. set memory 128m
op. sys. refuses to provide memory
r(909);
```

The number you type can be specified in megabytes or kilobytes. When you suffix numbers with **m** it means megabytes. When you suffix numbers with **k** (or nothing) it means kilobytes.

```
. set memory 4000k
(4000k)
. set memory 1000
(1000k)
```

❑ Technical Note

(This note is relevant only if you use Stata for Unix.) There is a detail in the operating system's handling of returned memory that we have glossed over. You probably think that the checking out and returning of memory from the operating system is handled like the checking out and returning of a book at a library. With some operating systems, it is handled that way, but others have a variation. Operating systems handle returned memory in one of three ways:

1. The instant memory is returned, it is marked as returned and is available for other programs to check out.

2. When memory is returned it is put in a special bin and, five or ten minutes from now, it will be marked as returned for other programs to check out. In the meantime, you could check it out again if you want, but no other program can.

3. When memory is returned it is put in the special bin and never moved from there. You can have the memory back, but no other program can ever have that memory.

Windows 95 and Windows NT follow policy 1. The various flavors of Unix differ on which policy they follow and this has implications.

Let's imagine you are pushing your Unix computer to its limits and have allocated lots of memory to Stata. You suddenly want to jump out of Stata and do something in Unix, so you use Stata's **shell** command to obtain a new shell:

```
. shell
op. sys. refused to start new process
r(702);
```

This can happen if there is no free memory. This reminds you that Stata has all the memory but you no longer need it, so you return most of it:

```
. set memory 4m
(4096k)
```

Now you try the `shell` command again. What will happen?

1. If you system follows policy 1, `shell` will work.

2. If you system follows policy 2, `shell` will not work, but five or ten minutes from now, it will start working again.

3. If you system follows policy 3, `shell` will not work.

The result hinges on whether the operating system really takes back, and when, the memory Stata returns. If your operating system follows policy 3, you must `exit` and restart Stata. If your operating system follows policy 2 and you are in a hurry, you can `exit` and restart, too.   ❏

Obtaining the memory report and how Stata uses memory

Type `memory` and Stata will give you a memory report. Below, we just started Stata:

```
. memory
    Total memory                    1,048,576 bytes    100.00%

    overhead (pointers)                     0              0.00%
    data                                    0              0.00%
                                  ------------
    data + overhead                         0              0.00%
    programs, saved results, etc.         352              0.03%
                                  ------------
    Total                                 352              0.03%
    Free                            1,048,224             99.97%
```

If you perform this experiment on your computer, you will probably see different numbers. Here is our memory report after we load the automobile data that comes with Stata:

```
. use auto
(1978 Automobile Data)

. memory
    Total memory                    1,048,576 bytes    100.00%

    overhead (pointers)                   296              0.03%
    data                                3,256              0.31%
                                  ------------
    data + overhead                     3,552              0.34%
    programs, saved results, etc.         960              0.09%
                                  ------------
    Total                               4,512              0.43%
    Free                            1,044,064             99.57%
```

Total memory refers to the total amount of memory Stata has allocated to its data areas—the number that can be specified at start-up time or reset by `set memory`. Well, almost. If you use Stata for Macintosh, total memory refers to a number somewhat smaller than that because Stata has to carve an area out of the total for another purpose. Stata for Macintosh users: just accept that the number is smaller than the number you specified and know that the larger the number you specify at start-up time, the larger the total memory will be and see the technical note below.

Overhead, data, and data + overhead refer to the amount of memory necessary to hold the data currently in memory. Start with the middle number.

3,256 bytes is the total amount of memory necessary to hold the automobile data and you could work this out for yourself from a `describe, detail`. The automobile data has 74 observations and each observation requires 44 bytes (called the width), and $74 \times 44 = 3{,}256$.

296 bytes is the pointer overhead associated with this data. Stata needs something called a pointer to keep track of where each observation is stored in memory. On this computer pointers are 4 bytes—but that varies—and the data has 74 observations, so $4 \times 74 = 296$.

Data + overhead is just the sum of the two numbers: $296 + 3{,}256 = 3{,}552$ is the total amount of memory Stata needs to store and keep track of this data.

Programs, saved results, etc., is the total amount of memory Stata has used to store just what it says: Stata's programs (ado-files), macros, matrices, value labels, and all sorts of other things. This is sometimes referred to as Stata's dynamic memory. The report shows 960 bytes this instant but the number changes frequently.

Here is a memory report from another session in which we have loaded a dataset with 69,515 observations on 23 variables and are in the midst of analyzing it using `xtgee`:

```
. memory
Total memory                       6,291,456 bytes     100.00%

overhead (pointers)                  278,060             4.42%
data                               2,363,510            37.57%
                                   ------------
data + overhead                    2,641,570            41.99%

programs, saved results, etc.         31,552             0.50%
                                   ------------
Total                              2,673,122            42.49%

Free                               3,618,334            57.51%
```

❑ Technical Note

Stata for Macintosh. The total amount of memory shown by `memory` is less than the amount you tell your Macintosh to allocate because we need to use some of that memory for other purposes. How much we need is given by $88\,\mathtt{matsize}^2 + 8\,\mathtt{matsize} + k$, where k is a constant for you (but varies slightly across Macintoshes). Thus, you will see total memory rise and fall according to the value to which you `set matsize`.

Let's compare `matsize = 40` with 80. For `matsize = 80`, we need $88 \cdot 80^2 + 8 \cdot 80 + k = 563{,}840 + k$. For `matsize = 40`, we need $88 \cdot 40^2 + 8 \cdot 40 + k = 141{,}120 + k$. The difference is then 422,720. Conclusion: if `matsize` was 40 and you `set matsize 80`, `memory` will report that total memory declines by 422,720 bytes. Since it is in "total memory" that Stata stores your data, reducing the value of `matsize` is one way of reallocating your memory.

❑

Using virtual memory

Virtual memory refers to using more memory than is physically present on your computer. This is a feature provided by the operating system, not Stata, and one that you as a Stata user may find yourself sometimes exploiting.

Virtual memory is slow. You will be unhappy if you need to use virtual memory on a daily basis. On the other hand, virtual memory can get you out of a bind and that is the right way to use it with Stata.

You do *NOT* need to set virtual on for Stata to use virtual memory. All set virtual on does is maybe make Stata run a little faster when the operating system is paging its brains out. set virtual on will not make Stata run fast, just faster.

Virtual memory is most efficient (which is not to say efficient) when the program being executed exhibits something called locality of reference. This is the idea that if the program accesses one location in memory, subsequent memory references will be to a location near that. If you set virtual on Stata's memory-management routines will go to extra work to arrange things so that the idea is true more often. Hence, Stata will run a little faster. If Stata is not using virtual memory, setting virtual on will make Stata run a little slower because Stata will be going to extra work for no good reason.

You set virtual on by typing the command,

```
. set virtual on
```

You can check whether virtual is on or off using query:

```
. query
----------------------------------------------------- Status
        type | float       display linesize | 79
     virtual | off                  pagesize | 22
        more | on            log linesize | 79
        beep | off                  pagesize | 0
        rmsg | off                     trace | off
     matsize | 40                   textsize | 100
     adosize | 30                      level | 95
    graphics | on
----------------------------------------------------- Files
         log | closed
        help | C:\STATA\stata.hlp
```

virtual is reported on the second line of the left column. To set virtual off, type the command,

```
. set virtual off
```

Saved Results

memory saves in _result():

1.	(current partition) max. obs.	7.	total programs, saved results, etc. (bytes)
2.	(current partition) max. max. obs.	8.	size of memory pointer (bytes)
3.	(current partition) max. var.	9.	number of variables
4.	(current partition) max. width	10.	width of data
5.	total memory (bytes)	11.	adosize
6.	total memory available to data (bytes)	12.	matsize

Note that results 1–4 refer to values associated with the current partition. At any instant Stata has partitioned the memory into observations and variables. The characteristics of the partition can change at any time including right in the middle of a command, so the first four numbers are really of little interest in that they do not reflect any real constraint. What they do reflect is efficiency. If something should occur that violates any of those limits, Stata will have to silently go to work to reform the partition, something it is able to do reasonably efficiently and without any disk accesses. Also note the contents of _result(2) are not a typographical error. It records the maximum number of observations in the current partition if the size of total programs, saved results, etc. (what is recorded in _result(7)) were zero. When Stata is faced with a request that violates the current partition's limits, it considers the possibility of discarding memory copies of ado-files that have not been used recently. Ado-files are loaded automatically on an as-needed basis and so how long they are kept in memory is only an efficiency issue. Stata considers reducing the memory requirement as an alternative to repartitioning.

The output produced by memory can be calculated from the saved results by

$$\text{total memory} = \text{\_result(1)}$$

$$\text{overhead (pointers)} = \text{\_N} \times \text{\_result(8)}$$

$$\text{data} = \text{\_N} \times \text{\_result(10)}$$

$$\text{programs, saved results, etc.} = \text{\_result(7)}$$

Also See

[U] **11 Setting the size of memory**

[R] **query**

Title

> **merge** — Merge datasets

Syntax

<u>merge</u> [*varlist*] using *filename* [, <u>nol</u>abel update replace <u>nokeep</u>]

If *filename* is specified without an extension, .dta is assumed.

Description

merge joins corresponding observations from the dataset currently in memory (called the master dataset) with those from the Stata-format dataset stored as *filename* (called the using dataset) into single observations.

Options

nolabel prevents Stata from copying the value label definitions from the disk dataset into the dataset in memory. Even if you do not specify this option, in no event do label definitions from the disk dataset replace label definitions already in memory.

update varies the action **merge** takes when an observation is matched. By default, the master data is held inviolate—values from the master data are retained when variables are found in both datasets. If update is specified, however, the values from the using dataset are retained in cases where the master data contains missing.

replace, allowed with update only, specifies that even in the case when the master data contains nonmissing values, they are to be replaced with corresponding values from the using data when the corresponding values are not equal. A nonmissing value, however, will never be replaced with a missing value.

nokeep causes **merge** to ignore observations in the using data that have no corresponding observation in the master. The default is to add these observations to the merged result and mark such observations with _merge = 1.

Remarks

Remarks are presented under the headings

> *The two kinds of merges*
> *One-to-one merge*
> *Match merge*
> *Updating data*

Distinguish carefully between merging and appending datasets, and the corresponding Stata commands **merge** and **append**. Appending refers to the addition of new observations on existing variables. If one thinks of data as a rectangle with observations going down and variables going across, appending increases the dataset's length. Merging adds new variables to existing observations, increasing the dataset's width.

Say you have data in which each observation records the characteristics of a particular automobile such as the car's price, weight, etc. If you have two such datasets, one for domestic and another for imported cars, and you wish to combine them into a single dataset, you are reading the wrong entry; see [R] **append**.

On the other hand, if you have two datasets, one recording price and ther other weight, mileage, etc., and you wish to combine them into a single set, continue reading; `merge` does this.

In addition to `merge`, another command, `joinby`, forms all pairwise combinations of observations within group. Say you have one dataset on mothers and fathers and another on their children. If you wish to combine them so that each parent is matched with every one of their children (each child is matched with both parents), so that a 2-parent, 3-child family results in $2 \times 3 = 6$ observations, see [R] **joinby**.

The two kinds of merges

`merge` joins the observations stored in memory with the observations stored in *filename*. The disk dataset must be a Stata-format dataset; that is, it must have been created with the `save` command.

Stata performs two kinds of merges. If no *varlist* is specified, Stata performs a *one-to-one* merge. In a one-to-one merge, the first observation of one dataset is joined with the first observation of the other dataset, the second observation is joined with the second, and so on. If a *varlist* is specified, however, Stata uses those variables to perform a *match* merge. In a match merge, observations are joined only if the values of the variables in the specified *varlist* match.

Regardless of the style of merge being performed, `merge` always adds a new variable called _merge to the dataset. This variable takes on the values 1, 2, or 3 to mark the source of the resulting observation. The coding is

1. The observation occurred only in the master dataset.

2. The observation occurred only in the using dataset.

3. The observation is the result of joining an observation from the master dataset with one from the using dataset.

When you use the `update` option, this coding is extended to include

4. Same as 3 except that missing values in the master were updated with values from the using.

5. Same as 3 except that some values in the master disagree with values in the using.

One-to-one merge

In a one-to-one merge, the first observation in the master dataset is joined with the first observation in the using dataset, the second observation is joined with the second, and so on. If variables with the same name occur in both the master and the using datasets, the joined observation retains those variables' *original* values, the values of the variables in the master dataset. When the master and using datasets contain different numbers of observations, missing values are joined with the remaining observations from the longer dataset.

▷ Example

You have two datasets stored on disk that you wish to merge into a single dataset. The first dataset, called odd.dta, contains the first five positive odd numbers. The second dataset, called even.dta, contains the fifth through eighth positive even numbers. (Our example is admittedly not realistic, but it does illustrate the concept.) We show you each of the datasets below:

```
. use odd
(First five odd numbers)

. list

        number      odd
1.          1        1
2.          2        3
3.          3        5
4.          4        7
5.          5        9

. use even
(5th through 8th even numbers)

. list

        number     even
1.           5       10
2.           6       12
3.           7       14
4.           8       16
```

We will join these two datasets using a one-to-one merge. Since the even data is already in memory (we just used it above), we type **merge using odd**. The result is

```
. merge using odd
number was int now float

. list

        number     even     odd    _merge
1.           5       10       1        3
2.           6       12       3        3
3.           7       14       5        3
4.           8       16       7        3
5.           5        .       9        2
```

The first thing you will notice is the new variable _merge. Every time Stata merges two datasets, it creates this variable and assigns the value of 1, 2, or 3 to each observation. The value 1 indicates that the resulting observation occurred only in the master dataset, 2 indicates the observation occurred only in the using dataset, and 3 indicates the observation occurred in both datasets and is thus the result of joining an observation from the master dataset with an observation from the using dataset.

In this case, the first four observations are marked by _merge equal to 3, and the last observation by _merge equal to 2. The first four observations are the result of joining observations from the two datasets, and the last observation is a result of adding a new observation from the using data. These values reflect the fact that the original data in memory had four observations, and the odd data stored on disk had five observations. The new last observation is from the odd data exclusively: number is 5, odd is 9, and even has been filled in with *missing*.

Notice that number takes on the values 5 through 8 for the first four observations. Those are the values of number from the original data in memory—the even data—and conflict with the value of number stored in the first four observations of the odd data. number in that dataset took on the values 1 through 4, and those values were lost during the merge process. When Stata joins observations and there is a conflict between the value of a variable in memory and the value stored in the using data, Stata *always* retains the value stored in memory.

When the command `merge using odd` was issued, Stata responded with "number was int now float". Let's `describe` the datasets in this example:

```
. describe using odd
Contains data                          First five odd numbers
   obs:            5                    18 Apr 1996 11:45
  vars:            2
  size:           60
--------------------------------------------------------------------------------
   1. number       float   %9.0g
   2. odd          float   %9.0g       Odd numbers
--------------------------------------------------------------------------------
Sorted by:
. describe using even
Contains data                          5th through 8th even numbers
   obs:            4                    2 Jun 1996 14:11
  vars:            2
  size:           40
--------------------------------------------------------------------------------
   1. number       int     %8.0g
   2. even         float   %9.0g       Even numbers
--------------------------------------------------------------------------------
Sorted by:   number
```

Note that `number` is stored as a `float` in `odd.dta`, but is stored as an `int` in `even.dta`; see [U] **19.2.2 Numeric storage types**. When you `merge` two datasets, Stata engages in automatic variable promotion; that is, if there are conflicts in numeric storage types, the more precise storage type will be used. The resulting dataset, therefore, will have `number` stored as a `float`, and Stata told you this when it said "number was int now float".

◁

Match merge

In a match merge, observations are joined if the values of the variables in the *varlist* are the same. Since the values must be the same, obviously the variables in the *varlist* must appear in both the master and the using datasets.

A match merge proceeds by taking an observation from the master dataset and one from the using dataset and comparing the values of the variables in the *varlist*. If the *varlist* values match, then the observations are joined. If the *varlist* values do not match, the observation from the *earlier* dataset (the dataset whose *varlist* value comes first in the sort order) is joined with a pseudo-observation from the *later* dataset (the other dataset). All the variables in the pseudo-observation contain missing values. The actual observation from the later dataset is retained and compared with the next observation in the earlier dataset, and the process repeats.

▷ Example

The result is not nearly so incomprehensible as the explanation. Let's return to the data used in the previous example and `merge` the two datasets on variable `number`. We first `use` the even data and then type `merge number using odd`:

```
. use even
(5th through 8th even numbers)
. merge number using odd
master data not sorted
r(5);
```

Rather than the data being merged, we suffer the error message "master data not sorted". Match merges require that the data be sorted in the order of the *varlist*, which in this case means ascending order of number. If you look at the previous example, you will observe that the data is in such an order, so the message is more than a little confusing. Before Stata can merge two datasets, however, the data must not only be sorted but Stata must *know* that they are sorted.

The basis of Stata's knowledge is the internal information it keeps on the sort order, and Stata reveals the extent of its knowledge whenever you describe the data:

```
. describe
Contains data from even.dta
  obs:           4                          5th through 8th even numbers
  vars:          2                          2 Jun 1996 14:11
  size:         40 (99.9% of memory free)
-----------------------------------------------------------------------------
  1. number        int    %8.0g
  2. even          float  %9.0g            Even numbers
-----------------------------------------------------------------------------
Sorted by:
```

The last line of the description shows that the data is "Sorted by:" nothing. We tell Stata to sort the data (or to learn that it is already sorted) with the sort command:

```
. sort number
. describe
Contains data from even.dta
  obs:           4                          5th through 8th even numbers
  vars:          2                          2 Jun 1996 14:11
  size:         40 (99.9% of memory free)
-----------------------------------------------------------------------------
  1. number        int    %8.0g
  2. even          float  %9.0g            Even numbers
-----------------------------------------------------------------------------
Sorted by:  number
```

Now when we describe the data, Stata informs us that the data is sorted by number. Now that Stata knows the data is sorted, let's try again:

```
. merge number using odd
using data not sorted
r(5);
```

Stata still refuses to carry out our request, this time complaining that the *using* data is not sorted. Both datasets, the master and the using, must be in ascending order of number before Stata can perform a merge.

As before, if you look at the previous example you will discover that odd.dta is in ascending order of number, but as before, Stata does not know this yet. We need to save the data we just sorted, use the odd data, sort it, and re-save it:

```
. save even, replace
file even.dta saved
. use odd
(First 5 odd numbers)
. sort number
. save odd, replace
file odd.dta saved
```

Now we should be able to merge the two datasets:

```
. use even
(5th through 8th even numbers)

. merge number using odd

. list
        number      even      odd    _merge
1.         5         10         9        3
2.         6         12         .        1
3.         7         14         .        1
4.         8         16         .        1
5.         1          .         1        2
6.         2          .         3        2
7.         3          .         5        2
8.         4          .         7        2
```

It worked! Let's understand what happened. Even though both datasets were sorted by number, we immediately discern that the result is no longer in ascending order of number. It will be easier to understand what happened if we re-sort the data and then list it again:

```
. sort number

. list
        number      even      odd    _merge
1.         1          .         1        2
2.         2          .         3        2
3.         3          .         5        2
4.         4          .         7        2
5.         5         10         9        3
6.         6         12         .        1
7.         7         14         .        1
8.         8         16         .        1
```

Notice that number now goes from 1 to 8, with no repeated values and no values left out of the sequence. Recall that the odd data defined observations for number between 1 and 5, whereas the even data defined observations between 5 and 8. Thus, the variable odd is defined for number equal to 1 through 5, and even is defined for number equal to 5 through 8.

For instance, in the first observation number is 1, even is *missing*, and odd is 1. The value of _merge, 2, indicates that this observation came from the using dataset—odd.dta. In the last observation number is 8, even is 16, and odd is *missing*. The value of _merge, 1, indicates that this observation came from the master dataset—even.dta.

The fifth observation is worth comment. number is 5, even is 10, and odd is 9. Both even and odd are defined, since both the even and the odd datasets had information for number equal to 5. The value of _merge, 3, also tells us that both datasets contributed to the formation of the observation.

◁

▷ Example

Although the previous example demonstrated, in glorious detail, how the match-merging process works, it was not a practical example of how you will ordinarily employ it. Here is a more realistic application.

You have two datasets containing information on automobiles. The identifying variable in each dataset is make, a string variable containing the manufacturer and the model. By *identifying* variable, we mean a variable that is unique for every observation in the data. Values for make—for instance, Honda Accord—are sufficient for identifying each observation.

One dataset, called `autotech.dta`, also contains `mpg`, `weight`, and `length`. The other dataset, called `autocost.dta`, contains `price` and `rep78`, the 1978 repair record.

```
. describe using autotech
Contains data                          1978 Automobile Data
  obs:            74                    2 Jun 1996 14:39
  vars:            4
  size:        2,072
-----------------------------------------------------------------------
  1. make         str18  %18s          Make and Model
  2. mpg          int    %8.0g         Mileage (mpg)
  3. weight       int    %8.0g         Weight (lbs.)
  4. length       int    %8.0g         Length (in.)
-----------------------------------------------------------------------
Sorted by:  make
. describe using autocost
Contains data                          1978 Automobile Data
  obs:            74                    2 Jun 1996 14:39
  vars:            3
  size:        1,924
-----------------------------------------------------------------------
  1. make         str18  %18s          Make and Model
  2. price        int    %8.0g         Price
  3. rep78        int    %8.0g         Repair Record 1978
-----------------------------------------------------------------------
Sorted by:  make
```

You desire, we assume, to merge these two datasets into a single dataset:

```
. use autotech
(Automobile Models)

. merge make using autocost
```

Let's now examine the result:

```
. describe
Contains data from autotech.dta
  obs:            74                    1978 Automobile Data
  vars:            7                    2 Jun 1996 14:39
  size:        2,442 (99.7% of memory free)
-----------------------------------------------------------------------
  1. make         str18  %18s          Make and Model
  2. mpg          int    %8.0g         Mileage (mpg)
  3. weight       int    %8.0g         Weight (lbs.)
  4. length       int    %8.0g         Length (in.)
  5. price        int    %8.0g         Price
  6. rep78        int    %8.0g         Repair Record 1978
  7. _merge       byte   %8.0g
-----------------------------------------------------------------------
Sorted by:
      Note:  data has changed since last save
```

We have a single dataset containing all the information from the two original datasets—or at least it appears that we do. Before accepting that conclusion, we need to verify the result. We think that we entered data for the same cars in each dataset, so every variable should be defined for every car. Although we know it is unlikely, we recognize the possibility that we made a mistake and accidentally left some cars out of one or the other dataset. We can reassure ourselves of our infallibility by tabulating _merge:

```
. tabulate _merge
    _merge |      Freq.     Percent        Cum.
-----------+-----------------------------------
         3 |         74      100.00      100.00
-----------+-----------------------------------
     Total |         74      100.00
```

We see that _merge is 3 for every observation in the data. We made no mistake—for every observation in autocost.dta, there was an observation in autotech.dta and vice versa.

Now pretend that we have another dataset containing additional information on these automobiles—automore.dta—and we want to merge that data as well. Before we can do so, we must sort the data we have in memory by make since after a merge the sort order may have changed:

```
. sort make
. merge make using automore
_merge already defined
r(110);
```

After sorting the data, Stata refused to merge the new dataset, complaining instead that _merge is already defined. Every time Stata merges datasets it wants to create a variable called _merge. In this case, there is an _merge variable left over from the last time we merged. We have two choices: We can rename the _merge variable or we can drop it. In this case _merge contains no useful information—we already verified that the previous merge went as expected—so we drop it and try again:

```
. drop _merge
. merge make using automore
```

Stata performed our request; whatever new variables were contained in automore.dta are now contained in our single, master dataset—perhaps. One should not jump to conclusions. After a match merge, you should *always* tabulate _merge to verify that the expected actually happened, as we do below:

```
. tabulate _merge
    _merge |      Freq.     Percent        Cum.
-----------+-----------------------------------
         1 |          1        1.33        1.33
         2 |          1        1.33        2.67
         3 |         73       97.33      100.00
-----------+-----------------------------------
     Total |         75      100.00
```

Surprise! In this case something strange did happen. Some 73 of the observations merged as we anticipated. However, the new data automore.dta added one new car to the dataset (identified by _merge equal to 2) and failed to define new variables for another car in our original dataset (identified by _merge equal to 1). Perhaps this is what should happen, but it is more likely that we have a mistake in automore.dta. We probably misidentified one car so that to Stata it appeared as data on a new car, resulting in one new observation and missing data on another.

If this happened to us, we would now figure out why it happened. We would type list make if _merge==1 to learn the identity of the car that did not appear in automore.dta, and we would type list make if _merge==2 to learn the identity of the car that automore.dta added to our data.

◁

❑ Technical Note

It is difficult to overemphasize the importance of tabulating _merge no matter how sure you are that you have no errors. It takes only a second and can save you hours of grief. Along the same lines, one-to-one merges are a bad idea. In the example above, we could have performed all the merges as one-to-one merges and saved a small amount of typing. Let's examine what would have happened.

We first merged `autotech.dta` with `autocost.dta` by typing `merge make using autocost`. We could perform a one-to-one merge by typing `merge using autocost`. The result would be the same; the datasets line up and are in the same sort order, so sequentially matching the observations from the two datasets would have resulted in a perfectly matched dataset.

In the second case, we merged the data in memory with `automore.dta` by typing `merge make using automore`. A one-to-one merge would have led to disaster, and we would never have known it! If we type `merge using automore`, Stata would sequentially, and blindly, join observations. Since there are the same number of observations in each dataset, everything would appear to merge perfectly.

We speculated in the previous example that we had an error in `automore.dta`. Remember that `automore.dta` included data on one new car and lacked data on an existing car. Even if there is no error, things have gone awry. No matter what, the data in memory and `automore.dta` do not match. For instance, assume that this new car is the first observation of `automore.dta` and that it is some (perhaps mistaken) model of Ford. Assume that the first observation of the data in memory is on a Chevrolet. Stata could and would silently join data on the Chevrolet with data on the Ford, and thereafter data on a Volvo with data on a Saab, and even data on a Volkswagen with data on a Cadillac. And you would never know.

Every dataset should carry a variable or a set of variables that *uniquely* identifies each observation, and then you should always use those variables when merging data. Ignore this advice at your own peril.

❑

❑ Technical Note

Circumstances may arise when you will merge two datasets knowing there will be mismatches. Say you have an analysis dataset on patients from the cancer ward of a particular hospital and you have just received another dataset containing their demographic information. Actually, this other dataset contains not just their demographic information but the demographic information on every patient in the hospital during the year. You could,

```
. merge patid using demog
. drop if _merge==1
```

Equivalently, you could

```
. merge patid using demog, nokeep
```

The `nokeep` option tells `merge` not to store observations from the using data that do not appear in the master. There is an advantage in this. When we merged and dropped, we stored the irrelevant observations and then discarded them, so the data in memory temporarily grew. When we merge with the `nokeep` option, the data never grows beyond what was absolutely necessary.

❑

❑ Technical Note

In our automobile example, we had a single identifying variable. Sometimes you will have identifying variables, variables that, taken together, are unique for every observation.

Let's imagine that, rather than having a single variable called `make`, we had two variables: `manuf` and `model`. `manuf` contains the manufacturer and `model` contains the model. Rather than having a single variable recording, say, "Honda Accord", we have two variables, one recording "Honda" and another recording "Accord". Stata can deal with data like this. You can go back through our previous example and substitute `manuf model` everywhere you see `make`. For instance, rather than typing `merge make using autocost`, we would have typed `merge manuf model using autocost`.

Now let's make one more change in our assumptions. Let's assume that `manuf` and `model` are not string variables but are instead numerically coded variables. Perhaps the number 15 stands for Honda in the `manuf` variable and the number 2 stands for Accord in the `model` variable. We do not have to remember our numeric codes because we have smartly created value labels telling Stata what number stands for what string of characters. We now go back to the step where we merged `autotech.dta` with `autocost.dta`:

```
. use autotech
(Automobile models)

. merge manuf model using autocost
(label manuf already defined)
(label model already defined)
```

Stata makes two minor comments but otherwise carries out our request. It notes that the labels `manuf` and `model` are already defined. The messages refer to the *value labels* named `manuf` and `model`.

Both datasets contain value label definitions that turn the numeric codes for manufacturer and model into words. When Stata merged the two datasets, it already had one set of definitions in memory (obtained when we typed `use autotech`) and thus ignored the second set of definitions contained in `autocost.dta`. Stata felt obliged to mention the second set of definitions while otherwise ignoring them since they *might* contain different codings. In this case, we know they are the same since we created them. (*Hint:* You should never give the same name to value labels containing different codings.)

❑

When one is performing a match merge, the master and/or using datasets may have multiple observations with the same *varlist* value. These multiple observations are joined sequentially, as in a one-to-one merge. If the datasets have an unequal number of observations with the same *varlist* value, the last such observation in the *shorter* dataset is replicated until the number of observations is equal.

▷ Example

The process of replicating the observation from the shorter dataset is known as *spreading* and can be put to practical use. Suppose you have two datasets. `dollars.dta` contains the dollar sales and costs of your firm, by region, for the last year:

```
. use dollars
(Regional Sales & Costs)
. list
         region      sales       cost
  1.         NE     360523     138097
  2.     N Cntrl    419472     227677
  3.      South     532399     330499
  4.       West     310565     165348
```

`sforce.dta` contains the names of the individuals in your sales force along with the region in which they operate:

```
. use sforce
(Sales Force)
. list
           name     region
  1.     Branton        NE
  2.      Franks        NE
  3.      Krantz   N Cntrl
  4.      Phipps   N Cntrl
  5.      Raggee   N Cntrl
  6.    Anderson     South
  7.     Dubnoff     South
  8.         Lee     South
  9.       Asher     South
 10.     Charles      West
 11.       Grant      West
 12.        Cobb      West
```

You now wish to merge these two datasets by `region`, spreading the sales and cost information across all observations for which it is relevant; that is, you want to add the variables `sales` and `costs` to the sales force data. The variable `sales` will assume the value $360,523 for the first two observations, $419,472 for the next three observations, and so on.

```
. merge region using dollars
(label region already defined)
. list
           name     region      sales       cost    _merge
  1.     Branton        NE     360523     138097         3
  2.      Franks        NE     360523     138097         3
  3.      Krantz   N Cntrl     419472     227677         3
  4.      Phipps   N Cntrl     419472     227677         3
  5.      Raggee   N Cntrl     419472     227677         3
  6.    Anderson     South     532399     330499         3
  7.     Dubnoff     South     532399     330499         3
  8.         Lee     South     532399     330499         3
  9.       Asher     South     532399     330499         3
 10.     Charles      West     310565     165348         3
 11.       Grant      West     310565     165348         3
 12.        Cobb      West     310565     165348         3
```

Even though there are 12 observations in the sales force data and only 4 observations in the sales and cost data, all the records merged. The `dollars.dta` contained one observation for the NE region. The `sforce.dta` contained two observations for the same region. Thus, the single observation in `dollars.dta` was matched to both the observations in `sforce.dta`. In technical jargon, the single record in `dollars.dta` was replicated, or *spread*, across the observations in `sforce.dta`.

◁

Updating data

merge with the **update** option varies merge's actions when an observation in the master is matched with an observation in the using data. Without the **update** option, merge leaves the values in the master data alone and adds the data for the new variables. With the **update** option, merge adds the new variables, but it also replaces missing values in the master observation with corresponding values from the using. (Missing values means numeric missing (.) and empty strings ("").)

The values for __merge are extended:

__merge	meaning
1	obs. from master data
2	obs. from using data
3	obs. from both, master agrees with using
4	obs. from both, missing in master updated
5	obs. from both, master disagrees with using

In the case of __merge $== 5$, the master values are retained unless **replace** is specified, in which case the master values are updated just as if they had been missing.

Pretend dataset 1 contains variables id, a, and b; dataset 2 contains id, a, and x. You merge the two datasets by id, dataset 1 being the master data in memory and dataset 2 the using data on disk. Consider two observations that match and call the values from the first dataset id_1, etc., and those from the second id_2, etc. The resulting dataset will have variables id, a, b, x, and __merge. merge's typical logic is

1. The fact that the observations match means $id_1 = id_2$. Set $id = id_1$.

2. Variable a occurs in both datasets. Ignore a_2 and set $a = a_1$.

3. Variable b occurs in only dataset 1. Set $b = b_1$.

4. Variable x occurs in only dataset 2. Set $x = x_2$.

5. Set __merge $= 3$.

With **update**, the logic is modified:

1. (unchanged.) Since the observations match, $id_1 = id_2$. Set $id = id_1$.

2. Variable a occurs in both datasets:

   a. If $a_1 = a_2$, set $a = a_1$ and set __merge $= 3$.

   b. If a_1 contains missing and a_2 is nonmissing, set $a = a_2$ and set __merge $= 4$, indicating an update was made.

   c. If a_2 contains missing, set $a = a_1$ and set __merge $= 3$ (indicating no update).

   d. If $a_1 \neq a_2$ and both contain nonmissing, set $a = a_1$ or, if **replace** was specified, $a = a_2$ but, regardless, set __merge $= 5$, indicating a disagreement.

Rules 3 and 4 remain unchanged.

▷ Example

In **original.dta** you have data on some cars including the make, price, and mileage rating. In **updates.dta** you have some updated data on these cars along with a new variable recording engine displacement. The datasets contain

```
. use original, clear
(original data)
. list
                    make      price       mpg
       1.    Chev. Chevette      3299        29
       2.     Chev. Malibu       4504         .
       3.       Datsun 510       5079        24
       4.       Merc. XR-7       6303         .
       5.      Olds Cutlass      4733        19
       6.    Renault Le Car      3895        26
       7.         VW Dasher      7140        23

. use updates, clear
(updates, mpg and displ)
. list
                    make        mpg      displ
       1.    Chev. Chevette        .        231
       2.     Chev. Malibu        22        200
       3.       Datsun 510        24        119
       4.       Merc. XR-7        14        302
       5.      Olds Cutlass       19        231
       6.    Renault Le Car       25         79
       7.         VW Dasher       23         97
```

Updating our data, we obtain

```
. use original, clear
(original data)
. merge make using updates, update
. list
                    make      price       mpg     displ     _merge
       1.    Chev. Chevette      3299        29       231          3
       2.     Chev. Malibu       4504        22       200          4
       3.       Datsun 510       5079        24       119          3
       4.       Merc. XR-7       6303        14       302          4
       5.      Olds Cutlass      4733        19       231          3
       6.    Renault Le Car      3895        26        79          5
       7.         VW Dasher      7140        23        97          3
```

All observations merged because all have _merge $\geq$ 3. The observations having _merge $==$ 3 have mpg just as it was recorded in the original data. In observation 1, mpg is 29 because the updated data had mpg $==$.; in observation 3, mpg remains 24 because the updated data also stated that mpg is 24.

The observations having _merge $==$ 4 have had their mpg data updated. The mpg variable was missing in observations 2 and 4 and new values were obtained from the update data.

The observation having _merge $==$ 5 has its mpg just as it was recorded in the original data, just as do the _merge $==$ 3 observations, but there is an important difference. There is a disagreement about the value of mpg; the original claims it is 26 and the updated, 25. Had we specified the replace option, mpg would now contain the updated 25 but the observation would still be marked _merge $==$ 5. replace affects only which value is retained in the case of disagreement.

◁

References

Nash, J. D. 1994. dm19: Merging raw data and dictionary files. *Stata Technical Bulletin* 20: 3–5. Reprinted in *Stata Technical Bulletin Reprints*, vol. 4, pp. 22–25.

Also See

[U] **28 Commands for combining data**

[R] **append**, [R] **cross**, [R] **joinby**, [R] **sort**

Title

mkspline — Linear spline construction

Syntax

mkspline *newvar₁* #₁ [*newvar₂* #₂ [...]] *newvar_k* = *oldvar* [if *exp*] [in *range*]

  [, <u>m</u>arginal]

mkspline *stubname* # = *oldvar* [if *exp*] [in *range*] [, <u>m</u>arginal <u>p</u>ctile]

Description

mkspline creates variables containing a linear spline of *oldvar*.

In the first syntax, mkspline creates *newvar₁*, ..., *newvar_k* containing a linear spline of *oldvar* with knots at the specified #₁, ..., #_{k−1}.

In the second syntax, mkspline creates # variables named *stubname*1, ..., *stubname*# containing a linear spline of *oldvar*. The knots are equally spaced over the range of *oldvar* or are placed at the percentiles of *oldvar*.

Options

marginal specifies that the new variables are to be constructed so that, when used in estimation, the coefficients represent the change in the slope from the preceding interval. The default is to construct the variables so that, when used in estimation, the coefficients will measure the slopes for the interval.

pctile is allowed only with the second syntax. It specifies that the knots are to be placed at percentiles of the data rather than equally spaced based on the range.

Remarks

Linear splines allow estimating the relationship between y and x as a piecewise linear function. A piecewise linear function is just that: it is a function composed of linear segments—straight lines. One linear segment represents the function for values of x below x_0. Another linear segment handles values between x_0 and x_1, and so on. The linear segments are arranged so that they join at x_0, x_1, ..., which are called the knots. An example of a piecewise linear function is shown below.

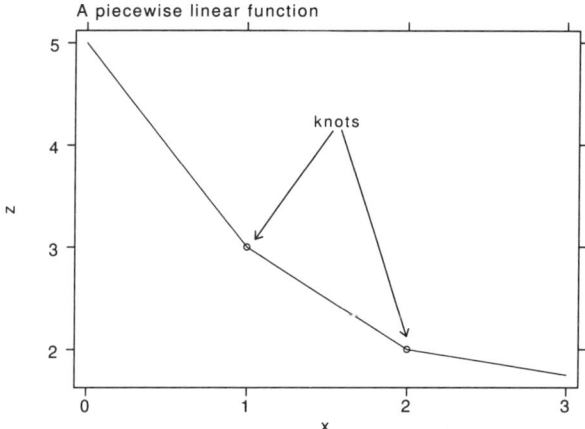

> ## Example

You wish to estimate a model of log income on education and age using a piecewise linear function for age:

$$\mathtt{lninc} = b_0 + b_1\, \mathtt{educ} + f(\mathtt{age}) + u$$

The knots are to be at ten-year intervals: 20, 30, 40, 50, and 60.

```
. mkspline age1 20 age2 30 age3 40 age4 50 age5 60 age6 = age, marginal
. regress lninc educ age1-age6
  (output omitted)
```

Since you specified the **marginal** option, you could test whether the age effect is the same in the 30–40 and 40–50 intervals by asking whether the **age4** coefficient were zero. With the **marginal** option, coefficients measure the change in slope from the preceding group. Specifying **marginal** changes only the interpretation of the coefficients; the same model is estimated in either case. That is, without the **marginal** option, the interpretation of the coefficients would have been

$$\frac{dy}{d\mathbf{age}} = \begin{cases} a_1 & \text{if } \mathbf{age} < 20 \\ a_2 & \text{if } 20 \le \mathbf{age} < 30 \\ a_3 & \text{if } 30 \le \mathbf{age} < 40 \\ a_4 & \text{if } 40 \le \mathbf{age} < 50 \\ a_5 & \text{if } 50 \le \mathbf{age} < 60 \\ a_6 & \text{otherwise.} \end{cases}$$

With the **marginal** option specified, the interpretation is

$$\frac{dy}{d\mathbf{age}} = \begin{cases} a_1 & \text{if } \mathbf{age} < 20 \\ a_1 + a_2 & \text{if } 20 \le \mathbf{age} < 30 \\ a_1 + a_2 + a_3 & \text{if } 30 \le \mathbf{age} < 40 \\ a_1 + a_2 + a_3 + a_4 & \text{if } 40 \le \mathbf{age} < 50 \\ a_1 + a_2 + a_3 + a_4 + a_5 & \text{if } 50 \le \mathbf{age} < 60 \\ a_1 + a_2 + a_3 + a_4 + a_5 + a_6 & \text{otherwise.} \end{cases}$$

◁

▷ Example

As a second example, pretend you have a binary outcome variable called outcome. You are beginning an analysis and wish to parameterize the effect of dosage on outcome. You wish to divide the data into five equal-width groups of dosage for the piecewise linear function.

```
. mkspline dose 5 = dosage
. logistic outcome dose1-dose5
(output omitted)
```

mkspline dose 5 = dosage creates five variables, dose1, dose2,...,dose5, equally spacing the knots over the range of dosage. If dosage varied between 0 and 100, mkspline dose 5 = dosage has the same effect as typing

```
. mkspline dose1 20 dose2 40 dose3 60 dose4 80 dose5 = dosage
```

The pctile option sets the knots to divide the data into five equal sample-size groups rather than five equal-width ranges. Typing

```
. mkspline dose 5 = dosage, pctile
```

places the knots at the 20th, 40th, 60th, and 80th percentiles of the data.

◁

Methods and Formulas

mkspline is implemented as an ado-file.

Let V_i, $i = 1, \ldots, n$ be the variables to be created, k_i, $i = 1, \ldots, n-1$ be the corresponding knots, and V be the original variable (the command is mkspline V_1 k_1 V_2 k_2 ... V_n = V). Then

$$V_1 = \min(V, k_1)$$
$$V_i = \max\left(\min(V, k_i), k_{i-1}\right) - k_{i-1} \quad i = 2, \ldots, n$$

If the marginal option is specified, the definitions are

$$V_1 = V$$
$$V_i = \max(0, V - k_{i-1}) \quad i = 2, \ldots, n$$

In the second syntax, mkspline *stubname* # = V, let m and M be the minimum and maximum of V. Without the pctile option, knots are set at $m + (M - m)(i/n)$ for $i = 1, \ldots, n-1$. If pctile is specified, knots are set at the $100(i/n)$ percentiles, for $i = 1, \ldots, n-1$. Percentiles are calculated by egen's pctile() function.

References

Gould, W. W. 1993. sg19: Linear splines and piecewise linear functions. *Stata Technical Bulletin* 15: 13–17. Reprinted in *Stata Technical Bulletin Reprints*, vol. 3, pp. 98–104.

Greene, W. H. 1993. *Econometric Analysis*. 2d ed. New York: Macmillan.

Johnston, J. 1984. *Econometric Methods*. 3d ed. New York: McGraw-Hill.

Panis, C. 1994. sg24: The piecewise linear spline transformation. *Stata Technical Bulletin* 18: 27–29. Reprinted in *Stata Technical Bulletin Reprints*, vol. 3, pp. 146–149.

Also See

[R] **fracpoly**

Title

ml — Maximum-likelihood estimation

Syntax

ml begin

ml function *progname*

ml method $\{$ lf | deriv0 | deriv1 | deriv2 $\}$

ml model b = *equationname(s)* $\big[$, constant(*cc...c*) depv(*dd...d*) from(b0) $\big]$

ml depnames *varlist*

ml sample *newvarname* $\big[$*varlist*$\big]$ $\big[$*weight*$\big]$ $\big[$if *exp*$\big]$ $\big[$in *range*$\big]$ $\big[$, noauto $\big]$

ml search , limits(*limitlist*) $\big[$ iterate(#) $\big]$

ml maximize *s* V $\big[$, fcnlabel(*string*) *maximize_options* $\big]$

ml post *anyshortname* $\big[$, lf0(#) pr2 obs(#) title(*string*) dof(#) $\big]$

ml mlout *shortname* $\big[$, eform(*string*) first level(#) $\big]$

ml report

ml query

where b, b0, and V are matrix names and *s* is a scalar name.

aweights, fweights, pweights, and iweights are allowed; see [U] **18.1.6 weight**.

To reset problem-size limits, see [R] **matsize**.

User-written *progname* arguments:

method	1st argument	2nd argument	3rd argument	4th argument	options
lf	*varname$_1$*	*varname$_2$*	$\big[$*varname$_3$*$\big]$	...	
deriv0	b	*s*			
deriv1	b	*s*	g		
deriv2	b	*s*	g	D	fast firstit lastit

varname$_1$ is existing variable—replace contents with log-likelihood value for observation; *varname$_2$*, *varname$_3$*, ..., are variables containing index values $x\beta$ for 1st equation, 2nd equation, ...

b is existing matrix containing parameter estimates. *s* is scalar name to be defined containing log-likelihood value for entire data; g is matrix name to be defined containing gradient vector; D is matrix name to be defined containing negative of 2nd derivatives. In case of deriv2, option fast indicates only *s* need be calculated; firstit indicates this is the first iteration; lastit indicates this is the last iteration.

Description

ml assists in maximum-likelihood estimation, allowing for both quick-and-dirty solutions and more formal implementations that provide first and second derivatives.

ml begin declares the beginning of an estimation problem.

ml function identifies the user-written program that calculates the likelihood or quasi-likelihood function.

ml method specifies the maximization method. The *progname* specified in ml function is assumed to calculate the log likelihood for each observation if the method is lf and the overall log likelihood (and possibly derivatives) otherwise.

ml model specifies the equation names (see [R] **eq**) to be estimated and declares that the resulting parameters are to be stored in **b** (a matrix name of your choosing). At this point, **b** will be created or recreated to be a row vector containing zeros or initial values obtained from another vector. Later, whatever values are in **b** will be used as the initial values for the estimation. The zero values inserted here may be adequate for some models.

ml depnames is an optional and rarely used command that specifies dependent or auxiliary variables required to calculate the likelihood function. Dependent variable names, if any, are set automatically by ml model. Use ml depnames only if you want to reset those names (ml query will report them). ml depnames must be specified *after* ml model if it is specified at all.

ml sample specifies the sample on which the estimation is to be based. *newvarname* is the name of a new variable to be added to the data; it will contain a flag indicating whether an observation is to be used. (If *newvarname* already exists, its contents will be replaced.) *newvarname* is both created and used by ml and that variable must not be dropped from the data until ml maximize has completed. The remaining variables (if any) in *varlist* are variables which are to be examined for missing values; observations that include missing values on these variables will be excluded from the estimation. Typically, *varlist* need not be specified because the variables in the equations previously specified in ml model are examined and observations having any missing values are excluded anyway (although noauto will prevent this). if *exp* and in *range* may also be specified; observations not meeting the criteria will also be excluded.

ml search is an optional command that carries out a search for initial values that are adequate for the constant terms of the model based on an allowed parameter range for the index of each equation. ml search may be used only with the lf linear-form optimization method. ml search uses a random technique to produce trial initial values; you must set the random number seed (see [R] **generate**) yourself if exact reproducibility is important.

ml maximize performs the maximization according to the ml function, ml method, ml model, ml sample, and possibly the ml search and ml depnames that came before it. The resulting log-likelihood value is placed in the scalar *s* (a name of your choosing) and the variance-covariance matrix of the estimators in matrix **V** (another name of your choosing). The parameter estimates themselves are placed in the matrix **b** identified in the previous ml model command.

ml post may optionally be used after ml maximize to save the estimation results in Stata's internal areas. (You may, of course, use matrix post instead—see [R] **matrix post**—or you might choose not to post the results at all.) *anyshortname* is a short name that you specify to identify the type of estimation. *anyshortname* is used by ml for internal tracking only—it is not displayed in the final results. If you were estimating, say, a Hobbs model, you might specify *anyshortname* as Hobbs.

`ml mlout` may be used repeatedly after `ml post` to display and redisplay the resulting output. *shortname* must be the *anyshortname* you specified when you performed the `ml post`.

`ml report` may be used to display results from an interrupted `ml maximize` (pressing of the *Break* key) as if it had finished. After an `ml report`, `matrix mlout` (but not `ml mlout`) may be used to redisplay results subsequently.

`ml query` reports what has been defined by the other `ml` commands and may be used at any time to report where you are in the definition process.

Options

constant(*cc...c*) specifies whether each equation is to include an intercept; `constant(1)` is the default. Begin by considering single-equation models. `constant(1)`, the default, means an intercept is to be included in the equation. `constant(0)` (synonym `nocons`) means no intercept is to be included.

In multiple-equation systems, `constant(1)`, the default, means that each equation is to include an intercept. `constant(0)` (synonym `nocons`) means none of the equations include an intercept.

If the first equation is to include an intercept but not the second, you specify `constant(10)`. If it is the other way around, you specify `constant(01)`. In constant(*cc...c*), the first *c* corresponds to the first equation; the second *c*, the second equation; and so on. If you do not specify as many *c*'s as equations, the last *c* is assume to correspond to all the remaining equations. That is why `constant(1)` means all the equations include an intercept.

If any of the equations omit the intercept, you may not use `ml search` to obtain initial values.

depv(*dd...d*) specifies the number of dependent variables in each equation; the dependent variables are assumed to appear first in the equation. The first *d* is the number of dependent variables in the first equation; the second *d*, in the second equation; and so on. The last *d* specified is assumed to correspond to all subsequent equations. The default is `depv(1)`, meaning all equations are assumed to contain one dependent variable. It commonly happens in multiple-equation estimation that some of the equations have dependent variables and other "equations" are merely lists of variables. For instance, in `heckman` (see [R] **heckman**), the first equation contains a dependent variable but the second "equation" merely specifies the variables thought to determine whether the previously mentioned dependent variable does not contain missing values. This could be specified as `ml model b = wage probit, depv(10)`. The 1 of the 10 means the first equation (`wage`) contains one dependent variable; the 0 means the second equation (`probit`) contains no dependent variables. If the equations were specified in reverse order, the corresponding option would be `depv(01)`.

from(**b0**) names a matrix (row vector) **b0** from which the initial values will be drawn. **b** and **b0** need not be in the same order or even of the same dimension—initialization is performed by column name. That is, the column names of **b0** should reflect the names of the parameters you wish to initialize, which must include the equation name if there is more than one equation being estimated. Parameters not initialized in this way (not found in **b0**) are set to zero. If `from()` is not specified, all parameters are set to zero. Named elements in **b0** that do not appear in any of the equations are ignored, but you are warned that initial values obtained from over-determined parameter vectors (vectors that correspond to a maximum-likelihood solution of a model with more explanatory variables) can be quite poor.

noauto suppresses marking as excluded from estimation observations for which any of the variables in the equations are missing. For instance, in heckman (see [R] **heckman**), two equations are specified, and the second equation is the list of variables thought to determine whether the dependent variable in the first equation is observed or missing. Without the noauto option, there never would be any such missing values because they would be automatically excluded from the estimation sample. When we coded heckman, we included noauto in the ml sample statement, and we included in *varlist* all the variables in the two equations except the dependent variable whose patterns of missing values the model intends to describe.

limits(*limitlist*) specifies lower and upper limits for each structural parameter to assist in the search for feasible, reasonably good initial values. If there is only one equation, *limitlist* contains two numeric values. If there is more than one equation, *limitlist* consists of a series of triplets—the first argument specifies the equation name and the remaining two the lower and upper limits. A search is then made in the restricted multidimensional space.

iterate(#) specifies the number of random solutions from which the best will be picked as an initial value. Random solutions that turn out not to be feasible—for which the likelihood function evaluates to missing—are not counted. iterate(5) is the default and the best is then selected from five (successful) attempts.

fcnlabel(*string*) provides a string used to label the function calculations in the output. If not specified, the default is Log Likelihood.

maximize_options control the maximization process; see [R] **maximize**. You should never have to specify the more technical of them, although we do recommend specifying the trace option.

lf0(#) specifies the value of the likelihood function for the restricted model. This is usually a model with only intercept terms. Specifying this option will then allow inclusion of a χ^2 test and pseudo-R^2 in the final output—see [R] **maximize** for the definitions—although the pseudo-R^2 will only be included if pr2 is also specified. Rather than a #, you may also specify lf0(i0) to indicate that the value of the log-likelihood function evaluated at the initial values (the values in b at the time you started ml maximize) is the intercept-only model.

pr2 specifies that the output should contain a pseudo-R^2 calculation based on percentage improvement in the likelihood function from lf0() up to zero. This will generally be appropriate for discrete data, but not for continuous data. To obtain the pseudo-R^2, you must specify both pr2 and lf0().

obs(#) specifies the number of observations to be displayed on the output. If obs() is not specified, the number of observations is automatically determined by either counting the number of observations in the estimation sample or summing the weights if fweight frequency weights or iweight importance weights are specified.

title(*string*) specifies a title to be placed on the output.

dof(#) specifies the number of degrees of freedom to be used for a Student's t test of significance. If this option is not specified, the normal distribution will be used for significance tests.

eform(*string*) specifies that the exponentiated form of the coefficients is to be output and reporting of constants is to be suppressed; *string* is used to label the exponentiated coefficients; see [R] **maximize**.

first requests that Stata display only the first equation and make it appear as if only one equation were estimated.

level(#) specifies the confidence level, in percent, for confidence intervals. The default is level(95) or as set by set level; see [U] **26.4 Specifying the width of confidence intervals**.

Remarks

Remarks are presented under the headings

Terminology
The matrix ml process
Initial values
The ml command sequence
Ancillary parameters
Multiple-equation models
Macros used

Terminology

Let us begin with a summary of terminology. Given some data $\mathbf{X}$, the likelihood of observing that data conditional on some model can be written $G(\mathbf{X}, \beta)$, where β is a vector of parameters to be estimated. The maximum-likelihood solution for β is to choose some vector $\mathbf{b}$ such that $G(\mathbf{X}, \mathbf{b})$ is maximized. Such solutions are typically obtained by an iterative technique; an initial guess $\mathbf{b}_0$ is somehow obtained and from that, $\mathbf{b}_1$ is found such that $G(\mathbf{X}, \mathbf{b}_1) > G(\mathbf{X}, \mathbf{b}_0)$. Now, given the $\mathbf{b}_1$, an even better solution $\mathbf{b}_2$ is found, where better means that $G(\mathbf{X}, \mathbf{b}_2) > G(\mathbf{X}, \mathbf{b}_1)$. This process is continued until it is said to converge (which can have a variety of definitions such as $|\mathbf{b}_i - \mathbf{b}_{i-1}|$ or $G(\mathbf{X}, \mathbf{b}_i) - G(\mathbf{X}, \mathbf{b}_{i-1})$ being small). If $G()$ is the log of the likelihood, and the model is appropriate, the variance-covariance matrix of the parameters can be estimated by the Hessian, the inverse matrix of second derivatives of $\ln G()$ with respect to β, evaluated at the obtained optimum $\mathbf{b}$. Throughout this section, we will assume that $G()$ is the log of the appropriate likelihood. An extensive theory of incorrect or improper likelihoods has been developed (see, for instance, Andrews et al. 1972) and is quite useful, but is not discussed here.

Quite often, the observations $\mathbf{X}$ are thought to be a series of observations $\mathbf{x}_1$, $\mathbf{x}_2$, ..., $\mathbf{x}_n$, that are independently and identically distributed. Thus,

$$G(\mathbf{X}, \beta) = \ln f(\mathbf{x}_1, \beta) + \ln f(\mathbf{x}_2, \beta) + \ldots + \ln f(\mathbf{x}_n, \beta)$$

where $f()$ is the density or probability function for each observation. To simplify notation, let us write $g(\mathbf{x}, \beta) = \ln f(\mathbf{x}, \beta)$. Sometimes, one of the elements of $\mathbf{x}$ is said to be an outcome or dependent variable that is determined by other values in $\mathbf{x}$, and that element of $\mathbf{x}$ is split out from the remaining values to write:

$$G(\mathbf{Y}, \mathbf{X}, \beta) = g(y_1, \mathbf{x}_1, \beta) + g(y_2, \mathbf{x}_2, \beta) + \ldots + g(y_n, \mathbf{x}_n, \beta)$$

At this point, we have done nothing more than label one of the variables differently from the rest. It is quite common, however, that the $\mathbf{x}$'s and β's are combined linearly, so that

$$G(\mathbf{Y}, \mathbf{X}, \beta) = G(\mathbf{Y}, \mathbf{X}\beta) = g(y_1, \mathbf{x}_1\beta) + g(y_2, \mathbf{x}_2\beta) + \ldots + g(y_n, \mathbf{x}_n\beta)$$

Models of this form are called regression models, and thus maximum-likelihood logit is also known as logistic regression, and maximum-likelihood exponential is referred to as exponential regression. (Maximum-likelihood Cox is called Cox regression, but it cannot be separated into independent and identically distributed pieces; maximizing a likelihood like the Cox likelihood is described in *Other optimization methods* below.)

In computational terms, there is a considerable economy that can be exploited in separable regression models. The term $\mathbf{x}_k\boldsymbol{\beta}$ is called the index I_k. During the iterative estimation procedure, one typically needs derivatives of the log-likelihood $G()$ with respect to each of the elements of $\boldsymbol{\beta}$, resulting in the so-called gradient vector. If the data are i.i.d., that gradient can be calculated as the sum of the gradients of the individual $g()$'s. If the model is also a separable regression model, rather than calculating the derivative of $g()$ for each element of $\boldsymbol{\beta}$, one can use the chain rule and calculate the derivative of $g()$ with respect to the index and then multiply that by the appropriate element of $\mathbf{x}$.

The lf method of ml—lf stands for linear form—does this; see *The matrix ml process* below for an example of the lf method.

The matrix ml process

First, we will consider an example of matrix ml, and then we will summarize the steps.

Consider the logistic regression likelihood function:

$$f(y, \mathbf{x}, \boldsymbol{\beta}) = f(y, \mathbf{x}\boldsymbol{\beta}) = \begin{cases} 1/\big(1 + \exp(-\mathbf{x}\boldsymbol{\beta})\big) & \text{if } y = 1 \\ \exp(-\mathbf{x}\boldsymbol{\beta})/\big(1 + \exp(-\mathbf{x}\boldsymbol{\beta})\big) & \text{if } y = 0 \end{cases}$$

The first step to implement this model is to write a program to calculate the log-likelihood value. As you will see, this program can be in different forms, but the simplest (corresponding to the lf optimization method) supplies the log likelihood on an observation-by-observation basis given the value of the dependent variable y and the index $\mathbf{x}\boldsymbol{\beta}$:

```
program define logit0
        local lnf "`1'"
        local I "`2'"
        quietly replace `lnf' = cond($S_mldepn, /*
                        */ -ln(1+exp(-`I')), /*
                        */ -(`I')-ln(1+exp(-`I')) )
end
```

The name we give our program—logit0—is arbitrary except that it cannot be a command name already in use by Stata. Our program expects two arguments—the name of an existing variable that is to be set to the likelihood value and the name of a variable that contains the value of the index $\mathbf{x}\boldsymbol{\beta}$. In addition, we need to know the dependent variable and that is supplied through the global macro S_mldepn. In the observation-by-observation calculation, we do not have to concern ourselves with the sample selection—the if *exp* and in *range*—because this will be handled by ml for us.

We are now ready to perform the maximization. We will do this interactively:

```
. ml begin
. ml function logit0
. ml method lf
. eq foreign mpg displ
. ml model b = foreign
. ml sample mysamp

. ml maximize f V
Iteration 0:  Log Likelihood = -51.292891
Iteration 1:  Log Likelihood = -21.486626
Iteration 2:  Log Likelihood = -20.755878
Iteration 3:  Log Likelihood = -20.752402
Iteration 4:  Log Likelihood = -20.752402

. ml post mylogit, title(My logit analysis)
```

```
. ml mlout mylogit
My logit analysis                              Number of obs   =        74
                                               Model chi2(2)   =        .
                                               Prob > chi2     =        .
Log Likelihood =    -20.7524016
------------------------------------------------------------------------------
  foreign |     Coef.   Std. Err.       z     P>|z|     [95% Conf. Interval]
----------+-------------------------------------------------------------------
      mpg |  -.191786    .091969     -2.085   0.037    -.3720419    -.01153
    displ |  -.0628496   .0197115    -3.188   0.001    -.1014833   -.0242158
    _cons |  12.66106    4.347169     2.912   0.004     4.140762   21.18135
------------------------------------------------------------------------------
```

Let us go through the steps one by one.

ml begin clears any previous problem; you must always start with this.

ml function specifies the name of our routine (the one we write) that calculates log-likelihood values.

ml method specifies the optimization method; we are using the lf linear-form technique.

We then took an aside and defined the equation we wanted to estimate although we could have defined the equation earlier, even before the ml begin. The equation we are going to estimate is the equivalent of logit foreign mpg displ, the outcome foreign will be fitted in terms of mpg and displ. Remember that when we do not explicitly specify the equation name, eq uses the first listed variable as both the equation name and as part of the contents of the equation; see [R] eq. We defined an equation named foreign containing foreign mpg displ.

The ml model statement informs ml of our desired model and creates a row vector b with suitable initial values. In this case, the elements of b were set to zero.

ml sample identifies the sample over which we wish to estimate the model. The variable mysamp did not exist prior to issuing this command; afterwards, it does. If we had wanted to restrict the sample to some subset of our data, we could have included an if *exp* or in *range* here. Since we did not, ml sample created mysamp based solely on missing values of the variables foreign, mpg, and displ. It knew to do this because we previously declared that we wished to estimate the equation foreign and foreign contains foreign mpg displ. (If we had previously declared estimation of multiple equations, the variables in all of those equations would have been checked for missing values.)

Finally, ml maximize estimates the model. We specified f and V. f will be the name of a scalar containing the value of the log-likelihood function and V will be the resulting variance-covariance matrix of the estimators. The estimates themselves will be placed in the vector b because, previously in our ml model statement, that is where we said we wanted them.

At this point, we could have just displayed the matrices b and V, along with the scalar f, to see the results; we really were done. Here is what would have happened:

```
. matrix list b
b[1,3]
          mpg        displ       _cons
r1  -.19178598  -.06284955   12.661057
. matrix list V
symmetric V[3,3]
             mpg         displ        _cons
  mpg    .0084583
displ    .00130367    .00038854
_cons   -.36756795   -.07948419    18.897879
```

```
. scalar list f
       f = -20.752402
```

Instead of doing this, however, we typed ml post, thus posting these results to Stata's internal estimation results. The ml post command is quite similar to the more general matrix post command (see [R] matrix post), except that it is easier to use since ml knows where everything is and knows everything that must be done to get the results correctly posted. We finally used ml mlout to see the results—another command similar to the matrix equivalent. In fact, we could have used matrix mlout, but ml mlout knows to put a header above the coefficient output. The formulas for the elements in the header are given in [R] maximize.

The advantages of posting and then displaying the results are that the output is better formatted and, having posted the results, we can use any of Stata's post-estimation features on our new estimates. We could now use, for example, predict or test commands.

Initial values

In our logistic-regression problem, we were fortunate that the zero vector was a feasible starting point. In general, we will not be so lucky and ml maximize will give up if the log-likelihood function cannot be calculated at the initial values we supply. Moreover, unless $G()$ is globally concave (as it is in the case of logit), there is no guarantee that the maximum found is a global maximum as opposed to a local one. Even with well-behaved functions, poor initial values can result in slow convergence. For all of these reasons, a good strategy for calculating initial values is crucial to the success of a likelihood-maximization effort.

In theory, one would like to start with consistent estimates for all parameters since one can guarantee that consistent initial values lead to efficient estimates. Unfortunately, this may be as difficult as solving the original problem. In the context of a linear-form model including an intercept, however, initial values of zero except for the intercept are often a workable starting point for the complete maximization. Sometimes such intercepts can be calculated directly by an analytic formula—they can in the case of logit—but at other times, no such closed-form solution is available.

Let's begin by taking the case of the closed-form solution. We want to estimate the logit model

$$\Pr(\texttt{foreign}_j) = p_j = \frac{\exp(I_j)}{1 + \exp(I_j)}$$

where $I_j = \beta_0 + \beta_1 \texttt{mpg}_j + \beta_2 \texttt{displ}_j$. We will start, however, by deriving the solution to the intercept-only model $I_j = \alpha$ and then, using $\beta_0 = \alpha$ and $\beta_1 = \beta_2 = 0$ for the initial values, turn the optimizer loose. Thus, we need to solve

$$p_j = \frac{\exp(\alpha)}{1 + \exp(\alpha)}$$

for α. Algebraic manipulation yields $\alpha = \ln(p_j/(1 - p_j))$. Logit has the property that the mean of the dependent variable equals the observed average probability, so we can calculate $\alpha = \ln(\overline{p}/(1 - \overline{p}))$ where $\overline{p}$ is the average value of foreign. In our data, $\overline{p}$ is

```
. summarize foreign

Variable |       Obs        Mean    Std. Dev.       Min        Max
---------+-----------------------------------------------------------
 foreign |        74    .2972973    .4601885         0          1
```

and so we obtain $\alpha = -.8602013$. We can automate this calculation and create a matrix which will contain the initial value we wish to impose:

```
. quietly summarize foreign
. local alpha = ln(_result(3)/(1-_result(3)))
. matrix ival = (`alpha')
. matrix colnames ival = _cons
. mat list ival

symmetric ival[1,1]
          _cons
r1   -.86020127
```

Remember, our goal is to produce initial values for the full model, which will be a 1×3 parameter vector. We do this by creating a vector of initial values—we called the vector ival—and then specifying from(ival) in the ml model statement. Our initial value vector need not be in the same order or even of the same dimension as the ultimate vector of initial values because ml will be able to determine from the column names which parameters we wish to set.

```
. ml begin
. ml function logit0
. ml method lf
. eq foreign mpg displ
. ml model b = foreign, from(ival)
. mat list b

b[1,3]
         mpg       displ       _cons
r1         0           0  -.86020127
```

We are stopping here just to show you that the initial-value vector has been created by ml model just as we intended.

```
. ml sample mysamp
. ml maximize f V
Iteration 0:  Log Likelihood =  -45.03321
Iteration 1:  Log Likelihood = -27.568062
Iteration 2:  Log Likelihood = -22.311313
Iteration 3:  Log Likelihood = -20.895142
Iteration 4:  Log Likelihood = -20.752687
Iteration 5:  Log Likelihood = -20.752402
Iteration 6:  Log Likelihood = -20.752402
```

We have our likelihood estimates. We will now continue to post and display the results and, this time, we will specify lf0(i0) on the ml post command. lf0(i0) means the value of the likelihood function at the initial values we previously supplied—which is reported above as iteration 0—is the intercept-only model. If you specify the lf0() option, ml mlout will report the χ^2 significance test. We will also specify pr2, meaning the pseudo-R^2 is to be calculated and reported as well:

```
. ml post mylogit, lf0(i0) pr2
. ml mlout mylogit
```

				Number of obs	=	74
				Model chi2(2)	=	48.56
				Prob > chi2	=	0.0000
Log Likelihood =	-20.7524016			Pseudo R2	=	0.5392

foreign	Coef.	Std. Err.	z	P>|z|	[95% Conf. Interval]	
mpg	-.191786	.0919395	-2.086	0.037	-.3719841	-.0115878
displ	-.0628495	.0196936	-3.191	0.001	-.1014484	-.0242507
_cons	12.66106	4.344298	2.914	0.004	4.146387	21.17572

Now let's consider the case where obtaining an analytic solution to the intercept-only model is too hard or impossible. In that case, one could first estimate an intercept-only model starting with zero and then use the intercept-only solution as the initial values for the full optimization.

```
. ml begin
. ml function logit0
. ml method lf
. eq foreign : foreign                  /* see note 1 */
. ml model b = foreign
. ml sample mysamp mpg displ            /* see note 2 */
. ml maximize f V
Iteration 0:  Log Likelihood = -51.292891
Iteration 1:  Log Likelihood = -45.046112
Iteration 2:  Log Likelihood =  -45.03321
Iteration 3:  Log Likelihood =  -45.03321

. mat list b                            /* see note 3 */

symmetric b[1,1]
          _cons
r1  -.86020127

. local f0=scalar(f)                    /* see note 4 */
. matrix ival = b                       /* see note 5 */
. ml begin                              /* see note 6 */
. ml function logit0
. ml method lf
. eq foreign mpg displ
. ml model b = foreign, from(ival)
. mat list b                            /* see note 7 */

b[1,3]
          mpg      displ      _cons
r1          0          0  -.86020127

. ml sample mysamp
. ml maximize f V
Iteration 0:  Log Likelihood =  -45.03321
Iteration 1:  Log Likelihood = -27.568062
Iteration 2:  Log Likelihood =  -22.31132
Iteration 3:  Log Likelihood = -20.895157
Iteration 4:  Log Likelihood = -20.752685
Iteration 5:  Log Likelihood = -20.752402
Iteration 6:  Log Likelihood = -20.752402

. ml post mylogit, lf0(`f0') pr2        /* see note 4 (sic) */
. ml mlout mylogit
```

		Number of obs	=	74
		Model chi2(2)	=	48.56
		Prob > chi2	=	0.0000
Log Likelihood =	-20.7524016	Pseudo R2	=	0.5392

foreign	Coef.	Std. Err.	z	P>|z|	[95% Conf. Interval]	
mpg	-.191786	.09195	-2.086	0.037	-.3720047	-.0115672
displ	-.0628495	.0196965	-3.191	0.001	-.1014539	-.0242452
_cons	12.66106	4.344936	2.914	0.004	4.145136	21.17697

Note 1: We define our equation in this strange way because eq foreign would be interpreted as a syntax error. The result of this is that the equation named foreign contains foreign and nothing else, so we wish to estimate solely on a constant.

Note 2: We include mpg and displ in the search for missing values because we ultimately will be estimating a model on those two variables and we want to exclude any observations that have missing values in obtaining the solution to the intercept-only model.

Note 3: We obtained the initial value we wanted; note this is the same number as we previously obtained analytically.

Note 4: We save the value of the likelihood function. We will later use this number in the `lf0()` option of `ml post` when we are all through so as to obtain the χ^2 test.

Note 5: We save the maximum-likelihood, constant-only parameter vector in the matrix `ival` which we will use later to initialize the full parameter vector.

Note 6: We start a new problem for the full model estimation.

Note 7: We are just showing you once again that `ml model` initialized the parameter vector as we intended.

There is a third way to obtain initial values: `ml search` will randomly choose values for intercept-only models and try them; it will retain the best attempt as the initial value. `ml search` is used after `ml sample` and before `ml maximize`. You, however, must specify a "reasonable" range for the index function(s). For instance,

```
. ml search, limits(-5 5)
```

would search the logit space in the range −5 to 5 and reset the parameter vector to the best values found after a handful of attempts.

Rerunning our example:

```
. ml begin
. ml function logit0
. ml method lf
. eq foreign mpg displ
. ml model b = foreign
. ml sample mysamp

. ml search, limits(-5 5)
search 1:  Log Likelihood = -54.947043
search 2:  Log Likelihood = -47.539624
search 3:  Log Likelihood = -57.979712
search 4:  Log Likelihood = -80.631491
search 5:  Log Likelihood = -77.383299
```

`ml search` tried five random initial values and then selected the best—the one corresponding to a log-likelihood value of −47.54. The `ml model b = foreign` previously set the initial values in b to all zeros. After the `ml search`, the values are

```
. mat list b

b[1,3]
          mpg       displ       _cons
r1          0           0   -1.4557853
```

Note that this is not the same value we obtained analytically or by an initial round of maximization earlier. This value is merely the best from five randomly chosen attempts. Even so, it is better than zero.

```
. ml maximize f V
Iteration 0:  Log Likelihood = -47.539624
Iteration 1:  Log Likelihood = -28.465395
Iteration 2:  Log Likelihood = -22.537005
Iteration 3:  Log Likelihood =  -20.93196
Iteration 4:  Log Likelihood = -20.752815
Iteration 5:  Log Likelihood = -20.752402
Iteration 6:  Log Likelihood = -20.752402
```

If you compare this `ml maximize` output with our previous runs, you will observe: (1) our initial log-likelihood value of -47.54 is better than the -51.29 of the zero model but not as good as the -45.03 of the correct intercept-only model; (2) the resulting log-likelihood value reported as of the last iteration is the same, -20.75, for all runs; and (3) the number of iterations is 6 in all cases.

You might now be tempted to think that improved initial values do not speed things along. As far as the well-behaved logit model is concerned, this is true, but you should not generalize. The logit function is globally concave and there is no point we could pick that would not guide us back onto the path to a solution (assuming the function can be calculated at all). It is more than globally concave—it is nearly quadratic—which fits nicely with our optimizer—and means that any bad point will instantly (in one iteration) put us back on the path to a good one. Do not expect to be so lucky when dealing with other likelihood functions.

There is a fourth way to proceed, and it is perhaps the best as long as the analytic solution is not available. Estimate the intercept-only model using maximum likelihood, as we did earlier, but use `ml search` to randomly choose a good initial value for that maximization. Then use the maximum-likelihood solution as the starting point for the full solution.

There is one more detail about `ml search`: The `iterate()` option specifies the number of random initial values to be attempted (from which the best is then chosen). The default is `iterate(5)`, but you can attempt more if you wish.

At the beginning of this section, we said that one would like to start with consistent estimates for all parameters since one can guarantee that consistent initial values lead to efficient estimates. Consistent means that, as the sample size tends toward infinity, the initial values tend toward the true parameters. Efficient means that there is no other estimator that has lower asymptotic mean square error.

It would be desirable to have consistent initial values in the full parameter space, but for a serious problem, that would involve a prohibitive amount of searching. In our experience, it works well to start with the maximum-likelihood solution for the intercepts. In order to know we have gotten to the maximum-likelihood solution for the intercepts, however, we need a consistent estimator for them. For this more limited problem, searching is feasible. A random search such as `ml search` will do this provided that the number of random values tried is sufficiently large and is tied in some way to the sample size N. We usually find that a number of samples on the order of $\ln(N)$ is a good choice.

The ml command sequence

To review, the command sequence for estimating a maximum-likelihood model is

required	`ml begin`	declare the start of a problem
required	`ml function`	declare name of calculation program
required	`ml method`	specify an optimization method
required	`ml model`	declare equations to be estimated
required	`ml sample`	determine estimation sample
optional	`ml search`	improve initial values
required	`ml maximize`	obtain maximum-likelihood results
optional	`ml post`	save results internally
optional	`ml mlout`	display or redisplay saved results

Ancillary parameters

Ancillary parameters are estimated parameters that do not have a corresponding variable associated with them—they are not coefficients. In linear regression, for instance, the parameters to be estimated are β in $E(y_j) = \mathbf{x}_j\beta$ and σ, the standard error of the residual. σ is an example of an ancillary parameter. In logistic regression, on the other hand, there is no ancillary parameter and so we have been able to ignore such problems so far.

We will examine the treatment of ancillary parameters using negative-binomial regression. Before attacking the programming, let's lay out the likelihood function. One way of viewing the negative binomial is that the number of times something occurs, y_i, is a function of $\mathbf{x}_i\beta$ and a parameter α. The likelihood for the i observation is given by

$$f(y_i) = \frac{\Gamma(m + y_i)}{\Gamma(y_i + 1)\Gamma(m)} \, p_i^m (1 - p_i)^{y_i}$$

where $m = 1/\alpha$, $p_i = 1/(1 + \alpha\mu_i)$, and $\mu_i = \exp(\mathbf{x}_i\beta)$. The log of the likelihood can be written as

$$\ln f(y_i) = \ln \Gamma(y_i + 1/\alpha) - \ln \Gamma(y_i + 1) - \ln \Gamma(1/\alpha) + y_i \ln(\alpha\mu_i/(1 + \alpha\mu_i)) - \ln(1 + \alpha\mu_i)/\alpha$$

Mathematically, numerical solutions for α are best handled by searching for $\ln \alpha$ because α is required to be greater than zero.

This is the function we wish to maximize. In terms of programming, remember $\mu_i = \exp(\mathbf{x}_i\beta)$, so $\ln \mu_i = \mathbf{x}_i\beta$ is a natural linear form. We already know how to deal with that.

We have left over, however, a parameter $\ln \alpha$. Pretend for a moment that we wished to allow the $\ln \alpha$ parameter to vary across the observations and planned to parameterize it $\ln \alpha_i = \mathbf{z}_i\gamma$. Then we would have a second linear-form equation. That is exactly what we are going to do, except that $\mathbf{z}_i$ will be restricted to be 1, resulting in an intercept-only equation.

Thus, there will be two equations and so two indexes. The first index will be $\mathbf{x}_i\beta$ and the second $\mathbf{z}_i\gamma$. Here is our program:

```
program define nb0 /* llvar xbeta zgamma */
        tempvar amu a
        quietly {
                local lnf     "`1'"
                local xbeta   "`2'"
                local zgamma  "`3'"
                gen double `a'   = exp(`zgamma')
                gen double `amu' = exp(`xbeta')*`a'
                replace `lnf' = /*
                */ lngamma($S_mldepn+1/`a')-lngamma($S_mldepn+1) - /*
                */ lngamma(1/`a')+$S_mldepn*ln(`amu'/(1+`amu')) - /*
                */ ln(1+`amu')/`a'
        }
end
```

Our program will receive three arguments—the first being the variable in which we are to store the calculated log-likelihood values, the second being the index of the first equation, and the third being the index of the second "equation". We will use the following data:

```
. list

        injuries   XYZowned
   1.        11          1
   2.         7          0
```

```
3.        7         0
4.       19         0
5.        9         0
6.        4         1
7.        3         0
8.        1         0
9.        3         1
```

The `ml` commands are

```
. ml begin
. ml func nb0
. ml method lf
. eq injuries XYZowned                    /* see note 1 */
. eq lnalpha :                            /* see note 2 */
. ml model b = injuries lnalpha, depv(10) /* see note 3 */
. ml sample mysamp
. ml search, limits(injuries 0 6  lnalpha -1 1)   /* see note 4 */
search 1:  Log Likelihood = -29.518455
search 2:  Log Likelihood = -27.534199
search 3:  Log Likelihood = -27.553961
search 4:  Log Likelihood = -32.795198
search 5:  Log Likelihood = -27.604258

. ml max f V
Iteration 0:   Log Likelihood = -27.534199
Iteration 1:   Log Likelihood = -25.999402
Iteration 2:   Log Likelihood = -25.914597
Iteration 3:   Log Likelihood = -25.914495
Iteration 4:   Log Likelihood = -25.914495

. ml post nbreg, title(Negative-Binomial Regression)
. ml mlout nbreg
```

```
Negative-Binomial Regression              Number of obs   =        9
                                          Model chi2(1)   =        .
                                          Prob > chi2     =        .
Log Likelihood =      -25.9144952
```

injuries	Coef.	Std. Err.	z	P>|z|	[95% Conf. Interval]	
injuries						
XYZowned	-.2451224	.5060919	-0.484	0.628	-1.237044	.7467995
_cons	2.036882	.2852203	7.141	0.000	1.47786	2.595903
lnalpha						
_cons	-1.028149	.6579723	-1.563	0.118	-2.317751	.2614533

Note 1: Our first equation is called `injuries` and contains `injuries XYZowned`. `injuries` is the dependent variable and `XYZowned` is the independent variable.

Note 2: Our second equation is called `lnalpha` and contains nothing, neither a dependent nor an independent variable. This "equation" is merely a list of things on which $\ln\alpha$ is to depend. Our $\ln\alpha$ will contain an intercept alone and so be a constant.

Note 3: We specify two equations and we specify `depv(10)`, meaning the first equation is to be interpreted as having one dependent variable and the second "equation" has no dependent variable.

Note 4: It is always a good idea to use `ml search` to obtain initial values rather than depending on a vector of zeros being satisfactory. Note the form of the `limit()` when there is more than one equation. We chose the limits for `injuries` to be 0 and 6 because the number of injuries is certainly more than $e^0 = 1$ and less than $e^6 \approx 403$—see the listing of the data above. Our limits of -1 and 1 for $\ln \alpha$ come from practical experience on reasonable values for this parameter.

❏ Technical Note

When you issue the `ml maximize` option, especially for the first time after programming a model, you should specify the `trace` option. We have not done this so as to conserve paper, but if there are problems, the trace will help you determine what is going wrong. Here is what the result would have been of specifying `trace` above:

```
. ml max f V, trace
            0   1.5305746  -.58037894
Iteration 0:  Log Likelihood = -27.534199
   -.18403127   1.9392818  -1.1471047
Iteration 1:  Log Likelihood = -25.999402
    -.2467879   2.0406448  -1.0294523
Iteration 2:  Log Likelihood = -25.914597
   -.24512172   2.0368826  -1.0281186
Iteration 3:  Log Likelihood = -25.914495
   -.24512244   2.0368819  -1.0281488
Iteration 4:  Log Likelihood = -25.914495
```

The `trace` option lists the parameter vector—the order of the coefficients is the same as the order printed in the more formal `ml mlout`.

❏

Multiple-equation models

Multiple-equation models are conceptually (and practically) no different from models with ancillary parameters. Given our code above, there is nothing stopping us from specifying a more complete second equation for $\ln \alpha$.

```
. ml begin
. ml func nb0
. ml method lf
. eq injuries XYZowned
. eq lnalpha : XYZowned                       /* see note 1 */
. ml model b = injuries lnalpha, depv(10)
. ml sample mysamp

. ml search, limits(injuries 0 6  lnalpha -1 1)
search 1:  Log Likelihood = -29.518455
search 2:  Log Likelihood = -27.534199
search 3:  Log Likelihood = -27.553961
search 4:  Log Likelihood = -32.795198
search 5:  Log Likelihood = -27.604258

. ml max f V
Iteration 0:  Log Likelihood = -27.534199
Iteration 1:  Log Likelihood = -25.943487
Iteration 2:  Log Likelihood = -25.734695
Iteration 3:  Log Likelihood = -25.732528
Iteration 4:  Log Likelihood = -25.732528

. ml post nbreg, title(Negative-Binomial Regression)
```

```
. ml mlout nbreg
Negative-Binomial Regression                      Number of obs   =        9
                                                  Model chi2(2)   =        .
                                                  Prob > chi2     =        .
Log Likelihood =      -25.7325279
-------------------------------------------------------------------------------
injuries |     Coef.   Std. Err.      z     P>|z|     [95% Conf. Interval]
---------+---------------------------------------------------------------------
injuries |
XYZowned |   -.2451225   .4577647    -0.535   0.592    -1.142325    .6520798
   _cons |    2.036882   .3112111     6.545   0.000     1.426919    2.646844
---------+---------------------------------------------------------------------
lnalpha  |
XYZowned |   -.9666323   1.736138    -0.557   0.578    -4.369401    2.436136
   _cons |   -.7969989   .7522319    -1.060   0.289    -2.271346    .6773486
-------------------------------------------------------------------------------
```

Note 1: This line is the only line that changed compared with our previous run in *Ancillary parameters* above. We changed the equation named lnalpha from containing nothing to containing XYZowned. ln α will now be a function of XYZowned (and a constant).

Since we have posted the results to Stata's internal areas, we can now test the joint significance of XYZowned:

```
. test XYZowned

 ( 1)  [injuries]XYZowned = 0.0
 ( 2)  [lnalpha]XYZowned = 0.0

        chi2(  2) =     0.60
      Prob > chi2 =     0.7420
```

Maximization difficulties

In real life, maximizing a likelihood function is trickier than it might appear above. In all of our examples, the successive changes in both the likelihood and the parameters become substantially smaller with each iteration. (You can see this for the log-likelihood value, but you cannot see it for the parameter vector because we typically have not specified trace.) This is called quadratic convergence and is a desirable property. If you observe convergence but it is not quadratic—the changes do not become progressively and substantially smaller—you should suspect trouble. Lack of quadratic convergence does not necessarily prove there is a problem, but if there is a problem, there will be lack of quadratic convergence.

It is possible that the function has no interior maximum—that the maximum occurs at infinite values of the parameters. In such cases, you will usually notice that the likelihood steps are not shrinking quickly. Moreover, if you specify trace, you may find that the change for one or more of the parameters is actually growing with each successive iteration.

There are two possible "solutions" to such problems. You can interrupt the maximization (by pressing *Break*) and study the nonconverged answer (ml report will help). Your goal is to find what parameters are causing the problem and to delete them, perhaps with some of the observations, and then reestimate the model. Or, you can let the iterative procedure continue until "convergence" and accept the answer with large values for some of the parameters, hoping that the second derivative approximations are sufficiently acceptable for inference. Which is better is up to you.

A likelihood function can have more than one maximum. Maximum-likelihood factor analysis (see [R] **factor**) has this problem whereas other likelihoods, such as logit, can be proven not to suffer from this problem. If you see a message "(nonconcave function encountered)" then you should certainly be alert to this possibility. One answer is to use `ml search` to produce different starting values, then follow the iterations to see if they converge to the same place. If you are searching for the single global maximum, you must repeat this procedure until you have seen enough of the local maximums to know which is the global.

Likelihood functions can have surfaces that are irregularly shaped. This is true of the Heckman selection model; see [R] **heckman**. This type of likelihood is especially vulnerable to slow convergence but, conditional on convergence, all is well.

Likelihood functions can have bounded feasible regions or, said differently, regions where the function is undefined. You should use functional transformation to avoid such regions. For instance, if α is restricted to be greater than 0, parameterize the model in terms of $\ln \alpha$. Ignoring the problem usually does not work well. If the derivatives suggest that the maximization routine should cross over the boundary, a great deal of effort will be put into trying to cross the boundary, and productive steps in another valid direction will be ignored. Penalty and mirroring strategies are also valid alternatives to transformation. In a penalty strategy, the likelihood function is adjusted downward near the boundary and this is done in a way to preserve continuity. In a mirroring strategy, a parameter which is restricted, say, to lie between ± 1, is aliased so that 1.2 is like .8 and so on.

Likelihood functions can be programmed incorrectly. This is especially true of the derivatives, which is one of the reasons we are so fond of (computationally slow) numerical derivatives. In any case, programming errors will generally result in slow convergence punctuated with commentary about steps that have backed up or encountered nonconcave functions. One common mistake with likelihoods is not using double precision. Another is accidentally omitting one of the parameters or eclipsing it—you think you have a function of three parameters and it is actually a function of two. If you use analytic derivatives, check them against Stata's numerically calculated derivatives. Stata can be made to print these on each iteration by setting the global macro `S_mldbug` to 1.

Other optimization methods

While the `lf` linear-form method on which we have concentrated so heavily is quite flexible, it is not flexible enough for all likelihood problems. There are some likelihood models, such as Cox proportional-hazards regression, where the likelihood must be calculated for the sample as a whole rather than observation-by-observation. There are other problems, such as factor analysis, that are not regression models at all.

The other techniques we provide will require more of your involvement in the maximization process than does `lf`. Three methods are available: `deriv0`, `deriv1`, and `deriv2`. In all cases, you must supply a complete likelihood function as a Stata program and, for `deriv1`, the first derivatives and, for `deriv2`, the second derivatives as well.

To explore the mechanics of this idea, we return to our first example, logistic regression. The calling program, and the general form of the output, remain mostly unchanged, except for the `ml function` and `ml method` calls.

```
program define logitd0
        local b "`1'"        /* parameter values */
        local f "`2'"        /* scalar name to contain function value */

        tempvar prdn rr
        matrix score double `prdn' = `b'
        qui replace `prdn' = 1/(1+exp(-`prdn'))
        qui gen double `rr' = sum(cond($S_mldepn,ln(`prdn'),ln(1-`prdn')))
        scalar `f' = `rr'[_N]
end
```

Note the use of double precision throughout.

This program would be executed by

```
. ml begin
. ml function logitd0
. ml method deriv0
```
(*remaining* ml *commands are the same as with the* lf *method*)

Our program is not sufficiently complicated. For instance, sample selection is not handled automatically for you as it is with lf. You still must issue the ml **sample** command, but it is your responsibility to make use of the marker variable ml **sample** creates. The name of the marker variable is stored in the global macro S_mlwgt. It contains zero if an observation is not to be used, so a better version of our program would read:

```
program define logitd0
        local b "`1'"       /* parameter values */
        local f "`2'"       /* scalar name to contain function value */

        tempvar prdn rr
        matrix score double `prdn' = `b' if $S_mlwgt
        qui replace `prdn' = 1/(1+exp(-`prdn')) if $S_mlwgt
        qui gen double `rr' = sum(cond($S_mldepn,ln(`prdn'),ln(1-`prdn')))
        scalar `f' = `rr'[_N]
end
```

In fact, $S_mlwgt contains not just a marker on whether the variable is to be used, but the weights (normalized as required) if weights are specified. Thus, an even better version of this program would read:

```
program define logitd0
        local b "`1'"       /* parameter values */
        local f "`2'"       /* scalar name to contain function value */

        tempvar prdn rr
        matrix score double `prdn' = `b' if $S_mlwgt
        qui replace `prdn' = 1/(1+exp(-`prdn')) if $S_mlwgt
        qui gen double `rr' = sum($S_mlwgt*cond($S_mldepn,ln(`prdn'),ln(1-`prdn')))
        scalar `f' = `rr'[_N]
end
```

It is also your responsibility to handle out-of-range parameters, something lf handled for you because it could observe that the likelihood is missing in certain observations. In the case of logistic regression, gross miscategorizations will cause us to take logs of numbers close to zero. In our program, after the **matrix score** and before the **replace**, we might include the lines:

```
qui count if $S_mlwgt!=0 & ((`prdn'>10 & $S_mldepn==0) | /*
        */ (`prdn'<-10 & $S_mldepn==1))
if _result(1)>0 {
        scalar `f' = -1e30
        exit
}
```

In any case, you get the idea. Everything is your responsibility. The deriv0, deriv1, and deriv2 methods are not intended for casual use. Even professional programmers would be well advised to use the lf method whenever possible or plan on spending considerable time testing and debugging their code.

If you wish to include analytic first derivatives—they will speed the calculation considerably—the program must be modified to calculate them. Later, you specify the ml method as deriv1:

```
program define logitd1
        local b "`1'"         /* starting values on entrance */
        local f "`2'"         /* scalar name to contain function value */
        local d "`3'"         /* derivative matrix */

        tempvar prdn rr
        matrix score double `prdn' = `b'
        qui replace `prdn' = 1/(1+exp(-`prdn'))
        gen double `rr' = ($S_mldepn - `prdn')
        mx_parm `b'
        qui matrix vecaccum `d' = `rr' $S_1 , $S_2
        qui replace `rr' = sum(cond($S_mldepn,log(`prdn'),log(1-`prdn')))
        scalar `f' = `rr'[_N]
end
```

Note that we did not include $S_mlwgt to handle sample selection and weights, nor did we include the logic for handling overflow. We wanted to keep the code readable but, were this real code, we would recommend adding the complication although we admit that, for quick-and-dirty work, we ourselves do not. If you do not add the handling of $S_mlwgt, remember that you should not specify if *exp*, in *range*, or weights with the ml sample command—your program would ignore them. Also, you must make sure to literally drop all observations in your data with missing values on the variables prior to using the estimator.

The mx_parm command in our program takes a vector as an argument and returns in the global macro $S_1 the variable list derived from the column names, exclusive of any constants. mx_parm returns in $S_2 either nothing or nocons, thus setting us up for a matrix vecaccum; see [R] **matrix accum**. You may use mx_parm in your programs if you wish.

❏ Technical Note

The gen double `rr' = ($S_mldepn - `prdn') in our program is deceptively simple. To get this, we noted that for a success the derivative of $\ln p$ with respect to $x_i\beta$, where p is the likelihood of the event that occurred, is $(1/p)(p)(1-p)$, whereas for a failure it is $(1/(1-p))(-p)(1-p)$.

❏

One might imagine that supplying first derivatives is better than supplying no derivatives—that method deriv1 is better than deriv0. That is true, but do not make the logical leap that therefore deriv1 is better than lf—that is not so. Taking advantage of linear form outweighs the value of analytic derivatives, both in accuracy and in speed. In the case of single-equation models, the linear-form program requires only three likelihood calculations per iteration—one for the function and two for the centered derivative calculation.

If speed is of concern, deriv2 is the best choice, but it requires not only that you provide analytic second derivatives but that you handle some housekeeping functions:

```
program define logitd2
        local b "`1'"         /* starting values on entrance */
        local f "`2'"         /* scalar name to contain function value */
        local d "`3'"         /* derivative matrix */
        local v "`4'"         /* matrix name to contain variance matrix */
        mac shift 4

        local options "LASTIT FIRSTIT FAST(string)"
        parse "`*'"
```

```
          if "`lastit'"~="" { exit }
          tempvar prdn rr
          matrix score double `prdn' = `b'
          qui replace `prdn' = 1/(1+exp(-`prdn'))
          if `fast'~=0 {
                  gen double `rr' = ($S_mldepn - `prdn') / (`prdn'*(1-`prdn'))
                  mx_parm `b'
                  qui matrix accum `v' = `rr' $S_1 [iw=`prdn'*(1-`prdn')], $S_2
                  matrix `d' = `v'[1,2...]
                  matrix `v' = `v'[2...,2...]
                  drop `rr'
          }
          qui gen double `rr' = sum(cond($S_mldepn,log(`prdn'),log(1-`prdn')))
          scalar `f' = `rr'[_N]
   end
```

This program has the same shortcoming as our previous drafts—it does not deal with sample selection, missing values, or user-specified weights, but all could be added.

Methods and Formulas

The `ml` maximizer is a modified Marquardt (1963) algorithm, which is itself a modified Newton–Raphson method. At each iteration, a log likelihood-derivative (gradient vector) g is calculated along with a matrix A, which is the negative of the Hessian. (Methods `lf` and `deriv0` make this calculation numerically, `deriv1` makes the second derivative calculation numerically based on the analytic first derivative results, and `deriv2` obtains all values from the user's analytical calculation.) A step of length $A^{-1}g$ is taken. The likelihood is now evaluated at the new value. If it is an increase, then another step is taken. Otherwise, an adaptive steepest-descent step is taken in the g direction. If an information message about a non-productive step appears, it means the maximizer took a tentative step that resulted in a lower likelihood. This situation is resolved within the modified Marquardt strategy, which is to augment the diagonal of the A matrix (by addition and multiplication), resulting in a step which is a compromise between a Newton–Raphson and a steepest-descent step.

If a parameter vector with a non negative-definite Hessian matrix is encountered, an information message is printed that a nonconcave function has been found. The modified Marquardt fixup is made, but the user should be aware that the likelihood declared to be a maximum could be a local maximum, not a global one.

If the matrix A is not positive definite, the modified Marquardt fixup is made to make the matrix positive definite. In the `lf` linear-form case, after such a fixup, a block diagonalization will be attempted unless the undocumented `style(1)` or `style(3)` option to `ml maximize` is specified.

Numerical derivatives are calculated using a more computational expensive variation on a technique suggested by Nash (1990, 219). The standard formula for numerical derivatives is $[f(b_i + h_i) - f(b_i)]/h_i$. Nash suggested $h_i = \epsilon(b_i + \epsilon)$, where ϵ is not less than machine precision. Setting h_i in this way ensures that $b_i + h_i$ differs from b_i in at least half its digits. We instead take the same idea but apply it to the numerator, finding an h_i such that $\epsilon_1(|f(b_i)| + \epsilon_1) \leq |f(b_i + h_i) - f(b_i)| \leq \epsilon_2(|f(b_i)| + \epsilon_2)$ for $\epsilon_1 < \epsilon_2$. We then calculate the derivative using a centered calculation, $[f(b_i + h_i/2) - f(b_i - h_i/2)]/h_i$.

If you have a function that you think, while not well behaved, has a unique maximum, and your optimization seems not to be able to find it, you should suspect the derivative calculation, especially if you are using the `lf` linear-form or `deriv0` methods—which use numerical derivatives. Analytic derivatives, or a different numerical technique, may prove helpful.

Macros used

S_mldepn. Name(s) of the dependent variables. The user-written likelihood program can count on these being in fixed order.

S_mlfunc. The name of the user-written likelihood function (used internally).

S_mlmeth. The name of the likelihood maximization method, or more precisely, the derivative calculation method (used internally).

S_mlwgt. The name of the weight variable (0 designates missing or excluded observations). The user program does not need to be concerned with this variable for lf linear-form maximization, but will need to use it for the matrix-based methods.

S_mlmb. The name of the parameter vector in which the estimates will ultimately be placed.

S_mlsf. The name of the scalar variable that holds the maximized value. Users are strongly advised, when referring to this variable, to use the construct scalar($S_mlsf) and not simply $S_mlsf. Remember, the name of the scalar was specified by the user and is typically simple—$S_mlsf might contain f—and Stata's expression name-resolution logic looks for data variables before scalars; see [R] **matrix scalar**.

S_mlmv. The name of the variance-covariance matrix of the parameters.

S_mlneq. The number of equations.

S_mleqn. The names of the equations.

S_mldbug. If set to 1, derivatives and other debugging information will be produced. To turn off debugging, clear the macro (type global S_mldbug).

Saved Results

ml maximize saves the parameter vector obtained from the most recent step in matrix S_mlbest. This matrix can be examined after pressing *Break* although using ml report is preferable.

The following global macros are set by ml post and do not disappear until another estimation is begun:

S_E_cmd	*anyshortname* specified with ml post
S_E_tdf	number of degrees of freedom for *t*, or . for normal
S_E_ttl	problem title
S_E_depv	dependent variable name
S_E_nobs	number of observations
S_E_chi2	chi-squared
S_E_mdf	degrees of freedom for model chi-squared
S_E_ll	log-likelihood at maximum
S_E_ll0	log-likelihood at initial values
S_E_pr2	pseudo *R*-squared

References

Andrews, D. F., P. Bickel, F. Hampel, P. Huber, W. H. Rogers, and J. W. Tukey. 1972. *Robust Estimates of Location: Survey and Advances.* Princeton. N.J.: Princeton University Press.

Marquardt, D. W. 1963. An algorithm for least squares estimation of nonlinear parameters. *Journal of the Society for Industrial and Applied Mathematics* 11: 431–441.

Nash, J. C. 1990. *Compact Numerical Methods for Computers: Linear Algebra and Function Minimisation.* 2d ed. New York: Adam Hilger.

Rogers, W. H. 1991. sbe2: Bailey-Makeham survival model. *Stata Technical Bulletin* 2: 11–14. Reprinted in *Stata Technical Bulletin Reprints*, vol. 1, pp. 64–68.

Also See

[R] **matrix**, [R] **matrix post**, [R] **maximize**, [R] **nl**

Title

mlogit — Multinomial (polytomous) logistic regression

Syntax

$\left[\text{by } \textit{varlist}:\right]$ mlogit $\left[\textit{depvar indepvars } \left[\textit{weight}\right] \left[\text{if } \textit{exp}\right] \left[\text{in } \textit{range}\right]\right]$

$\left[, \text{ basecategory}(\#) \text{ constraints}(\textit{clist}) \text{ level}(\#) \text{ rrr noconstant}\right.$

$\textit{maximize\_options} \left.\right]$

where *clist* is of the form $\#\left[-\#\right]\left[, \#\left[-\#\right] \ldots\right]$

fweights and aweights are allowed; see [U] **18.1.6 weight**.

mlogit shares the features of all estimation commands; see [U] **26 Estimation and post-estimation commands**.

To reset problem-size limits, see [R] **matsize**.

Description

mlogit estimates maximum-likelihood multinomial logit models, also known as polytomous logistic regression. Constraints may be defined to perform constrained estimation. Some people refer to conditional logistic regression as multinomial logit. If you are one of them, see [R] **clogit**.

A maximum of 50 categories can be estimated with Intercooled Stata; 20 categories with Small Stata.

Options

basecategory(#) specifies the value of *depvar* that is to be treated as the base category. The default is to choose the most frequent category.

constraints(*clist*) specifies the linear constraints to be applied during estimation. The default is to perform unconstrained estimation. Constraints are defined with the **constraint** command; see [R] **constraint**. constraints(1) specifies that the model is to be constrained according to constraint 1; constraints(1-4) specifies constraints 1 through 4; constraints(1-4,8) specifies constraints 1 through 4 and 8. It is not considered an error to specify nonexistent constraints so long as some of the constraints exist. Thus, constraint(1-999) would specify that all defined constraints be applied.

level(#) specifies the confidence level, in percent, for confidence intervals. The default is level(95) or as set by **set level**; see [U] **26.4 Specifying the width of confidence intervals**.

rrr reports the estimated coefficients transformed to relative risk ratios, i.e., e^b rather than b; see *Description of model* below for an explanation of this concept. Standard errors and confidence intervals are similarly transformed. This option affects how results are displayed, not how they are estimated. rrr may be specified at estimation or when replaying previously estimated results.

noconstant suppresses the constant term in the regression.

maximize_options control the maximization process; see [R] **maximize**. You should never have to specify them.

Remarks

Remarks are presented under the headings

Description of model
Estimating unconstrained models
Obtaining predicted values
Testing hypotheses about coefficients
Estimating constrained models

mlogit performs maximum-likelihood estimation of models with discrete dependent (left-hand-side) variables. It is intended for use when the dependent variable takes on more than two outcomes and the outcomes have no natural ordering. If the dependent variable takes on only two outcomes, estimates are identical to those produced by logistic or logit; see [R] **logistic** and [R] **logit**. If the outcomes are ordered, see [R] **ologit**.

Description of model

For an introduction to multinomial logit models, see, for instance, Aldrich and Nelson (1984, 73–77), Greene (1993, chapter 21), and Hosmer and Lemeshow (1989, 216–238). For a description with an emphasis on the difference in assumptions and data requirements for conditional and multinomial logit, see Judge et al. (1985, 768–772).

Consider the outcomes 1, 2, 3, ..., m recorded in y, and the explanatory variables X. For expositional purposes, assume there are $m = 3$ outcomes. Think of these three outcomes as "buy an American car", "buy a Japanese car", and "buy a European car". The values of y are then said to be "unordered". Even though the outcomes are coded 1, 2, and 3, the numerical values are arbitrary in the sense that $1 < 2 < 3$ does not imply that outcome 1 (buy American) is less than outcome 2 (buy Japanese) is less than outcome 3 (buy European). It is this unordered categorical property of y that distinguishes the use of mlogit from regress (which is appropriate for a continuous dependent variable), from ologit (which is appropriate for ordered categorical data), and from logit (which is appropriate for two outcomes and which can therefore be thought of as ordered).

In the multinomial logit model, we estimate a set of coefficients $\beta^{(1)}$, $\beta^{(2)}$, and $\beta^{(3)}$ corresponding to each outcome category:

$$\Pr(y = 1) = \frac{e^{X\beta^{(1)}}}{e^{X\beta^{(1)}} + e^{X\beta^{(2)}} + e^{X\beta^{(3)}}}$$

$$\Pr(y = 2) = \frac{e^{X\beta^{(2)}}}{e^{X\beta^{(1)}} + e^{X\beta^{(2)}} + e^{X\beta^{(3)}}}$$

$$\Pr(y = 3) = \frac{e^{X\beta^{(3)}}}{e^{X\beta^{(1)}} + e^{X\beta^{(2)}} + e^{X\beta^{(3)}}}$$

The model, however, is unidentified in the sense that there is more than one solution to $\beta^{(1)}$, $\beta^{(2)}$, and $\beta^{(3)}$ that leads to the same probabilities for $y = 1$, $y = 2$, and $y = 3$. To identify the model, one of $\beta^{(1)}$, $\beta^{(2)}$, or $\beta^{(3)}$ is arbitrarily set to 0—it does not matter which. That is, if we arbitrarily set $\beta^{(1)} = 0$, the remaining coefficients $\beta^{(2)}$ and $\beta^{(3)}$ would measure the change relative to the $y = 1$ group. If we instead set $\beta^{(2)} = 0$, the remaining coefficients $\beta^{(1)}$ and $\beta^{(3)}$ would measure the change relative to the $y = 2$ group. The coefficients would differ because they have different interpretations, but the predicted probabilities for $y = 1, 2,$ and 3 would still be the same. Thus, either parameterization would be a solution to the same underlying model.

Setting $\beta^{(1)} = 0$, the equations become

$$\Pr(y = 1) = \frac{1}{1 + e^{X\beta^{(2)}} + e^{X\beta^{(3)}}}$$

$$\Pr(y = 2) = \frac{e^{X\beta^{(2)}}}{1 + e^{X\beta^{(2)}} + e^{X\beta^{(3)}}}$$

$$\Pr(y = 3) = \frac{e^{X\beta^{(3)}}}{1 + e^{X\beta^{(2)}} + e^{X\beta^{(3)}}}$$

The relative probability of $y = 2$ to the base category is

$$\frac{\Pr(y = 2)}{\Pr(y = 1)} = e^{X\beta^{(2)}}$$

Let us call this ratio the relative risk and let us further assume that X and $\beta_k^{(2)}$ are vectors equal to $(x_1, x_2, \ldots, x_k)$ and $(\beta_1^{(2)}, \beta_2^{(2)}, \ldots, \beta_k^{(2)})'$, respectively. The ratio of the relative risk for a one-unit change in x_i is then

$$\frac{e^{\beta_1^{(2)} x_1 + \ldots + \beta_i^{(2)}(x_i+1) + \ldots + \beta_k^{(2)} x_k}}{e^{\beta_1^{(2)} x_1 + \ldots + \beta_i^{(2)} x_i + \ldots + \beta_k^{(2)} x_k}} = e^{\beta_i^{(2)}}$$

Thus, the exponentiated value of a coefficient is the relative risk ratio for a one unit change in the corresponding variable, it being understood that risk is being measured as the risk of the category relative to the base category.

Estimating unconstrained models

▷ Example

You have data on the type of health insurance available to 616 psychologically depressed subjects in the U.S. (Tarlov et al. 1989; Wells et al. 1989). The insurance is categorized as being either an indemnity plan (i.e., regular fee-for-service insurance which may have a deductible or coinsurance rate) or a prepaid plan (a fixed up-front payment allowing subsequent unlimited use as provided, for instance, by an HMO). The third possibility is that the subject has no insurance whatsoever. You wish to explore the demographic factors associated with each subject's insurance choice. As an introduction to the data, one of the demographics factors is the race of the participant, coded as white or nonwhite:

```
. tabulate insure nonwhite, chi2 col

          | nonwhite
   insure |         0          1 |     Total
----------+----------------------+----------
    Indem |       251         43 |       294
          |     50.71      35.54 |     47.73
----------+----------------------+----------
  Prepaid |       208         69 |       277
          |     42.02      57.02 |     44.97
----------+----------------------+----------
 Uninsure |        36          9 |        45
          |      7.27       7.44 |      7.31
----------+----------------------+----------
    Total |       495        121 |       616
          |    100.00     100.00 |    100.00

          Pearson chi2(2) =   9.5599   Pr = 0.008
```

Although `insure` appears to take on the values Indem, Prepaid, and Uninsure, it actually takes on the values 1, 2, and 3. The words appear because a value label has been associated with the numeric variable `insure`; see [U] **19.6.3 Value labels**.

When you estimate a multinomial logit model, you can tell `mlogit` which group to use as the base category or you can let `mlogit` choose. To estimate a model of `insure` on `nonwhite`, letting `mlogit` choose the base category, we type

```
. mlogit insure nonwhite

Iteration 0:  Log Likelihood =-556.59502
Iteration 1:  Log Likelihood =-551.78935
Iteration 2:  Log Likelihood =-551.78348
Iteration 3:  Log Likelihood =-551.78348

Multinomial regression                      Number of obs =      616
                                            chi2(2)       =     9.62
                                            Prob > chi2   =   0.0081
Log Likelihood = -551.78348                 Pseudo R2     =   0.0086

------------------------------------------------------------------------------
   insure |      Coef.   Std. Err.       z     P>|z|     [95% Conf. Interval]
----------+-------------------------------------------------------------------
Prepaid   |
 nonwhite |   .6608212   .2157321     3.063    0.002     .2379942    1.083648
    _cons |  -.1879149   .0937644    -2.004    0.045    -.3716896   -.0041401
----------+-------------------------------------------------------------------
Uninsure  |
 nonwhite |   .3779585    .407589     0.927    0.354    -.4209012    1.176818
    _cons |  -1.941934   .1782185   -10.896    0.000    -2.291236   -1.592632
------------------------------------------------------------------------------
(Outcome insure==Indem is the comparison group)
```

`mlogit` chose the indemnity group as the base or comparison group and presented coefficients for the outcomes prepaid and uninsured. According to the model, the probability of prepaid for whites (`nonwhite` $= 0$) is

$$\Pr(\texttt{insure} = \texttt{Prepaid}) = \frac{e^{-.188}}{1 + e^{-.188} + e^{-1.942}} = 0.420$$

Similarly, for nonwhites, the probability of prepaid is

$$\Pr(\texttt{insure} = \texttt{Prepaid}) = \frac{e^{-.188+.661}}{1 + e^{-.188+.661} + e^{-1.942+.378}} = 0.570$$

These results agree with the column percentages presented by tabulate since the `mlogit` model is fully saturated. That is, there are enough terms in the model to fully explain the column percentage in each cell. Note that the model chi-squared and the tabulate chi-squared are in almost perfect agreement; both are testing that the column percentages of `insure` are the same for both values of `nonwhite`.

◁

▷ Example

By specifying the `basecategory()` option, you can control which category of the outcome variable is treated as the comparison group. Left to its own, `mlogit` chose to make category 1, indemnity, the base category. If we wanted to make category 2, prepaid, the base, we type

```
. mlogit insure nonwhite, base(2)

Iteration 0:   Log Likelihood =-556.59502
Iteration 1:   Log Likelihood =-551.78935
Iteration 2:   Log Likelihood =-551.78348
Iteration 3:   Log Likelihood =-551.78348

Multinomial regression                        Number of obs =      616
                                              chi2(2)       =     9.62
                                              Prob > chi2   =   0.0081
Log Likelihood = -551.78348                   Pseudo R2     =   0.0086

------------------------------------------------------------------------
   insure |     Coef.   Std. Err.       z    P>|z|   [95% Conf. Interval]
----------+-------------------------------------------------------------
Indem     |
 nonwhite |  -.6608212   .2157321    -3.063   0.002   -1.083648   -.2379942
    _cons |   .1879149   .0937644     2.004   0.045    .0041401    .3716896
----------+-------------------------------------------------------------
Uninsure  |
 nonwhite |  -.2828628   .3977302    -0.711   0.477    -1.0624     .4966741
    _cons |  -1.754019   .1805145    -9.717   0.000   -2.107821   -1.400217
------------------------------------------------------------------------
(Outcome insure==Prepaid is the comparison group)
```

The `basecategory()` option requires that we specify the numeric value of the category, so we could not type `base(Prepaid)`.

Although the coefficients now appear to be different, note that the summary statistics reported at the top are identical. With this parameterization, the probability of prepaid insurance for whites is

$$\Pr(\texttt{insure} = \texttt{Prepaid}) = \frac{1}{1 + e^{.188} + e^{-1.754}} = 0.420$$

This is the same answer we obtained previously.

◁

▷ Example

By specifying `rrr`, which we can do at estimation time or when we redisplay results, we see the model in terms of relative risk ratios:

```
. mlogit, rrr
Multinomial regression                          Number of obs =      616
                                                chi2(2)       =     9.62
                                                Prob > chi2   = 0.0081
Log Likelihood = -551.78348                     Pseudo R2     = 0.0086

------------------------------------------------------------------------------
    insure |      RRR    Std. Err.       z     P>|z|     [95% Conf. Interval]
-----------+------------------------------------------------------------------
Indem      |
  nonwhite |   .516427    .1114099    -3.063   0.002     .3383588    .7882073
-----------+------------------------------------------------------------------
Uninsure   |
  nonwhite |   .7536232   .2997387    -0.711   0.477     .3456254    1.643247
------------------------------------------------------------------------------
(Outcome insure==Prepaid is the comparison group)
```

Looked at this way, the relative risk of choosing an indemnity over a prepaid plan is 0.52 for nonwhites relative to whites.

◁

▷ Example

One of the advantages of mlogit over tabulate is that continuous variables can be included in the model and you can include multiple categorical variables. In examining the data on insurance choice, you decide you want to control for age, gender, and site of study (the study was conducted in three sites):

```
. mlogit insure age male nonwhite site2 site3
Iteration 0:  Log Likelihood =-555.85446
Iteration 1:  Log Likelihood =-534.72983
Iteration 2:  Log Likelihood =-534.36536
Iteration 3:  Log Likelihood =-534.36165
Iteration 4:  Log Likelihood =-534.36165
Multinomial regression                          Number of obs =      615
                                                chi2(10)      =    42.99
                                                Prob > chi2   = 0.0000
Log Likelihood = -534.36165                     Pseudo R2     = 0.0387

------------------------------------------------------------------------------
    insure |    Coef.    Std. Err.       z     P>|z|     [95% Conf. Interval]
-----------+------------------------------------------------------------------
Prepaid    |
       age |  -.011745    .0061946    -1.896   0.058    -.0238862    .0003962
      male |   .5616934   .2027465     2.770   0.006     .1643175    .9590693
  nonwhite |   .9747768   .2363213     4.125   0.000     .5115955    1.437958
     site2 |   .1130359   .2101903     0.538   0.591    -.2989296    .5250013
     site3 |  -.5879879   .2279351    -2.580   0.010    -1.034733   -.1412433
     _cons |   .2697127   .3284422     0.821   0.412    -.3740222    .9134476
-----------+------------------------------------------------------------------
Uninsure   |
       age |  -.0077961   .0114418    -0.681   0.496    -.0302217    .0146294
      male |   .4518496   .3674867     1.230   0.219     -.268411    1.17211
  nonwhite |   .2170589   .4256361     0.510   0.610    -.6171725    1.05129
     site2 |  -1.211563   .4705127    -2.575   0.010    -2.133751   -.2893747
     site3 |  -.2078123   .3662926    -0.567   0.570    -.9257327    .510108
     _cons |  -1.286943   .5923219    -2.173   0.030    -2.447872   -.1260135
------------------------------------------------------------------------------
(Outcome insure==Indem is the comparison group)
```

These results suggest that the inclination of nonwhites to choose prepaid care is even stronger than it was without controlling. We also see that subjects in site 2 are less likely to be uninsured.

◁

Obtaining predicted values

▷ Example

After estimation, `predict` can be used to obtain predicted probabilities, index values, and standard errors of the index or differences in the index. For instance, in the preceding example we estimated a model of insurance-choice on various characteristics. We can obtain the predicted probabilities for outcome 1 by typing

```
. predict p1, outcome(1)
(1 missing value generated)

. summarize p1

Variable |     Obs       Mean    Std. Dev.      Min        Max
---------+-----------------------------------------------------
      p1 |     615    .4504065    .1125962    .1964103   .7885724
```

If you look back at the previous example, while we claimed to have 616 subjects in our data, the multinomial logit model was estimated on 615 observations—there was one observation containing a missing value for one of the explanatory variables. This missing value means that no prediction can be made.

Although we typed `outcome(1)`, specifying 1 for the indemnity category, we could have typed `outcome(Indem)`. For instance, to obtain the probabilities for prepaid, we could type

```
. predict p2, outcome(prepaid)
equation prepaid not found
r(303);

. predict p2, outcome(Prepaid)
(1 missing value generated)

. summarize p2

Variable |     Obs       Mean    Std. Dev.      Min        Max
---------+-----------------------------------------------------
      p2 |     615    .4504065    .1125962    .1964103   .7885724
```

When specifying the label, it must be specified exactly as it appears in the underlying value label (or how it appears in the `mlogit` output), and that includes capitalization.

Here, we have used `predict` to obtain probabilities for the same sample on which we estimated. That is not necessary. We could use another dataset that had the independent variables defined (in our example, `age`, `male`, `nonwhite`, `site2`, and `site3`) and use `predict` to obtain predicted probabilities.

◁

❏ Technical Note

`predict` can also be used to obtain the "index" values—the $\sum x_i \widehat{\beta}_i^{(k)}$—as well as the probabilities:

```
. predict idx1, outcome(Indem) index
(1 missing value generated)
```

```
. summarize idx1
Variable |      Obs        Mean    Std. Dev.       Min        Max
---------+-----------------------------------------------------------
    idx1 |      615           0           0          0          0
```

The indemnity category was our base category—the category for which all the coefficients were set to 0—and so the index is always 0. For the prepaid category:

```
. predict idx2, outcome(Prepaid) index
(1 missing value generated)
. predict idx3, outcome(Uninsure) index
. summarize idx2 idx3
Variable |      Obs        Mean    Std. Dev.       Min        Max
---------+-----------------------------------------------------------
    idx2 |      615   -.0627473    .4905472  -1.298198   1.493112
    idx3 |      615   -1.992153     .603006  -3.112741  -.8258458
```

We can obtain the standard error of the index by specifying the **stdp** option:

```
. predict se2, outcome(Prepaid) stdp
(1 missing value generated)
. list p2 idx2 se2 in 1/5
             p2         idx2         se2
  1.   .3709022   -.4831167    .2437772
  2.   .4977667     .055111    .1694686
  3.   .4113073   -.1712106    .1793498
  4.   .5424927    .3788345    .2513701
  5.   .4927324     .034113    .1640012
```

(We obtained the probability **p2** in the previous example.)

Finally, **predict** can calculate the standard error of the difference in the index values between two outcomes with the **stddp** option:

```
. predict se_2_3, outcome(Prepaid,Uninsure) stddp
(1 missing value generated)
. list idx2 idx3 se_2_3 in 1/5
           idx2         idx3      se_2_3
  1.  -.4831167   -3.073253    .5469354
  2.    .055111   -2.715986    .4331917
  3.  -.1712106   -1.579621    .3053815
  4.   .3788345   -1.462007    .4492552
  5.    .034113   -2.729924     .425924
```

In the first observation, the difference in the indexes is $-.483 - (-3.073) = 2.59$. The standard error of that difference is .547.

❏

▷ Example

It is more difficult to interpret the results from **mlogit** than **clogit** or **logit** since there are multiple equations. For example, suppose one of the independent variables in your model takes on the values 0 and 1 and you are attempting to understand the effect of this variable. Assume the coefficient on this variable for the second outcome, $\beta^{(2)}$, is positive. You might then be tempted to reason that the probability of the second outcome is higher if the variable is 1 rather than 0. Most of the time, that will be true; occasionally, you will be surprised. It could be that the probability of some other category will increase even more (say $\beta^{(3)} > \beta^{(2)}$) and thus the probability of outcome 2 actually falls relative to that outcome.

Prediction can be used to aid interpretation.

Continuing with our previously estimated insurance-choice model, we wish to describe the model's predictions by race. For this purpose, we can use the "method of recycled predictions", in which we vary characteristics of interest across the whole dataset and average the predictions. That is, we have data on both whites and nonwhites, and our individuals have other characteristics as well. We will first pretend that all the people in our data are white but hold their other characteristics constant. We then calculate the probabilities of each outcome. Next we will pretend that all the people in our data are nonwhite, still holding their other characteristics constant. Again we calculate the probabilities of each outcome. The difference in those two sets of calculated probabilities, then, is the difference due to race, holding other characteristics constant.

```
. gen byte nonwhold = nonwhite          /* save real race      */
. replace nonwhite = 0                  /* make everyone white  */
(121 real changes made)
. predict wpind, outcome(Indem)         /* predict probabilities */
. predict wpp, outcome(Prepaid)
. predict wpnoi, outcome(Uninsure)
. replace nonwhite = 1                  /* make everyone nonwhite */
(615 real changes made)
. predict nwpind, outcome(Indem)
. predict nwpp, outcome(Prepaid)
. predict nwpnoi, outcome(Uninsure)
. replace nonwhite = nonwhold           /* restore real race    */
(494 real changes made)
. summarize wpind wpp wpnoi nwpind nwpp nwpnoi

    Variable |     Obs       Mean    Std. Dev.       Min        Max
-------------+--------------------------------------------------------
       wpind |     615   .5159406    .0866958    .3092903    .71939
         wpp |     615   .4069474    .0991605    .1964103    .633162
       wpnoi |     615    .077112    .0360347    .0273596   .1302816
      nwpind |     615   .3127002    .0815687    .1565233    .535021
        nwpp |     615   .6289396    .0980804    .3871782   .8172187
      nwpnoi |     615   .0583602     .028816    .0209648   .0933868
```

Earlier in this entry we presented a cross-tabulation of insurance type and race. Those values were unadjusted. The means reported above are the values adjusted for age, sex, and site. Combining the results gives

	Unadjusted		Adjusted	
	white	nonwhite	white	nonwhite
Indemnity	.51	.36	.52	.31
Prepaid	.42	.57	.41	.63
Uninsured	.07	.07	.08	.06

We find, for instance, that while 57% of nonwhites in our data had prepaid plans, after adjusting for age, sex, and site, 63% of nonwhites choose prepaid plans.

◁

❑ Technical Note

Classification of predicted values followed by comparison of the classifications with the observed outcomes is a second way predicted values can help interpret a multinomial logit model. This is a variation on the notions of sensitivity and specificity for logistic regression. Here, we will adopt a three-part classification with respect to indemnity and prepaid: definitely predicting indemnity, definitely predicting prepaid, and ambiguous.

```
. predict indem, outcome(Indem) index          /* obtain indexes      */
. predict prepaid, outcome(Prepaid) index
. gen diff = prepaid-indem                      /* obtain difference   */
. predict sediff, outcome(Indem,Prepaid)  stddp    /* and its standard error */
. gen type = 1 if diff/sediff < -1.96          /* definitely indemnity */
(481 missing values generated)
. replace type = 3 if diff/sediff > 1.96       /* definitely prepaid  */
(93 real changes made)
. replace type = 2 if type==. & diff/sediff!=. /* ambiguous           */
(388 real changes made)
. label def type 1 "Def Ind" 2 "Ambig" 3 "Def Prep"
. label values type type                        /* label results       */
. tabulate insure type
```

```
           | type
    insure |  Def Ind      Ambig   Def Prep |     Total
-----------+---------------------------------+----------
     Indem |       78        183         33 |       294
   Prepaid |       44        177         56 |       277
  Uninsure |       12         28          5 |        45
-----------+---------------------------------+----------
     Total |      134        388         94 |       616
```

One substantive point learned by this exercise is that the predictive power of this model is modest. There are a substantial number of misclassifications in both directions, though there are more correctly classified observations than misclassified observations.

A second interesting point is that the uninsured look overwhelmingly as though they might have come from the indemnity system rather than the prepaid system.

❏

Testing hypotheses about coefficients

▷ Example

Hypotheses about the coefficients are tested with test just as they are after any estimation command; see [R] test. The only important point to note is test's syntax for dealing with multiple equation models. You are warned that test bases its results on the estimated covariance matrix and that a likelihood-ratio test may be preferred; see *Estimating constrained models* below for an example of lrtest.

If one simply lists variables after the test command, one is testing that the corresponding coefficients are zero across all equations:

```
. test site2 site3
 ( 1)  [Prepaid]site2 = 0.0
 ( 2)  [Uninsure]site2 = 0.0
 ( 3)  [Prepaid]site3 = 0.0
 ( 4)  [Uninsure]site3 = 0.0

         chi2(  4) =     19.74
       Prob > chi2 =     0.0006
```

One can test that all the coefficients (except the constant) in a single equation are zero by simply typing the outcome in square brackets:

```
. test [Uninsure]
 ( 1)  [Uninsure]age = 0.0
 ( 2)  [Uninsure]male = 0.0
 ( 3)  [Uninsure]nonwhite = 0.0
 ( 4)  [Uninsure]site2 = 0.0
 ( 5)  [Uninsure]site3 = 0.0
           chi2(  5) =      9.31
         Prob > chi2 =    0.0973
```

Specification of the outcome is just as with `predict`; you can specify the label if the outcome variable is labeled, or you can specify the numeric value of the outcome. We would have obtained the same test as above had we typed `test [3]`, since 3 is the value of `insure` for the outcome uninsured.

The two syntaxes can be combined. To test that the coefficients on the site variables are 0 in the equation corresponding to the outcome prepaid, we can type

```
. test [Prepaid]: site2 site3
 ( 1)  [Prepaid]site2 = 0.0
 ( 2)  [Prepaid]site3 = 0.0
           chi2(  2) =     10.78
         Prob > chi2 =    0.0046
```

We specified the outcome and then followed that with a colon and the variables we wanted to test.

We can also test that coefficients are equal across equations. To test that all coefficients except the constant are equal for the prepaid and uninsured outcomes:

```
. test [Prepaid=Uninsure]
 ( 1)  [Prepaid]age - [Uninsure]age = 0.0
 ( 2)  [Prepaid]male - [Uninsure]male = 0.0
 ( 3)  [Prepaid]nonwhite - [Uninsure]nonwhite = 0.0
 ( 4)  [Prepaid]site2 - [Uninsure]site2 = 0.0
 ( 5)  [Prepaid]site3 - [Uninsure]site3 = 0.0
           chi2(  5) =     13.80
         Prob > chi2 =    0.0169
```

To test that only the site variables are equal:

```
. test [Prepaid=Uninsure]: site2 site3
 ( 1)  [Prepaid]site2 - [Uninsure]site2 = 0.0
 ( 2)  [Prepaid]site3 - [Uninsure]site3 = 0.0
           chi2(  2) =     12.68
         Prob > chi2 =    0.0018
```

Finally, we can test any arbitrary constraint by simply entering the equation, specifying the coefficients as described in [U] **20.5 Accessing coefficients and standard errors**. The following hypothesis is senseless but illustrates the point:

```
. test ([Prepaid]age+[Uninsure]site2)/2 = 2-[Uninsure]nonwhite
 ( 1)  .5 [Prepaid]age + [Uninsure]nonwhite + .5 [Uninsure]site2 = 2.0
           chi2(  1) =     22.45
         Prob > chi2 =    0.0000
```

Please see [R] **test** for more information on `test`. All that is said about combining hypotheses across `test` commands (the `accum` option) is relevant after `mlogit`.

◁

Estimating constrained models

mlogit can estimate models with subsets of coefficients constrained to be zero, subsets of coefficients constrained to be equal both within and across equations, and with subsets of coefficients arbitrarily constrained to equal linear combinations of other estimated coefficients.

Prior to estimating a constrained model, you define the constraints using the constraint command; see [R] **constraint**. Constraints are numbered and the syntax for specifying a constraint is exactly the same as the syntax for testing constraints; see *Testing hypotheses about coefficients* above. Once the constraints are defined, you estimate using mlogit, specifying the constraint() option. Typing constraint(4) would use the constraint you previously saved as 4. Typing constraint(1,4,6) would use the previously stored constraints 1, 4, and 6. Typing constraint(1-4,6) would use the previously stored constraints 1, 2, 3, 4, and 6.

Sometimes, you will not be able to specify the constraints without knowledge of the omitted group. In such cases, assume the omitted group is whatever group is convenient for you and include the basecategory() option when you type the mlogit command.

▷ Example

Among other things, constraints can be used as a means of hypothesis testing. In our insurance-choice model, we previously tested the hypothesis that there is no distinction between having indemnity insurance and being uninsured. This we did with the test command. Indemnity-style insurance was the omitted group, so we typed

```
. test [Uninsure]
 ( 1)   [Uninsure]age = 0.0
 ( 2)   [Uninsure]male = 0.0
 ( 3)   [Uninsure]nonwhite = 0.0
 ( 4)   [Uninsure]site2 = 0.0
 ( 5)   [Uninsure]site3 = 0.0
            chi2(  5) =      9.31
          Prob > chi2 =    0.0973
```

(Had indemnity not been the omitted group, we would have typed test [Uninsure=Indem].)

The results produced by test are based on the estimated covariance matrix of the coefficients and so are an approximation. Since the probability of being uninsured is quite low, the log likelihood may be nonlinear for the uninsured. Conventional statistical wisdom is not to trust the asymptotic answer under these circumstances, but to perform a likelihood-ratio test instead.

Stata has a lrtest likelihood-ratio test command; to use it we must estimate both the unconstrained and the constrained models. The unconstrained model is what we have previously estimated. Following the instruction in [R] **lrtest**, we first save the unconstrained model results:

```
. lrtest, saving(0)
```

To estimate the constrained model, we must reestimate our model with all the coefficients except the constant set to 0 in the Uninsure equation. We define the constraint and then reestimate:

```
. constraint define 1 [Uninsure]
. mlogit insure age male nonwhite site2 site3, constr(1)
 ( 1)   [Uninsure]age = 0.0
 ( 2)   [Uninsure]male = 0.0
 ( 3)   [Uninsure]nonwhite = 0.0
 ( 4)   [Uninsure]site2 = 0.0
 ( 5)   [Uninsure]site3 = 0.0
```

```
Iteration 0:  Log Likelihood =-555.85446
Iteration 1:  Log Likelihood =-539.80523
Iteration 2:  Log Likelihood =-539.75644
Iteration 3:  Log Likelihood =-539.75643
```

Multinomial regression					Number of obs =	615
					chi2(5) =	32.20
					Prob > chi2 =	0.0000
Log Likelihood = -539.75643					Pseudo R2 =	0.0290

insure	Coef.	Std. Err.	z	P>|z|	[95% Conf. Interval]	
Prepaid						
age	-.0107025	.0060039	-1.783	0.075	-.0224699	.0010649
male	.4963616	.1939683	2.559	0.010	.1161908	.8765324
nonwhite	.942137	.2252094	4.183	0.000	.5007347	1.383539
site2	.2530912	.2029465	1.247	0.212	-.1446767	.6508591
site3	-.5521774	.2187237	-2.525	0.012	-.9808678	-.1234869
_cons	.1792752	.3171372	0.565	0.572	-.4423023	.8008527
Uninsure						
age	0	.	.	.	.	.
male	0	.	.	.	.	.
nonwhite	0	.	.	.	.	.
site2	0	.	.	.	.	.
site3	0	.	.	.	.	.
_cons	-1.87351	.1601099	-11.701	0.000	-2.18732	-1.5597

(Outcome insure==Indem is the comparison group)

We can now perform the likelihood-ratio test:

```
. lrtest
Mlogit:  likelihood-ratio test                    chi2(5)    =    10.79
                                                  Prob > chi2 =   0.0557
```

The likelihood ratio chi-squared is 10.79 with 5 degrees of freedom—just slightly greater than the magic $P = .05$ level. Thus, we should not call this difference significant.

◁

❑ Technical Note

In certain circumstances, a multinomial logit model should be estimated with conditional logit; see [R] **clogit**. With substantial data manipulation, clogit is capable of handling the same class of models with some interesting additions. For example, if we had available the price and deductible of the most competitive insurance plan of each type, this information could not be used by mlogit but could be incorporated by clogit.

❑

Saved Results

See [R] **maximize** for the results stored by mlogit.

Methods and Formulas

The model for multinomial logit is

$$\Pr(Y_i = k) = \frac{\exp\left(\sum\limits_{j=0}^{p} x_{ij}\beta_{jk}\right)}{\sum\limits_{m=1}^{r} \exp\left(\sum\limits_{j=0}^{p} x_{ij}\beta_{jm}\right)}$$

This model is described in Greene (1993, chapter 21).

Newton–Raphson maximum likelihood is used; see [R] **maximize**.

In the case of constrained equations, the set of constraints is orthogonalized and a subset of maximizable parameters is selected. For example, a parameter that is constrained to zero is not a maximizable parameter. If two parameters are constrained to be equal to each other, only one is a maximizable parameter.

Let $\mathbf{r}$ be the vector of maximizable parameters. Note that $\mathbf{r}$ is physically a subset of the solution parameters $\mathbf{b}$. A matrix $\mathbf{T}$ and a vector $\mathbf{m}$ are defined

$$\mathbf{b} = \mathbf{Tr} + \mathbf{m}$$

with the consequence that

$$\frac{df}{d\mathbf{b}} = \frac{df}{d\mathbf{r}}\mathbf{T}'$$

$$\frac{d^2 f}{d\mathbf{b}^2} = \mathbf{T}\frac{d^2 f}{d\mathbf{r}^2}\mathbf{T}'$$

$\mathbf{T}$ consists of a block form in which one block is a permutation of the identity matrix and the other part describes how to calculate the constrained parameters from the maximizable parameters.

References

Aldrich, J. H. and F. D. Nelson. 1984. *Linear Probability, Logit, and Probit Models.* Newbury Park, CA: Sage Publications.

Greene, W. H. 1993. *Econometric Analysis.* 2d ed. New York: Macmillan.

Hamilton, L. C. 1993. sqv8: Interpreting multinomial logistic regression. *Stata Technical Bulletin* 13: 24–28. Reprinted in *Stata Technical Bulletin Reprints*, vol. 3, p. 176–181.

Hosmer, D. W., Jr., and S. Lemeshow. 1989. *Applied Logistic Regression.* New York: John Wiley & Sons.

Judge, G. G., W. E. Griffiths, R. C. Hill, H. Lütkepohl, and Tsoung-Chao Lee. 1985. *The Theory and Practice of Econometrics.* 2d. ed. New York: John Wiley & Sons.

Tarlov, A. R., J. E. Ware, Jr., S. Greenfield, E. C. Nelson, E. Perrin, and M. Zubkoff. 1989. The medical outcomes study. *Journal of the American Medical Association* 262: 925–930.

Wells, K. E., R. D. Hays, M. A. Burnam, W. H. Rogers, S. Greenfield, and J. E. Ware, Jr. 1989. Detection of depressive disorder for patients receiving prepaid or fee-for-service care. *Journal of the American Medical Association* 262: 3298–3302.

Also See

[U] **20.5 Accessing coefficients and standard errors**, [U] **26 Estimation and post-estimation commands**

[R] **clogit**, [R] **constraint**, [R] **glogit**, [R] **lincom**, [R] **logistic**, [R] **lrtest**, [R] **maximize**, [R] **ologit**, [R] **predict**, [R] **test**, [R] **testnl**, [R] **xi**

Title

> **more** — Pause until key is depressed

Syntax

<u>more</u>

<u>set</u> <u>more</u> { on | off }

Description

more causes Stata to display --more-- and pause until any key is depressed.

set more on, which is the default, tells Stata that when a --more-- message is displayed, wait until a key is depressed before continuing.

set more off tells Stata not to display the --more-- message, and, therefore, don't pause.

Remarks

When you see --more-- at the bottom of the screen

Press ...	and Stata...
letter *l* or *Enter*	displays the next line
letter *q*	acts as if you pressed *Break*
space bar or any other key	displays the next screen

In addition, Stata for Windows and Stata for Macintosh users can press the **More** button to display the next screen.

--more-- is Stata's way of telling you it has something more to show you, but showing you that something more will cause the information on the screen to scroll off.

If you type set more off, --more-- conditions will never arise—Stata's output will scroll by at full speed.

If you type set more on, --more-- conditions will be restored at the appropriate places.

Programmers: Do-file writers sometimes include set more off in their do-files because they do not care to interactively review the output. They want Stata to proceed at full speed because they plan on making a log of the output which they will review later.

Do-filers need not bother to set more on at the end of their do-file. Stata automatically restores the previous set more when the do-file (or program) concludes.

The more programming command

Ado-file programmers need take no special action to have `--more--` conditions arise when the screen is full. Stata handles that automatically.

If, however, you wish to force a `--more--` condition early, you can include the `more` command in your program. The syntax of `more` is

    `more`

`more` takes no arguments.

Also See

[U] **14 —more— conditions**

[R] **query**

Title

> **mvencode** — Change missing to coded missing value and vice versa

Syntax

> mvencode *varlist* [if *exp*] [in *range*] , m̲v(#) [o̲verride]
>
> mvdecode *varlist* [if *exp*] [in *range*] , m̲v(#)

Description

> mvencode changes all occurrences of missing to # in the specified *varlist*.
>
> mvdecode changes all occurrences of # to missing in the specified *varlist*.

Options

> mv(#) specifies the numeric value to which or from which missing is to be changed and is not optional.
>
> override specifies that the protection provided by mvencode is to be overridden. Without this option, mvencode refuses to make the requested change if # is already used in the data.

Remarks

> One occasionally reads datasets where missing (e.g., failed to answer a survey question, or the data was not collected, or whatever) is coded with a special numeric value. Popular codings are 9, 99, −9, −99, and the like. If missing were encoded as −99,
>
> ```
> . mvdecode _all, mv(-99)
> ```
>
> would translate the special code to the Stata missing value '.'. Use this command cautiously since, even if −99 were not a special code, all −99's in the data would be changed to missing.
>
> Conversely, one occasionally needs to export a dataset to software that does not understand that '.' means missing value, so one codes missing with a special numeric value. To change all missings to −99:
>
> ```
> . mvencode _all, mv(-99)
> ```
>
> mvencode is smart: it will automatically recast variables upward if necessary, so even if a variable is stored as a byte, its missing values can be recoded to, say, 999. In addition, mvencode refuses to make the change if # (−99 in this case) is already used in the data, so you can be certain that your coding is unique. You can override this feature by including the override option.

▷ Example

> Our automobile data (described in [U] **13 Stata's on-line tutorials and sample datasets**) contains 74 observations and 12 variables. Let us first attempt to translate whatever missing values there are in the data to 1:

```
. mvencode _all, mv(1)
make:    string variable ignored
rep78:   already 1 in    2 observations
foreign: already 1 in   22 observations
no action taken
r(9);
```

Our attempt failed. mvencode first informed us that make is a string variable—this is not a problem but is reported merely for our information. String variables are ignored by mvencode. It next informed us that rep78 already was coded 1 in 2 observations and that foreign was already coded 1 in 22 observations. Thus, 1 would be a poor choice for encoding missing values because, after encoding, you could not tell a real 1 from a coded missing value 1.

We could force mvencode to encode the data with 1 anyway by typing mvencode _all, mv(1) override and that would be appropriate if the 1's in our data already represented missing data. They do not however, and we will code missing as 999:

```
. mvencode _all, mv(999)
make:    string variable ignored
rep78:   5 missing values
```

This worked, and we are informed that the only changes necessary were to 5 observations of rep78.

◁

▷ Example

Let us now pretend that we just read in the automobile data from some raw dataset where all the missing values were coded 999. We can convert the 999's to real missings by typing

```
. mvdecode _all, mv(999)
make:    string variable ignored
rep78:   5 missing values
```

We are informed that make is a string variable and so was ignored and that rep78 contained 5 observations with 999. Those observations have now been changed to contain missing.

◁

Methods and Formulas

mvencode and mvdecode are implemented as ado-files.

Also See

[R] **generate**, [R] **recode**

Title

mvreg — Multivariate regression

Syntax

mvreg *depvarlist* : *varlist* [*weight*] [if *exp*] [in *range*] [, <u>nocons</u> <u>corr</u> <u>no</u>header

<u>not</u>able <u>l</u>evel(*#*)]

<u>aw</u>eights and <u>fw</u>eights are allowed; see [U] **18.1.6 weight**.

mvreg shares the features of all estimation commands; see [U] **26 Estimation and post-estimation commands**.

To reset problem-size limits, see [R] **matsize**.

Description

mvreg estimates multivariate regression models. mvreg typed without arguments redisplays the previous mvreg results.

Options

nocons omits the constant term from the estimation.

corr displays the correlation matrix of the residuals between the equations.

noheader suppresses display of the table reporting F statistics, R-squared, and root mean square error above the coefficient table.

notable suppresses display of the coefficient table.

level(*#*) specifies the confidence level, in percent, for confidence intervals. The default is level(95) or as set by set level; see [U] **26.4 Specifying the width of confidence intervals**.

Remarks

Multivariate regression differs from multiple regression in that *several* dependent variables are jointly regressed on the same independent variables. Multivariate regression is related to Zellner's seemingly unrelated regression (see [R] **sureg**) but, since the same set of independent variables are used for each dependent variable, the syntax is simpler and the calculations faster.

The individual coefficients and standard errors produced by mvreg are identical to those that would be produced by regress estimating each equation separately. The difference is that mvreg, being a joint estimator, also estimates the between-equation covariances, so you can test coefficients across equations and, in fact, the test syntax makes such tests more convenient.

▷ Example

Using the automobile data, we estimate a multivariate regression for "space" variables (hdroom, trunk, and turn) in terms of a set of other variables including three "performance variables" (displ, gratio, and mpg):

```
. mvreg hdroom trunk turn : price mpg displ gratio length weight
```

Equation	Obs	Parms	RMSE	"R-sq"	F	P
hdroom	74	7	.7390205	0.2996	4.777213	0.0004
trunk	74	7	3.052314	0.5326	12.7265	0.0000
turn	74	7	2.132377	0.7844	40.62042	0.0000

	Coef.	Std. Err.	t	P>|t|	[95% Conf. Interval]	
hdroom						
price	-.0000528	.000038	-1.392	0.168	-.0001286	.0000229
mpg	-.0093774	.0260463	-0.360	0.720	-.061366	.0426112
displ	.0031025	.0024999	1.241	0.219	-.0018873	.0080922
gratio	.2108071	.3539588	0.596	0.553	-.4956975	.9173118
length	.015886	.012944	1.227	0.224	-.0099504	.0417223
weight	-.0000868	.0004724	-0.184	0.855	-.0010296	.0008561
_cons	-.4525117	2.170073	-0.209	0.835	-4.783995	3.878972
trunk						
price	.0000445	.0001567	0.284	0.778	-.0002684	.0003573
mpg	-.0220919	.1075767	-0.205	0.838	-.2368159	.1926322
displ	.0032118	.0103251	0.311	0.757	-.0173971	.0238207
gratio	-.2271321	1.461926	-0.155	0.877	-3.145149	2.690884
length	.170811	.0534615	3.195	0.002	.0641014	.2775206
weight	-.0015944	.001951	-0.817	0.417	-.0054885	.0022997
_cons	-13.28253	8.962868	-1.482	0.143	-31.17249	4.607428
turn						
price	-.0002647	.0001095	-2.418	0.018	-.0004833	-.0000462
mpg	-.0492948	.0751542	-0.656	0.514	-.1993031	.1007136
displ	.0036977	.0072132	0.513	0.610	-.0106999	.0180953
gratio	-.1048432	1.021316	-0.103	0.919	-2.143399	1.933712
length	.072128	.0373487	1.931	0.058	-.0024204	.1466764
weight	.0027059	.001363	1.985	0.051	-.0000145	.0054264
_cons	20.19157	6.261549	3.225	0.002	7.693467	32.68967

We should have specified the corr option so that we would also see the correlations between the residuals of the equations. We can correct our omission because mvreg—like all estimation commands—typed without arguments redisplays results. The noheader and notable (read no-table) options suppress redisplaying the output we have already seen:

```
. mvreg, notable noheader corr

Correlation matrix of residuals:

         hdroom    trunk     turn
hdroom   1.0000
 trunk   0.4986   1.0000
  turn  -0.1090  -0.0628   1.0000

Breusch-Pagan test of independence: chi2(3) =    19.566, Pr = 0.0002
```

The Breusch–Pagan test is significant, so the residuals of these three space variables are not independent of each other.

The three performance variables among our independent variables are mpg, displ, and gratio. We can jointly test the significance of these three variables, in all the equations, by typing

```
. test mpg displ gratio
 ( 1)  [hdroom]mpg = 0.0
 ( 2)  [trunk]mpg = 0.0
 ( 3)  [turn]mpg = 0.0
 ( 4)  [hdroom]displ = 0.0
 ( 5)  [trunk]displ = 0.0
 ( 6)  [turn]displ = 0.0
 ( 7)  [hdroom]gratio = 0.0
 ( 8)  [trunk]gratio = 0.0
 ( 9)  [turn]gratio = 0.0
       F(  9,     67) =     0.33
             Prob > F =     0.9622
```

These three variables are not, as a group, significant. We might have suspected this from their individual significance in the individual regressions, but this multivariate test provides an overall assessment with a single p-value.

We can also perform a test for the joint significance of all three equations:

```
. test [hdroom]
 (output omitted )
. test [trunk], accum
 (output omitted )
. test [turn], accum
 ( 1)  [hdroom]price = 0.0
 ( 2)  [hdroom]mpg = 0.0
 ( 3)  [hdroom]displ = 0.0
 ( 4)  [hdroom]gratio = 0.0
 ( 5)  [hdroom]length = 0.0
 ( 6)  [hdroom]weight = 0.0
 ( 7)  [trunk]price = 0.0
 ( 8)  [trunk]mpg = 0.0
 ( 9)  [trunk]displ = 0.0
 (10)  [trunk]gratio = 0.0
 (11)  [trunk]length = 0.0
 (12)  [trunk]weight = 0.0
 (13)  [turn]price = 0.0
 (14)  [turn]mpg = 0.0
 (15)  [turn]displ = 0.0
 (16)  [turn]gratio = 0.0
 (17)  [turn]length = 0.0
 (18)  [turn]weight = 0.0
       F( 18,     67) =    19.34
             Prob > F =     0.0000
```

The set of variables as a whole is strongly significant. We might have suspected this, too, from the individual equations.

◁

❑ Technical Note

The mvreg command provides a good way to deal with multiple comparisons. If we wanted to assess the effect of length, we might be dissuaded from interpreting any of its coefficients except that in the trunk equation. [trunk]length—the coefficient on length in the trunk equation—has a p-value of .002, but in the remaining two equations, it has p-values of only .224 and .058.

A conservative statistician might argue that there are 18 tests of significance in mvreg's output (not counting those for the intercept), so p-values above $.05/18 = .0028$ should be declared insignificant at the 5% level. A more aggressive but, in our opinion, reasonable approach would be to first note that the three equations are jointly significant, so we are justified in making some interpretation. Then, we would work through the individual variables using test, possibly using $.05/6 = .0083$ (6 because there are 6 independent variables) for the 5% significance level. For instance, examining length:

```
. test length

 ( 1)   [hdroom]length = 0.0
 ( 2)   [trunk]length = 0.0
 ( 3)   [turn]length = 0.0

       F(  3,    67) =    4.94
            Prob > F =    0.0037
```

The reported significance level of .0037 is less than .0083, so we will declare this variable significant. [trunk]length is certainly significant with its p-value of .002, but what about in the remaining two equations with p-values .224 and.058? Performing a joint test:

```
. test [hdroom]length [turn]length

 ( 1)   [hdroom]length = 0.0
 ( 2)   [turn]length = 0.0

       F(  2,    67) =    2.91
            Prob > F =    0.0613
```

At this point, reasonable statisticians could disagree. The .06 significance value suggests no interpretation but these were the two least-significant values out of three, so one would expect the p-value to be a little high. Perhaps an equivocal statement is warranted: there seems to be an effect, but chance cannot be excluded.

❏

Saved Results

mvreg saves in the S_ macros:

S_E_cmd	mvreg
S_E_nobs	number of observations
S_E_neq	number of equations
S_E_elis	dependent variable names
S_E_tdf	residual degrees of freedom
S_E_par	number of parameters (including constant)
S_E_r2	R-squared for each equation
S_E_sd	RMSE for each equation
S_E_f	F statistic for each equation
S_E_pv	significance of F for each equation
S_3	degrees of freedom for Breusch–Pagan chi-squared if corr option
S_4	Breusch–Pagan chi-squared if corr option

In addition, mvreg saves the matrix S_E_rcv containing the covariances between the residuals of the equations.

Methods and Formulas

mvreg is implemented as an ado-file.

Given q equations and p independent variables (including the constant), the parameter estimates are given by the $p \times q$ matrix

$$\mathbf{B} = (\mathbf{X'WX})^{-1}\mathbf{X'WY}$$

where $\mathbf{Y}$ is a $n \times q$ matrix of dependent variables and $\mathbf{X}$ is a $n \times p$ of independent variables. $\mathbf{W}$ is a weighting matrix equal to $\mathbf{I}$ if no weights are specified. If weights are specified, let $\mathbf{v}: 1 \times n$ be the specified weights. If fweight frequency weights are specified, $\mathbf{W} = \mathrm{diag}(\mathbf{v})$. If aweight analytic weights are specified, $\mathbf{W} = \mathrm{diag}[\mathbf{v}/(\mathbf{1'v})(\mathbf{1'1})]$, which is to say, the weights are normalized to sum to the number of observations.

The residual covariance matrix is

$$\mathbf{R} = (\mathbf{Y'WY} - \mathbf{B'}(\mathbf{X'WX})\mathbf{B})/(n - p)$$

The estimated covariance matrix of the estimates is $\mathbf{R} \otimes (\mathbf{X'WX})^{-1}$. These results are identical to those produced by sureg when the same list of independent variables is specified repeatedly; see [R] **sureg**.

The Breusch and Pagan (1980) χ^2 statistic—a Lagrange multiplier statistic—is given by

$$\lambda = n \sum_{i=1}^{q} \sum_{j=1}^{i-1} r_{ij}^2$$

where r_{ij} is the estimated correlation between the residuals of the equations and n is the number of observations. It is distributed as χ^2 with $q(q-1)/2$ degrees of freedom.

References

Breusch, T. and A. Pagan. 1980. The LM test and its applications to model specification in econometrics. *Review of Economic Studies* 47: 239–254.

Also See

Title

nbreg — Negative binomial regression

Syntax

nbreg *depvar* $\lceil$*varlist*$\rceil$ $\lceil$*weight*$\rceil$ $\lceil$if *exp*$\rceil$ $\lceil$in *range*$\rceil$ $\lceil$, <u>l</u>evel(#) <u>irr</u> <u>e</u>xposure(*varname*)

    <u>o</u>ffset(*varname*) *maximize_options* $\rceil$

gnbreg *eqname₁ eqname₂* $\lceil$*weight*$\rceil$ $\lceil$if *exp*$\rceil$ $\lceil$in *range*$\rceil$ $\lceil$, <u>l</u>evel(#) <u>irr</u> <u>e</u>xposure(*varname*)

    <u>o</u>ffset(*varname*) *maximize_options* $\rceil$

fweights and aweights are allowed; see [U] **18.1.6 weight**.

These commands share the features of all estimation commands; see [U] **26 Estimation and post-estimation commands**, but also see the warning below.

To reset problem-size limits, see [R] **matsize**.

Description

nbreg estimates a negative binomial maximum-likelihood regression of *depvar* on *varlist*, where *depvar* is a nonnegative count variable. In this model, the count variable is believed to be generated by a Poisson-like process, only the variation is greater than that of a true Poisson. This extra variation is referred to as overdispersion. See [R] **poisson** before reading this entry.

gnbreg is a generalized negative binomial regression; here, the overdispersion parameter α is further parameterized. *eqname₁* contains *depvar* and *indepvars* for the log of the expected count; *eqname₂* contains a list of variables on which α is thought to depend.

nbreg and gnbreg typed without arguments redisplay previous estimation results.

Also note that although aweights are allowed, they are not recommended; see Rogers (1991).

Options

level(#) specifies the confidence level, in percent, for confidence intervals. The default is level(95) or as set by set level; see [U] **26.4 Specifying the width of confidence intervals**.

irr reports estimated coefficients transformed to incidence rate ratios, i.e., e^b rather than b. Standard errors and confidence intervals are similarly transformed. This option affects how results are displayed, not how they are estimated or stored. irr may be specified at estimation or when replaying previously estimated results.

exposure(*varname*) and offset(*varname*) are different ways of specifying the same thing. exposure() specifies a variable that reflects the amount of exposure over which the *depvar* events were observed for each observation; ln(*varname*) with coefficient constrained to be 1 is entered into the log-link function. offset() specifies a variable that is to be entered directly into the log-link function with coefficient constrained to be 1; thus exposure is assumed to be $e^{varname}$.

maximize_options control the maximization process; see [R] **maximize**. You should never have to specify them, although we often recommend specifying trace.

Remarks

Remarks are presented under the headings

nbreg
gnbreg
Predicted values

Negative binomial regression is used to estimate models of the number of occurrences (counts) of an event when the event has extra-Poisson variation; that is, it has overdispersion. The Poisson regression model is

$$y_i \sim \text{Poisson}(\mu_i)$$

where

$$\mu_i = \exp(\mathbf{x}_i\boldsymbol{\beta} + \text{offset}_i)$$

for observed counts y_i with covariates $\mathbf{x}_i$ for the ith observation. One derivation of the negative binomial is that individual units follow a Poisson regression model, but there is an omitted variable u_i such that e^{u_i} follows a gamma distribution with mean 1 and variance α:

$$y_i \sim \text{Poisson}(\mu_i^*)$$

where

$$\mu_i^* = \exp(\mathbf{x}_i\boldsymbol{\beta} + \text{offset}_i + u_i)$$

and

$$e^{u_i} \sim \text{Gamma}(1/\alpha, 1/\alpha)$$

We refer to α as the overdispersion parameter. The larger α is, the greater the overdispersion. The Poisson model corresponds to $\alpha = 0$.

nbreg parameterizes α as $\ln\alpha$. gnbreg allows $\ln\alpha$ to be modeled as $\ln\alpha_i = \mathbf{z}_i\boldsymbol{\gamma}$, a linear combination of covariates $\mathbf{z}_i$

nbreg

It is not uncommon to posit a Poisson regression model and observe a lack of model fit. The following data appeared in Rodríguez (1993):

```
. list
```

	cohort	age_mos	deaths	exposure
1.	1	0.5	168	278.4
2.	1	2.0	48	538.8
3.	1	4.5	63	794.4
4.	1	9.0	89	1550.8
5.	1	18.0	102	3006.0
6.	1	42.0	81	8743.5
7.	1	90.0	40	14270.0
8.	2	0.5	197	403.2
9.	2	2.0	48	786.0
10.	2	4.5	62	1165.3
11.	2	9.0	81	2294.8
12.	2	18.0	97	4500.5
13.	2	42.0	103	13201.5
14.	2	90.0	39	19525.0
15.	3	0.5	195	495.3
16.	3	2.0	55	956.7

```
17.        3       4.5      58      1381.4
18.        3       9.0      85      2604.5
19.        3      18.0      87      4618.5
20.        3      42.0      70      9814.5
21.        3      90.0      10      5802.5

. gen logexp = ln(exposure)

. quietly tab cohort, gen(coh)

. poisson deaths coh2 coh3, offset(logexp)


Iteration 0: Log Likelihood = -4103.7302
Iteration 1: Log Likelihood = -2419.342
Iteration 2: Log Likelihood = -2170.1772
Iteration 3: Log Likelihood = -2159.5483
Iteration 4: Log Likelihood = -2159.5161
Iteration 5: Log Likelihood = -2159.5156

Poisson regression, normalized by exp(logexp)     Number of obs    =       21
Goodness-of-fit chi2(18)      =   4190.688          Model chi2(2)    =   49.161
Prob > chi2                   =     0.0000          Prob > chi2      =   0.0000
Log Likelihood                = -2159.516          Pseudo R2        =   0.0113
```

deaths	Coef.	Std. Err.	z	P>|z|	[95% Conf. Interval]	
coh2	-.3020404	.0573319	-5.268	0.000	-.4144088	-.189672
coh3	.0742143	.0589726	1.258	0.208	-.0413698	.1897984
_cons	-3.899488	.0411345	-94.798	0.000	-3.98011	-3.818866

The extreme significance of the goodness-of-fit χ^2 indicates the Poisson regression model is inappropriate—suggesting to us that we should try a negative binomial model:

```
. nbreg deaths coh2 coh3, offset(logexp)
Iteration 0:  Log Likelihood = -148.36388
(nonconcave function encountered)
Iteration 1:  Log Likelihood = -131.96225
Iteration 2:  Log Likelihood = -131.61132
(output omitted)
Iteration 7:  Log Likelihood = -131.58186
Iteration 0:  Log Likelihood = -131.58186
Iteration 1:  Log Likelihood = -131.38365
Iteration 2:  Log Likelihood =  -131.3799
Iteration 3:  Log Likelihood =  -131.3799

Negative Binomial Regression                  Number of obs    =       21
                                              Model chi2(2)    =     0.40
                                              Prob > chi2      =   0.8171
Log Likelihood =   -131.3798965               Pseudo R2        =   0.0015
```

deaths	Coef.	Std. Err.	z	P>|z|	[95% Conf. Interval]	
_lnmean						
coh2	-.2675996	.7236753	-0.370	0.712	-1.685977	1.150778
coh3	-.4573789	.7236974	-0.632	0.527	-1.8758	.9610421
_cons	-2.086731	.5118523	-4.077	0.000	-3.089943	-1.083519
_lnalpha						
_cons	.5940055	.2583312	2.299	0.021	.0876856	1.100325

```
    alpha      1.811229   [_lnalpha]_cons = ln(alpha)
                   (LR test against Poisson, chi2(1) =  4056.271 P =  0.0000)
```

The first set of iterations record **nbreg**'s iterations to estimate a model with only an intercept and α; the second, shorter log, is for the model with all the parameters.

Our original Poisson model is a special case of the negative binomial—it corresponds to $\alpha = 0$. **nbreg**, however, estimates α indirectly, estimating instead $\ln \alpha$. In our model, $\ln \alpha = 0.594$, meaning that $\alpha = 1.81$ (**nbreg** undoes the transformation for us at the bottom of the output).

The Z statistic printed in the table for $\ln \alpha$ is a test of $\ln \alpha = 0$, which is equivalent to $\alpha = 1$. This test, however, is not very meaningful.

In order to test $\alpha = 0$ (equivalent to $\ln \alpha = -\infty$), **nbreg** performs a likelihood-ratio test. The staggering χ^2 value of 4,056 asserts that the probability that we would observe this data conditional on $\alpha = 0$, i.e., conditional on the process being Poisson, is virtually zero. The data is not Poisson. It is not accidental that this χ^2 value is quite close to the goodness-of-fit statistic from the Poisson regression itself.

❑ Technical Note

The negative binomial model deals with cases where there is more variation than would be expected were the process Poisson. The negative binomial model is not helpful if there is less than Poisson variation—if the variance of the count variable is less than its mean. But underdispersion is uncommon. Poisson models arise because of independently generated events. Overdispersion comes about if some of the parameters (causes) of the Poisson processes are unknown. To obtain underdispersion, the sequence of events would have to somehow be regulated; that is, events would not be independent, but controlled based on past occurrences.

❑

gnbreg

gnbreg is a generalization of **nbreg**. Whereas in **nbreg** a single $\ln \alpha$ is estimated, **gnbreg** allows $\ln \alpha$ to vary observation by observation as a linear combination of another set of covariates: $\ln \alpha_i = \mathbf{z}_i \gamma$.

We will assume the number of deaths is a function of age whereas the $\ln \alpha$ parameter is a function of cohort. To estimate the model, we type

```
. eq deaths age_mos
. eq lnalpha: coh2 coh3
. gnbreg deaths lnalpha, offset(logexp)
```

That is, we define our two equations and then perform the estimation.

eq (see [R] **eq**) has two syntaxes: we can specify an equation name followed by a colon and the contents of the equation, or we can skip specifying the equation name and the colon. In that case, the first variable is interpreted as both the equation name and part of the contents of the equation. Thus, we define an equation named **deaths** containing **deaths age_mos** and we define an equation named **lnalpha** containing **coh2 coh3**.

For the first equation specified, the first variable is interpreted as the dependent variable and any remaining variables are interpreted as the independent variables for the regression part of our estimation. The second "equation" is interpreted as merely a list of variables on which $\ln \alpha$ is thought to depend.

Here is the result of estimating our model:

```
. eq deaths age_mos
. eq lnalpha: coh2 coh3
. gnbreg deaths lnalpha, offset(logexp)
Iteration 0:  Log Likelihood = -148.36388
(nonconcave function encountered)
Iteration 1:  Log Likelihood = -131.96225
(output omitted)
Iteration 7:  Log Likelihood = -131.58186
Iteration 0:  Log Likelihood = -131.58186
(unproductive step attempted)
Iteration 1:  Log Likelihood = -123.88483
(output omitted)
Iteration 14:  Log Likelihood = -117.56163
```

```
Negative Binomial Regression              Number of obs   =      21
                                          Model chi2(3)   =   28.04
                                          Prob > chi2     =  0.0000
Log Likelihood =   -117.5616350           Pseudo R2       =  0.1066

------------------------------------------------------------------------------
    deaths |     Coef.   Std. Err.      z    P>|z|     [95% Conf. Interval]
---------+--------------------------------------------------------------------
deaths   |
 age_mos |  -.0516655   .0051736    -9.986   0.000    -.0618055   -.0415255
   _cons |  -1.867285    .215492    -8.665   0.000    -2.289642   -1.444928
---------+--------------------------------------------------------------------
lnalpha  |
    coh2 |   .0936286   .7024872     0.133   0.894    -1.283221    1.470478
    coh3 |   .0811418   .7025635     0.115   0.908    -1.295857    1.458141
   _cons |  -.4756568   .5012835    -0.949   0.343    -1.458154    .5068407
------------------------------------------------------------------------------
          (LR test against Poisson, chi2(1) =  1108.866 P =  0.0000)
```

We find that age is a significant determinant of the number of deaths. The standard errors for the variables in the $\ln \alpha$ equation suggest that the overdispersion parameter does not vary across cohorts. We can test this by typing

```
. test [lnalpha]
 ( 1)  [lnalpha]coh2 = 0.0
 ( 2)  [lnalpha]coh3 = 0.0
        chi2(  2) =    0.02
      Prob > chi2 =    0.9904
```

There is no evidence of variation by cohort in this data.

Predicted values

After **nbreg** and **gnbreg**, **predict** returns a prediction of the log of the counts. To obtain the predicted count when there is no offset, type

```
. predict lncount
. gen count = exp(lncount)
```

If there is an offset variable, say, **offset**, you type

```
. predict lncount
. gen count = exp(lncount + offset)
```

nbreg and **gnbreg** are similar to **poisson** in this way; see [R] **poisson**.

Saved Results

See *Saved Results* in [R] **ml**; the macro S_E_cmd contains nbreg or gnbreg.

Methods and Formulas

nbreg and gnbreg are implemented as ado-files.

See [R] **poisson** and Feller (1968, 156–164) for an introduction to the Poisson distribution.

A negative binomial distribution can be regarded as a gamma mixture of Poisson random variables. The number of times something occurs, y_i, is distributed as Poisson($\nu_i \mu_i$). That is, its conditional likelihood is

$$f(y_i \mid \nu_i) = \frac{(\nu_i \mu_i)^{y_i} e^{-\nu_i \mu_i}}{\Gamma(y_i + 1)}$$

where $\mu_i = \exp(\mathbf{x}_i \boldsymbol{\beta} + \text{offset}_i)$ and ν_i is an unobserved parameter with a Gamma($1/\alpha, 1/\alpha$) density:

$$g(\nu) = \frac{\nu^{(1-\alpha)/\alpha} e^{-\nu/\alpha}}{\Gamma(1/\alpha)}$$

This gamma distribution has mean 1 and variance α, where α is our ancillary parameter.

The unconditional likelihood for the ith observation is therefore

$$f(y_i) = \int_0^\infty f(y_i \mid \nu) g(\nu) \, d\nu$$

$$= \frac{\Gamma(m + y_i)}{\Gamma(y_i + 1)\Gamma(m)} \, p_i^m (1 - p_i)^{y_i}$$

where $p_i = 1/(1 + \alpha \mu_i)$ and $m = 1/\alpha$. Solutions for α are handled by searching for $\ln \alpha$ since α is required to be greater than zero.

In the case of **gnbreg**, α is allowed to vary across the observations according to the parameterization $\ln \alpha_i = \mathbf{z}_i \boldsymbol{\gamma}$.

Maximization is via the lf linear-form method described in [R] **matrix ml**.

References

Feller, W. 1968. *An Introduction to Probability Theory and Its Applications*, vol. 1. 3rd ed. New York: John Wiley & Sons.

Rodriguez, G. 1993. sbe10: An improvement to poisson. *Stata Technical Bulletin* 11: 11–14. Reprinted in *Stata Technical Bulletin Reprints*, vol. 2, pp. 94–98.

Rogers, W. H. 1991. sbe1: Poisson regression with rates. *Stata Technical Bulletin* 1: 11–12. Reprinted in *Stata Technical Bulletin Reprints*, vol. 1, pp. 62–68.

——. 1993. sg16.4: Comparison of nbreg and glm for negative binomial. *Stata Technical Bulletin* 16: 7. Reprinted in *Stata Technical Bulletin Reprints*, vol. 3, pp. 82–84.

Also See

[U] **20.5 Accessing coefficients and standard errors**, [U] **26 Estimation and post-estimation commands**

[R] **glm**, [R] **lincom**, [R] **linktest**, [R] **lrtest**, [R] **maximize**, [R] **poisson**, [R] **predict**, [R] **test**, [R] **testnl**, [R] **vce**, [R] **xi**

Title

> **newey** — Regression with Newey–West standard errors

Syntax

newey *depvar* [*varlist*] [*weight*] [*if exp*] [*in range*] , lag(#)

[t(*varname$_t$*) force <u>nocon</u>stant <u>l</u>evel(#)]

aweights are allowed; see [U] **18.1.6 weight**.

newey shares the features of all estimation commands; see [U] **26 Estimation and post-estimation commands**.

To reset problem-size limits; see [R] **matsize**.

Description

newey produces Newey–West standard errors for coefficients estimated by OLS regression. The error structure is assumed to be heteroscedastic and possibly autocorrelated up to some lag.

Note that if **lag(0)** is specified, the variance estimates produced by **newey** are simply the Huber/White/sandwich robust variances estimates calculated by **regress, robust**; see [R] **regress**.

Options

lag(#) is not optional; it specifies the maximum lag to consider in the autocorrelation structure. If you specify **lag() > 0**, then you must also specify option **t()**, described below. If you specify **lag(0)**, the output is exactly the same as **regress, robust**.

t(*varname$_t$*) specifies the variable recording the time of each observation. You must specify **t()** if **lag() > 0**. *varname$_t$* must record values indicating the observations are equally spaced in time or **newey** will refuse to estimate the model. If observations are not equally spaced but you wish to treat them as if they were, you must specify the **force** option.

You need only specify **t()** the first time you estimate a model with a particular dataset. After that, it need not be specified again except to change the variable's identity; **newey** remembers your previous **t()** option.

force specifies that estimation is to be forced even though **t()** shows the data not to be equally spaced. **newey** requires observations be equally spaced so that calculations based on lags correspond to a constant time change. If you specify a **t()** variable indicating observations are not equally spaced, **newey** will refuse to estimate the model. If you also specify **force**, **newey** will estimate the model and assume that the lags based on the data ordered by **t()** are appropriate.

noconstant specifies that the estimated regression should not include an intercept term.

level(#) specifies the confidence level, in percent, for confidence intervals. The default is **level(95)** or as set by **set level**; see [U] **26.4 Specifying the width of confidence intervals**.

Remarks

The Huber/White/sandwich robust variance estimator (see, for example, White 1980) produces consistent standard errors for OLS regression coefficient estimates in the presence of heteroscedasticity. The Newey–West (1987) variance estimator is an extension that produces the consistent estimates when there is autocorrelation in addition to possible heteroscedasticity.

The Newey–West variance estimator handles autocorrelation up to and including a lag of m, where m is specified by stipulating a $lag(m)$ option. Thus, it assumes that any autocorrelation at lags greater than m can be ignored.

▷ Example

newey, lag(0) is equivalent to regress, robust:

```
. regress price weight displ, robust
Regression with robust standard errors          Number of obs =       74
                                                F(  2,   71) =    14.44
                                                Prob > F      =   0.0000
                                                R-squared     =   0.2909
                                                Root MSE      =   2518.4

------------------------------------------------------------------------------
             |               Robust
       price |      Coef.   Std. Err.       t    P>|t|     [95% Conf. Interval]
-------------+----------------------------------------------------------------
      weight |   1.823366   .7808755     2.335   0.022     .2663446    3.380387
       displ |   2.087054   7.436967     0.281   0.780    -12.74184    16.91595
       _cons |    247.907   1129.602     0.219   0.827    -2004.454    2500.269
------------------------------------------------------------------------------

. newey price weight displ, lag(0)
Regression with Newey-West standard errors      Number of obs  =       74
maximum lag : 0                                 F(  2,   71) =    14.44
                                                Prob > F      =   0.0000

------------------------------------------------------------------------------
             |             Newey-West
       price |      Coef.   Std. Err.       t    P>|t|     [95% Conf. Interval]
-------------+----------------------------------------------------------------
      weight |   1.823366   .7808755     2.335   0.022     .2663446    3.380387
       displ |   2.087054   7.436967     0.281   0.780    -12.74184    16.91595
       _cons |    247.907   1129.602     0.219   0.827    -2004.454    2500.269
------------------------------------------------------------------------------
```

◁

▷ Example

We have time-series measurements on variables usr and idle and now wish to estimate an OLS model, but obtain Newey–West standard errors allowing for a lag of up to 3:

```
. newey usr idle, lag(3) t(time)
Regression with Newey-West standard errors      Number of obs  =       30
maximum lag : 3                                 F(  1,   28) =    10.90
                                                Prob > F      =   0.0026

------------------------------------------------------------------------------
             |             Newey-West
         usr |      Coef.   Std. Err.       t    P>|t|     [95% Conf. Interval]
-------------+----------------------------------------------------------------
        idle |  -.2281501   .0690927    -3.302   0.003    -.3696801     -.08662
       _cons |   23.13483   6.327031     3.657   0.001     10.17449    36.09516
------------------------------------------------------------------------------
```

◁

Saved Results

newey saves in the S_# macros:

S_E_cmd	newey
S_E_depv	dependent variable
S_E_nobs	number of observations
S_E_f	F statistic
S_E_mdf	F model degrees of freedom
S_E_tdf	F total degrees of freedom
S_E_lag	maximum lag

Methods and Formulas

newey is implemented as an ado-file.

newey calculates the estimates

$$\widehat{\beta}_{\mathrm{OLS}} = (\mathbf{X}'\mathbf{X})^{-1}\mathbf{X}'\mathbf{y}$$
$$\widehat{\mathrm{Var}}(\widehat{\beta}_{\mathrm{OLS}}) = (\mathbf{X}'\mathbf{X})^{-1}\mathbf{X}'\widehat{\Omega}\mathbf{X}(\mathbf{X}'\mathbf{X})^{-1}$$

That is, the coefficient estimates are simply those of OLS linear regression.

For the case of lag(0) (no autocorrelation), the variance estimates are calculated using the White formulation:

$$\mathbf{X}'\widehat{\Omega}\mathbf{X} = \mathbf{X}'\widehat{\Omega}_0\mathbf{X} = \frac{n}{n-k}\sum_i \widehat{e}_i^2 \mathbf{x}_i'\mathbf{x}_i$$

Here $\widehat{e}_i = y_i - \mathbf{x}_i\widehat{\beta}_{\mathrm{OLS}}$, where $\mathbf{x}_i$ is the ith row of the $\mathbf{X}$ matrix, n is the number of observations, and k is the number of predictors in the model, including the constant if there is one. Note that the above formula is exactly the same as that used by **regress, robust** with the regression-like formula (the default) for the multiplier q_c; see the *Methods and Formulas* section of [R] **regress**.

If lag() > 0, the variance estimates are calculated using the Newey–West (1987) formulation

$$\mathbf{X}'\widehat{\Omega}\mathbf{X} = \mathbf{X}'\widehat{\Omega}_0\mathbf{X} + \frac{n}{n-k}\sum_{l=1}^{m}\left(1 - \frac{l}{m+1}\right)\sum_{i=l+1}^{n}\widehat{e}_i\widehat{e}_{i-l}(\mathbf{x}_i'\mathbf{x}_{i-l} + \mathbf{x}_{i-l}'\mathbf{x}_i)$$

where m is the maximum lag.

References

Newey, W. and K. West. 1987. A simple, positive semi-definite, heteroskedasticity and autocorrelation consistent covariance matrix. *Econometrica* 55: 703–708.

White, H. 1980. A heteroskedasticity-consistent covariance matrix estimator and a direct test for heteroskedasticity. *Econometrica* 50: 1–16.

Also See

[U] **20.5 Accessing coefficients and standard errors**, [U] **26 Estimation and post-estimation commands**

[R] **lincom**, [R] **linktest**, [R] **regress**, [R] **svyreg**, [R] **test**, [R] **testnl**, [R] **vce**, [R] **xtgls**

Title

nl — Nonlinear least squares

Syntax

nl *fcn depvar* [*varlist*] [*weight*] [if *exp*] [in *range*] [, level(#) init(...) lnlsq(#)

leave eps(#) nolog trace iterate(#) *fcn_options*]

nlpred *newvar* [if *exp*] [in *range*] [, resid]

nlinit # *parameter_list*

aweights and fweights are allowed; see [U] **18.1.6 weight**.

nl shares the features of all estimation commands, see [U] **26 Estimation and post-estimation commands**, but also see the warning below.

To reset problem-size limits, see [R] **matsize**.

Description

nl fits an arbitrary nonlinear function to the dependent variable *depvar* by least squares. You provide the function itself in a separate program with a name of your choosing, except that the first two letters of the name must be nl. *fcn* refers to the name of the function without the first two letters. For example, you type nl nexpgr ... to estimate with the function defined in the program nlnexpgr.

nl typed without arguments redisplays the results of the last estimation.

nlpred will calculate predicted values and residuals after nl.

nlinit is useful when writing nlfcns.

Warning: nlpred, not predict, is used after estimation with nl to obtain predicted values.

Options

level(#) specifies the confidence level, in percent, for confidence intervals. The default is level(95) or as set by set level; see [U] **26.4 Specifying the width of confidence intervals**.

init(...) specifies initial values for parameters that are to be used to override the default initial values. Examples are provided below.

lnlsq(#) fits the model defined by nlfcn using "log least squares", defined as least squares with shifted lognormal errors. In other words, $\ln(depvar - \#)$ is assumed normally distributed. Sums of squares and deviance are adjusted to the same scale as *depvar*.

leave leaves behind after estimation a set of new variables with the same names as the estimated parameters containing the derivative of $E(y)$ with respect to the parameter.

eps(#) specifies the convergence criterion for successive parameter estimates and for the residual sum of squares. eps(1e-5) is the default.

574

nolog suppresses the iteration log.

trace expands the iteration log to provide more details, including values of the parameters at each step of the process.

iterate(#) specifies the maximum number of iterations before giving up and defaults to 100.

fcn_options refer to any options allowed by nlfcn.

resid tells nlpred to calculate residuals rather than predicted values.

Remarks

Remarks are presented under the headings

> *nlfcns*
> *Some common nlfcns*
> *Log-normal errors*
> *Weights*
> *Errors*
> *General comments on fitting nonlinear models*
> *More on nlfcns*

nl fits an arbitrary nonlinear function to the dependent variable *depvar* by least squares. The specific function is specified by writing an nlfcn, described below. The values to be fitted in the function are called the parameters.

The fitting process is iterative (modified Gauss–Newton). It starts with a set of initial values for the parameters (guesses as to what the values will be and which you also supply) and finds another set of values that fit the function even better. Those are then used as a starting point and another improvement is found, and the process continues until no further improvement is possible.

nlfcns

nl uses the function defined by nlfcn. nlfcn has two purposes: to identify the parameters of the problem and set default initial values, and to evaluate the function for a given set of parameter estimates.

▷ Example

You have variables y and x in your data and wish to fit a negative-exponential growth curve with parameters B_0 and B_1:

$$y = B_0 \left(1 - e^{-B_1 x}\right)$$

First, you write a program to calculate the predicted values:

```
program define nlnexpgr
        if "`1´" == "?" {              /* if query call ...            */
                global S_1 "B0 B1"     /*    declare parameters        */
                global B0=1            /*    and initialize them       */
                global B1=.1
                exit
        }
        replace `1´=$B0*(1-exp(-$B1*x))  /* otherwise, calculate function */
end
```

To estimate the model, you type `nl nexpgr y`. `nl`'s first argument specifies the name of the function, although you do not type the `nl` prefix. You type `nexpgr`, meaning the function is `nlnexpgr`. `nl`'s second argument specifies the name of the dependent variable. Replicating the example in the SAS manual (1985, 588–590):

```
. use sasxmpl1

. nl nexpgr y
(obs = 20)
Iteration 0:  residual SS =  .1999027
Iteration 1:  residual SS =  .0026142
Iteration 2:  residual SS =  .0005769
Iteration 3:  residual SS =  .0005768
```

```
  Source |      SS        df      MS                  Number of obs =        20
---------+-----------------------------              F( 2,    18) = 275732.74
   Model | 17.6717234      2  8.83586172             Prob > F      =    0.0000
Residual |   .00057681    18  .000032045            R-squared     =    1.0000
---------+-----------------------------              Adj R-squared =    1.0000
   Total | 17.6723003     20  .883615013            Root MSE      =  .0056608
                                                     Res. dev.     = -152.317

(nexpgr)
-----------------------------------------------------------------------------
      y |    Coef.   Std. Err.      t     P>|t|     [95% Conf. Interval]
-----------------------------------------------------------------------------
     B0 |  .9961885   .0016138   617.303   0.000    .9927981    .9995789
     B1 |  .0419539   .0003983   105.346   0.000    .0411172    .0427906
-----------------------------------------------------------------------------
```

    (SE's, P values, CI's, and correlations are asymptotic approximations)

Notice that the initial values of the parameters were provided in the `nlnexpgr` program. You can, however, override these initial values on the `nl` command line. To estimate the model using .5 for the initial value of B0 rather than 1, you can type `nl nexpgr y, init(B0=.5)`. To also change the initial value of B1 from .1 to .2, you type `nl nexpgr y, init(B0=.5, B1=.2)`.

◁

The outline of all nlfcns is the same:

```
program define nlfcn
        if "`1'" == "?" {
                global S_1 "parameter names"
                ( initialize parameters )
                exit
        }
        replace `1' = ...
end
```

On a query call, indicated by `` `1' `` being "?", the nlfcn is to place the names of the parameters in the global macro S_1 and initialize the parameters. Parameters are stored as macros, so if nlfcn declares that the parameters are A, B, and C (via `global S_1 "A B C"`), it must then place initial values in the corresponding parameter macros A, B, and C (via `global A=0`, `global B=1`, etc.). After initializing the parameter macros, it is done.

On a calculation call, `` `1' `` does not contain "?"; it instead contains the name of a variable that is to be filled in with the predicted values. The current values of the parameters are stored in the macros previously declared on the query call (e.g., $A, $B, and $C).

▷ Example

You wish to fit the CES production functions defined by

$$\ln q = B_0 + A \ln\left(D\,l^R + (1-D)k^R\right)$$

where the parameters to be estimated are B_0, A, D, and R. q, l, and k refer to total output and labor and capital inputs. In your data, you have the variables `lnq`, `labor`, and `capital`. The nlfcn is

```
program define nlces
        if "`1'" == "?" {
                global S 1 "B0 A D R"
                global B0 = 1
                global A = -1
                global D = .5
                global R = -1
                exit
        }
        replace `1'=$B0 + $A*ln($D*labor^$R + (1-$D)*capital^$R)
end
```

Again using data from the SAS manual (1985, 591–592):

```
. use sasxmpl2

. nl ces lnq
(obs = 30)
Iteration 0:  residual SS =  37.09651
Iteration 1:  residual SS =  35.48615
Iteration 2:  residual SS =  22.69042
Iteration 3:  residual SS =  1.845374
  (output omitted )
Iteration 19:  residual SS =  1.761039
```

Source	SS	df	MS			
Model	59.5286148	3	19.8428716			
Residual	1.76103929	26	.06773228			
Total	61.2896541	29	2.11343635			

```
Number of obs =        30
F(  3,   26) =    292.96
Prob > F      =    0.0000
R-squared     =    0.9713
Adj R-squared =    0.9680
Root MSE      =  .2602543
Res. dev.     =  .0775148
```

(ces)

lnq	Coef.	Std. Err.	t	P>|t|	[95% Conf. Interval]	
B0*	.1244882	.0783432	1.589	0.124	-.0365486	.2855251
A	-.336291	.2721672	-1.236	0.228	-.8957387	.2231568
D	.3366743	.1361148	2.473	0.020	.0568863	.6164623
R	-3.011047	2.323489	-1.296	0.206	-7.787048	1.764954

```
* Parameter taken as constant term in model & ANOVA table
  (SE's, P values, CI's, and correlations are asymptotic approximations)
```

If the nonlinear model contains a constant term, `nl` will find it and indicate its presence by placing an asterisk next to the parameter name when displaying results. In the output above, B0 is a constant. (`nl` determines that a parameter B0 is a constant term because the partial derivative $f = \partial E(y)/\partial$B0 has a coefficient of variation (s.d./mean) less than `eps()`. Usually, $f = 1$ for a constant, as it does in this case.)

◁

nl's output closely mimics that of **regress**; see [R] **regress**. The model F test, R-squared, sums of squares, etc., are calculated as **regress** calculates them, which means in this case that they are corrected for the mean. If no "constant" is present, as was the case in the negative-exponential growth example previously, the usual caveats apply to the interpretation of the F and R-squared statistics; see comments and references in Goldstein (1992).

When making its calculations, nl creates the partial derivative variables for all the parameters, giving each the same name as the corresponding parameter. Unless you specify **leave**, these are discarded when nl completes the estimation. Therefore, your data must not have data variables that have the same names as parameters. We recommend using uppercased names for parameters and lowercased names (as is common) for variables.

After estimating with nl, typing nl by itself will redisplay previous estimates. Typing **correlate,** **_coef** will show the asymptotic correlation matrix of the parameters, and typing **nlpred myvar** will create new variable **myvar** containing the predicted values. Typing **nlpred res, resid** will create **res** containing the residuals.

nlfcn's have a number of additional features that are described in *More on nlfcns* below.

Some common nlfcns

An important feature of **nl**, in addition to estimating arbitrary nonlinear regressions, is the facility for adding prewritten common *fcns*.

Three *fcns* are provided for exponential regression with one asymptote:

exp3	$Y = b_0 + b_1 b_2^X$
exp2	$Y = b_1 b_2^X$
exp2a	$Y = b_1 \left(1 - b_2^X\right)$

For instance, typing **nl exp3 ras dvl** estimates the three-parameter exponential model (parameters b_0, b_1, and b_2) using $Y = $ **ras** and $X = $ **dvl**.

Two *fcns* are provided for the logistic function (symmetric sigmoid shape; not to be confused with logistic regression):

log4	$Y = b_0 + b_1 / \left(1 + \exp\left(-b_2(X - b_3)\right)\right)$
log3	$Y = b_1 / \left(1 + \exp\left(-b_2(X - b_3)\right)\right)$

Finally, two *fcns* are provided by the Gompertz function (asymmetric sigmoid shape):

gom4	$Y = b_0 + b_1 \exp\left(-\exp\left(-b_2(X - b_3)\right)\right)$
gom3	$Y = b_1 \exp\left(-\exp\left(-b_2(X - b_3)\right)\right)$

❏ Technical Note

You may find the functions above useful, but the important thing to note is that, if there is a nonlinear function you use often, you can package the function once and for all. Consider the function we packaged called **exp2**, which estimates the model $Y = b_1 b_2^X$. The code for the function is

```
program define nlexp2
        version 5.0
        if "`1'"=="?" {
                global S_2 "2-param. exp. growth curve, $S_E_depv=b1*b2^`2'"
                global S_1 "b1 b2"
                *
                * Approximate initial values by regression of log Y on X
                *
                local exp "[$S_E_wgt $S_E_exp]"
                tempvar Y
                gen `Y' = log($S_E_depv) $S_E_if $S_E_in
                regress `Y' `2' `exp'
                global b1 - exp(_b[_cons])
                global b2 = exp(_b[`2'])
                exit
        }
        replace `1'=$b1*$b2^`2'
end
```

Because we were packaging this function for repeated use, we went to the trouble of obtaining good initial values, which in this case we could obtain by taking the log of both sides,

$$Y = b_1 b_2^X$$

$$\ln(Y) = \ln(b_1 b_2^X) = \ln(b_1) + \ln(b_2)X$$

and then using linear regression to estimate $\ln(b_1)$ and $\ln(b_2)$. If this had been a quick-and-dirty implementation, we probably would not have bothered (initializing b_1 and b_2 to 1, say) and so forced ourselves to specify better initial values with nl's initial() option when they were not good enough.

The only other thing we did to complete the packaging was store nlexp2 as an ado-file called nlexp2.ado. The alternatives would have been to type the code into Stata interactively or to place the code in a do-file. Those approaches are adequate for occasional use, but we wanted to be able to type nl exp2 without having to worry whether the program nlexp2 was defined. When nl attempts to execute nlexp2, if the program is not in Stata's memory, Stata will search the disk(s) for an ado-file of the same name and, if found, automatically load it. All we had to do was name the file with the .ado suffix and then place it in a directory where Stata could find it. In our case, we put nlexp2.ado in Stata's system directory for StataCorp-written ado-files. In your case, you should put the file in the directory Stata reserves for user-written ado-files, which is to say, c:\ado (DOS or Windows), ~/ado (Unix), or ~:Ado (Macintosh). See [U] 23 Ado-files.

❏

Log-normal errors

A nonlinear model with identically normally distributed errors may be written

$$y_i = f(\mathbf{x}_i, \boldsymbol{\beta}) + u_i, \qquad u_i \sim \mathrm{N}(0, \sigma^2) \tag{1}$$

for $i = 1, \ldots, n$. If the y_i are thought to have a k-shifted lognormal instead of a normal distribution, that is, $\ln(y_i - k) \sim \mathrm{N}(\zeta_i, \tau^2)$, and the systematic part $f(\mathbf{x}_i, \boldsymbol{\beta})$ of the original model is still thought appropriate, the model becomes

$$\ln(y_i - k) = \zeta_i + v_i = \ln\big(f(\mathbf{x}_i, \boldsymbol{\beta}) - k\big) + v_i, \qquad v_i \sim \mathrm{N}(0, \tau^2) \tag{2}$$

This model is estimated if `lnlsq(k)` is specified.

If model (2) is correct, the variance of $(y_i - k)$ is proportional to $\big(f(\mathbf{x}_i, \boldsymbol{\beta}) - k\big)^2$. Probably the most common case is $k = 0$, sometimes called "proportional errors" since the standard error of y_i is proportional to its expectation, $f(\mathbf{x}_i, \boldsymbol{\beta})$. Assuming the value of k is known, (2) is just another nonlinear model in $\boldsymbol{\beta}$ and it may be fitted as usual. However, we may wish to compare the fit of (1) with that of (2) using the residual sum of squares or the deviance D, $D = -2 \times$ log-likelihood, from each model. To do so, we must allow for the change in scale introduced by the log transformation.

Assuming, then, the y_i to be normally distributed, Atkinson (1985, 85–87, 184), by considering the Jacobian $\prod |\partial \ln(y_i - k)/\partial y_i|$, showed that multiplying both sides of (2) by the geometric mean of $y_i - k$, $\dot{y}$, gives residuals on the same scale as those of y_i. The geometric mean is given by

$$\dot{y} = e^{n^{-1}\sum \ln(y_i - k)}$$

which is a constant for a given dataset. The residual deviance for (1) and for (2) may be expressed as

$$D(\widehat{\boldsymbol{\beta}}) = \Big(1 + \ln(2\pi\widehat{\sigma}^2)\Big)n \tag{3}$$

where $\widehat{\boldsymbol{\beta}}$ is the maximum-likelihood estimate (MLE) of $\boldsymbol{\beta}$ for each model and $n\widehat{\sigma}^2$ is the RSS from (1), or that from (2) multiplied by $\dot{y}^2$.

Since (1) and (2) are models with different error structures but the same functional form, the arithmetic difference in their RSS or deviances is not easily tested for statistical significance. However, if the deviance difference is "large" (> 4, say), one would naturally prefer the model with the smaller deviance. Of course, the residuals for each model should be examined for departures from assumptions (nonconstant variance, nonnormality, serial correlations, etc.) in the usual way.

Consider alternatively modeling

$$E(y_i) = 1/(C + Ae^{Bx_i}) \tag{4}$$

$$E(1/y_i) = E(y_i') = C + Ae^{Bx_i} \tag{5}$$

where C, A, and B are parameters to be estimated. We will use the data $(y, x) = (.04, 5)$, $(.06, 12)$, $(.08, 25)$, $(.1, 35)$, $(.15, 42)$, $(.2, 48)$, $(.25, 60)$, $(.3, 75)$, and $(.5, 120)$ (Danuso 1991).

Model	C	A	B	RSS	Deviance
(4)	1.781	25.74	$-.03926$	$-.001640$	-51.95
(4) with `lnlsq(0)`	1.799	25.45	$-.04051$	$-.001431$	-53.18
(5)	1.781	25.74	$-.03926$	8.197	24.70
(5) with `lnlsq(0)`	1.799	27.45	$-.04051$	3.651	17.42

There is little to choose between the two versions of the logistic model (4), whereas for the exponential model (5) the fit using `lnlsq(0)` is much better (a deviance difference of 7.28). The reciprocal transformation has introduced heteroscedasticity into y_i' which is countered by the proportional errors property of the lognormal distribution implicit in `lnlsq(0)`. The deviances are not comparable between the logistic and exponential models because the change of scale has not been allowed for, although in principle, it could be.

Weights

Weights are specified the usual way—analytic and frequency weights are supported; see
[U] **26.12 Weighted estimation**. Use of analytic weights implies that the y_i have different variances. Model (1) may therefore be rewritten

$$y_i = f(\mathbf{x}_i, \boldsymbol{\beta}) + u_i, \qquad u_i \sim N(0, \sigma^2/w_i) \tag{1a}$$

where w_i are (positive) weights, assumed known and normalized such that their sum equals the number of observations. The residual deviance for (1a) is

$$D(\widehat{\boldsymbol{\beta}}) = \big(1 + \ln(2\pi\widehat{\sigma}^2)\big)n - \sum \ln(w_i) \tag{3a}$$

(compare with equation 3), where

$$n\widehat{\sigma}^2 = \text{RSS} = \sum w_i\big(y_i - f(\mathbf{x}_i, \widehat{\boldsymbol{\beta}})\big)^2$$

Defining and fitting a model equivalent to (2) when weights have been specified as in (1a) is not straightforward and has not been attempted. Thus, deviances using and not using the lnlsq() option may not be strictly comparable when analytic weights (other than 0 and 1) are used.

Errors

nl will stop with error 196 if an error occurs in your nlfcn program and it will report the error code raised by nlfcn.

nl is reasonably robust to the inability of nlfcn to calculate predicted values for certain parameter values. nl assumes that predicted values can be calculated at the initial value of the parameters. If this is not so, an error message is issued with return code 480.

Thereafter, as nl changes the parameter values, it monitors nlfcn's returned predictions for unexpected missing values. If detected, nl backs up. That is, nl finds a linear combination of the previous, known-to-be-good parameter vector and the new, known-to-be-bad vector, a combination where the function can be evaluated, and continues its iterations from that point.

nl does require, however, that once a parameter vector is found where the predictions can be calculated, small changes to the parameter vector can be made in order to calculate numeric derivatives. If a boundary is encountered at this point, an error message is issued with return code 481.

When specifying lnlsq(), an attempt to take logarithms of $y_i - k$ when $y_i \leq k$ results in an error message with return code 482.

If iterate() iterations are performed and estimates still have not converged, results are presented with a warning and the return code set to 430.

General comments on fitting nonlinear models

In many cases, achieving convergence is problematic. For example, a unique maximum-likelihood (minimum-RSS) solution may not exist. A large literature exists on different algorithms that have been used, on strategies for obtaining good initial parameter values, and on tricks for parameterizing the model to make its behavior as "linear-like" as possible. Selected references are Kennedy and Gentle (1980, ch. 10) for computational matters, and Ross (1990) and Ratkowsky (1983) for all three aspects. Much of Ross's considerable experience is enshrined in the computer package MLP (Ross 1987), an invaluable resource. Ratkowsky's book is particularly clear and approachable, with useful discussion on the meaning and practical implications of "intrinsic" and "parameter-effects" nonlinearity. An excellent general text, though (in places) not for the mathematically faint-hearted, is Gallant (1987). Also see Davidson and MacKinnon (1993, Chapters 2, 3, and 5).

The success of `nl` will be enhanced if care is paid to the form of the model fitted, along the lines of Ratkowsky and Ross. For example, Ratkowsky (1983, 49–59) analyses three possible 3-parameter "yield-density" models for plant growth:

$$E(y_i) = \begin{cases} (\alpha + \beta x_i)^{-1/\theta} \\ (\alpha + \beta x_i + \gamma x_i^2)^{-1} \\ (\alpha + \beta x_i^\phi)^{-1} \end{cases}$$

All three models give similar fits. However, he shows that the second formulation is dramatically more "linear-like" than the other two and therefore has better convergence properties. In addition, the parameter estimates are virtually unbiased and normally distributed and the asymptotic approximation to the standard errors, correlations and confidence intervals is much more accurate than for the other models. Even within a given model, the way the parameters are expressed (e.g., ϕ^{x_i} or $e^{\theta x_i}$) affects the degree of linear-like behavior.

Our advice is that even if you cannot get a particular model to converge, don't give up. Experiment with different ways of writing it or with slightly different alternative models that also fit well.

More on nlfcns

Note that the syntax for `nl` is

　　　　`nl` *fcn depvar* [*varlist*] [...] [, ... *fcn_options*]

The syntax for an nlfcn is

　　　　nlfcn {*varname* | **?**} [*varlist*] [, *fcn_options*]

The *varlist*, if specified with `nl`, will be passed to nlfcn along with any options not intended for `nl`. Thus, it is possible to write nlfcns that are quite general.

When nlfcn is called with a **?**, the *varlist* and *fcn_options*, if any, are still passed. In addition, `S_E_depv` contains the identity of the dependent variable; `S_E_if` and `S_E_in` contain the `if` *exp* and `in` *range* specified on the `nl` command line; and `S_E_wgt` and `S_E_exp` contain the weight and expression.

nlfcn is required to post the names of the parameters to `S_1` and to provide default initial values for all the parameters. In addition, it may post up to two titles in `S_2` and `S_3` that will be subsequently used to title the output. The `S_E_` macros provide useful information for filling in titles and generating initial parameters estimates.

When nlfcn is called without a **?**, it is required to calculate the predicted values conditional on the current value of the parameters. Note that nlfcn is not required to process `if` *exp* or `in` *range*. Restriction to the estimation sample will be handled by `nl`.

Thus, at the beginning of this insert, we gave an example for calculating a negative-exponential growth model. A better version of the nlfcn would have been

```
program define nlexpgr
        version 5.0
        if "`1'" == "?" {
                global S_1 "B0 B1"
                global B0=1
                global B1=.1
                global S_2 "negative-exp. growth"
                global S_3 "$S_E_depv = B0*(1-exp(-B1*`2'))"
                exit
        }
        replace `1'=$B0*(1-exp(-$B1*`2'))
end
```

This version would title the output and allow the independent variable to be specified on the nl command line:

```
. nl nexpgr y xval
```

An even more sophisticated version of nlnexpgr might use S_E_depv, `2´, S_E_if, and S_E_in to generate more reasonable starting values of B0 and B1.

nlinit is intended for use by nlfcns. Its syntax is

nlinit *# parameter_list*

nlinit initializes each parameter in *parameter_list* to contain #. For example:

```
nlinit 0 A B C
nlinit 1 D E
```

Saved Results

nl saves in the S_# macros:

S_1	number of observations	S_7	R-squared
S_2	model sum of squares	S_8	adjusted R-squared
S_3	model degrees of freedom	S_9	residual root mean square
S_4	residual sum of squares	S_10	residual deviance
S_5	residual degrees of freedom	S_11	geometric mean $(y-k)^2$ if lnlsq(), otherwise 1
S_6	model F statistic	S_12	0 if convergence failed, otherwise 1

Note that S_1 through S_9 correspond to the successive elements of _result() following regress; see [R] **regress**.

The final parameter estimates are available in the parameter macros defined by nlfcn. The standard errors of the parameters are available through _se[*parameter*]; see [U] **20.5 Accessing coefficients and standard errors**.

nlpred and nlinit save nothing in S_# macros or _result().

Methods and Formulas

nl is implemented as an ado-file.

Acknowledgments

nl was written by Patrick Royston of the Royal Postgraduate Medical School, London. The original version of this routine was published in Royston (1992). Francesco Danuso's menu-driven nonlinear regression program (1991) provided the inspiration.

References

Atkinson, A. C. 1985. *Plots, Transformations and Regression*. Oxford: Oxford Science Publications.

Danuso, F. 1991. sg1: Nonlinear regression command. *Stata Technical Bulletin* 1: 17–19. Reprinted in *Stata Technical Bulletin Reprints*, vol. 1, pp. 96–98.

Davidson, R. and J. G. MacKinnon. 1993. *Estimation and Inference in Econometrics*. New York: Oxford University Press.

Gallant, A. R. 1987. *Nonlinear Statistical Models.* New York: John Wiley & Sons.

Goldstein, R. 1992. srd7: Adjusted summary statistics for logarithmic regressions. *Stata Technical Bulletin* 5: 17–21. Reprinted in *Stata Technical Bulletin Reprints*, vol. 1, pp. 178–183.

Kennedy, W. J., Jr. and J. E. Gentle. 1980. *Statistical Computing.* New York: Marcel Dekker.

Ratkowsky, D. A. 1983. *Nonlinear Regression Modeling.* New York: Marcel Dekker.

Ross, G. J. S. 1987. *MLP User Manual, release 3.08.* Oxford: Numerical Algorithms Group.

——. 1990. *Nonlinear Estimation.* New York: Springer-Verlag.

Royston, P. 1992. sg1.2: Nonlinear regression command. *Stata Technical Bulletin* 7: 11–18. Reprinted in *Stata Technical Bulletin Reprints*, vol. 2, pp. 112–120.

——. 1993. sg1.4: Standard nonlinear curve fits. *Stata Technical Bulletin* 11: 17. Reprinted in *Stata Technical Bulletin Reprints*, vol. 2, p. 121.

SAS Institute Inc. 1985. *SAS User's Guide: Statistics, Version 5 Edition.* Cary, NC.

Also See

[U] **20.5 Accessing coefficients and standard errors**, [U] **26 Estimation and post-estimation commands**

[R] **ml**, [R] **vce**, [R] **xi**

Title

notes — Place notes in data

Syntax

notes [*varname*]: *text*

notes

notes [list] *evarlist* [in #[/#]]

notes drop *evarlist* [in #[/#]]

where *evarlist* is a *varlist* but may also contain the word _dta and # is a number or the letter l.

If *text* includes the letters TS surrounded by blanks, the TS is removed and a time stamp is substituted in its place.

Description

notes attaches notes to the data in memory. These notes become a part of the data and are saved when the data is saved and retrieved when the data is used; see [R] **save**. notes can be attached to the data generically or specifically to a variable within the data.

Remarks

A note is nothing formal; it is merely a string of text—probably words in your native language—reminding you to do something or cautioning you against something or anything else you might feel like jotting down. People who work with real data invariably end up with paper notes plastered around their terminal saying things like "Send the new sales data to Bob" or "Check the income variable in salary95; I don't believe it" or "The gender dummy was significant!" It would be better if these notes were attached to the data. Attached to the terminal, they tend to fall off and get lost.

Adding a note to your data requires typing note or notes (they are synonyms), a colon (:), and whatever you feel worth remembering. The note is added to the data currently in memory.

```
. note:  Send copy to Bob once verified.
```

You can replay your notes by typing notes (or note) by itself.

```
. notes
_dta:
  1.  Send copy to Bob once verified.
```

Once you resave your data, you can replay the note in the future, too. You add more notes just as you created the first:

```
. note: Mary wants a copy, too.
. notes
_dta:
  1.  Send copy to Bob once verified.
  2.  Mary wants a copy, too.
```

You can place time stamps on your notes by placing the word TS (in capitals) in the text of your note:

```
. note: TS merged updates from JJ&F

. notes

_dta:
   1.  Send copy to Bob once verified.
   2.  Mary wants a copy, too.
   3.  15 Oct 1994 16:01 merged updates from JJ&F
```

The notes we have added so far are attached to the data generically, which is why Stata prefixes them with _dta when it lists them. You can attach notes to variables:

```
. note mpg: is the 44 a mistake?  Ask Bob.

. note mpg: what about the two missing values?

. notes

_dta:
   1.  Send copy to Bob once verified.
   2.  Mary wants a copy, too.
   3.  15 Oct 1994 16:04 merged updates from JJ&F

mpg:
   1.  is the 44 a mistake? Ask Bob.
   2.  what about the two missing values?
```

Up to 9,999 generic notes can be attached to _dta and another 9,999 notes can be attached to each variable.

Selectively listing notes

notes by itself lists all the notes. In full syntax, notes is equivalent to typing notes _all in 1/1. Here are some variations:

notes _dta	list all generic notes
notes mpg	list all notes for variable mpg
notes _dta mpg	list all generic notes and mpg notes
notes _dta in 3	list generic note 3
notes _dta in 3/5	list generic notes 3 through 5
notes mpg in 3/5	list mpg notes 3 through 5
notes _dta in 3/l	list generic notes 3 through last

Deleting notes

notes drop works much like listing notes except that typing notes drop by itself does not delete all notes; type notes drop _all. Some variations:

notes drop _dta	delete all generic notes
notes drop _dta in 3	delete generic note 3
notes drop _dta in 3/5	delete generic notes 3 through 5
notes drop _dta in 3/l	delete generic notes 3 through last
notes drop mpg in 4	delete mpg note 4

Warnings

1. Notes are stored with the data and, as with other updates you make to the data, the additions and deletions are not permanent until you save the data; see [R] **save**.

2. The maximum length of a single note is 1,000 characters with Small Stata and 5,400 characters with Intercooled.

Methods and Formulas

notes is implemented as an ado file.

Also See

[U] **19.8 Characteristics**

[R] **save**

Title

> **nptrend** — Test for trend across ordered groups

Syntax

nptrend *varname* [if *exp*] [in *range*] , by(*groupvar*) [nodetail score(*scorevar*)]

Description

nptrend performs a nonparametric test for trend across ordered groups.

Options

by(*groupvar*) is not optional; it specifies the group on which the data is to be ordered.

nodetail suppresses the listing of group rank sums.

score(*scorevar*) defines scores for groups. When not specified, the values of *groupvar* are used for the scores.

Remarks

nptrend performs the nonparametric test for trend across ordered groups developed by Cuzick (1985) and is an extension of the Wilcoxon rank-sum test (ranksum; see [R] **signrank**). A correction for ties is incorporated into the test. nptrend is a useful adjunct to the Kruskal–Wallis test; see [R] **kwallis**.

In addition to nptrend, for non-grouped data the signtest and spearman commands can be useful; see [R] **signrank** and [R] **spearman**. The Cox and Stuart test, for instance, applies the sign test to differences between equally spaced observations of *varname*. The Daniels test calculates Spearman's rank correlation of *varname* with a time index. Under appropriate conditions, the Daniels test is more powerful than the Cox and Stuart test. See Conover (1980) for a discussion of these tests and their asymptotic relative efficiency.

▷ Example

The following data (Altman 1991, 217) shows ocular exposure to ultraviolet radiation for 32 pairs of sunglasses classified into 3 groups according to the amount of visible light transmitted.

Group	Transmission of visible light	Ocular exposure to ultraviolet radiation
1	< 25%	1.4 1.4 1.4 1.6 2.3 2.3
2	25 to 35%	0.9 1.0 1.1 1.1 1.2 1.2 1.5 1.9 2.2 2.6 2.6 2.6 2.8 2.8 3.2 3.5 4.3 5.1
3	> 35%	0.8 1.7 1.7 1.7 3.4 7.1 8.9 13.5

Entering this data into Stata, we have

```
. list
         group    exposure
  1.        1         1.4
  2.        1         1.4
  3.        1         1.4
  4.        1         1.6
  5.        1         2.3
  6.        1         2.3
  7.        2          .9
  (output omitted )
 31.        3         8.9
 32.        3        13.5
```

We use `nptrend` to test for a trend of (increasing) exposure across the 3 groups by typing

```
. nptrend exposure, by(group)
     group     score       obs    sum of ranks
         1         1         6              76
         2         2        18             290
         3         3         8             162

         z  =  1.52
     P>|z|  =  0.13
```

When the groups are given any equally spaced scores (such as -1, 0, 1), we will obtain the same answer as above. To illustrate the effect of changing scores, an analysis of these data with scores 1, 2, and 5 (admittedly not very sensible in this case) produces

```
. gen mysc = cond(group==3,5,group)
. nptrend exposure, by(group) score(mysc)
     group     score       obs    sum of ranks
         1         1         6              76
         2         2        18             290
         3         5         8             162

         z  =  1.46
     P>|z|  =  0.14
```

This example suggests that the analysis is not all that sensitive to the scores chosen.

◁

❑ Technical Note

The grouping variable may be either a string variable or a numeric variable. If it is a string variable and no score variable is specified, the natural numbers 1, 2, 3, . . . are assigned to the groups in the sort order of the string variable. This may not always be what you expect. For example, the sort order of the strings "one", "two", "three" is "one", "three", "two".

❑

Saved Results

`nptrend` saves in the S_# macros:

S_1	number of observations	S_3	z statistic
S_2	test statistic	S_4	significance value

Methods and Formulas

nptrend is implemented as an ado-file.

nptrend is based on a method due to Cuzick (1985). The following description of the statistic is from Altman (1991, 215–217). We have k groups of sample sizes n_i $(i = 1, \dots, k)$. The groups are given scores, l_i, which reflect their ordering, such as 1, 2, and 3. The scores do not have to be equally spaced, but they usually are. The total set of $N = \sum n_i$ observations are ranked from 1 to N and the sums of the ranks in each group, R_i, are obtained. L, the weighted sum of all the group scores, is

$$L = \sum_{i=1}^{k} l_i n_i$$

The statistic T is calculated as

$$T = \sum_{i=1}^{k} l_i R_i$$

Under the null hypothesis, the expected value of T is $E(T) = .5(N+1)L$, and its standard error is

$$\mathrm{se}(T) = \sqrt{\frac{n+1}{12}\left(N \sum_{i=1}^{k} l_i^2 n_i - L^2\right)}$$

so that the test statistic, z, is given by $z = [T - E(T)]/\mathrm{se}(T)$, which has an approximately standard Normal distribution when the null hypothesis of no trend is true.

The correction for ties affects the standard error of T. Let $\tilde{N}$ be the number of unique values of the variable being tested ($\tilde{N} \le N$), and let t_j be the number of times the jth unique value of the variable appears in the data. Define

$$a = \frac{\sum_{j=1}^{\tilde{N}} t_j(t_j^2 - 1)}{N(N^2 - 1)}$$

The corrected standard error of T is $\widetilde{\mathrm{se}}(T) = \sqrt{1-a}\ \mathrm{se}(T)$.

Acknowledgments

nptrend was written by K. A. Stepniewska and D. G. Altman of the Imperial Cancer Research Fund, London.

References

Altman, D. G. 1991. *Practical Statistics for Medical Research*. London: Chapman & Hall.

Conover, W. J. 1980. *Practical Nonparametric Statistics*. New York: John Wiley & Sons.

Cuzick, J. 1985. A Wilcoxon-type test for trend. *Statistics in Medicine* 4: 87–90.

Stepniewska, K. A. and D. G. Altman. 1992. snp4: Non-parametric test for trend across ordered groups. *Stata Technical Bulletin* 9: 21–22. Reprinted in *Stata Technical Bulletin Reprints*, vol. 2, p. 169.

Also See

[R] **kwallis**, [R] **signrank**, [R] **spearman**

Title

obs — Increase number of observations in dataset

Syntax

<u>set</u> <u>obs</u> #

Description

<u>set obs</u> changes the number of observations in the current dataset. # must be at least as large as the current number of observations. If there are variables in memory, the values of all new observations are set to missing.

Remarks

▷ Example

<u>set obs</u> can be useful for concocting artificial datasets. For instance, if you wanted to graph the function $y = x^2$ over the range 1 to 100, you could

```
. drop _all
. set obs 100
obs was 0, now 100
. generate x = _n
. generate y = x^2
. graph y x
( graph not shown)
```

◁

Also See

[R] **describe**, [R] **range**

Title

ologit — Maximum-likelihood ordered logit estimation

Syntax

$\Big[$ by *varlist*:$\Big]$ <u>olog</u>it *depvar* $\big[$*varlist*$\big]$ $\big[$*weight*$\big]$ $\big[$**if** *exp*$\big]$ $\big[$**in** *range*$\big]$ $\big[$, <u>t</u>able

    <u>l</u>evel(#) *maximize_options* $\big]$

ologitp *newvarlist* $\big[$**if** *exp*$\big]$ $\big[$**in** *range*$\big]$

aweights and fweights are allowed; see [U] **18.1.6 weight**.

ologit shares the features of all estimation commands; see [U] **26 Estimation and post-estimation commands**.

To reset problem-size limits, see [R] **matsize**.

ologit may be used with sw to perform stepwise estimation; see [R] **sw**.

Description

    ologit estimates ordered logit models of ordinal variable *depvar* on the independent variables *varlist*. The actual values taken on by the dependent variable are irrelevant except that larger values are assumed to correspond to "higher" outcomes. Up to 50 outcomes are allowed in Intercooled Stata; 20 outcomes in Small Stata.

    ologitp can be used to obtain predicted probabilities after ologit; see *Hypothesis tests and predictions* below.

    Also see [R] **oprobit** for ordered probit models; [R] **logistic** and [R] **logit** for ordinary (two-outcome) logistic models; [R] **probit** for ordinary (two-outcome) probit models; [R] **mlogit** for multinomial logit multiple-outcome models when the outcomes cannot be ordered; and [R] **clogit** for conditional logistic regression.

Options

    table requests a table showing how the probabilities for the categories are computed from the fitted equation.

    level(#) specifies the confidence level, in percent, for confidence intervals. The default is level(95) or as set by set level; see [U] **26.4 Specifying the width of confidence intervals**.

    maximize_options control the maximization process; see [R] **maximize**. You should never have to specify them.

Remarks

Ordered logit models are used to estimate relationships between an ordinal dependent variable and a set of independent variables. An *ordinal* variable is a variable that is categorical and ordered, for instance, "poor", "good", and "excellent", which might be the answer to one's current health status or the repair record of one's car. If there are only two outcomes, see [R] **logistic**, [R] **logit**, and [R] **probit**. This entry is concerned only with more than two outcomes. If the outcomes cannot be ordered (e.g., residency in the north, east, south and west), see [R] **mlogit**. This entry is concerned only with models in which the outcomes can be ordered.

In ordered logit, an underlying score is estimated as a linear function of the independent variables and a set of *cut* points. The probability of observing outcome i corresponds to the probability that the estimated linear function, plus random error, is within the range of the cut points estimated for the outcome:

$$\Pr(\text{outcome}_j = i) = \Pr(\kappa_{i-1} < \beta_1 x_{1j} + \beta_2 x_{2j} + \ldots + \beta_k x_{kj} + u_j \le \kappa_i)$$

u_j is assumed to be logistically distributed in ordered logit. In either case, one estimates the coefficients $\beta_1, \beta_2, \ldots, \beta_k$ along with the cut points $\kappa_1, \kappa_2, \ldots, \kappa_{I-1}$, where I is the number of possible outcomes. κ_0 is taken as $-\infty$ and κ_I is taken as $+\infty$. All of this is a direct generalization of the ordinary two-outcome logit model.

▷ Example

You wish to analyze the 1977 repair records of 66 foreign and domestic cars; a variation of the automobile data described in [U] **13 Stata's on-line tutorials and sample datasets**. The 1977 repair records, like those in 1978, take on values poor, fair, average, good, and excellent. Here is a cross-tabulation of the data:

```
. tab rep77 foreign, chi2

Repair      | Foreign
Record 1977|  Domestic     Foreign |      Total
-----------+----------------------+----------
     Poor |        2           1 |          3
     Fair |       10           1 |         11
  Average |       20           7 |         27
     Good |       13           7 |         20
      Exc |        0           5 |          5
-----------+----------------------+----------
    Total |       45          21 |         66

          Pearson chi2(4) =  13.8619   Pr = 0.008
```

Although it appears that `foreign` takes on the values "Domestic" and "Foreign", it is actually a numeric variable taking on the values 0 and 1. Similarly, `rep77` takes on the values 1, 2, 3, 4, and 5, corresponding to "Poor", "Fair", and so on. The more meaningful words appear because we attached value labels to the data; see [U] **19.6.3 Value labels**.

Since the chi-squared value is significant, you could claim that there is a relationship between `foreign` and `rep77`. Literally, however, you can only claim that the distributions are different; the chi-squared test is not directional. One way to model these data is to model the categorization that took place when the data were created. Cars have a true frequency-of-repair, which we will assume is given by $S_j = \beta \, \text{foreign}_j + u_j$, and a car is categorized as "poor" if $S_j \le \kappa_0$, as "fair" if $\kappa_0 < S_j \le \kappa_1$, and so on:

```
. ologit rep77 foreign, table

Iteration 0:  Log Likelihood =-89.895098
Iteration 1:  Log Likelihood =-85.951765
Iteration 2:  Log Likelihood =-85.908227
Iteration 3:  Log Likelihood =-85.908161

Ordered Logit Estimates                    Number of obs =       66
                                           chi2(1)       =     7.97
                                           Prob > chi2   = 0.0047
Log Likelihood = -85.908161                Pseudo R2     = 0.0444

------------------------------------------------------------------------------
   rep77 |    Coef.   Std. Err.      z     P>|z|     [95% Conf. Interval]
---------+--------------------------------------------------------------------
 foreign |  1.455878   .5308946    2.742   0.006     .4153436    2.496412
---------+--------------------------------------------------------------------
   _cut1 | -2.765562   .5988207           (Ancillary parameters)
   _cut2 |  -.9963603  .3217704
   _cut3 |  .9426153   .3136396
   _cut4 |  3.123351   .5423237
------------------------------------------------------------------------------

   rep77 |      Probability              Observed
---------|-----------------------------------------
    Poor | Pr(        xb+u<_cut1)          0.0455
    Fair | Pr(_cut1<xb+u<_cut2)            0.1667
 Average | Pr(_cut2<xb+u<_cut3)            0.4091
    Good | Pr(_cut3<xb+u<_cut4)            0.3030
     Exc | Pr(_cut4<xb+u)                  0.0758
```

Our model is $S_j = 1.46\,\text{foreign}_j + u_j$; the expected value for foreign cars is 1.46 and, for domestic cars, 0; foreign cars have better repair records.

The "ancillary parameters" _cut1, _cut2, _cut3, and _cut4 correspond to the κ's in our previous notation—they model the categorization. For instance, the probability that a foreign car is categorized as having a poor repair record is given by the probability that $1.46 + u_j \le -2.77$ or, equivalently, $u_j \le -4.23$.

The estimated cut points tell us how to interpret the score and the table below the estimates—produced because we specified the option table—reminds us of the interpretation. A car is estimated as having a poor repair record if the score is less than the estimated _cut1. (Actually, the table could say less than or equal, but since the logistic distribution is continuous, the probability of any particular value is zero, so it does not matter.)

For a foreign car, the probability of a poor record is the probability that $1.46 + u_j \le -2.77$ or, equivalently, $u_j \le -4.23$. Making this calculation requires familiarity with the logistic distribution: the probability is $1/(1 + e^{4.23}) = .014$. On the other hand, for domestic cars, the probability of a poor record is the probability $u_j \le -2.77$, which is .059.

This, it seems to us, is a far more reasonable prediction than we would have made based on the table alone. The table showed that 2 out of 45 domestic cars had poor records while 1 out of 21 foreign cars had poor records—corresponding to probabilities $2/45 = .044$ and $1/21 = .048$. The predictions from our model imposed a smoothness assumption—foreign cars should not, overall have better repair records without the difference revealing itself in each category. The fact that, in our data, the fractions of foreign and domestic cars in the poor category are virtually identical is due only to the randomness associated with small samples.

Thus, if we were asked to predict the true fractions of foreign and domestic cars that would be classified in the various categories, we would choose the numbers implied by the ordered logit model:

	tabulate		logit	
	Domestic	Foreign	Domestic	Foreign
Poor	.044	.048	.059	.014
Fair	.222	.048	.210	.065
Average	.444	.333	.450	.295
Good	.289	.333	.238	.467
Excellent	.000	.238	.043	.159

See *Hypothesis tests and predictions* below for a more complete explanation of how to generate predictions from an ordered logit model.

◁

❑ Technical Note

In this case, ordered logit provides an alternative to ordinary two-outcome logistic models with an arbitrary dichotomization, which might otherwise have been tempting. We could, for instance, have summarized this data by converting the 5-outcome `rep77` variable to a 2-outcome variable, combining cars in the average, fair, and poor categories to make one outcome and cars in the good and excellent categories to make the second.

Another, even less appealing alternative would have been to use ordinary regression, arbitrarily labeling "excellent" as 5, "good" as 4, and so on. The problem is that with different but equally valid labelings (say 10 for "excellent"), we would obtain different estimates. We would have no way of choosing one metric over another. That is not, however, true of `ologit`. The actual values used to label the categories make no difference other than through the order they imply.

In fact, our labeling was 5 for "excellent", 4 for "good", and so on. The words "excellent" and "good" appear in our output because we attached a value label to the variables; see [U] **19.6.3 Value labels**. If we were to now go back and type `replace rep77=10 if rep77==5`, changing all the 5's to 10's, we would still obtain exactly the same results when we reestimated our model.

❑

▷ Example

In the example above, we used ordered logit as a way to model a table. We are not, however, limited to including only a single explanatory variable nor to including only categorical variables. We can explore the relationship of `rep77` with any of the variables in our data. We might, for instance, model `rep77` not only in terms of the origin of manufacture, but including `length` (a proxy for size) and `mpg`:

```
. ologit rep77 foreign length mpg
Iteration 0:  Log Likelihood =-89.895098
Iteration 1:  Log Likelihood =-78.775147
Iteration 2:  Log Likelihood =-78.256299
Iteration 3:  Log Likelihood =-78.250722
Iteration 4:  Log Likelihood =-78.250719

Ordered Logit Estimates                        Number of obs =      66
                                               chi2(3)       =   23.29
                                               Prob > chi2   =  0.0000
Log Likelihood = -78.250719                    Pseudo R2     =  0.1295
```

```
      rep77 |     Coef.   Std. Err.       z    P>|z|     [95% Conf. Interval]
  ----------+--------------------------------------------------------------
    foreign |   2.896807   .7906411     3.664   0.000     1.347179   4.446435
     length |   .0828275     .02272     3.646   0.000     .0382972   .1273579
        mpg |   .2307677   .0704548     3.275   0.001     .0926788   .3688566
  ----------+--------------------------------------------------------------
      _cut1 |   17.92748   5.551191              (Ancillary parameters)
      _cut2 |   19.86506    5.59648
      _cut3 |   22.10331   5.708935
      _cut4 |   24.69213   5.890754
  --------------------------------------------------------------------------
```

foreign still plays a role, and an even larger role than previously. We find that larger cars tend to have better repair records as do cars with better mileage ratings.

◁

Hypothesis tests and predictions

See [U] **26 Estimation and post-estimation commands** for instructions on obtaining the variance-covariance matrix of the estimators, predicted values, and hypothesis tests. Also see [R] **lrtest** for performing likelihood-ratio tests.

In addition to what is said in [U] **26 Estimation and post-estimation commands**, be aware that the predicted values obtained from predict are the predicted *scores*, not predicted *probabilities*. To get the predicted probabilities we need to do some additional computations. This is most easily accomplished using ologitp.

▷ Example

In a previous example, we estimated the model ologit rep77 foreign length mpg. The predict command can be used to obtain the predicted score S_j for each automobile and standard formulas (given in the following technical note) used to translate those into probability statements. ologitp, used after ologit, does precisely this.

You type the command followed by the names of the new variables to hold the predicted probabilities, ordering the names from low to high. In our data, the lowest outcome is "poor" and the highest "excellent". We have five categories and so must type five names following ologitp; the choice of name is up to us:

```
. ologitp poor fair avg good exc
. list score exc good make model rep78 if rep77==.
           score        exc       good       make      model     rep78
    3.    18.99191   .0033341   .0393055       AMC     Spirit        .
   10.    20.08064   .0098392    .107004     Buick       Opel        .
   32.    18.63714   .0023406   .0279497      Ford     Fiesta     Good
   44.    20.55367    .015697   .1594413     Merc.    Monarch   Average
   53.    22.03044    .065272   .4165187   Peugeot        604        .
   56.    19.43574    .005187    .059727     Plym.    Horizon   Average
   57.    21.07457   .0261461   .2371826     Plym.    Sapporo        .
   63.    21.19858   .0294961   .2585824     Pont.    Phoenix        .
```

The eight cars listed were introduced after 1977 and so do not have 1977 repair records in our data. We predicted what their 1977 repair records might have been using the fitted equation. We see that, based on its characteristics, the Peugeot 604 had about a $41.65 + 6.53 = 48.2$ percent chance of a good or excellent repair record. The Ford Fiesta, which had only a 3 percent chance of a good or excellent repair record, in fact had a good record when it was introduced in the following year.

◁

❑ Technical Note

For ordered logit, the predicted score is defined as $S_j = x_{1j}\beta_1 + x_{2j}\beta_2 + \ldots + x_{kj}\beta_k$. The ordered-logit predictions are then the probability that $S_j + u_j$ lies between a pair of cut points κ_{i-1} and κ_i. Some handy formulas are

$$\Pr(S_j + u_j < \kappa) = 1/(1 + e^{S_j - \kappa})$$
$$\Pr(S_j + u_j > \kappa) = 1 - 1/(1 + e^{S_j - \kappa})$$
$$\Pr(\kappa_1 < S_j + u_j < \kappa_2) = 1/(1 + e^{S_j - \kappa_2}) - 1/(1 + e^{S_j - \kappa_1})$$

predict will predict the score S_j for each automobile. Rather than using ologitp, we could calculate the predicted probabilities by hand. If we wished to obtain the predicted probability that the repair record is excellent and the probability that it is good, we look back at ologit's output to obtain the cut points. We find that "good" corresponds to the interval _cut3 $< S_j + u <$ _cut4 and "excellent" to the interval $S_j + u >$ _cut4:

```
. predict score
. gen probgood = 1/(1+exp(score-_b[_cut4])) - 1/(1+exp(score-_b[_cut3]))
. gen probexc = 1 - 1/(1+exp(score-_b[_cut4]))
```

The results of our calculation will be exactly the same as that produced by ologitp. Note that we refer to the estimated cut points just as we would any coefficient, so _b[_cut3] refers to the value of the _cut3 coefficient; see [U] **20.5 Accessing coefficients and standard errors**.

❑

Saved Results

ologit is a member of the class described in [R] **maximize**; see that entry for saved results. ologitp saves no results.

Methods and Formulas

ologitp is implemented as an ado-file.

A straightforward textbook description of the model fit by ologit, as well as the models fit by oprobit, clogit, and mlogit, can be found in Greene (1993, chapter 21). When you have a qualitative dependent variable, several estimation procedures are available. A popular choice is multinomial logistic regression (see [R] **mlogit**), but if you use this procedure when the response variable is ordinal, you are discarding information because multinomial logit ignores the ordered aspect of the outcome. Ordered logit and probit models provide a means to exploit the ordering information.

There is more than one "ordered logit" model. The model fit by ologit, which we will call the ordered logit model, is also known as the proportional odds model. Another popular choice, not fitted by ologit, is known as the stereotype model. All ordered logit models have been derived by starting with a binary logit/probit model and generalizing it to allow for more than two outcomes.

The proportional odds ordered logit model is so called because, if one considers the odds odds$(k) = P(Y \leq k)/P(Y > k)$, then odds$(k_1)$ and odds(k_2) have the same ratio, for all independent variable combinations. The model is based on the principle that the only effect of combining adjoining categories in ordered categorical regression problems should be a loss of efficiency in the estimation of the regression parameters (McCullagh 1980). This model was also described by Zavoina and McKelvey (1975), and previously by Aitchison and Silvey (1957) in a different algebraic form. Brant (1990) offers a set of diagnostics for the model.

Peterson and Harrell (1990) suggest a model that allows non-proportional odds for a subset of the explanatory variables. `ologit` does not allow this, but a test of `ologit` with respect to the Peterson and Harrell model using a "score test" concept is scheduled to appear in a forthcoming issue of the *Stata Technical Bulletin*; see [U] **2.4 The Stata Technical Bulletin**.

The stereotype model rejects the principle on which the ordered logit model is based. Anderson (1984) argues that there are two distinct types of ordered categorical variables: "grouped continuous", like income, where the "type a" model applies; and "assessed", like extent of pain relief, where the stereotype model applies. Greenland (1985) independently developed the same model. The stereotype model starts with a multinomial logistic regression model and imposes constraints on this model.

Goodness of fit for `ologit` can be evaluated by comparing the likelihood value with that obtained by estimating the model with `mlogit`. Let L_1 be the log-likelihood value reported by `ologit` and L_0 be the log-likelihood value reported by `mlogit`. If there are p independent variables (excluding the constant) and c categories, `mlogit` will fit $p(c-1)$ additional parameters. One can then perform a "likelihood-ratio test", i.e., calculate $-2(L_1 - L_0)$ and compare with $\chi^2(p(c-2))$. This test is only suggestive because the ordered logit model is not nested within the multinomial logit model. A large value of $-2(L_1 - L_0)$ should, however, be taken as evidence of poorness of fit. Marginally large values, on the other hand, should not be taken too seriously.

The coefficients and cut points are estimated using maximum-likelihood as described in [R] **maximize**. In our parameterization, no constant appears as the effect is absorbed into the cut points.

`ologit` and `oprobit` begin by tabulating the dependent variable. Category $i = 1$ is defined as the minimum value of the variable, $i = 2$ as the next ordered value, and so on, for the empirically determined I categories.

The probability of observing an observation in the case of ordered logit is

$$
\mathrm{Pr}(\text{outcome} = i) = \mathrm{Pr}\left(\kappa_{i-1} < \sum_j \beta_j x_j + u \le \kappa_i\right)
$$

$$
= \frac{1}{1 + \exp(-\kappa_i + \sum \beta_j x_j)} - \frac{1}{1 + \exp(-\kappa_{i-1} + \sum \beta_j x_j)}
$$

Note that κ_0 is defined as $-\infty$ and κ_I as $+\infty$.

In the case of ordered probit, the probability of observing an observation is

$$
\mathrm{Pr}(\text{outcome} = i) = \mathrm{Pr}\left(\kappa_{i-1} < \sum_j \beta_j x_j + u \le \kappa_i\right)
$$

$$
= F\left(\kappa_i - \sum_j x_j \beta_j\right) - F\left(\kappa_{i-1} - \sum_j x_j \beta_j\right)
$$

References

Aitchison, J. and S. D. Silvey. 1957. The generalization of probit analysis to the case of multiple responses. *Biometrika* 44: 131–140.

Anderson, J. A. 1984. Regression and ordered categorical variables (with discussion). *Journal of the Royal Statistical Society*, Series B 46: 1–30.

Brant, R. 1990. Assessing proportionality in the proportional odds model for ordinal logistic regression. *Biometrics* 46: 1171–1178.

Greene, W. H. 1993. *Econometric Analysis*. 2d ed. New York: Macmillan.

Greenland, S. 1985. An application of logistic models to the analysis of ordinal response. *Biometrical Journal* 27: 189–197.

McCullagh, P. 1977. A logistic model for paired comparisons with ordered categorical data. *Biometrika* 64: 449–453.

——. 1980. Regression models for ordinal data (with discussion). *Journal of the Royal Statistical Society*, Series B 42: 109–142.

McCullagh, P. and J. A. Nelder. 1991. *Generalized Linear Models*. 2d ed. London: Chapman & Hall.

Peterson, B. and F. E. Harrell, Jr. 1990. Partial proportional odds models for ordinal response variables. *Applied Statistics* 39: 205–217.

Zavoina, W. and R. D. McKelvey. 1975. A statistical model for the analysis of ordinal level dependent variables. *Journal of Mathematical Sociology* 4: 103–120.

Also See

[U] **20.5 Accessing coefficients and standard errors**, [U] **26 Estimation and post-estimation commands**

[R] **clogit**, [R] **lincom**, [R] **linktest**, [R] **logistic**, [R] **logit**, [R] **lrtest**, [R] **maximize**, [R] **mlogit**, [R] **oprobit**, [R] **predict**, [R] **probit**, [R] **sw**, [R] **test**, [R] **testnl**, [R] **vce**

Title

oneway — One-way analysis of variance

Syntax

$\big[$ by *varlist*: $\big]$ <u>one</u>way *response_var factor_var* $\big[$ *weight* $\big]$ $\big[$ if *exp* $\big]$ $\big[$ in *range* $\big]$ $\big[$, <u>noa</u>nova

    <u>nol</u>abel <u>miss</u>ing <u>w</u>rap <u>t</u>abulate $\big[$ <u>no</u>$\big]$<u>m</u>eans $\big[$ <u>no</u>$\big]$<u>st</u>andard $\big[$ <u>no</u>$\big]$<u>f</u>req $\big[$ <u>no</u>$\big]$<u>o</u>bs

    <u>b</u>onferroni <u>sc</u>heffe <u>si</u>dak $\big]$

aweights and fweights are allowed; see [U] **18.1.6 weight**.

Description

The oneway command reports one-way analysis-of-variance (ANOVA) models and performs multiple-comparison tests.

If you wish to estimate more complicated ANOVA layouts or wish to estimate analysis-of-covariance (ANOCOVA) models, see [R] **anova**.

See [R] **encode** for examples of estimating ANOVA models on string variables.

See [R] **loneway** for an alternative oneway command with slightly different features.

Options

noanova suppresses the display of the ANOVA table.

nolabel causes the numeric codes to be displayed rather than the value labels in the ANOVA and multiple-comparison test tables.

missing requests that missing values of *factor_var* be treated as a category rather than as observations to be omitted from the analysis.

wrap requests that Stata take no action on wide tables to make them readable. Unless wrap is specified, wide tables are broken into pieces to enhance readability.

tabulate produces a table of summary statistics of the *response_var* by levels of the *factor_var*. The table includes the mean, standard deviation, frequency, and, if the data is weighted, the number of observations. Individual elements of the table may be included or suppressed by the $\big[$ no$\big]$means, $\big[$ no$\big]$standard, $\big[$ no$\big]$freq, and $\big[$ no$\big]$obs options. For example, typing

oneway response factor, tabulate means standard

would produce a summary table that contained only the means and standard deviations. You could achieve the same result by typing

oneway response factor, tabulate nofreq

$\big[$ no$\big]$means includes only or suppresses only the means from the table produced by the tabulate option. See tabulate option above.

$\big[$ no$\big]$standard includes only or suppresses only the standard deviations from the table produced by the tabulate option. See tabulate option above.

[no]freq includes only or suppresses only the frequencies from the table produced by the tabulate option. See tabulate option above.

[no]obs includes only or suppresses only the reported number of observations from the table produced by the tabulate option. If the data is not weighted, the number of observations is identical to the frequency and by default only the frequency is reported. If the data is weighted, the frequency refers to the sum of the weights. See tabulate option above.

bonferroni reports the results of a Bonferroni multiple-comparison test.

scheffe reports the results of a Scheffé multiple-comparison test.

sidak reports the results of a Šidák multiple-comparison test.

Remarks

The oneway command reports one-way analysis-of-variance (ANOVA) models. To perform a one-way layout of a variable called endog on exog, you type oneway endog exog.

▷ Example

You run an experiment varying the amount of fertilizer used in growing apple trees. You test four concentrations, using each concentration in three groves of twelve trees each. Later in the year, you measure the average weight of the fruit.

If all had gone well, you would have had three observations on the average weight for each of the four concentrations. Instead, two of the groves were mistakenly leveled by a confused man on a large bulldozer. You are left with the following data:

```
. use apple
(Apple trees)

. describe

Contains data from apple.dta
  obs:            10                          Apple trees
  vars:            2                          10 Apr 1996 14:48
  size:          140 (99.9% of memory free)
-------------------------------------------------------------------------
  1. treat       int      %8.0g              Fertilizer
  2. wgt         double   %10.0g             Avg. weight (g)
-------------------------------------------------------------------------
Sorted by:

. list

          treat           wgt
   1.         1          117.5
   2.         1          113.8
   3.         1          104.4
   4.         2           48.9
   5.         2           50.4
   6.         2           58.9
   7.         3           70.4
   8.         3           86.9
   9.         4           87.7
  10.         4           67.3
```

To obtain the one-way analysis-of-variance results, you type

```
. oneway wgt treat
                      Analysis of Variance
        Source            SS        df      MS             F     Prob > F
    -----------------------------------------------------------------------
    Between groups    5295.54433     3    1765.18144      21.46    0.0013
    Within groups     493.591667     6    82.2652778
    -----------------------------------------------------------------------
        Total         5789.136       9    643.237333
    Bartlett's test for equal variances:   chi2(3)=1.3900    Prob>chi2=0.708
```

You find significant (at better than the 1% level) differences among the four concentrations.

◁

□ **Technical Note**

Rather than using the **oneway** command, we could have performed this analysis using **anova**. The first example in [R] **anova** repeats this same analysis. You may wish to compare the output.

You will find the **oneway** command quicker than the **anova** command and, as you will learn, **oneway** allows you to perform multiple-comparison tests. On the other hand, **anova** will let you generate predictions, examine the covariance matrix of the estimators, and perform more general hypothesis tests.

□

□ **Technical Note**

Although the output is a usual analysis-of-variance table, let's run through it anyway. The between-group sum of squares for the model is 5295.5 with 3 degrees of freedom. This results in a mean square of $5295.5/3 \approx 1765.2$. The corresponding F statistic is 21.46 and has a significance level of 0.0013. Thus, the model appears to be significant at the 0.13% level.

The second line summarizes the within-group (residual) variation. The within-group sum of squares is 493.59 with 6 degrees of freedom, resulting in a mean square error of 82.27.

The between- plus the residual-group variations sum to the total sum of squares and is reported as 5789.1 in the last line of the table. This is the total sum of squares of **wgt** after removal of the mean. Similarly, the between plus residual degrees of freedom sum to the total degrees of freedom, 9. Remember that there are 10 observations. Subtracting 1 for the mean, we are left with 9 total degrees of freedom.

At the bottom of the table is reported Bartlett's test for equal variances. The value of the statistic is 1.39. The corresponding significance level (χ^2 with 3 degrees of freedom) is 0.708, so we cannot reject the assumption that the variances are homogeneous.

□

Obtaining observed means

▷ **Example**

We typed **oneway wgt treat** to obtain an ANOVA table of weight of fruit by fertilizer concentration. Although we obtained the table, we did not obtain any information on which fertilizer seems to work the best. If we add the **tabulate** option, we obtain that additional information:

```
. oneway wgt treat, tabulate
                |       Summary of Avg. weight (g)
    Fertilizer  |      Mean    Std. Dev.        Freq.
    ------------+-----------------------------------
             1  |    111.90         6.75             3
             2  |     52.73         5.39             3
             3  |     78.65        11.67             2
             4  |     77.50        14.42             2
    ------------+-----------------------------------
         Total  |     80.62        25.36            10

                        Analysis of Variance
        Source              SS          df       MS              F        Prob > F
    -----------------------------------------------------------------------------
    Between groups      5295.54433       3    1765.18144        21.46       0.0013
    Within groups       493.591667       6    82.2652778
    -----------------------------------------------------------------------------
        Total            5789.136        9    643.237333

    Bartlett's test for equal variances:  chi2(3)=1.3900   Prob>chi2=0.708
```

We find that the average weight is largest when we used fertilizer concentration 1.

◁

Multiple-comparison tests

▷ Example

oneway also has the ability to perform multiple-comparison tests, using either Bonferroni, Scheffé, or Šidák normalizations. For instance, to obtain the Bonferroni multiple-comparison test, we specify the bonferroni option:

```
. oneway wgt treat, bonferroni
                        Analysis of Variance
        Source              SS          df       MS              F        Prob > F
    -----------------------------------------------------------------------------
    Between groups      5295.54433       3    1765.18144        21.46       0.0013
    Within groups       493.591667       6    82.2652778
    -----------------------------------------------------------------------------
        Total            5789.136        9    643.237333

    Bartlett's test for equal variances:  chi2(3)=1.3900   Prob>chi2=0.708

        Comparison of Avg. weight (g) by Fertilizer
                    (Bonferroni)
    Row Mean-|
    Col Mean |        1          2          3
    ---------+---------------------------------
           2 |    -59.17
             |     0.001
             |
           3 |    -33.25      25.92
             |     0.042       0.122
             |
           4 |    -34.40      24.77      -1.15
             |     0.036       0.146      1.000
```

The results of the Bonferroni test are presented as a matrix. The first entry, −59.17, represents the difference between fertilizer concentrations 2 and 1 (labeled "Row Mean - Col Mean" in the upper stub of the table). Remember that in the previous example we requested the tabulate option. Looking back, we find that the means of concentrations 1 and 2 are 111.90 and 52.73, respectively. Thus, 52.73 − 111.90 = −59.17.

Underneath that number is reported "0.001". This is the Bonferroni-adjusted significance of the difference. The difference is significant at the 0.1% level. Looking down the column, we see that concentration 3 is also worse than concentration 1 (4.2% level) as is concentration 4 (3.6% level).

Based on this evidence, I would use concentration 1 if I grew apple trees.

◁

▷ Example

We can just as easily obtain the Scheffé-adjusted significance levels. Rather than specifying the bonferroni option, we specify the scheffe option.

We will also add the noanova option to prevent Stata from redisplaying the ANOVA table:

```
. oneway wgt treat, noanova scheffe
     Comparison of Avg. weight (g) by Fertilizer
                        (Scheffe)
    Row Mean-|
    Col Mean |         1         2         3
    ---------+---------------------------------
           2 |  -59.1667
             |     0.001
             |
           3 |    -33.25   25.9167
             |     0.039     0.101
             |
           4 |     -34.4   24.7667     -1.15
             |     0.034     0.118     0.999
```

The differences are the same as we obtained in the Bonferroni output, but the significance levels are not. According to the Bonferroni-adjusted numbers, the significance of the difference between fertilizer concentrations 1 and 3 is 4.2%. The Scheffé-adjusted significance level is 3.9%.

We will leave it to you to decide which results are more accurate.

◁

▷ Example

Let's conclude this example by obtaining the Šidák-adjusted multiple-comparison tests. We do this to illustrate Stata's capabilities to calculate these results. It is understood that searching across adjustment methods until you find the results you want is not a valid technique for obtaining significance levels.

```
. oneway wgt treat, noanova sidak
     Comparison of Avg. weight (g) by Fertilizer
                    (Sidak)
Row Mean-|
Col Mean |          1          2          3
---------|-------------------------------------
       2 |     -59.17
         |      0.001
         |
       3 |     -33.25      25.92
         |      0.041      0.116
         |
       4 |     -34.40      24.77      -1.15
         |      0.035      0.137      1.000
```

We find results that are similar to the Bonferroni-adjusted numbers.

◁

Weighted data

▷ Example

oneway can work with weighted data as well as unweighted data. Let's assume that you wish to perform a one-way layout of the death rate on the four Census regions of the United States using state data. Your data contains three variables, drate (the death rate), region (the region), and pop (the population of the state).

To estimate the model, you type oneway drate region [weight=pop], although one typically abbreviates weight as w. We will also add the tabulate option so that you can see how the table of summary statistics differs for weighted data:

```
. oneway drate region [w=pop], tabulate
(analytic weights assumed)
Census   |         Summary of Death Rate
region   |     Mean   Std. Dev.      Freq.        Obs.
---------+---------------------------------------------
      NE |    97.15        5.82   49135283           9
 N Cntrl |    88.10        5.58   58865670          12
   South |    87.05       10.40   74734029          16
    West |    75.65        8.23   43172490          13
---------+---------------------------------------------
   Total |    87.34       10.43   2.259e+08          50
                   Analysis of Variance
    Source              SS         df       MS          F      Prob > F
-----------------------------------------------------------------------
Between groups     2360.92281       3   786.974272     12.17     0.0000
Within groups      2974.09635      46   64.6542685
-----------------------------------------------------------------------
   Total           5335.01916      49   108.877942
Bartlett's test for equal variances:  chi2(3)=5.4971   Prob>chi2=0.139
```

When the data is weighted, the summary table has four rather than three columns. The column labeled "Freq." reports the sum of the weights. The overall frequency is $2.259 \cdot 10^8$, meaning that there are approximately 226 million people in the U.S.

The ANOVA table is appropriately weighted. Also see [U] **18.1.6 weight**.

◁

Saved Results

oneway saves in _result():

1. number of observations	6. F statistic
2. between group sum of squares	7–9. (not used)
3. between group degrees of freedom	10. Bartlett's χ^2
4. within group sum of squares	11. Bartlett's degrees of freedom
5. within group degrees of freedom	

Methods and Formulas

The model of one-way analysis of variance is

$$y_{ij} = \mu + \alpha_i + \epsilon_{ij}$$

for levels $i = 1, \ldots, k$ and observations $j = 1, \ldots, n_i$. Define $\overline{y}_i$ as the (weighted) mean of y_{ij} over j and $\overline{y}$ as the overall (weighted) mean of y_{ij}. Define w_{ij} as the weight associated with y_{ij}, which is 1 if the data is unweighted. w_{ij} is normalized to sum to $n = \sum_i n_i$ if aweights are used and is otherwise unnormalized. w_i refers to $\sum_j w_{ij}$ and w refers to $\sum_i w_{ij}$.

The between group sum of squares is then

$$S_1 = \sum_i w_i(\overline{y}_i - \overline{y})^2$$

The total sum of squares is

$$S = \sum_i \sum_j w_{ij}(y_{ij} - \overline{y})^2$$

The within group sum of squares is given by $S_e = S - S_1$.

The between group mean square is $s_1^2 = S_1/(k - 1)$ and the within group mean square is $s_e = S_e/(w - k)$. The test statistic is $F = s_1^2/s_e^2$. See, for instance, Snedecor and Cochran (1989).

Bartlett's test

Bartlett's test assumes that you have m independent, normal random samples and tests the hypothesis $\sigma_1^2 = \sigma_2^2 = \ldots = \sigma_m^2$. The test statistic, M, is defined

$$M = \frac{(T - m)\ln\widehat{\sigma}^2 - \sum(T_i - 1)\ln\widehat{\sigma}_i^2}{1 + \frac{1}{3(m-1)}\sum\frac{1}{T_i-1} - \frac{1}{T-m}}$$

where there are T overall observations and T_i observations in the ith group and

$$(T_i - 1)\widehat{\sigma}_i^2 = \sum_{j=1}^{T_i}(y_{ij} - \overline{y}_i)^2$$

$$(T - m)\widehat{\sigma}^2 = \sum_{i=1}^{m}(T_i - 1)\widehat{\sigma}_i^2$$

An approximate test of the homogeneity of variance is based on the statistic M with critical values obtained from the χ^2 distribution of $m - 1$ degrees of freedom. See Bartlett (1937) or Judge et al. (1985, 447–449).

Multiple-comparison tests

Let's begin by reviewing the logic behind these adjustments. The "standard" t statistic for the comparison of two means is

$$t = \frac{\overline{y}_i - \overline{y}_j}{s\sqrt{\frac{1}{n_i} + \frac{1}{n_j}}}$$

where s is the overall standard deviation, $\overline{y}_i$ is the measured average of y in group i, and n_i is the number of observations in the group. We perform hypothesis tests by calculating this t statistic. We simultaneously choose a critical level α and look up the t statistic corresponding to that level in a table. We reject the hypothesis if our calculated t exceeds the value we looked up. Alternatively, since we have a computer at our disposal, we calculate the significance-level e corresponding to our calculated t statistic and, if $e < \alpha$, we reject the hypothesis.

All of this logic works well when we are performing a *single* test. Now consider what happens when we perform a number of separate tests, say n of them. Let's assume, just for discussion, that we set α equal to 0.05 and that we will perform 6 tests. For each test we have a 0.05 probability of falsely rejecting the equality-of-means hypothesis. Overall, then, our chances of falsely rejecting *at least one* of the hypotheses is $1 - (1 - .05)^6 \approx .26$ if the tests are independent.

The idea behind multiple-comparison tests is to control for the fact that we will perform multiple tests and to hold down our overall chances of falsely rejecting each hypothesis to α rather than letting it grow with each additional test we perform. (See Miller 1981 and Hochberg and Tamhane 1987 for rather advanced texts on multiple-comparison procedures.)

The Bonferroni adjustment (see Miller 1981; also see Winer, Brown, and Michels 1991, 158–166) does this by (falsely but approximately) asserting that the critical level we should use, a, is the true critical level α divided by the number of tests n, that is, $a = \alpha/n$. For instance, if we are going to perform 6 tests each at the .05 significance level, we want to adopt a critical level of $.05/6 \approx .00833$.

We can just as easily apply this logic to e, the significance level associated with our t statistic, as to our critical level α. If a comparison has a calculated significance of e, then its "real" significance, adjusted for the fact of n comparisons, is $n \cdot e$. If a comparison has a significance level of, say, .012, and we perform 6 tests, then its "real" significance is .072. If we adopt a critical level of .05, we cannot reject the hypothesis. If we adopt a critical level of .10, we can reject.

Of course, this calculation can go above 1, but that just means that there is no $\alpha < 1$ for which we could reject the hypothesis. (This situation arises due to the crude nature of the Bonferroni adjustment.) Stata handles this case by simply calling the significance level 1. Thus, the formula for the Bonferroni significance level is

$$e_b = \min(1, en)$$

where $n = k(k-1)/2$ is the number of comparisons.

The Šidák adjustment (Šidák 1967; also see Winer, Brown, and Michels 1991, 165–166) is slightly different and provides a tighter bound. It starts with the assertion that

$$a = 1 - (1 - \alpha)^{1/n}$$

Turning this formula around and substituting calculated significance levels, we obtain

$$e_s = \min\left(1, 1 - (1 - e)^n\right)$$

For example, if the calculated significance is 0.012 and we perform 6 tests, the "real" significance is approximately 0.07.

The Scheffé test (Scheffé 1953, 1959; also see Winer, Brown, and Michels 1991, 191–195) differs in derivation, but it attacks the same problem. Let there be k means for which we want to make all the pairwise tests. Two means are declared significantly different if

$$t \geq \sqrt{(k-1)F(\alpha; k-1, \nu)}$$

where $F(\alpha; k-1, \nu)$ is the α-critical value of the F distribution with $k-1$ numerator and ν denominator degrees of freedom. Scheffé's test has the nicety that it never declares a contrast significant if the overall F test is nonsignificant.

Turning the test around, Stata calculates a significance level

$$\widehat{e} = F\left(\frac{t^2}{k-1}, k-1, \nu\right)$$

For instance, you have a calculated t statistic of 4.0 with 50 degrees of freedom. The simple t test says the significance level is .00021. The F test equivalent, 16 with 1 and 50 degrees of freedom, says the same. If you are doing three comparisons, however, you calculate an F test of 8.0 with 2 and 50 degrees of freedom, which is .0010.

References

Altman, D. G. 1991. *Practical Statistics for Medical Research.* London: Chapman & Hall.

Bartlett, M. S. 1937. Properties of sufficiency and statistical tests. *Proceedings of the Royal Society*, Series A 160: 268–282.

Hochberg, Y. and A. C. Tamhane. 1987. *Multiple Comparison Procedures.* New York: John Wiley & Sons.

Judge, G. G., W. E. Griffiths, R. C. Hill, H. Lütkepohl, and Tsoung-Chao Lee. 1985. *The Theory and Practice of Econometrics.* 2d ed. New York: John Wiley & Sons.

Miller, R. G., Jr. 1981. *Simultaneous Statistical Inference.* 2d ed. New York: Springer-Verlag.

Scheffé, H. 1953. A method for judging all contrasts in the analysis of variance. *Biometrika* 40: 87–104.

———. 1959. *The Analysis of Variance.* New York: John Wiley & Sons.

Šidák, Z. 1967. Rectangular confidence regions for the means of multivariate normal distributions. *Journal of the American Statistical Association* 62: 626–633.

Snedecor, G. W. and W. G. Cochran. 1989. *Statistical Methods.* 8th ed. Ames, IA: Iowa State University Press.

Winer, B. J., D. R. Brown, and K. M. Michels. 1991. *Statistical Procedures in Experimental Design.* 3d ed. New York: McGraw-Hill.

Also See

[U] 24.8 **Accessing results calculated by other programs**

[R] **anova**, [R] **encode**, [R] **loneway**, [R] **table**

Title

oprobit — Maximum-likelihood ordered probit estimation

Syntax

[by *varlist*:] <u>oprobit</u> *depvar* [*varlist*] [*weight*] [if *exp*] [in *range*] [, <u>t</u>able

<u>level</u>(#) *maximize_options*]

oprobitp *newvarlist* [if *exp*] [in *range*]

aweights and fweights are allowed; see [U] **18.1.6 weight**.

oprobit shares the features of all estimation commands; see [U] **26 Estimation and post-estimation commands**.

To reset problem-size limits, see [R] **matsize**.

oprobit may be used with sw to perform stepwise estimation; see [R] **sw**.

Description

oprobit estimates ordered probit models of ordinal variable *depvar* on the independent variables *varlist*. The actual values taken on by the dependent variable are irrelevant except that larger values are assumed to correspond to "higher" outcomes. Up to 50 outcomes are allowed in Intercooled Stata; 20 outcomes in Small Stata.

oprobitp can be used to obtain predicted probabilities after oprobit; see *Hypothesis tests and predictions* below.

Also see [R] **ologit** for ordered logit models; [R] **logistic** and [R] **logit** for ordinary (two-outcome) logistic models; [R] **probit** for ordinary (two-outcome) probit models; [R] **mlogit** for multinomial logit multiple-outcome models when the outcomes cannot be ordered; and [R] **clogit** for conditional logistic regression.

Options

table requests a table showing how the probabilities for the categories are computed from the fitted equation.

level(#) specifies the confidence level, in percent, for confidence intervals. The default is level(95) or as set by set level; see [U] **26.4 Specifying the width of confidence intervals**.

maximize_options control the maximization process; see [R] **maximize**. You should never have to specify them.

Remarks

An ordered probit model is used to estimate relationships between an ordinal dependent variable and a set of independent variables. An *ordinal* variable is a variable that is categorical and ordered, for instance, "poor", "good", and "excellent", which might be the answer to one's current health status or the repair record of one's car. If there are only two outcomes, see [R] **logistic**, [R] **logit**, and [R] **probit**. This entry is concerned only with more than two outcomes. If the outcomes cannot be ordered (e.g., residency in the north, east, south and west), see [R] **mlogit**. This entry is concerned only with models in which the outcomes can be ordered.

In ordered probit, an underlying score is estimated as a linear function of the independent variables and a set of *cut* points. The probability of observing outcome i corresponds to the probability that the estimated linear function, plus random error, is within the range of the cut points estimated for the outcome:

$$\Pr(\text{outcome}_j = i) = \Pr(\kappa_{i-1} < \beta_1 x_{1j} + \beta_2 x_{2j} + \ldots + \beta_k x_{kj} + u_j \le \kappa_i)$$

u_j is assumed to be normally distributed. In either case, one estimates the coefficients $\beta_1, \beta_2, \ldots, \beta_k$ along with the cut points $\kappa_1, \kappa_2, \ldots, \kappa_{I-1}$, where I is the number of possible outcomes. κ_0 is taken as $-\infty$ and κ_I is taken as $+\infty$. All of this is a direct generalization of the ordinary two-outcome probit model.

▷ Example

In [R] **ologit**, we use a variation of the automobile data (see [U] **13 Stata's on-line tutorials and sample datasets**) to analyze the 1977 repair records of 66 foreign and domestic cars. We use ordered logit to explore the relationship of rep77 in terms of foreign (origin of manufacture), length (a proxy for size), and mpg. Here we estimate the same model using ordered probit rather than ordered logit:

```
. oprobit rep77 foreign length mpg
Iteration 0:   Log Likelihood =-89.895098
Iteration 1:   Log Likelihood =-78.141221
Iteration 2:   Log Likelihood =-78.020314
Iteration 3:   Log Likelihood =-78.020025
Ordered Probit Estimates                      Number of obs =       66
                                              chi2(3)       =    23.75
                                              Prob > chi2   =   0.0000
Log Likelihood = -78.020025                   Pseudo R2     =   0.1321

------------------------------------------------------------------------------
   rep77 |     Coef.   Std. Err.      z     P>|z|     [95% Conf. Interval]
---------+--------------------------------------------------------------------
 foreign |   1.704861   .4246786    4.014   0.000     .8725057    2.537215
  length |   .0468675   .012648     3.706   0.000     .022078     .0716571
     mpg |   .1304559   .0378627    3.445   0.001     .0562464    .2046654
---------+--------------------------------------------------------------------
   _cut1 |   10.1589    3.076749             (Ancillary parameters)
   _cut2 |   11.21003   3.107522
   _cut3 |   12.54561   3.155228
   _cut4 |   13.98059   3.218786
------------------------------------------------------------------------------
```

We find that larger cars tend to have better repair records as do cars with better mileage ratings.

◁

Hypothesis tests and predictions

See [U] **26 Estimation and post-estimation commands** for instructions on obtaining the variance-covariance matrix of the estimators, predicted values, and hypothesis tests. Also see [R] **lrtest** for performing likelihood-ratio tests.

In addition to what is said in [U] **26 Estimation and post-estimation commands**, be aware that the predicted values obtained from `predict` are the predicted *scores*, not predicted *probabilities*. To get the predicted probabilities we need to do some additional computations. This is most easily accomplished using `oprobitp`.

▷ Example

In the above example, we estimated the model `oprobit rep77 foreign length mpg`. The `predict` command can be used to obtain the predicted score S_j for each automobile and standard formulas (given in the following technical note) used to translate those into probability statements. `oprobitp`, used after `oprobit`, does precisely this.

You type the command followed by the names of the new variables to hold the predicted probabilities, ordering the names from low to high. In our data, the lowest outcome is "poor" and the highest "excellent". We have five categories and so must type five names following `oprobitp`; the choice of name is up to us:

```
. oprobitp poor fair avg good exc
. list pscore make model good exc if rep77==.
```

	pscore	make	model	good	exc
3.	10.74377	AMC	Spirit	.0351813	.0006044
10.	11.35933	Buick	Opel	.1133763	.0043803
32.	10.54229	Ford	Fiesta	.0222789	.0002927
44.	11.62798	Merc.	Monarch	.1700846	.0093209
53.	12.52981	Peugeot	604	.4202766	.0734199
56.	10.99454	Plym.	Horizon	.0590294	.001413
57.	11.92174	Plym.	Sapporo	.2466034	.0197543
63.	11.99277	Pont.	Phoenix	.266771	.0234156

◁

❑ Technical Note

For ordered probit, the predicted score is defined as $S_j = x_{1j}\beta_1 + x_{2j}\beta_2 + \ldots + x_{kj}\beta_k$. Ordered probit is identical to ordered logit except that one uses a different distribution function for calculating probabilities. The ordered-probit predictions are then the probability that $S_j + u_j$ lies between a pair of cut points κ_{i-1} and κ_i. The formulas in the case of ordered probit are

$$\Pr(S_j + u < \kappa) = F(\kappa - S_j)$$
$$\Pr(S_j + u > \kappa) = 1 - F(\kappa - S_j) = F(S_j - \kappa)$$
$$\Pr(\kappa_1 < S_j + u < \kappa_2) = F(\kappa_2 - S_j) - F(\kappa_1 - S_j)$$

Thus, to perform two of the five calculations performed by `oprobitp`, we could type

```
. predict pscore
. gen pexc = normprob(pscore-_b[_cut4])
. gen pgood = normprob(_b[_cut4]-pscore) - normprob(_b[_cut3]-pscore)
```

❑

Saved Results

oprobit is a member of the class described in [R] **maximize**; see that entry for saved results. oprobitp saves no results.

Methods and Formulas

oprobitp is implemented as an ado-file.

Please see the *Methods and Formulas* section of [R] **ologit**.

References

Aitchison, J. and S. D. Silvey. 1957. The generalization of probit analysis to the case of multiple responses. *Biometrika* 44: 131–140.

Greene, W. H. 1993. *Econometric Analysis*. 2d ed. New York: Macmillan.

Also See

[U] 20.5 Accessing coefficients and standard errors, [U] 26 Estimation and post-estimation commands

[R] **clogit**, [R] **lincom**, [R] **linktest**, [R] **logistic**, [R] **logit**, [R] **lrtest**, [R] **maximize**, [R] **mlogit**, [R] **ologit**, [R] **predict**, [R] **probit**, [R] **sw**, [R] **test**, [R] **testnl**, [R] **vce**, [R] **xi**

Title

> **order** — Reorder variables in dataset

Syntax

order *varlist*

move *varname₁* *varname₂*

aorder [*varlist*]

Description

order changes the order of the variables in the current dataset. The variables specified in *varlist* are moved, in order, to the front of the dataset.

move also reorders variables. move relocates *varname₁* to the position of *varname₂* and shifts the remaining variables, including *varname₂*, to make room.

aorder alphabetizes the variables specified in *varlist* and moves them to the front of the dataset. If no *varlist* is specified, _all is assumed.

Remarks

▷ Example

When using order, you must specify a *varlist*, but it is not necessary to specify all the variables in the dataset. For example:

```
. describe
Contains data from auto.dta
  obs:            74                          1978 Automobile Data
  vars:            6
  size:        2,368 (99.7% of memory free)
-------------------------------------------------------------------------
  1. price      int     %8.0g               Price
  2. weight     int     %8.0g               Weight (lbs.)
  3. mpg        int     %8.0g               Mileage (mpg)
  4. make       str18   %18s                Make and Model
  5. length     int     %8.0g               Length (in.)
  6. rep78      int     %8.0g               Repair Record 1978
-------------------------------------------------------------------------
Sorted by:
     Note:  data has changed since last save
. order make mpg
```

(Continued on next page.)

614

```
. describe
Contains data from auto.dta
  obs:             74                         1978 Automobile Data
  vars:             6
  size:         2,368 (99.7% of memory free)
-----------------------------------------------------------------------------
    1. make        str18   %18s              Make and Model
    2. mpg         int     %8.0g             Mileage (mpg)
    3. price       int     %8.0g             Price
    4. weight      int     %8.0g             Weight (lbs.)
    5. length      int     %8.0g             Length (in.)
    6. rep78       int     %8.0g             Repair Record 1978
-----------------------------------------------------------------------------
Sorted by:
      Note:  data has changed since last save
```

If we now wanted length to be the last variable in our dataset, we could type order make mpg price weight rep78 length but it would be easier to use move:

```
. move length rep78

. describe
Contains data from auto.dta
  obs:             74                         1978 Automobile Data
  vars:             6
  size:         2,368 (99.7% of memory free)
-----------------------------------------------------------------------------
    1. make        str18   %18s              Make and Model
    2. mpg         int     %8.0g             Mileage (mpg)
    3. price       int     %8.0g             Price
    4. weight      int     %8.0g             Weight (lbs.)
    5. rep78       int     %8.0g             Repair Record 1978
    6. length      int     %8.0g             Length (in.)
-----------------------------------------------------------------------------
Sorted by:
      Note:  data has changed since last save
```

We now change our mind and decide that we would prefer that the variables be alphabetized.

```
. aorder

. describe
Contains data from auto.dta
  obs:             74                         1978 Automobile Data
  vars:             6
  size:         2,368 (99.6% of memory free)
-----------------------------------------------------------------------------
    1. length      int     %8.0g             Length (in.)
    2. make        str18   %18s              Make and Model
    3. mpg         int     %8.0g             Mileage (mpg)
    4. price       int     %8.0g             Price
    5. rep78       int     %8.0g             Repair Record 1978
    6. weight      int     %8.0g             Weight (lbs.)
-----------------------------------------------------------------------------
Sorted by:
      Note:  data has changed since last save
```

◁

❑ Technical Note

If your dataset contains variables named `year1`, `year2`, ..., `year19`, `year20`, `aorder` will order them correctly even though to most computer programs, `year10` is alphabetically between `year1` and `year2`. ❑

Methods and Formulas

`aorder` is implemented as an ado-file.

Also See

[R] **edit**, [R] **describe**, [R] **rename**

Title

orthpoly — Orthogonal polynomials

Syntax

orthpoly *varname* [*weight*] [if *exp*] [in *range*] , { generate(*varlist*)

poly(*matname*) } [degree(#)]

Note: Either one of generate() or poly() or both must be specified.

Description

orthpoly computes orthogonal polynomials for a variable *varname*.

Options

degree(#) specifies the highest degree polynomial to include. Orthogonal polynomials of degree 1, 2, ..., $d = $ # are computed. Default is $d = 1$.

generate(*varlist*) creates d new variables (of type double) containing orthogonal polynomials of degree 1, 2, ..., d evaluated at *varname*. The *varlist* must either contain exactly d new variable names or be abbreviated using the styles *newvar1-newvar d* or *newvar*. For both styles of abbreviation, new variables *newvar1*, *newvar2*, ..., *newvar d* are generated.

poly(*matname*) creates a $(d+1) \times (d+1)$ matrix called *matname* containing the coefficients of the orthogonal polynomials. The orthogonal polynomial of degree $i \leq d$ is

matname[i, $d+1$] + *matname*[i, 1]*varname* + *matname*[i, 2]*varname*^{2}
+ $\cdots$ + *matname*[i, i]*varname*^{i}

Note that the coefficients corresponding to the constant term are placed in the last column of the matrix. The rationale for this arrangement is shown in the example below.

Remarks

When fitting polynomial terms in a regression, orthogonal polynomials are often recommended for two reasons. The first is numerical accuracy. The natural polynomials 1, x, x^2, x^3, ... are highly collinear, and including several terms in a model would create problems for an unsophisticated regression routine. Stata's regress command, however, can face a large amount of collinearity and still produce accurate results. Stata users are likely to find orthogonal polynomials useful for the second reason: ease of interpreting results. When orthogonal polynomials are used, $\mathbf{X'X}$ is diagonal, partial sums of squares become the same as sequential sums of squares, and significance tests are orthogonal.

Illustrations of syntax:

```
. orthpoly weight, deg(4) generate(pw1 pw2 pw3 pw4)
. orthpoly weight, deg(4) generate(pw1-pw4)
. orthpoly weight, deg(4) generate(pw*)
```

```
. orthpoly weight, deg(4) poly(P)
. orthpoly weight, deg(4) gen(pw1-pw4) poly(P)
```

▷ Example

Suppose we wish to fit the model

$$\text{mpg} = \beta_0 + \beta_1\,\text{weight} + \beta_2\,\text{weight}^2 + \beta_3\,\text{weight}^3 + \beta_4\,\text{weight}^4 + \epsilon$$

We will first compute the regression with natural polynomials, and then do it with orthogonal polynomials.

```
. use auto
(1978 Automobile Data)
. gen double w1 = weight
. gen double w2 = w1*w1
. gen double w3 = w2*w1
. gen double w4 = w3*w1
. regress mpg w1-w4

     Source |       SS       df       MS              Number of obs =      74
------------+------------------------------           F(  4,    69) =   36.06
      Model | 1652.73666     4   413.184164           Prob > F      =  0.0000
   Residual | 790.722803    69   11.4597508           R-squared     =  0.6764
------------+------------------------------           Adj R-squared =  0.6576
      Total | 2443.45946    73   33.4720474           Root MSE      =  3.3852

------------------------------------------------------------------------------
        mpg |      Coef.   Std. Err.      t    P>|t|     [95% Conf. Interval]
------------+-----------------------------------------------------------------
         w1 |   .0289302   .1161939     0.249   0.804    -.2028704    .2607307
         w2 |  -.0000229   .0000566    -0.404   0.687    -.0001359    .0000901
         w3 |   5.74e-09   1.19e-08     0.482   0.631    -1.80e-08    2.95e-08
         w4 |  -4.86e-13   9.14e-13    -0.532   0.596    -2.31e-12    1.34e-12
      _cons |   23.94421   86.60667     0.276   0.783    -148.8314    196.7198
------------------------------------------------------------------------------

. orthpoly weight, generate(pw*) deg(4)
. regress mpg pw1-pw4

     Source |       SS       df       MS              Number of obs =      74
------------+------------------------------           F(  4,    69) =   36.06
      Model | 1652.73666     4   413.184164           Prob > F      =  0.0000
   Residual | 790.722803    69   11.4597508           R-squared     =  0.6764
------------+------------------------------           Adj R-squared =  0.6576
      Total | 2443.45946    73   33.4720474           Root MSE      =  3.3852

------------------------------------------------------------------------------
        mpg |      Coef.   Std. Err.      t    P>|t|     [95% Conf. Interval]
------------+-----------------------------------------------------------------
        pw1 |  -4.638252   .3935245   -11.786   0.000    -5.423312   -3.853192
        pw2 |   .8263545   .3935245     2.100   0.039     .0412947    1.611414
        pw3 |  -.3068616   .3935245    -0.780   0.438    -1.091921    .4781982
        pw4 |   -.209457   .3935245    -0.532   0.596    -.9945168    .5756027
      _cons |    21.2973   .3935245    54.119   0.000     20.51224    22.08236
------------------------------------------------------------------------------

. orthpoly weight, poly(P) deg(4)
. matrix bp = get(_b)
. matrix b = bp*P
. matrix list b

b[1,5]
            deg1        deg2        deg3        deg4       _cons
y1     .02893016   -.00002291   5.745e-09   -4.862e-13   23.944212
```

Compare the p-values of the terms in the natural-polynomial regression with those in the orthogonal-polynomial regression. With orthogonal polynomials, it is easy to see that the cubic and quartic terms are nonsignificant and that the constant, linear, and quadratic terms each have $p < 0.05$.

The example also illustrates how the matrix P obtained with the `poly()` option can be used to transform coefficients for orthogonal polynomials to coefficients for natural polynomials. The row vector `bp` contains the coefficients from the orthogonal-polynomial regression; `matrix b = bp*P` transforms them to coefficients of natural polynomials. These are, as they should be, the same as the coefficients from the natural-polynomial regression.

◁

Methods and Formulas

`orthpoly` is implemented as an ado-file.

`orthpoly` uses the Christoffel–Darboux recurrence formula. They are normalized so that

$$\mathbf{X'DX} = N\mathbf{I}$$

where $\mathbf{D} = \mathrm{diag}(w_1, w_2, \ldots, w_n)$ with w_i the weights, and $N = \sum_{i=1}^{n} w_i$. If weights are not specified, $w_i = 1$. If the weights are `aweight`s, they are first normalized to sum to the number of observations.

References

Abramowitz, M. and I. A. Stegun, eds. 1968. *Handbook of Mathematical Functions*, 7th printing. Washington, D.C.: National Bureau of Standards.

Sribney, W. M. 1995. sg37: Orthogonal polynomials. *Stata Technical Bulletin* 25: 17–18. Reprinted in *Stata Technical Bulletin Reprints*, vol 5, p. 96–98.

Also See

[U] **26 Estimation and post-estimation commands**

[R] **matrix**, [R] **regress**

Title

> **outfile** — Write ASCII-format dataset

Syntax

<u>ou</u>tfile [*varlist*] using *filename* [if *exp*] [in *range*] [, <u>c</u>omma <u>d</u>ictionary

    <u>nol</u>abel <u>noq</u>uote replace <u>w</u>ide]

Description

outfile writes data to a disk file in ASCII format, a format that can be read by other programs. The new file is *not* in Stata format; see [R] **save** for instructions on saving data for subsequent use in Stata.

The data saved by outfile can be read back by infile; see [R] **infile**. If *filename* is specified without an extension, '.raw' is assumed unless the dictionary option is specified, in which case '.dct' is assumed.

Options

comma causes Stata to write the file in comma-separated-value format. In this format, values are separated by commas rather than blanks. Missing values are written as two consecutive commas.

dictionary writes the file in Stata's data dictionary format. See [R] **infile (fixed format)** for a description of dictionaries. comma may not be specified with dictionary.

nolabel causes Stata to write the numeric values of labeled variables. The default is to write the labels enclosed in double quotes.

noquote prevents Stata from placing double quotes around the contents of string variables.

replace permits outfile to overwrite an existing dataset. replace may not be abbreviated.

wide causes Stata to write the data with one observation per line. The default is to split observations into lines of 80 characters or less.

Remarks

outfile enables data to be sent to a disk file for processing by a non-Stata program. Each observation is written as one or more records—records that will not exceed 80 characters unless you specify the wide option. The values of the variables are written using their current display formats, and unless the comma option is specified, each is prefixed with two blanks.

If you specify the dictionary option, the data is written in the same way, but in front of the data outfile writes a data dictionary describing the contents of the file.

▷ Example

You have entered into Stata data on seven employees in your firm. The data contains employee name, employee identification number, salary, and sex:

```
. list
              name      empno     salary       sex
  1.    Carl Marks      57213      24000      male
  2.    Irene Adler     47229      27000    female
  3.    Adam Smith      57323      24000      male
  4.    David Wallis    57401      24500      male
  5.    Mary Rogers     57802      27000    female
  6.    Carolyn Frank   57805      24000    female
  7.    Robert Lawson   57824      22500      male
```

If you now wish to use a program other than Stata with this data, you must somehow get the data over to that other program. The standard Stata-format dataset created by **save** will not do the job—it is written in a special format that only Stata understands. Most programs, however, understand ASCII datasets—standard text datasets that are like those produced by a text editor. You can tell Stata to produce such a dataset using **outfile**. Typing **outfile using employee** creates a dataset called **employee.raw** that contains all the data. We can use the Stata **type** command to review the resulting file:

```
. outfile using employee

. type employee.raw
      "Carl Marks"       57213      24000      "male"
     "Irene Adler"       47229      27000    "female"
      "Adam Smith"       57323      24000      "male"
    "David Wallis"       57401      24500      "male"
     "Mary Rogers"       57802      27000    "female"
   "Carolyn Frank"       57805      24000    "female"
   "Robert Lawson"       57824      22500      "male"
```

We see that the file contains the four variables and that Stata has surrounded the string variables with double quotes.

◁

❑ Technical Note

outfile is careful to columnize the data in case you want to read it using formatted input. In the example above, the first string has a **%16s** display format. Stata wrote two leading blanks and then placed the string in a 16-character field. As Stata always does, it right-justified the string. The two numbers each have a **%9.0g** format. Each number is written as two blanks followed by the number, right-justified in a 9-character field. The last entry is really a numeric variable, but it has an associated value label. Its format is **%9.0g**, so Stata wrote two blanks and then right-justified the value label in a 9-character field.

❑

❑ Technical Note

The **nolabel** option prevents Stata from substituting value label strings for the underlying numeric value; see [U] **19.6.3 Value labels**. As we just said, the last variable in our data is really a numeric variable:

```
. outfile using employ2, nolabel
```

```
. type employ2.raw
      "Carl Marks"      57213      24000        0
     "Irene Adler"      47229      27000        1
     "Adam Smith"      57323      24000        0
   "David Wallis"      57401      24500        0
    "Mary Rogers"      57802      27000        1
  "Carolyn Frank"      57805      24000        1
  "Robert Lawson"      57824      22500        0
```

❏

❏ Technical Note

If you do not want Stata to place double quotes around the contents of string variables, specify the noquote option:

```
. outfile using employ3, noquote
. type employ3.raw
      Carl Marks      57213      24000       male
     Irene Adler      47229      27000     female
     Adam Smith      57323      24000       male
   David Wallis      57401      24500       male
    Mary Rogers      57802      27000     female
  Carolyn Frank      57805      24000     female
  Robert Lawson      57824      22500       male
```

❏

▷ Example

Stata never writes over an existing file unless told to do so explicitly. For instance, if the file employee.raw already exists and you attempted to overwrite it by typing outfile using employee, here is what would happen:

```
. outfile using employee
file employee.raw already exists
r(602);
```

You can tell Stata that it is okay to overwrite a file by specifying the replace option: outfile using employee, replace.

◁

❏ Technical Note

Some programs prefer data that is separated by commas rather than by blanks. Stata will produce such a dataset if you specify the comma option:

```
. outfile using employee, comma
. type employee.raw
"Carl Marks",57213,24000,"male"
"Irene Adler",47229,27000,"female"
"Adam Smith",57323,24000,"male"
"David Wallis",57401,24500,"male"
"Mary Rogers",57802,27000,"female"
"Carolyn Frank",57805,24000,"female"
"Robert Lawson",57824,22500,"male"
```

❏

▷ Example

Finally, outfile can create data dictionaries that infile can read. Dictionaries are perhaps the best way to organize your raw data. A dictionary describes your data so that you do not have to remember the order of the variables, the number of variables, the variable names, or anything else. The file in which you store your data becomes self-documenting so that when you come back to it at some future date, you can understand what it is. See [R] **infile (fixed format)** for a full description of data dictionaries.

When you specify the dictionary, Stata writes a .dct file:

```
. outfile using employee, dict

. type employee.dct
dictionary {
        str15   name                "Employee name"
        float   empno               "Employee number"
        float   salary              "Annual salary"
        float   sex       :sexlbl   "Sex"
}
        "Carl Marks"    57213    24000    "male"
        "Irene Adler"   47229    27000    "female"
        "Adam Smith"    57323    24000    "male"
      "David Wallis"    57401    24500    "male"
       "Mary Rogers"    57802    27000    "female"
      "Carolyn Frank"   57805    24000    "female"
      "Robert Lawson"   57824    22500    "male"
```

◁

Also See

[U] **27 Commands to input data**

[R] **infile**, [R] **outsheet**

Title

outsheet — Write spreadsheet-style dataset

Syntax

outsheet [*varlist*] using *filename* [if *exp*] [in *range*] [, nonames nolabel noquote

comma replace]

If *filename* is specified without a suffix, .out is assumed.

Description

outsheet writes data in tab- or comma-separated ASCII format into a file. This is the format that most spreadsheet programs prefer.

Options

nonames specifies that variable names are not to be written in the first line of the file; the file is to contain data values only.

nolabel specifies that the numeric values of labeled variables are to be written into the file rather than the label associated with each value.

noquote specifies that string variables are not to be enclosed in double quotes.

comma specifies comma-separated format rather than the default tab-separated format.

replace specifies that it is okay to overwrite *filename* if it already exists.

Remarks

If you wish to move your data into another program, you have the following alternatives:

1. The use of an external data-transfer program; see [U] **27.4 Transfer programs**.
2. Cutting and pasting from Stata's data editor if you use Stata for Windows or Stata for Macintosh; see [U] **5 Starting and stopping Stata for Windows 95**.
3. Using outsheet.
4. Using outfile; see [R] **outfile**.

Concerning alternatives 3 and 4, outsheet is typically preferred if you are moving the data to a spreadsheet and outfile is probably better if you are moving data to another statistical package.

If your goal is to send data to another Stata user, you could use outsheet or outfile, but easiest is simply to send the .dta dataset. This will work even if you use Stata for Windows and your cohort uses Stata for Macintosh. All Statas can read each other's .dta files.

▷ Example

    `outsheet` copies the data currently loaded in memory into the specified file. About all that can go wrong is the file you specify already exists:

```
. outsheet using tosend
file tosend.out already exists
r(602);
```

In that case, you can **erase** the file (see [R] **erase**), specify `outsheet`'s `replace` option, or use a different filename. When all goes well, `outsheet` is silent:

```
. outsheet using tosend, replace

. _
```

If you are copying the data to a program other than a spreadsheet, remember to specify the `noname` option:

```
. outsheet using foral, nonames

. _
```

◁

Also See

[U] **27 Commands to input data**

[R] **insheet**, [R] **outfile**

Author Index

A

Abramowitz, M., [U] **20 Functions and expressions**, [R] **orthpoly**
Afifi, A. A., [R] **anova**, [R] **sw**
Agresti, A., [R] **tabulate**
Aitchison, J., [R] **ologit**, [R] **oprobit**
Aldrich, J. H., [R] **logit**, [R] **mlogit**, [R] **probit**
Allen, M. J., [R] **alpha**
Altman, D. G., [R] **anova**, [R] **fracpoly**, [R] **kappa**, [R] **kwallis**, [R] **nptrend**, [R] **oneway**, [R] **st stcox**
Amemiya, T., [R] **cnreg**, [R] **glogit**
Anagnoson, J. T., [U] **2 Resources for learning and using Stata**
Andersen, E. B., [R] **clogit**
Anderson, J. A., [R] **ologit**
Andrews, D. F., [R] **ml**, [R] **rreg**
Arbuthnott, J., [R] **signrank**
Armitage, P., [R] **ltable**, [R] **means**
Armstrong, R. D., [R] **qreg**
Atkinson, A. C., [R] **boxcox**, [R] **nl**
Azen, S. P., [R] **anova**

B

Baker, R. J., [R] **glm**
Balanger, A., [R] **sktest**
Baltagi, B. H., [R] **xtreg**
Bancroft, T. A., [R] **sw**
Bartlett, M. S., [R] **factor**, [R] **oneway**
Bassett, G., Jr., [R] **qreg**
Beale, E. M. L., [R] **sw**, [R] **test**
Beaton, A. E., [R] **rreg**
Beck, N., [R] **xtgls**
Becker, R. A , [R] **graph matrix**
Becketti, S., [R] **fracpoly**, [R] **graph axis labels**, [R] **graph printing**, [R] **graph twoway**, [R] **pause**, [R] **runtest**, [R] **spearman**
Belle, G. van, [R] **dstdize**, [R] **epitab**
Belsley, D. A., [R] **fit**
Bendel, R. B., [R] **sw**
Beniger, J. R., [R] **cumul**, [R] **graph bar**, [R] **graph histogram**, [R] **graph pie**
Berk, K. N., [R] **sw**
Berk, R. A., [R] **rreg**
Berkson, J., [R] **logit**, [R] **probit**
Bernstein, I. H., [R] **alpha**, [R] **loneway**
Berry, G., [R] **ltable**, [R] **means**
Beyer, W. H., [R] **qc**
Bickel, P. J., [R] **ml**, [R] **rreg**
Binder, D. A., [U] **26 Estimation and post-estimation commands**, [R] **_robust**, [R] **svyreg**
Birdsall, T. G., [R] **logistic**
Bland, M., [R] **signrank**

Bliss, C. I., [R] **probit**
Bloomfield, P., [R] **qreg**
Boice, J. D., [R] **bitest**, [R] **epitab**
Bollen, K. A., [R] **fit**
Bortkewitsch, L. von, [R] **poisson**
Box, G. E. P., [R] **boxcox**, [R] **lnskew0**
Boyd, N. F., [R] **kappa**
Brant, R., [R] **ologit**
Breslow, N. E., [R] **clogit**, [R] **epitab**, [R] **st stcox**, [R] **st sts test**
Breusch, T., [R] **mvreg**, [R] **sureg**, [R] **xtreg**
Brier, G. W., [R] **brier**
Brook, R., [R] **brier**
Brown, D. R., [R] **anova**, [R] **oneway**
Buchner, D. M., [R] **ladder**
Burnam, M. A., [R] **lincom**, [R] **mlogit**
Burr, I. W., [R] **qc**

C

Carlile, T., [R] **kappa**
Carroll, R. J., [R] **rreg**
Chadwick, J., [R] **poisson**
Chamberlain, G., [R] **clogit**
Chambers, J. M., [U] **13 Stata's on-line tutorials and sample datasets**, [R] **diagplots**, [R] **graph box**, [R] **graph by**, [R] **graph matrix**, [R] **graph oneway**, [R] **graph star**, [R] **graph twoway**, [R] **grmeanby**, [R] **ksm**
Charlett, A., [R] **fracpoly**
Chatterjee, S., [R] **corc**, [R] **eivreg**, [R] **fit**, [R] **poisson**, [R] **regress**
Chiang, C. L., [R] **ltable**
Clark, V. A., [R] **ltable**
Clarke, M. R. B., [R] **factor**
Clarke, R. D., [R] **poisson**
Clayton, D., [R] **epitab**
Cleveland, W. S., [U] **13 Stata's on-line tutorials and sample datasets**, [R] **diagplots**, [R] **graph box**, [R] **graph by**, [R] **graph lines**, [R] **graph matrix**, [R] **graph oneway**, [R] **graph star**, [R] **graph twoway**, [R] **ksm**
Cochran, W. G., [R] **anova**, [R] **correlate**, [R] **dstdize**, [R] **means**, [R] **oneway**, [R] **signrank**, [R] **svy**, [R] **svymean**, [R] **svyreg**
Cochrane, D., [R] **corc**, [R] **prais**
Cohen, J., [R] **kappa**
Collett, D., [R] **clogit**, [R] **logistic**, [R] **st sts test**, [R] **st stweib**
Conover, W. J., [R] **centile**, [R] **ksmirnov**, [R] **kwallis**, [R] **nptrend**, [R] **spearman**, [R] **tabulate**
Cook, R. D., [R] **boxcox**, [R] **fit**
Cornfield, J., [R] **epitab**
Cox, D. R., [R] **boxcox**, [R] **lnskew0**, [R] **st stcox**, [R] **st sts**, [R] **st stweib**
Cox, N. J., [U] **1 Read this—it will help**, [U] **21 Printing and preserving output**
Cramér, H., [R] **tabulate**

Subject Index

This is the combined subject index for the *Stata Reference Manual* and the *Stata User's Guide*.

Semicolons set off the most important entries from the rest. Sometimes no entry will be set off with semicolons; this means all entries are equally important.

A

confidence intervals, [U] **26.4 Specifying the width of confidence intervals**, [R] **level**
    for means, proportions, and counts, [R] **ci**, [R] **ttest**, [R] **svymean**
    for medians and percentiles, [R] **centile**
    for linear combinations of coefficients, [R] **lincom**, [R] **svylc**
    for odds and risk ratios, [R] **epitab**, [R] **lincom**
CONFIG.SYS DOS system file, [U] **D. Installation of Stata for DOS**
confirm command, [R] **confirm**
connect() graph option, [R] **graph connect**
console,
    controlling scrolling of output, [R] **more**
    obtaining input from, [R] **display (for programmers)**
constrained estimation, [R] **constraint**
    linear regression, [R] **cnsreg**
    multinomial logistic regression, [R] **mlogit**
    programming, [R] **matrix constraint**
constraint command, [R] **constraint**; [R] **matrix constraint**
contents of data, [R] **describe**; [R] **codebook**
contingency tables, [R] **epitab**, [R] **tabulate**; [R] **table**
control charts, [R] **qc**
convergence criteria, [R] **maximize**
Convex, *see* Unix
Cook's D, [R] **fit**, [R] **predict**
Cook−Weisberg test for heteroscedasticity, [R] **fit**
copy and paste, [U] **32 More on Stata for Windows**, [U] **33 More on Stata for Macintosh**, [R] **edit**, [R] **graph printing Macintosh**, [R] **graph printing Windows**
copying matrices, [R] **matrix define**, [R] **matrix get**, [R] **matrix mkmat**
corc command, [R] **corc**; [U] **26 Estimation and postestimation commands**, [U] **35 Overview of model estimation in Stata**
Cornfield confidence intervals, [R] **epitab**
correcting data, *see* editing data
correlate command, [R] **correlate**; [R] **matrix post**
correlated errors, *see* robust
correlation, [R] **correlate**
    canonical, [R] **canon**
    intracluster, [R] **loneway**
    Kendall's rank correlation, [R] **spearman**
    pairwise, [R] **correlate**
    partial, [R] **pcorr**
    Pearson's product-moment, [R] **correlate**
    Spearman's rank correlation, [R] **spearman**
correlation matrices, [R] **correlate**, [R] **matrix define**, [R] **vce**
cos() function, [U] **20.3.1 Mathematical functions**, [R] **functions**
cosine function, [U] **20.3.1 Mathematical functions**, [R] **functions**
count command, [R] **count**
count() egen function, [R] **egen**

count-time data, [R] **ct**; [R] **ct ctset**, [R] **ct cttost**, [R] **nbreg**, [R] **poisson**, [R] **st sttoct**
counts, making dataset of, [R] **collapse**
courses in Stata, [U] **2.5 NetCourses**
covariance matrix of estimators, [R] **vce**; [R] **correlate**, [R] **matrix get**, [R] **matrix post**
covariate patterns, [R] **logistic**
COVRATIO, [R] **fit**
cox command, [R] **cox**; [U] **26 Estimation and postestimation commands**, [U] **35 Overview of model estimation in Stata**
Cox proportional hazards model, [R] **st stcox**; [R] **cox**
cprplot command, [R] **fit**
Cramér's V, [R] **tabulate**
crclib command, [U] **23.8 How do I install STB updates?**
Cronbach's alpha, [R] **alpha**
cross command, [R] **cross**
cross-product matrices, [R] **matrix accum**
cross-sectional time-series data, *see* xt
cross-tabulations, *see* tables
crude estimates, [R] **epitab**
cs and csi commands, [R] **epitab**
ct, [R] **ct**, [R] **ct ctset**, [R] **ct cttost**, [R] **st sttoct**
ctset command, [R] **ct ctset**
cttost command, [R] **ct cttost**
cubic splines, graphing, [R] **graph connect**
cumul command, [R] **cumul**
cumulative distribution, empirical, [R] **cumul**
cumulative distribution functions, [U] **20.3.2 Statistical functions**, [R] **functions**
cumulative incidence data, [R] **epitab**, [R] **poisson**
cusum command, [R] **cusum**

D

data, [U] **19 Data**; [R] **data types**
    appending, *see* appending data
    categorical, *see* categorical data
    certifying, *see* certifying data
    characteristics of, [U] **19.8 Characteristics**, [R] **char**
    combining, *see* combining datasets
    contents of, [R] **describe**; [R] **codebook**
    count-time, *see* count-time data
    cross-sectional time-series, *see* xt
    documenting, [R] **codebook**, [R] **notes**
    editing, *see* editing data
    entering, *see* inputting data interactively
    exporting, *see* exporting data
    generating, [R] **generate**; [R] **egen**
    importing, [R] **infile**, [R] **insheet**; [U] **27.4 Transfer programs**
    inputting, *see* data, importing
    labeling, *see* labeling data
    large, dealing with, *see* memory
    listing, [R] **edit**, [R] **list**
    missing values, *see* missing values
continued on next page

continued on next page

G

logistic and logit regression, [R] **logistic**, [R] **logit**
  conditional, [R] **clogit**
  fixed-effects, [R] **clogit**
  generalized estimating equations, [R] **xtgee**
  generalized linear model, [R] **glm**
  multinomial, [R] **mlogit**; [R] **clogit**
  ordered, [R] **ologit**
  polytomous, [R] **mlogit**
  random-effects, [R] **xtgee**
  with grouped data, [R] **glogit**
  with panel data, [R] **clogit**, [R] **xtgee**
  with survey data, [R] **svyreg**
logit command, [R] **logit**; [U] **26 Estimation and
    post-estimation commands**, [U] **35 Overview
    of model estimation in Stata**
logit regression, *see* logistic and logit regression
logo, Stata, [R] **graph printing**
loneway command, [R] **loneway**
long, [U] **19.2.2 Numeric storage types**, [R] **data
    types**
long lines in ado-files and
    do-files, [U] **24.12.2 Comments and long lines
    in ado-files**, [R] **#delimit**
longitudinal data, *see* xt
lookfor command, [R] **describe**
lookup command, [R] **lookup**; [U] **12 Stata's on-line
    help and lookup facilities**
loop, endless, *see* endless loop
looping, [R] **while**
Lotus 1-2-3, reading data from, *see* spreadsheets
Lotus .PIC files, [R] **graph printing**
lower() string function, [U] **20.3.4 String functions**,
    [R] **functions**
lowercase-string function, [U] **20.3.4 String functions**,
    [R] **functions**
lowess, [R] **ksm**
lpredict command, [R] **logistic**
LRECLs, [R] **infile (fixed format)**
L-R plot, [R] **fit**
lroc command, [R] **logistic**
lrtest command, [R] **lrtest**
ls command, [R] **dir**
lsens command, [R] **logistic**
lstat command, [R] **logistic**
ltable command, [R] **ltable**
ltolerance() option, [R] **maximize**
ltrim() string function, [U] **20.3.4 String functions**,
    [R] **functions**
lv command, [R] **lv**
lvr2plot command, [R] **fit**

M

ma() egen function, [R] **egen**
Macintosh, [U] **33 More on Stata for Macintosh**
  copy and paste, [U] **33 More on Stata for
    Macintosh**, [R] **edit**, [R] **graph printing
    Macintosh**

Macintosh, *continued*
  creating PICT and EPS files, [U] **33 More on Stata
    for Macintosh**, graph printing Macintosh
  dialog box, [R] **window control**, [R] **window dialog**,
    [R] **window stopbox**
  getting started, *Getting Started with Stata for
    Macintosh* manual
  help, [R] **help**
  identifying in programs, [U] **24.3.9 Built-in global
    system macros**
  installation, [U] **C. Installation of Stata for
    Macintosh**; [U] **23.8 How do I install STB
    updates?**
  invocation, [U] **7 Starting and stopping Stata for
    Macintosh**
  keyboard use, [U] **17 Keyboard use**
  pause, [R] **sleep**
  printing graphs, [R] **graph printing Macintosh**
  Review window, saving contents of, [U] **33 More on
    Stata for Macintosh**
  setting file icon, [R] **touch**
  specifying filenames, [U] **18.6 File-naming
    conventions**
  windows, [R] **window**
macro command, [R] **macro**
macros, [U] **24.3 Macros**, [R] **macro**, [R] **parse**,
    [R] **scalar**
    and see S_ macros; S_E_ macros
MAD regression, [R] **qreg**
main effects, [R] **anova**
makeCns matrix subcommand, [R] **matrix constraint**
man command, [R] **help**
Mann–Whitney two-sample statistic, [R] **signrank**
Mantel–Haenszel test, [R] **epitab**, [R] **st stir**
mapping strings to numbers, [R] **encode**, [R] **label**
margin() graph option, [R] **graph combining**
marginal tax rate egen function, [R] **egen**
mark command, [R] **mark**
markout command, [R] **mark**
matched case-control data, [R] **clogit**, [R] **epitab**
matched-pairs tests, [R] **signrank**, [R] **ttest**; [R] **hotel**
matcproc command, [R] **matrix constraint**
mathematical functions and expressions,
    [U] **20.3 Functions**, [R] **functions**, [R] **matrix
    define**
matname command, [R] **matrix mkmat**
matrices, [R] **matrix**
  accessing internal, [R] **matrix**, [R] **matrix get**
  accumulating, [R] **matrix accum**
  appending rows and columns, [R] **matrix define**,
    [R] **matrix substitute**
  Cholesky decomposition, [R] **matrix define**
  coefficient matrices, [R] **matrix post**
  column names, *see* matrices, row and column names
  constrained estimation, [R] **matrix constraint**
  copying, [R] **matrix define**, [R] **matrix get**
  correlation, [R] **matrix define**
  covariance matrix of estimators, [R] **matrix post**
  cross-product, [R] **matrix accum**

continued on next page

messages and return codes, *see* error messages and return codes

Metafile, Windows, [U] **32 More on Stata for Windows**, [R] **graph printing Windows**

Microsoft Windows, *see* Windows

midsummaries, [R] **lv**

mild outliers, [R] **lv**

Mills' ratio, [R] **heckman**

min() built-in function, [U] **20.3.5 Special functions**, [R] **functions**

min() egen function, [R] **egen**

minimum absolute deviations, [R] **qreg**

minimum squared deviations, [R] **fit**, [R] **regress**; [R] **areg**, [R] **cnsreg**; [R] **nl**

minimums and maximums, *see* maximums and minimums

missing values, [U] **19.2.1 Missing values**, [U] **20 Functions and expressions**
  counting, [R] **codebook**, [R] **inspect**
  encoding and decoding, [R] **mvencode**
  imputing, [R] **impute**
  replacing, [R] **merge**

misspecification effects, [R] **svymean**, [R] **svyreg**

mkmat command, [R] **matrix mkmat**

mkspline command, [R] **mkspline**

ml command, [R] **ml**

mlogit command, [R] **mlogit**; [U] **26 Estimation and post-estimation commands**, [U] **35 Overview of model estimation in Stata**

mlout matrix subcommand, [R] **matrix constraint**, [R] **matrix post**

mod() function, [U] **20.3.1 Mathematical functions**, [R] **functions**

model sensitivity, [R] **fit**, [R] **rreg**

model specification test, [R] **linktest**; [R] **fit**, [R] **xtreg**

modifying data, *see* editing data

modulus function, [U] **20.3.1 Mathematical functions**, [R] **functions**

modulus transformations, [R] **boxcox**

moment matrices, [R] **matrix accum**

monitors, [R] **graph monitors**; [R] **ansi**
  note on Toshiba computers, [R] **stata**

Monte Carlo simulations, [R] **postfile**, [R] **simul**

month() function, [U] **30.5 Other date functions**; [U] **20.3.3 Date functions**, [R] **functions**

more command and parameter, [U] **14 –more– conditions**, [R] **more**, [R] **query**

more condition, [U] **14 –more– conditions**, [U] **22.1.6 Preventing –more– conditions**, [R] **query**

move command, [R] **order**

moving averages, [R] **egen**

mtr() egen function, [R] **egen**

multinomial logistic regression, [R] **mlogit**; [R] **clogit**

multiple comparison tests, [R] **oneway**

multiple regression, *see* linear regression

multiplication operator, *see* arithmetic operators

multivariate analysis,
  canonical correlation, [R] **canon**
  factor analysis, [R] **factor**
  Heckman selection model, [R] **heckman**
  Hotelling's T-squared, [R] **hotel**
  outliers, [R] **hadimov**
  regression, [R] **mvreg**
  Zellner's seemingly unrelated, [R] **sureg**

mvdecode and mvencode commands, [R] **mvencode**

mvreg command, [R] **mvreg**; [U] **26 Estimation and post-estimation commands**, [U] **35 Overview of model estimation in Stata**

mx_param command, [R] **ml**

N

_n and _N built-in variables, [U] **18.3 Naming conventions**

name space and conflicts, matrices and scalars, [R] **matrix**, [R] **matrix define**

names, [U] **18.3 Naming conventions**
  conflicts, [R] **matrix**, [R] **matrix define**, [R] **scalar**
  matrix row and columns, [R] **matrix**, [R] **matrix define**, [R] **matrix post**, [R] **matrix rowname**

natural log function, [U] **20.3.1 Mathematical functions**, [R] **functions**

nbreg command, [R] **nbreg**; [U] **26 Estimation and post-estimation commands**, [U] **35 Overview of model estimation in Stata**

nchi() function, [U] **20.3.2 Statistical functions**, [R] **functions**

negation operator, *see* arithmetic operators

negative binomial regression, [R] **nbreg**; [R] **glm**

nested effects, [R] **anova**

NetCourses, [U] **2.5 NetCourses**

newey command, [R] **newey**; [U] **26 Estimation and post-estimation commands**, [U] **35 Overview of model estimation in Stata**, [R] **xtgls**

Newey–West standard errors, [R] **newey**

newlines, data without, [R] **infile (fixed format)**

newsletter, [U] **2 Resources for learning and using Stata**

Newton–Raphson method, [R] **ml**

nl, nlinit, and nlpred commands, [R] **nl**

noaxis graph option, [R] **graph axis rendition**

nobreak command, [R] **break**

noisily prefix, [R] **quietly**

noncentral chi-squared distribution function, [U] **20.3.2 Statistical functions**, [R] **functions**

nonconformities, quality control, [R] **qc**

nonconstant variance, *see* heteroscedasticity

nonlinear least squares, [R] **nl**

nonparametric tests
  association, [R] **spearman**
  equality of distributions, [R] **ksmirnov**, [R] **kwallis**, [R] **signrank**
  equality of medians, [R] **signrank**
  equality of proportions, [R] **bitest**, [R] **prtest**

continued on next page

S

continued on next page

T

t distribution
cdf, [U] **20.3.2 Statistical functions**, [R] **functions**
confidence interval for mean, [R] **ci**
testing equality of means, [R] **ttest**; [R] **hotel**,
[R] **svymean**

tab characters, show, [R] **type**

tab1 and tab2 commands, [R] **tabulate**

tabdisp command, [R] **tabdisp**

tabi command, [R] **tabulate**

table command, [R] **table**

tables
contingency, [R] **table**, [R] **tabulate**
epidemiologic, [R] **epitab**
formatting numbers in, [R] **format**
frequency, [R] **tabulate**; [R] **table**, [R] **tabsum**,
[R] **xttab**
life, [R] **ltable**
N-way, [R] **table**; [R] **tabdisp**
of means, [R] **table**, [R] **tabsum**
of statistics, [R] **table**; [R] **tabdisp**
printing, [U] **21 Printing and preserving output**

tabulate and tabi commands, [R] **tabulate**

tan() function, [U] **20.3.1 Mathematical functions**,
[R] **functions**

tangent function, [U] **20.3.1 Mathematical functions**,
[R] **functions**

tau, [R] **spearman**

technical support, [U] **2.7 Technical support**

TEMP DOS environment variable, [R] **macro**

tempfile command, [R] **macro**

tempname command, [R] **macro**, [R] **matrix**,
[R] **scalar**

temporary files, [R] **macro**; [U] **24.7.3 Temporary files**,
[R] **preserve**, [R] **scalar**

temporary names, [R] **macro**, [R] **matrix**, [R] **scalar**

temporary variables, [R] **macro**; [U] **24.7.1 Temporary
variables**

tempvar command, [R] **macro**

termcap(5), [U] **17 Keyboard use**

terminal
obtaining input from, [R] **display (for
programmers)**
suppressing output, [R] **quietly**

terminfo(4), [U] **9.12 Remote Graphics Support
(RGS)**, [U] **17 Keyboard use**

test command, [R] **test**; [U] **26.8 Performing
hypothesis tests on the coefficients**; [R] **anova**

test-based confidence intervals, [R] **epitab**

testnl command, [R] **testnl**

testparm command, [R] **test**

tests
association, [R] **tabulate**
binomial proportion, [R] **bitest**
Breusch–Pagan, [R] **mvreg**, [R] **sureg**
epidemiological tables, [R] **epitab**
equality of coefficients, [R] **test**, [R] **testnl**,
[R] **svytest**

equality of distributions, [R] **kwallis**, [R] **ksmirnov**,
[R] **signrank**
equality of means, [R] **ttest**; [R] **hotel**
equality of medians, [R] **signrank**
equality of proportions, [R] **bitest**, [R] **prtest**
equality of survivor functions, [R] **st sts test**
equality of variance, [R] **sdtest**
heterogeneity, [R] **epitab**
heteroscedasticity, [R] **fit**
internal consistency, [R] **alpha**
interrater agreement, [R] **kappa**
likelihood ratio, [R] **lrtest**
model coefficients, [R] **lrtest**, [R] **test**, [R] **testnl**,
[R] **svytest**
model specification, [R] **linktest**; [R] **fit**, [R] **xtreg**
normality, [R] **sktest**, [R] **swilk**; [R] **boxcox**,
[R] **ladder**
serial independence, [R] **runtest**
trend, [R] **nptrend**

textsize parameter, [R] **graph textsize**

time of day, [U] **24.3.9 Built-in global system macros**

time-series data, [R] **corc**, [R] **graph connect**, [R] **egen**,
[R] **hlu**, [R] **matrix accum**, [R] **newey**,
[R] **prais**, [R] **xtgee**, [R] **xtgls**, *also see* xt

time stamp, [R] **describe**

tis command, [R] **xt**

titles of graphs, [R] **graph titles**; [R] **graph box**

tlabel() graph option, [R] **graph axis labels**

TMPDIR Unix environment variable, [R] **macro**

tobit command, [R] **cnreg**; [U] **26 Estimation and
post-estimation commands**, [U] **35 Overview of
model estimation in Stata**

tobit regression, [R] **cnreg**

tolerance() option, [R] **maximize**

totals, survey data, [R] **svymean**

touch command, [R] **touch**

tprob() function, [U] **20.3.2 Statistical functions**,
[R] **functions**

trace of matrix, [R] **matrix define**

trace, set, [R] **program**

tracing iterative maximization process, [R] **maximize**

transferring data
copying and pasting, [R] **edit**
from Stata, [U] **27.4 Transfer programs**,
[R] **outsheet**; [R] **outfile**
into Stata, [U] **27 Commands to input data**,
[R] [U] **27.4 Transfer programs**, [R] **infile**,
[R] **insheet**

transformations
log, [R] **lnskew0**
modulus, [R] **boxcox**
power, [R] **boxcox**; [R] **lnskew0**
to achieve normality, [R] **boxcox**; [R] **ladder**
to achieve zero skewness, [R] **lnskew0**

transposing data, [R] **xpose**

transposing matrices, [R] **matrix define**

trend, test for, [R] **nptrend**

trigonometric functions, [U] **20.3.1 Mathematical
functions**, [R] **functions**

X

X Windows, [U] **9.10 Using X Windows,**
    [U] **9.11 Using X Windows remotely,**
    [U] **9.13 How Stata displays graphs (pipeline**
    drivers), [R] **pd,** [R] **xwindow**
xchart command, [R] **qc**
xi command, [R] **xi**
xlabel() graph option, [R] **graph axis labels**
xpose command, [R] **xpose**
xscale() graph option, [R] **graph axis scale**
xt (panel or cross-sectional data), [R] **clogit,** [R] **xt,**
    [R] **xtgee,** [R] **xtgls,** [R] **xtpois,** [R] **xtprobit**
xtcorr command, [R] **xtgee**
xtdata command, [R] **xtdata;** [R] **xt**
xtdes command, [R] **xtdes;** [R] **xt**
xtgee command, [R] **xtgee;** [U] **26 Estimation and**
    post-estimation commands, [U] **35 Overview of**
    model estimation in Stata
xtgls command, [R] **xtgls;** [U] **26 Estimation and**
    post-estimation commands, [U] **35 Overview of**
    model estimation in Stata
xthaus command, [R] **xtreg;** [R] **xt**
xtile command, [R] **pctile**
xtpois command, [R] **xtpois;** [U] **26 Estimation and**
    post-estimation commands, [U] **35 Overview of**
    model estimation in Stata
xtprobit command, [R] **xtprobit;** [U] **26 Estimation**
    and post-estimation commands,
    [U] **35 Overview of model estimation in Stata**
xtpred command, [R] **xtreg;** [R] **xt**
xtreg command, [R] **xtreg;** [R] **xt;** [U] **26 Estimation**
    and post-estimation commands,
    [U] **35 Overview of model estimation in Stata**
xtsum command, [R] **xtsum;** [R] **xt**
xttab command, [R] **xttab;** [R] **xt**
xttest0 command, [R] **xtreg;** [R] **xt**
xttrans command, [R] **xttrans;** [R] **xt**

Y

year() function, [U] **20.3.3 Date functions,**
    [U] **30.5 Other date functions,** [R] **functions**
ylabel() graph option, [R] **graph axis labels**
yscale() graph option, [R] **graph axis scale**

Z

Zellner's seemingly unrelated regression, [R] **sureg**
zero matrix, [R] **matrix define**